The Hidden Debt to Islamic Civilisation

by S E Al-Djazairi

Bayt Al-Hikma Press

2005

ISBN-10: 0-9551156-0-4 (hbk)
ISBN-13: 978-0-9551156-0-8 (hbk)
ISBN-10: 0-9551156-1-2 (pbk)
ISBN-13: 978-0-9551156-1-5 (pbk)

Published by Bayt Al-Hikma Press
http://BaytAlHikma.co.uk
Printed and Bound in Europe by the Alden Group, Oxford

Acknowledgments

I am deeply grateful to a great number of people, including C.M. Zaimeche for reading through the manuscript, L. Ball for helping in the design and edition, and finance.
Errors in this work are mine.

CONTENTS

PREFACE

`Time would fail me,' Savage says, `if I attempted to enumerate and expatiate on how the Ummayad capital of Cordova, and, to a lesser degree, the cities of Egypt as well as those of what is now Iraq, made themselves preceptresses of the Western world in architecture, mathematics, medicine and music.'[1]
Lopez, in his study on Oriental influences in the economic awakening of the West, observes that the latter `will emancipate itself only after a long and diligent learning from the Orient.'[2]

This is a lengthy and complex learning, the study of its many aspects requiring sifting through a vast material to study how the Islamic element was diffused between places, by different individuals, and at various times. Paper alone, for instance, would require a book; and the same for geometry, the astrolabe, the chemist's laboratory, the experimental method, etc. Each piece will have to be followed meticulously and dealt with competently. But who has the competence to deal with everything? Then is needed a good understanding of many languages: Latin, French, English, Hebrew, German, Spanish, Italian and, of course Arabic, to collect information available in all such languages, the old and the new. And, of course, is also needed a good knowledge of history; and evidently a good knowledge of Islamic civilisation, and Western civilisation. Writing of the long learning the West derived from Islam is, indeed, a challenging procedure. And the limited scope of this work is obvious, requiring others to follow and explain this subject much better.

---

[1] H.L. Savage: Fourteenth Century Jerusalem and Cairo through Western eyes, In N.A. Faris ed: *The Arab Heritage*, Princeton University Press, 1944. pp 199-220: at p.199.
[2] R Lopez: Les Influences Orientales et l'Eveil economique de l'Occident; *Cahiers d'Histoire Mondiale*; Vol 1: 1953-4; pp 594-622; p. 598.

INTRODUCTION

Western historians, in general, have removed the Islamic source with regard to every single change that affected science and civilisation at the origin of Western civilisation, and modern civilisation, and then, each and everyone has substituted a number of explanations for such changes within their field of study. This systematic suppression of the Islamic source of modern science and civilisation has been, however, noted by individual historians who have re-considered the history of their subject. Thus, in his `History of Dams,' Norman Smith, began his chapter devoted to Islamic dams, by noting how historians of civil engineering have ignored the Muslim period, and have claimed that nothing was done by the Muslims, even worse, they have blamed the Muslims for the decline of irrigation and other engineering activities, and their eventual extinction, which is `both unjust and untrue.'[3]

Winder, too, observes, that even in one of the standard works dealing with the legacy of Islamic civilisation, Islamic mechanical engineering is completely set aside.[4]

A similar point is raised by Pacey, who points to the same generalised opinion that hydraulic engineering made little progress under the Muslims, whilst in truth, Muslims extended the application of mechanical and hydraulic technology enormously.[5]

In the development of agriculture, Cherbonneau makes the same observation, questioning the absence of reference to the Muslim contribution, insisting that `If we took the bother to open up and consult the old manuscripts, so many views will be changed, so many prejudices will be destroyed.'[6]

Studying the history of Cartography, Harley and Woodward have noted how it seems nobody has mapped anything from the fall of Rome in the late 5th century to the fall of Constantinople in the 15th, again, completely setting aside any Islamic contribution.[7]

---

[3] N. Smith: *A History of Dams,* The Chaucer Press, London,1971. p.75.

[4] R.B. Winder: Al-Jazari, in *The Genius of Arab Civilisation; Source of Renaissance*; ed J.R.Hayes; Phaidon; 1976; p. 188.

[5] A.Pacey: *Technology in World Civilization, a Thousand Year History*, The MIT Press, Cambridge, 1990, at p.8.

[6] A. Cherbonneau: *Kitab al-Filaha* of Abu Khayr al-Ichbili, in *Bulletin d'Etudes Arabes*, pp 130-44; at p. 130.

[7] J.B. Harley and D. Woodward ed: *The History of Cartography*; Volume 2; Book 1; Cartography in the Traditional Islamic and South Asian Societies; The University of Chicago Press; Chicago and London; 1992; preface p. 1.

Addressing the history of astronomy, Krisciunas did not fail to notice how astronomical research has been made to fall `into a dazed slumber following Ptolemy (c 90-168 CE) not to reawaken until the time of Copernicus (1473-1543),' totally bypassing centuries of Muslim contributions, except to acknowledge them as book burning fanatics.[8]

In mathematics, O'connor and Robertson make the same point, that, the widely held opinion is that after a brilliant period for mathematics when the Greeks laid the foundations for modern mathematics, there was a period of stagnation before the Europeans took over where the Greeks left off; whilst in truth O'cconor and Robertson note, modern mathematics owes so much to Muslim mathematicians centuries before the 16th.[9]

Talbot Rice, equally, hardly fails to note how the historians of art have set aside the Islamic role, turning it into pale imitation of others, whilst he offers both text and photographic evidence to prove the inanity of these widely held theories.[10]

This systematic suppression of the Islamic role in the rise of modern science and civilisation, through its impact on the West, has led to conclusions that hostility to Islam was the principal reason for it. Watt, thus, observes:

`When one keeps hold of all the facets of the medieval confrontation of Christianity and Islam, it is clear that the influence of Islam on Western Christendom is greater than is usually realised.... But, Because Europe was reacting against Islam, it belittled the influence of the Saracens and exaggerated its dependence on its Greek and Roman heritage.'[11]

The same enmity towards Islam is seen by Glubb as the reason why `the indebtedness of Western Christendom to Arab civilisation was systematically played down, if not completely denied.'[12]

Draper, equally, talks of the systematic manner in which the literature of Europe has contrived to put out of sight our scientific obligations to the Muslims; injustice founded on religious rancour and national conceit.[13]

---

[8] K. Krisciunas: *Astronomical Centers of the World*; Cambridge University Press, Cambridge, 1988; at p. 23.

[9] J. J O'Connor and E. F Robertson: Arabic Mathematics: a forgotten brilliance at: http://www-history.mcs.st-andrews.ac.uk/history/index.html

[10] D.Talbot Rice: *Islamic Art*; Thames and Hudson; London; 1979 ed; pp. 172; 174; 183.

[11] W. Montgomery Watt: L'Influence de l'Islam sur l'Europe Medievale (127-156): In *Revue d'Etudes Islamiques*; Vol 41; pp 127-56; at pp. 155-6.

[12] Sir John Glubb: *A Short History of the Arab Peoples*, Hodder and Stoughton, London, 1969, p.289.

[13] J.W. Draper: A *History of the Intellectual Development of Europe*; 2 Vols: London, 1875; revised ed; Vol 2; p. 42.

Even Prince Charles observes: `There is also much ignorance about the debt our own culture and civilisation owe to the Islamic world... which stems from the straightjacket of history, which we have inherited.... Because we have tended to see Islam as the enemy of the West, as an alien culture, society, and system of belief, we have tended to ignore or erase its great relevance to our own history.'[14]

Although the systematic suppression of the Islamic role from mainstream Western history has been noted, hardly anything has been said how this is done. This is the object of this work. This author seeks to answer the matter by addressing deficient historical writing where it is at its most vulnerable: its incapacity to rest on anything substantial when the issue is addressed from as wide a spectrum as possible. Indeed, Western `historians' dispose of enough expertise to build whole theories around the changes that affected their science or subject, and it is easy for them to fabricate whole histories, just as Hartner puts it, by `twisting and suppressing facts at the author's pleasure.'[15]By using their expertise in their specific subject, adding all the nitty gritty of academia, referencing, statements backed by other statements from similarly minded historians, they can convince whomsoever fails to see the wider picture, or is not knowledgeable enough to challenge them.[16] However, by addressing as wide spectrum as possible of changes that took place in the medieval period, this author was able to see a number of patterns. First, all new medieval scientific developments and changes in aspects of civilisation, anywhere, any time, took place as soon as contact was made with an Islamic source. Second, major changes show the same timing (12th century principally), when contact was made with Islamic culture, or when the first crusaders began returning from the East. Third, all changes took place in contact with the same geographical sources (Spain, Sicily, Southern Italy, the East during the Crusades) (all under

---

[14] H.R.H Prince of Wales: Islam and the West, Oxford Centre for Islamic Studies, Oxford, 1993.

[15] W. Hartner Essay review of O. Neugebauer: A History of Ancient Mathematical Astronomy, Verlag, 1975; in *Journal for the History of Astronomy*; 9; pp 201-12; at p. 201.

[16] On the manners and forms history is distorted, see, for instance, the following:
J. Fontana: *The Distorted Past*, Blackwell, 1995.
P. Geyl: *Use and Abuse of History*, Yale University Press, 1955:p.78.
M. Daumas: The History of Technology: Its limits; its methods; trans into English and notes by A. Rupert Hall; in *History of Technology*, 1976; pp 85-112;
D.H. Fischer: *Historians' Fallacies*, London: Routledge & Kegan Paul, 1971.Introduction: xxi.
Lies My Teacher Told Me by James W. Loewen at:
http://www.uvm.edu/~jloewen/intro.html

Islamic control, or direct influence). Fourth, all regions within Western Christendom, which experienced the first revolutions in science and aspects of civilisation (Lorraine, Salerno, Montpellier, Catalonia, etc,) were the nearest to Islamic sources of influence, or did so soon after the entry of Islamic learning into such places. Fifth, each of these regions showed forms and manners of change in precisely the very aspect of science and civilisation they borrowed from Islam. Sixth, all changes bear the same substance of content (Islamic content). Seventh, all changes have the same agents of transmission (Muslim masons and scholars, Christians residing amongst Muslims..). Eighth, all early Western Christian scholars were either Arabic minded scholars (Adelard of Bath, Gerbert of Aurillac, Daniel of Morley…), or scholars who travelled to the Muslim world (Leonardo Fibonacci..). Ninth, any changes that took place prior to the 12th-13th century also show the same patterns of influence. And so on and so forth.

All these points, which are easy to conceal if one change is dealt with on its-own become impossible to conceal if tens of changes are considered together, as the same patterns repeat themselves. More importantly, if each historian can give diverse causes and explanations for changes which affected his or her science or subject, which seem plausible if any such change or science is looked at individually, when all such subjects are put together, however, one is faced with literally tens of causes, all very different, often conflicting, and yet, suddenly, spontaneously, producing the same impact, and at the same time, and in the same places. Which, of course, is basically unscientific, for, it is impossible for diverging causes to produce the same effects, in the same place, at the same time, in the same pattern, and with the same substance.

This work seeks to dismantle the established Western version of history, which does away with the Islamic influence on the West, and on modern science and civilisation.

In its first part, it shows how historians demean as much as possible the Islamic role in the rise of modern science and civilisation, insisting that modern science and civilisation owe to the Western recovery of Greek learning in its Arabic version. This part also dwells on the generalised technique of distorting historical reality through a selective suppression of facts and of bibliographical sources, and even the suppression of whole centuries from knowledge. The underlying reasons for such hostile approach to the Islamic role in the rise of science and civilisation are also examined.

The second part shows that changes which took place in Western Christendom, whether university learning, windmills, individual sciences, the beginning of hospitals, the introduction of paper, changes in arts and architecture, etc, rather than owing their source to tens of differing, even conflicting causes, as Western history generally holds, all, in fact, owe to the same Islamic sources. This is made obvious by looking at these sources through three major parameters, each addressed in a distinct chapter:

-The first chapter looks at the role of scholars, pilgrims, tradesmen, rulers, etc, who disseminated Islamic learning.

-The second chapter looks at the particular role of some regions and countries in their acquisition and then diffusion of Islamic sciences and civilisation.

-The third deals with the impact translations from Arabic, especially in the 12th century, had on modern science and civilisation.

In the third part, focus is on areas of influence, here highlighting the Islamic substance of influence. This is addressed in four distinct areas, each, again, in a distinct chapter:

The first chapter deals with the Islamic impact on Western learning in its wider form.

The second deals with Islamic influences on particular sciences.

The third covers influences on trade, industry and farming.

The final chapter looks at the arts, architecture, and culture, highlighting, once more, the strong Islamic influences.

******

Throughout, this work will remain highly critical of mainstream Western history. However, it must be insisted upon two crucial elements: first, that although criticism can be addressed to mainstream modern historians and modern study of history, older Western historians, in general, and many of today's historians, even if the latter constitute the minority, have imposed on themselves high standards of impartiality and excellence. Second, and more importantly, it is only thanks to the erudition of this minority of Western historians that this work is possible. They might have their views on Islam, as a faith, with which this author disagrees, but it is they who have preserved and conveyed much of what relates to Islamic civilisation this author has relied upon to complete this work.

Part One

MAINSTREAM WESTERN APPROACH TO THE ISLAMIC ROLE IN THE RISE OF MODERN SCIENCE AND CIVILISATION

Today's Western vast superiority over the Islamic world is military, economic, scientific, communications, information, etc. Looking at the Islamic lands today, all that can be seen are dysfunctional economies and institutions, undemocratic political systems, and above all, an inexistent scientific contribution to humanity of any sort or form. An image of generalised ineptness compounded by a daily media barrage telling of Islamic terror, intolerance, barbarism, etc. Yet, some ten-twelve centuries or so ago, the picture was the very reverse. As Lombard says:

`Nous vivions dans des clairières. L'Islam, lui, brillait de tous ses feux...' (We were living in the wilderness; Islam then was glaring with a thousand lights).[17]

Draper depicts such contrast:

`When Europe was hardly more enlightened than Caffraria is now, the Saracens were cultivating and even creating science. Their triumphs in philosophy, mathematics, astronomy, chemistry, medicine, proved to be more glorious, more durable, and therefore more important than their military actions had been.'[18]

When the Muslims entered Spain in the early 8th century, in the Spanish Asturias, Scott observes, the local inhabitants lived in `rude hovels constructed of stones and unhewn timber, thatched with straw, floored with rushes and provided with a hole in the roof to enable the smoke to escape; their walls and ceilings were smeared with soot and grease.'[19] The people, Scott pursues, were `in appearance and intelligence, scarcely removed from the condition of savages.'[20]

The only few blessed with the capacity to read in Western Christendom

---

[17] The article appeared in *Le Temps stratégique* No 20, Spring 1987; but can be found at http://www.archipress.org/batin/ts20lombard.htm.

[18] J.W. Draper: *A History of the Intellectual Development; op cit;* Vol I; p. 412.

[19] S.P. Scott: *History of the Moorish Empire in Europe*; The Lippincot Company; Philadelphia; 1904. Vol 1; p.339.

[20] Ibid.

were ecclesiastics, few souls lost in wide stretches of rural ignorance.[21] The monasteries were `islands in a sea of ignorance and barbarism, saving learning from extinction in Western Europe at a time when no other forces worked strongly to that end,' says Haskins.[22] This, at the time, Campbell notes, when the Caliphs of Baghdad and Cordova endowed and fostered education among their subjects (both Muslims and non Muslims) to such an extent that in the latter city every boy and girl of twelve was able to read and write.[23]

This is so big a contrast, that the 11th century Spanish Muslim, Said al-Andalusi, in his book *The Categories of Nations,* when singling out the peoples who had cultivated the sciences, finds no place for Western Christendom.[24]

It was Islam, as will be lengthily shown in this work, which, in the expression of Lombard: `dragged Western Christendom out of its `barbarian night.'[25] It was Islam which promoted trade and culture, and the Islamic advance, which dragged the West into `an astonishing progress and the re-launching of its civilisation,' pursues Lombard.[26] An opinion also adhered to by Smith:

`The dark ages of Europe would have been doubly, nay trebly dark; for the Arabs who alone by their arts and sciences, by their agriculture, their philosophy, and their virtues, shone out amidst the universal gloom of ignorance and crime, who gave to Spain and to Europe an Averroes and an Avicenna, the Alhambra and the Al-Kazar….. It was the Arabs who developed the sciences of agriculture and astronomy, and created those of Algebra and chemistry; who adorned their cities with colleges and libraries, as well as with mosques and palaces; who supplied Europe with a school of philosophers from Cordova, and a school of physicians from Salerno.'[27]

The discovery of Islamic learning, Levey points out, did not just arrive at a time when the movement of ideas was `at a relative standstill,' but the Muslims also came along with a new outlook, with a sense of enquiry into

---

[21] C.H. Haskins: *The Renaissance of the Twelfth Century*, Harvard University Press, 1927: 32-4.

[22] Ibid.

[23] D. Campbell: *Arabian Medicine, and its Influence on the Middle Ages*; Philo Press; Amsterdam; 1926; reprinted 1974: pp.xiii-xiv.

[24] P. Benoit and F. Micheau: The Arab Intermediary: in *A history of Scientific Thought*; M. Serres editor; Blackwell, 1995; pp 191-221; p. 202.

[25] M. Lombard: Nous Vivions; op cit.

[26] Ibid.

[27] R.B. Smith: *Mohammed and Mohammedanism*; London; Smith Elder; 1876 pp. 125-6; and 217.

the old, and finally to a point `where Western Europe could take over this thoroughly examined knowledge and endow its ripeness with a completely fresh approach of its own.'[28]

Such Islamic role in the awakening of Western Christendom is generally passed in silence, though. Dawson points out how:
`We are so accustomed to regarding our culture as essentially Western, that it is difficult to remember that there was a time when the most civilised regions of Western Europe belonged to an alien Oriental culture.'[29]
Briffault is more radical in his assessment:
`The debt of Europe to the heathen dog, could find no place in the scheme of Christian history, and the garbled falsification has imposed itself on all subsequent conceptions.'[30] `The history of the rebirth of Europe from barbarism,' he adds, `is constantly being written without any reference whatsoever, except to mention `the triumphs of the Cross over the Crescent,' and `the reclamation of Spain from the Moorish yoke," to the influence of Arab civilisation-the history of the Prince of Denmark without Hamlet.'[31]
Equally, Draper speaks of:
`The systematic manner in which the literature of Europe has contrived to put out of sight our scientific obligations to the Muhammadans…'[32]
`The Arab has left his intellectual heritage on Europe…' and `such their (Muslims) splendour, their luxury, their knowledge; such some of the obligations we are under to them-obligations which Christian Europe, with singular insincerity, has ever been fain to hide. The cry against the misbeliever has long outlived the Crusades.'[33]

One of the many reasons for this denial, briefly noted here, is: had the Islamic role in the rise of the West and modern civilisation been accepted, how would then have been justified the Western colonial history of the Islamic lands, when such colonisation was justified on the ground of a civilising mission of `an inferior.' Today, equally, the Western `civilising mission' of Islamic society parallels depictions of Islamic barbarism, with little or no ground for any acknowledgment of any Islamic role in the rise of modern science and civilisation.

---

[28] M. Levey: *Early Arabic Pharmacology*, Leiden, E.J. Brill,, 1973, p. 71.
[29] C. Dawson: *Medieval Essays*: Sheed and Ward: London; 1953; p. 219.
[30] R. Briffault: *The Making of Humanity*, George Allen and Unwin Ltd, 1928, p. 189.
[31] Ibid.
[32] J.W. Draper: A *History*; op cit; Vol 2; p. 42.
[33] Ibid. p. 44.

It is this matter of denial of the Islamic role in the rise of modern science and civilisation that this first part deals with.

The first chapter looks at the contrast between Islam and Western civilisations during the Middle Ages so as to demonstrate that, contrary to what mainstream Western history tells us, it was impossible for the West to suddenly, and spontaneously, emerge from a state of wretchedness into sudden light without external Islamic influence. It is all the more the case, as the first parts of Western Christendom to emerge into higher learning were precisely those that had the first contacts with Islam.

The manner mainstream Western history demeans such an impact, and the reasons behind such denial are then addressed in the second chapter. The third chapter refutes such interpretation of history in good length.

1. CONTRASTING CIVILISATIONS

The sharp contrast that existed between Islam and Western Christendom over the Middle Ages period (7th-13th century, most particularly) highlights the fact that modern Western civilisation did not come out of nowhere for, next to it, `mingling with it' as Dawson puts it, was a brilliant civilisation.[34] Many of the features of such high civilisation can be found in Europe soon after the two came into direct contact (during the 12th century, most of all). This contrast also serves to show that it was impossible for the Christian West to jump from nowhere to deliver our modern civilisation, and spontaneously, as is made to appear by most of modern historians. Historians, it must be noted, who fail to realise that it is a fundamental basic principle that nothing happens out of nothing; unless, of course it is created by God, and one is a believer. Of course one is not going to argue on this last point, nor is one going to dwell on every detail of Islamic `brilliance' and Western Christian `wretchedness.' Here are just some overall observations to highlight the contrasts at the levels of learning and society.

1. Learning

In the land of Islam, learning (*ilm*), by which is meant the whole world of the intellect, Pedersen holds, engaged the interest of Muslims more than anything else during `the golden age of Islam and for a good while thereafter' (8th-13th century).[35] The life that evolved in the mosques spread outward to put its mark upon influential circles everywhere. Princes and rich men gathered people of learning and letters around them, and it was quite common for a prince, one or more times a week, to hold a concourse (majlis), at which representatives of the intellectual life would assemble and, with their princely host participating, discuss those topics that concerned them, just as they were accustomed to do when meeting in their own millieu.[36] `Never before and never since', admits Briffault `on such a scale has the spectacle been witnessed of the ruling classes throughout the length and breadth of a vast empire given over entirely to

[34] C. Dawson: Medieval Essays; op cit; p. 220.
[35] J. Pedersen: *The Arabic Book,* tr by G. French; Princeton University Press; 1984. p. 37.
[36] Ibid.

a frenzied passion for the acquirement of knowledge. Learning seemed to have become with them the chief business of life. Caliphs and emirs hurried from their Diwans to closet themselves in their libraries and observatories. They neglected their affairs of the state to attend lectures and converse on mathematical problems with men of science.'[37]

Science became hobby; paupers and kings competing to obtain knowledge; Islam's religious encouragement of science `breaking the monopolies of the hermits, of churches and temples,' note al-Faruqui.[38] During `the most splendid period' of Islamic Spain, Scott remarks, ignorance was regarded so disgraceful that those without education `concealed the fact as far as possible, just as they would have hidden the commission of a crime.'[39] In Muslim Spain, Scott notes, there was not a village where `the blessings of education' could not be enjoyed by the children of the most indigent peasant, and in Cordova were eight hundred public schools frequented alike by Muslims, Christians, and Jews, and where instruction was imparted by lectures. The Spanish Muslim received knowledge at the same time and under the same conditions as the literary pilgrims from Asia Minor and Egypt, from Germany, France, and Britain.[40]

As early as in the 9th century were established centres for advanced learning in the Muslim world; and by the end of the 11th century `university-type institutions' were established in most of the chief cities.[41] The earliest such institution was the first scientific academy of its genre: *Bayt al-Hikma*, or House of Wisdom, was established in Baghdad in the 9th century. It was primarily a research institute, with, as Artz lists, a library, scientific equipment, a translation bureau, and an observatory. Instruction was given in rhetoric, logic, metaphysics and theology, algebra, geometry, trigonometry, physics, biology, medicine, and surgery.[42] In 1065, a great university was founded in Baghdad, and then, in 1234, a second, even more advanced, was set up; this one, Artz notes, had magnificent buildings, including quarters for four law faculties.[43] The university also maintained dormitories, a hospital, and a

---

[37] R. Briffault: *The Making of Humanity*, op cit; p 188.

[38] I.R. and L.L. Al Faruqi: *The Cultural Atlas of Islam*; Mc Millan Publishing Company New York, 1986. p.232.

[39] S.P. Scott: History; op cit, Vol 3: p. 424.

[40] Ibid. pp 467-8.

[41] W.M. Watt: *The Influence of Islam on Medieval Europe*; Edinburgh University Press; 1972; p. 12.

[42] F.B. Artz: *The Mind of the Middle Ages*; 3rd ed; The University of Chicago Press, 1980. p. 151.

[43] Ibid. pp.151-2.

huge library, where it was easy to consult the books, and where pens and paper and lamps were supplied free to the students.[44]
In all other early Islamic institutions of higher learning, which were established around then (Al-Azhar: Cairo; Al-Qarrawiyyin: Fes..) the students were maintained thanks to endowments of diverse sorts. In the curriculum, scientific subjects took a large place, including astronomy and engineering at Al-Azhar,[45] medicine also at Al-Azhar and the mosque of Ibn Tulun in Egypt;[46] courses on grammar, rhetoric, logic, elements of mathematics and astronomy at Al-Qarrawiyyin,[47]and possibly history, geography and elements of chemistry.[48] At Al-Qayrawan and Zaytuna in Tunisia, alongside the Quran and jurisprudence were taught grammar, mathematics, astronomy and medicine.[49] At Al-Qayrawan, classes in medicine were delivered by Ziad. B. Khalfun, Ishak B. Imran and Ishak B. Sulayman,[50] whose works were subsequently translated by Constantine The African in the 11th century to establish the first faculty of medicine in Western Europe: Salerno. In Iraq, pharmacology, engineering, astronomy and other subjects were taught in the mosques of Baghdad, and students came from Syria, Persia and India to learn these sciences.[51]

In Western Christendom, and in sharp contrast, learning `had few friends and many detractors.'[52]The Church ran the only schools, and churchmen were the only educated class, acting as secretaries, advisers, scribes, and accountants to princes and barons. Engineers, architects, doctors, lawyers, diplomats, and jurists were all clerics.[53] Such men of

---

[44] Ibid.
[45]M. Alwaye: `Al-Azhar...in thousand years.' Majallatu'l Azhar: (Al-Azhar Magazine, English Section 48 (July 1976: 1-6 in M. Sibai: *Mosque Libraries An Historical Study;* Mansell Publishing Limited; London; 1987. p 30.
[46]J. Pedersen: Some aspects of the history of the madrassa *Islamic Culture* 3 (October 1929) pp 525-37, p. 527.
[47] R. Le Tourneau: *Fes in the age of the Merinids*, trans from French by B.A. Clement, University of Oklahoma Press, 1961, p. 122.
[48] Ibid.
[49] H. Djait et al: *Histoire de la Tunisie* (le Moyen Age); Societe Tunisienne de Difusion, Tunis; p. 378.
[50] Al-Bakri, Massalik, 24; Ibn Abi Usaybi'a, *Uyun al-anba*, ed. and tr A. Nourredine and H. Jahier, Algiers 1958, 2.9, in M.Talbi: Al-Kayrawan; in *Encyclopaedia of Islam*, vol IV, new series; Leiden; Brill; pp. 824-32; at pp 829-30.
[51] Al-Khuli: D*awr al-masajid*, op cit, p. 20, in M. Sibai, Mosque Libraries, op cit p. 30.
[52] N. Daniel: *The Cultural Barrier,* Edinburgh University Press, 1975; p. 170.
[53]Z. Oldenbourg: *The Crusades*; trans from the French by A. Carter; Weinfeld and Nicolson; London; 1965. p.9.

education, dwelling in monasteries, were separated one from another by wide stretches or rural ignorance.[54] Monasteries, however, Haskins points out, were not always such centres of light. Thus, in the rule of St.Benedict, which came to prevail generally throughout the West, the central point was the *Opus Dei*, the daily chanting of the office in the choir, which consumed generally four to four and half hours, and tended with its later developments to occupy six or seven. From three to five hours daily, depending on the season, were left free for reading, by which was meant study and meditation on the Bible or the fathers, such as Basil and Cassian, not discursive reading in other works.[55] Hill, too, outlines the narrow objectives of cathedral teaching, which includes the preparation of clerics and priests, whilst the scientific learning consisted in basic arithmetical computations, the propositions of Euclid (without the proofs), and astronomy based mainly on the folklore of Germanic tribes, rudimentary geometry and chemistry consisting of basic metallurgy and the dyeing of cloth.[56]

In his dedication of his *Philosophia* to John of Oxford, Bishop of Norwich from 1175 to 1200, the English scholar, Daniel of Morley writes a long quotation, of which extracts:

`When, some time ago, I went away to study, I stopped a while in Paris. There, I saw asses rather than men occupying the chairs and pretending to be very important. They had desks in front of them heaving under the weight of two or three immovable tomes, painting Roman Law in golden letters. With leaden styluses in their hands they inserted asterisks and obeluses here and there with a grave and reverent air. But because they did not know anything, they were no better than marble statues: by their silence alone they wished to seem wise, and as soon as they tried to say anything, I found them completely unable to express a word. When I discovered things were like this, I did not want to get infected by similar petrification.... But when I heard that the doctrine of the Arabs, which is devoted entirely to the quadrivium, was all the fashion in Toledo in those days, I hurried there as quickly as I could...'[57]

Daniel pursues that he was begged to return to England from Spain by his friends, but was `disappointed' with what he found. Asked by his friend the bishop about `the wonderful things in Toledo,' the teaching there, and the movements of the celestial bodies, Daniel submitted a

---

[54] C.H. Haskins: The Renaissance; op cit; pp. 32-4.

[55] Ibid.

[56] D.R. Hill: *Islamic Science and Engineering*, Edinburgh University Press. 1993. p. 220.

[57] In C. Burnett: *The Introduction of Arabic Learning into England.* The Panizzi Lectures, 1996. The British Library, London, 1997. pp.61-2.

treatise for his scrutiny. Its first book was about the lower part of the universe, its second about the higher. He then begs the reader that `he should not despise the simple and clear opinions of the Arabs, but should note that Latin philosophers make heavy weather of these subjects quite unnecessarily, and, through their ignorance, have put figments of their imagination veiled in obscure language, so that their unsteady floundering in this subject might be covered by a blanket of unintelligibility.'[58]

The contrast between the two civilisations stretches to every subject of science. Medical knowledge and practice, for instance, shows that Christian/Latin `cures' consisted primarily in excessive bleeding, severe amputations, use of magic, which more than often led to the death of the patient.[59] At least up to the 13th century, a common method of treatment for practically every ailment in the West was bleeding by leeches or at times by the use of the knife. Bleeding even of weakened wounded warriors was common, magic charms and curious drugs- for example, the drinking of urine for its supposedly beneficial qualities, were also prescribed.[60] For every emergency or illness there was a friend in the skies as outlined here by Durant.[61] St Sebastian and St Roch were mighty in time of pestilence. St Apollinia, whose jaw had been broken by the executioner, healed the toothache; St Blaise cured sore throat. St Corneille protected oxen; St Gall chickens, St Antony pigs.[62] Islam, on the other hand shuns saints and sainthood; Daniel noting how Islamic theologians always fought popular beliefs in saints, relics and miracles.[63] Draper observes how: `whilst the Christian peasant fever stricken or overtaken by accident, tried to the nearest saint shrine and expected a miracle; the Spanish Moor relied on the prescription or lancet of his physician, or the bandage and knife of his surgeon.'[64]

As far as mathematics went, as Briffault notes, whilst the Muslims perfected the decimal system of notation by introducing the use of the cipher or zero, created Algebra and carried it to the solution of equations of the fourth degree, and trigonometry, substituting sines and tangents

---

[58] Daniel of Morley, Philosophia, ed. G. Maurach, pp 204-55; in C. Burnett: The Introduction of Arabic learning, op cit, p. 62.

[59] M. Watt: The Influence, op cit, pp 65-6.

[60] D. J. Geanakoplos: *Medieval Western Civilisation, and the Byzantine and Islamic Worlds*, D.C. Heath and Company, Toronto, 1979.p.358

[61] W. Durant: *The Age of Faith*, Simon and Shuster, New York; 6th printing; 1950. p. 737.

[62] E. Male: l'Art religieux du 13em siecle en France; pp. 309-11; in W. Durant: The Age of faith, p.743.

[63] N. Daniel: The Arabs and Mediaeval Europe; op cit. p.11

[64] J.W. Draper: A History, op cit, vol II, p. 40.

for the chord of the Greeks, and `thus multiplied a thousand-fold the powers of human inquiry, the highest mathematical knowledge of the Christian West did not extend beyond `a laboured use of the rule of three.'[65]The simplest operations of arithmetic were performed by means of the abacus-the same device of wires and beads that is used `in our kindergartens.'[66]In 9th century Europe, according to Allen, arithmetic was a sort of occult art, which was to solve mysteries rather than problems.[67]And when Gerbert, later pope Silvester II (999-1003), who had visited Spain and learnt Muslim sciences, constructed a new form of abacus, and brought Arabic numerals north, his mathematics was rejected,[68]and was even deemed dangerous `Saracen' magic.[69]

The narrow intellectual boundaries were compounded by the narrow physical perceptions of the world. Thus, whilst Muslims, through a number of geographers of great stature, Ibn Fadlan, Al-Biruni, Al-Muqaddasi and so on, unveiled the mysteries of lands as diverse as Scandinavia, India, Africa, China, and central Asia, from as early as the 9th century,[70]only in the late 13th century, John of Montecorvino, an Italian missionary to India and to China (c.1247-c.1328) wrote his first letter from the Coromandel Coast, in 1291-1292, known only through an Italian version made by the Dominican Menentillus of Spoleto; this being the earliest Christian account of India, thus over four centuries after similar accounts by Muslims (Ibn Sa'ad, Suleyman etc).[71] In its description of India, climate, peoples, products, Hinduism, Hindu manners and customs, hence and only then, it became apparent in

---

[65] R.Briffault: *The Making of Humanity*, op cit; p. 194.

[66] Ibid.

[67] R. Allen: Gerbert Pope Silvester II; *The English Historical Review*: Year 1892: pp 625-668; p.631.

[68] W.M. Watt: The Influence of Islam; op cit; pp. 58-9.

[69] See L.Cochrane: *Adelard of Bath;* British Museum Press, 1994; J. Draper: A History; op cit.

[70] See for instance:

-G.Ferrand: *Relations de Voyages et textes geographiques Arabes, Persans and Turks relatifs a l'Extreme orient du VIIem au XVIIIem Siecles*; Ernest Leroux, Paris, 1913-4

-A. Miquel: *La Geography Humaine du Monde Musulman*; in 4 vols; Paris; The Hague; 1967

J.T. Reinaud: *Relations de voyages faites par les Arabes et les Persans dans l'Inde et la Chine*; Paris; Imprimerie Royale; 2 Vols; 1845.

C.de La Ronciere: *La Decouverte de l'Afrique au Moyen Age: l'Interieur du Continent;* Vol 1; Published as Vol 5 of the Memoires de la Societe Royale de Geography d'Egypte; Cairo; 1924.

[71] G.Sarton: *Introduction to the History of Science*; 3 vols; The Carnegie Institute of Washington; 1927-48. Vol II. pp 1054-6.

Western Christendom the vast extent and the diversity of that continent.[72]

The book and its institution, the library, offer more contrasts between the two cultures. In Merw in Eastern Persia, around 1216-1218, there were 10 libraries, two in the chief mosque and the remainder in the madrasas.[73] In Shiraz, was founded a library by Adud al-Daula (d.983), which, in the words of al-Muqaddasi (b.946-d.end of 10th century), was: `a complex of buildings surrounded by gardens with lakes and waterways. The buildings were topped with domes, and comprised an upper and a lower story with a total, according to the chief official, of 360 rooms.... In each department, catalogues were placed on a shelf... the rooms were furnished with carpets...'[74]
In Marrakech, the Kutubya Mosque was so named, because around 200 Kutubiya or book sellers had assembled their booths around that Mosque erected by the Almohad ruler Abd al-Mumin, and they had given their name to it.[75] And in Spain, Al-Hakem's (ruler 961-976) collection was estimated at between 400,000 to 600,000 books.[76] Nur Eddin Zangi's (ruler 1146-1173) gave many libraries to Damascus;[77] Al Qadi al-Fadil presented Cairo's schools with 100,000 volumes on various subjects for the use of students;[78] and the Almohad rulers did the same in Morocco; the sultans in fact collecting both works, and authors, whom they wanted to have very close to them.[79]It was also impossible to find a mosque or a learning institution of any sort without a collection of books placed at the disposal of students or readers.[80]Amongst scholars, there was none who could be found without a collection of books of his own, the number of these libraries somehow equal to the number of learned people, in their thousands.[81] The library of the physician Ibn al-Mutran, for instance, had, according to Ibn Abi Usaybi'a (1203-69) more than

---

[72]Ibid.
[73] Yaqut: Mu'jam in J. Pedersen, The Arabic Book, p. 128.
[74] AL-Muqaddasi: *Ahsan al-Taqasim fi Ma'arifat al-Aqalim* (The best divisions in the knowledge of the Climes), edited by de Goeje, Leiden, 1885. p. 449.
[75] R. Landau: *Morocco*: Elek Books Ltd, London 1967. p.80.
[76] J. Pedersen: The Arabic Book, op cit, p. 120.
[77] A Shalaby: *History of Muslim Education*. Beirut: Dar al Kashaf, 1954. p. 102.
[78] Al-Makrizi: *Khitat*: Ed A Al-Mulaiji. 3 Vols. Beirut: Dar al-Urfan. 1959. vol II, p. 366.
[79] G. Deverdun: *Marrakech*; Editions Techniques Nord Africaines; Rabat; 1959. pp. 264-5.
[80] A. Shalaby: *History; op cit*; p 95:
[81] Ibid. p. 107.

3000 volumes; and three copyists worked constantly in his service.[82] And we hear of a private library in Baghdad, in the 9th century, which required 120 camels to move it from one place to another.[83]

In Western Christendom, the library, Draper explains, hardly meant a special room, still less a special building. Its common word was *armarium*, which means wardrobe or book-press, and that is what the `library' was, ordinarily kept in the church, or in an alcove of the cloister with shelves in the wall.[84] Such collections of books were perforce small, and the earliest monastic catalogues list but a few volumes, perhaps a score or so.[85] Lanfranc's *Consuetudines* at the end of the 11th century assumes that all the books of a monastery can be piled on a single rug.[86] By the 12th century, few libraries could approach the size of that of Reichenau, which numbered 415 volumes in the 9th century, or that of Lorsch with 590, and Bobbio with 666 in the 10th century.[87] Even in the 12th century, such libraries as that of Corbie, containing 342 volumes, and of Durham with 546, were rare, whilst Cluny, rich in everything, had 500 books.[88] In the case of these larger collections something to be deducted to allow for duplicates, of which the catalogues of the greater libraries show a considerable number. Thus Cluny possessed nearly a dozen copies of Boethius' *De consolatione philosophiae*.[89]Every monastery had a library of service books, with usually some copies of Bibles and theological works; often certain elementary text-books, though these cannot always be assumed.[90]The library catalogue of the rich abbey of Troarn in Normandy, dated 1446, was composed almost entirely of books of devotion, and few Norman abbeys or nunneries can show more.[91] Collections of books remained very small for centuries, even in the largest institutions, in France, the 14th century king's library had only about 400 titles.[92] The libraries of

---

[82] In F. Micheau: The Scientific Institutions in the Medieval Near East, in *The Encyclopaedia of the History of Arabic Science*, Ed by R. Rashed; Routledge; London; 1996; pp 985-1007, at p. 988:

[83] F.B. Artz: The Mind; op cit; p.153.

[84] J. Draper: History; op cit; Vol II; p. 71.

[85] Ibid.

[86] Ibid.

[87] J.S. Beddie: Libraries in the Twelfth Century; *Anniversary Essays in Medieval History by Students of Charles Homer Haskins*; Boughton Mifflin Company; Boston; 1929; pp. 1-23; p. 2-3.

[88] Ibid.

[89] Ibid.

[90] C.H. Haskins: The Renaissance; op cit; pp. 34-6

[91] Ibid.

[92] F.B. Artz: The Mind; op cit; p.153.

the Sorbonne in Paris in the 14th and the Vatican in the 15th century contained roughly over 2000 books each.[93]

Whilst in Islam, there was the odd case of a scholar running foul of a ruler, or powerful vizier, and hence being exiled, and possibly imprisoned, there is no case of one learned man being burnt at the stake for his `heretical' ideas. Even the Almohads, deemed the most Orthodox of all Muslim dynasties, were not just behind a brilliant civilisation,[94] but also sponsored scholarship.[95] Maimonides, who is generally said by many to have been victim of the `extreme Orthodox Muslim' Almohads, in fact mainly suffered at the hands of non Muslims. Rabbi Solomon ben Abraham of Montpellier denounced his books to the Dominican inquisition at Montpellier as containing heresies dangerous to Christianity as well as Judaism. All his publications were burned in public ceremonies at Montpellier in 1234, and at Paris in 1242.[96] After he left for the East, and when worn out by fatigue, Saladin's vizier, seeing his exhaustion, pensioned him until he died in 1204, aged sixty nine.[97]

In the Christian West, Lacroix explains, from the time of Plotinus and Porphyrus (Greek Antiquity) to that of Cardan and Paracelsus (15th century `Renaissance',) no man of eminence could assist the progress of science or make any great scientific discovery without being reputed a magician, or stigmatised as `a sorcerer-a fatal appellation which, attached to the name of a noble victim of his love for science, disturbed his repose, often interrupted his labours, and sometimes put his liberty and life in peril.'[98] Frederick II who sought to promote learning attracted much fear and suspicion because amongst others he fostered learning in areas such as medicine, which was viewed with deep seated hostility and fear, and `Andalusians' (that is those with Islamic learning from

---

[93] J.F. d'Amico, `Manuscripts,' in *The Cambridge History of Renaissance Philosophy*, ed. C Schmitt and Q. Skinner (New York: Cambridge University Press, 1988), pp 11-24 at pp. 15 ff. D'Amico follows K. Christ, *The Handbook of Medieval Library History*, trans. T.M. Otto (London: Methuen, 1984).

[94] To have a glimpse of Almohad art and civilization see:
E.L. Provencal: *La Civilisation Arabe en Espagne*; Paris; 1948;
G. Marcais: *Manuel d'Art Musulman*; Paris; 1926.
H. Terrasse: *L'Art Hispano-Mauresque des origins au 13em siecle*; Paris; 1937.

[95] See G. Deverdun: *Marrakech*; op cit;
Entries on Ibn Rushd and Marrakech in *Dictionary of the Middle Ages*; J.R. Strayer Editor in Chief; Charles Scribner's Sons; New York; 1980 fwd.

[96] W. Durant: The Age of faith, P. 415.

[97] Ibid. p. 414.

[98] P. Lacroix: *Science and Literature in the Middle Ages*, Frederick Ungar Publishing Co, New York, 1964.p.204.

Spain) were regarded with considerable trepidation by the old guard.[99]Learned men of Christendom, the likes of Raymond Lulli, Albertus Magnus, Roger Bacon, Vincent of Beauvais, who, after having composed a great number of remarkable works upon scholastic philosophy, could not escape unjust suspicions and persecutions.[100] Henry of Aragon, lord of Villena in Spain, gathered a great library, which was publicly burned on the charge that he had intercourse with the devil.[101]The Florentine encyclopaedist, Cecco d'Ascoli was accused of being in communication with the devil, and burnt at the stake in Rome in 1327.[102]

2. Contrasting Societies:

Economic and Social conditions mirrored the contrasts in learning. Marcais explains that cities have played a considerable part in the history of Islam, which is somehow paradoxical when remembering that those who carried the faith throughout the world, from the Himalayas to the Pyrenees, were mainly Arabs and Bedouins `who never slept between four walls.'[103]A point also noted by Udovitch, who contrasts the desert and oases `the setting of its birth,' with the cities and towns `the setting of Islam's growth and maturity.'[104] From Mecca and Medina, the centres of power, culture, and wealth moved to such urban sites as Damascus, Baghdad, Cairo, Al-Qayrawan, Fes, and Cordoba.[105]Western Christendom, on the other hand, went the other way, according to Lombard, who notes how the cities of antiquity disappeared due to economic crises, (5th century) invasions, and brigandage; the town was now merely a cramped *castrum* for defence and refuge; the period marked by the triumph of the large estate and of rural economy `Barbarisation and ruralisation spreading over almost the whole of the

---

[99] Maria Rosa Menocal: *The Arabic Role in Medieval Literary History,* University of Pennsylvania Press, Philadelphia, 1987. p.64.
[100] P. Lacroix: Science; op cit. p.204.
[101] Calvert: Moorish Remains in Spain; in W. Durant: The Age of Faith; op cit; p. 426.
[102] P. Lacroix: Science; op cit. p.204.
[103] G. Marcais: l'Urbanisme Musulman, in *Melanges d'Histoire et d'Archeologie de l'Occident Musulman*; Vol 1; Gouvernement General de l'Algerie; Alger; 1957; pp 219-31; at p. 219.
[104] A.L. Udovitch: Urbanism; in *Dictionary of the Middle Ages*; op cit, Vol 12, pp 306-10.
[105] Ibid.

Western World.'[106] Southern is of the same opinion, contrasting the West, a society primarily agrarian, feudal, and monastic, at a time when the strength of Islam lay in its great cities, wealthy courts, and long lines of communication.[107]The greatest centres of Islamic civilisation, Artz notes, `as far at least as it was to influence the civilization of Europe,' were Damascus, Baghdad, Cairo, and Cordova.[108]In fact, medieval Baghdad, Cairo, Damascus, Aleppo, Tyre, Tripoli, Tunis, Mosul were already modern cities such as would not begin to flower in the West until the 17th century or even the 19th century.[109] The great cities of the East possessed conduits of running water; and everywhere could be found numerous pools and baths.[110] The streets were paved, and many were actual mosaics of different coloured stones, and often shaded with canopies stretched between the roofs of the buildings to give shelter from sun and rain.[111] The houses were large buildings, several storeys high, housing numerous families, with terraces on the roofs, internal galleries and balconies, and fountains in the centre of the courtyards.[112] Every city also had its countless gardens, and on the outskirts were great orchards full of orange and lemon trees, apples, pomegranates, and cherries.[113]

Damascus, for instance, was built at a point where five streams converge, and was well supplied with parks, fountains, and public baths; public buildings, and great charitable foundations for the care of the sick, orphans, and the aged and by the 10th century had a population of 140,000.[114]The city was a great commercial and manufacturing centre, each craft with its quarter, whilst outside the city the landed aristocrats and the wealthier merchants had magnificent homes surrounded with gardens. In the middle of the city stood the huge palace and the gardens of the caliph and, beside them, the greatest of all Islamic mosques, built by twelve thousand workmen, employed for eight years.[115]Its vast mosaic floor was covered with rich carpets, the walls were faced with marble and tiles, and the interior was lighted with seventy-four stained glass windows and thousands of hanging lamps of metal and of

---

[106] M. Lombard: *The Golden Age of Islam*; trans J. Spencer; North Holland publishers; 1975. p. 119.
[107] R.W. Southern: *Western Views of Islam in the Middle Ages*, Harvard University Press, 1978. p. 7.
[108] F.B. Artz: The Mind; op cit; pp 148-50.
[109] Z. Oldenbourg: *The Crusades*; op cit; pp. 497-8.
[110] Ibid. p. 476.
[111] Ibid. pp. 476; 498.
[112] Ibid. p. 476.
[113] Ibid.
[114] F.B. Artz: The Mind; op cit; pp 148-50.
[115] Ibid.

enamelled glass. And in its construction, the master masons used for the first time in a Muslim building the horse-shoe arch.[116]

Samarra, the second great capital of the Abbasid caliphate, was situated along the Tigris some sixty miles (ninety-seven kilometres) north of Baghdad. The city was founded in 835 by caliph al-Mu'tasim (r. 833-841). It was subject to meticulous planning; several thoroughfares running almost the entire length and breadth of the city.[117] The main thoroughfare extended the entire length of the city. With later extensions it ran some 20 miles (32 kilometres) and was reported to have been 300 feet (91 meters) wide at one point. The great government buildings, the Friday mosque and the city markets were all situated along al-Sarjah; and it was throughout the entire history of the city the main line from which most of the city's traffic radiated toward the Tigris and inland.[118] The market areas were subsequently enlarged and the port facilities expanded as part of an energetic program that included the refurbishing and strengthening of already existing structures.[119] The new mosque was an enormous structure; and as it was to serve the entire population of Samarra (which resided for the most part along the first two thoroughfares inland), three major traffic areas had to be constructed along the width of the urban area. Each artery was reported to have been about 150 feet (46 meters) wide so as to handle the enormous traffic. Each artery was flanked by rows of shops, representing all sorts of commercial and artisanal establishments. The arteries were in turn connected to ample side streets containing the residences of the general populace.[120] The Great thoroughfare was extended from the outer limits of Samarra, and feeder channels that brought drinking water flanked both sides of the road.[121]

Cordova, in the 10th century, is said to have had 200,000 houses, 600 mosques, and 900 public baths, and its thoroughfares, for a distance of miles, brilliantly illuminated, substantially paved, kept in excellent repair, regularly patrolled by guardians of the peace.[122] Its workshops employed 13,000 weavers, as well as its armourers and leather works, whose products were famous throughout the civilised world.[123]

---

[116] Ibid.
[117] J. Lassner: Samarra; Dictionary of Middle Ages; op cit; vol 10;pp. 642-3.
[118] Ibid.
[119] Ibid.
[120] Ibid. p. 643.
[121] Ibid.
[122] S.P. Scott: *History; op cit;* Vol 3; pp 520-2.
[123] C. Dawson: Medieval Essays; op cit; p. 220.

And long indeed would be the list of early Islamic cities which could boast huge expanses of gardens.[124] Al-Fustat, in Cairo, with its multi-storey dwellings, had thousands of private gardens, some of great splendour.[125] Basra in Iraq is described by the early geographers as a veritable Venice, with mile after mile of canals criss-crossing the gardens and orchards;[126] Nisbin, also in Iraq was said to have 40 000 gardens of fruit trees, and Damascus 110 000.[127] One Garden in the city of Samarra in the 9th century consisted of 432 acres, 172 of which being gardens with pavilions, halls and basins.[128]In Turkey, Ettinghausen says: `devotion, if not mania' for pretty flowers was prevalent everywhere; fondness for tulips in 16th century Turkey, in particular, having a profound influence on Europe.[129] In North Africa, one learns of a multitude of gardens, surrounding and inside cities such as Tunis, Algiers, Tlemcen, and Marrakech, places which today are not conspicuous for their greenery.[130]

Other than their glamour and magnificence, Islamic cities, as seats of the government or its representatives, also guaranteed relative security; as local markets or international emporiums, they provided economic opportunities; and with their mosques and madrasas, their churches, synagogues, and schools, their bathhouses and other amenities, they contained all that was needed for leading a religious and cultured life.[131]In Aleppo, for instance, at the time of the crusades, in the middle of the war and at a moment when the city was in economic doldrums, there were still a number of Christian churches.[132] Muslim cities, cosmopolitan by nature, Oldenbourg adds, were great centres of commerce, into which caravans flowed from all corners of the East and the West.[133] The tooled leather work, the work in metal, glass-making and silk-weaving, the tile and ceramic creations, the illuminated manuscripts, and the wrought jewels made in these Islamic centres

---

124 A.M. Watson: *Agricultural Innovation in the Early Islamic World*; Cambridge University Press; 1983. p.117.
125 G. Wiet: *Cairo, City of Art and Commerce*; Norman Oklahoma; 1964; pp. 17;19;22.
126 Al-Duri: *Tarikh al-Iraq*; Baghdad; 1948 pp; 26.28.
127 Yaqut, Ibn Abd Allah al-Hamawi: *Jacut's Geographisches Worterbuch,* ed. F. Wustenfeld. 6 vols. Leipzig, 1866-70. vol iv; p. 787.
128 R. Ettinghausen: Introduction; in *The Islamic Garden*, Ed by E.B. MacDougall and R. Ettinghausen; Dumbarton Oaks; Washington; 1976; p. 3.
129 Ibid. p.5.
130 Al-Bakri: Description: 9 ff; Torres balbas: La Ruinas; 275 ff; G.Marcais: les Jardins de l'islam; all in A. Watson: Agricultural Innovation; op cit; p. 118.
131 A.L. Udovitch: Urbanism; op cit; p. 310.
132 Z. Oldenbourg: *The Crusades*; op cit; pp. 497-8.
133Ibid. p. 498.

found markets all over Asia and Europe.[134]Muslim cities were also administrative centres employing thousands of clerks; cultural centres where sometimes tens of thousands of manuscripts were preserved in public and private libraries, where schools of literature and philosophy of all persuasions met, where men assembled in public squares to discuss the Qu'ran; each of these cities a world in miniature; even the small cities, like Homs and Shaizar, had `an opulence and comfort which European kings might have envied.'[135] Their streets were paved with stones, and were cleaned, policed, and illuminated at night, whilst water was brought to the public squares and to many of the houses by conduits.[136] In large Muslim cities there were schools for all, free for young children and sometimes even for university students; there were public baths at every street corner, as well as many private pools.[137]

It is difficult to imagine Western Europe without cities, notes Geanakoplos, but during the period of the `Dark Ages,' and in contrast to the civilisation of Islam, urban centres had virtually disappeared, except for some of the nuclei of Roman cities in Paris, Rome, London, Cologne, Italy and southern France.[138] These were, however, only shadows of the old Roman towns, hardly constituting cities in the modern sense of the word; they were, essentially, sites of fortresses or of Episcopal sees; usually inhabited by the bishop or secular lord and his servants.[139] Whether from a cultural, economic and artistic point of view, there was no possible comparison between Western Europe and the Muslim East, admits Oldenbourg; `Compared to Baghdad, Paris, Mainz, London and Milan were not even like modern provincial cities compared to a capital. `They were little better than African villages or townships, where only the churches and the occasionally princely residence bore witness that this was an important centre.'[140] Western `cities' lacked any substantial group of merchants or artisans and were in consequence largely dependent on the local agricultural economy.[141] Paris, for instance, consisted of only the Ile de la Cite, a small fortified island in the middle of the Seine, where the royal residence, the Episcopal palace, and the cathedral were the most important buildings,

[134] F.B. Artz: The Mind; op cit; pp 148-50.
[135] Z. Oldenbourg: The Crusades; op cit; p. 498.
[136] F.B. Artz: The Mind; op cit; pp 148-50.
[137] Z. Oldenbourg: *The Crusades*; op cit; pp. 497-8.
[138] D.J. Geanakoplos: *Medieval Western; op cit;* p.187.
[139] Ibid.
[140] Z. Oldenbourg: *The Crusades*; op cit; p. 497.
[141] D.J. Geanakoplos: *Medieval Western; op cit;* p.187.

whilst Rouen, the capital of the duchy of Normandy, was centred on the ducal palace, the bishop's residence, and a great monastery.[142] Some merchant-craftsmen and peddler type sold their wares in nearby regions where protection could be secured, and local markets, rising in major concentrations of populations, were negligible in both number and importance, their purpose being only to serve local needs.[143]The population, sparse as it was, was perpetually thinned by pestilence and want, and nor was the state of the townsman better than that of the rustic; his bed was a bag of straw, with a hard round of log for his pillow.[144] If he was in easy circumstances, his clothing was of leather, if poor, a wisp of straw wrapped round his limbs kept off the cold.[145] Scott notes how in Paris, there were no pavements until the 13th century; in London none until the 14th; the streets of both capitals were often impassable; at night shrouded in inky darkness; at all times dominated by outlaws.[146] It was not until the close of the reign of Charles II, that even a defective system of street lighting was adopted. In London the mortality of the plague is a convincing proof of the unsanitary conditions that prevailed; the supply of water was derived from the polluted river or from wells reeking- with contamination.[147]

3. Contacts and Impacts

In a period when the Christian West was `fighting desperately with barbarism,' Carra de Vaux says, it was the Muslims who kept `alive the higher intellectual life and the study of science.'[148]
And if, the zenith of Muslim activity may be placed in the 9th and 10th centuries, it was continued down to the 15th, and from the 12th century, De Vaux adds, everyone in the West `who had any taste for science, some desire for light, turned to the East or to the Moorish West.'[149]

---

142 Ibid.
143 Ibid.
144 J. Draper: History, Vol II; op cit; p. 230:
145 Ibid.
146 S.P. Scott: History; op cit; Vol 3; pp 520-2.
147 Ibid.
148 Baron Carra de Vaux: Astronomy and Mathematics, in *The Legacy of Islam*, ed T. Arnold and A. Guillaume; 1st edition; Oxford; 1931; pp.376-97; at p. 377.
149 Ibid.

The Muslim East, Oldenbourg observes, was then regarded as the land not only of wealth and luxury but also of technical and artistic progress; a model to be imitated as far as possible, but one which people had as yet no idea of equalling.[150] To the west, it was in Spain, in Sicily, in the trading cities of the French and Italian Rivieras, and at the feudal courts of Provence and Catalonia, Dawson observes, that Western Christendom came under the influence of `the brilliant civilisation' that had developed in Western Islam in the 10th to the 12th century.[151] It was at Toledo, Salerno, and Barcelona and Montpellier and Palermo, Dawson spells out, that the Christians `put themselves to school' and laid the foundations of the new scientific culture of the West.[152] Western scholars' eyes, he points out, were not just opened to the riches they were discovering, but above all to their own scientific backwardness.'[153]

Travellers, merchants, pilgrims, students, all brought back the same impressions of wonder and even envy, so much so, it must have at times appeared to them that wealth and comfort went hand in hand `with the ability to read Arabic.'[154]A frustrating reality caught by the devoutly Christian figure, Alvaro of Cordova (mid 9th century):

`The pity of it! Christians have forgotten their own tongue and scarce one in a thousand can be found able to compose in fair Latin a letter to a friend! but when it comes to writing Arabic, how many there are who can express themselves in that language with the greatest elegance, and even compose verses which surpass in formal correctness those of the Arabs themselves.'[155]

It is precisely any Western region which made contact with Islam, which first experienced changes instantaneously before the rest. Christian Catalonia in Spain was first to emerge from barbarism. Catalonia was the nearest Christian part to Islamic Andalusia, and as Burnett notes, 10th century Cordova far outstripped in size and opulence any city in the Latin West, and it was no surprise that Islamic astronomy and culture should overflow into its nearest Christian neighbour: Catalonia.[156] From Catalonia, the monastery of Ripoll, in particular, elements of such learning

---

[150]Z. Oldenbourg: *The Crusades*; op cit; p. 474.
[151] C. Dawson: *Medieval Essays; op cit;* p. 140.
[152] Ibid.
[153] Ibid.
[154] Maria Rosa Menocal: The Arabic Role; op cit; p.63.
[155]Alvaro: *Indiculus luminosus,* chap. 35, in MPL, CXXI, 554-56; trans. R.Dozy: *Spanish Islam,* Trans. F. G. S. Styokes, London, 1913. p. 268.
[156] C. Burnett: The Introduction of Arabic Learning; op cit. p.3.

were carried north by successive Western scholars (Gerbert. John of Gorze, etc).[157]

Further north, it is precisely, Lorraine, in France, the first place north of the Pyrenees to acquire Islamic astronomical and mathematical learning, which then thrived in its schools, before it diffused such knowledge through much of the Christian West.[158]This follows precisely the contacts established between the German Emperor and Islamic Spain. The German envoy, John of Gorze (in Lorraine), travelled to Cordoba where he stayed three years, and on his return initiated a revival in mathematics and astronomy in the school cathedrals of the region. From there, such knowledge spread to France, and above all England, Lotharingians disseminating the first elements of mathematics and astronomy, and also the knowledge of the astrolabe in such places.[159]

It is also to Sicily, after it was taken by the Normans from the Muslims (late 11th), as Haskins, Sarton, and others have shown, that Western learned men travelled to acquire science and notions of good living, and arts.[160] It is from Sicily that knowledge of administration and finance was derived.[161]And it is from Sicily that aspects of nautical science and various trades and skills also passed north.[162]

It is Salerno, in the south of Italy, which became the first centre of higher learning of the Christian West, precisely once Constantine the African, who, born in Tunisia, had travelled, settled there and made his translations of Muslim doctors of the East and those of Al-Qayrawan.[163]Translations, which made Salerno the first faculty of medicine, its offshoots giving birth to the universities of Palermo and Padua, and from there further north;

---

157 J. W. Thompson: Introduction of Arabic science into Lorraine in the tenth Century," *ISIS* 12 (1929): 187-91.
-L.Cochrane: Adelard of Bath; op cit; C.H. Haskins: Studies; op cit; C. Burnett: The Introduction; op cit; etc.

158 See M.C. Welborn: `Lotharingia as a center of Arabic and scientific influence in the eleventh century,' *ISIS* 16 (1931) pp.188-99; J. W. Thompson: Introduction of Arabic science; op cit.

159 Ibid.

160 C.H. Haskins: *Studies in the History of Mediaeval Science*; Frederick Ungar Publishing Co. New York. 1967 ed.
-D. Matthew: *The Norman Kingdom of Sicily*: Cambridge University Press; 1992.

161 C.H. Haskins: England and Sicily in the 12th century; *The English Historical Review*: Vol XXVI (1911) pp 433-447 and 641-665.

162 See Part two of this work, under appropriate heading.

163 See M. Mc Vaugh: Constantine the African, *Dictionary of Scientific Biography*, Ed C. C. Gillispie; C. Scribner's Sons, New York, 1970 fwd, vol 3, pp. 393-5.

translations, which supplied a basic foundation of medical literature on which the West would build for several centuries.[164]

The south of France, the nearest region to Spain, not surprisingly, via the Jewish intermediaries, was also one of the first regions to thrive in all forms and manners of science and learning, arts and culture, which it then distributed all over the continent.[165]

And it is no surprise, nor coincidence, that it was Spain and Portugal, the two places where the Muslims stayed the longest, and where their impact was the strongest, that emerged as the most advanced powers in the early modern times (15th-17th centuries). The Iberian peoples, the Portuguese and the Spaniards, as seafarers and discoverers, opened up the routes across the oceans by making use of the knowledge handed down by Muslim science.[166]

And, once more, as the subsequent chapters will detail to great lengths, each and every region changed and impacted on the rest of Western Christendom, and precisely, according to what it borrowed from Islam. Salerno acquired Islamic medicine, and changed and influenced the rest exactly in this area;[167] not in astronomy or mathematics, which it could have done had the influence been other than Islamic. Lorraine did change and impact on the rest not in medical sciences or geography, it did precisely in the subjects it borrowed from Islam: astronomy and mathematics.[168] Western commercial techniques did not arrive in England or France, first; instead they did via the Italians, the very people who were engaged in near exclusive trade with the Muslims.[169] The Arabic system of reckoning and other mathematical knowledge precisely arrived to Europe with Leonardo Fibonacci, no-one else; Leonardo, whose father had sent

---

164 D.C. Lindberg: The transmission of Greek and Arabic learning to the West; in *Science in the Middle Ages*; ed D.C. Lindberg; The University of Chicago Press. Chicago; 1978 pp 52-90. p. 62.

165 D. Romano: `La Transmission des Sciences Arabes par les Juifs en Languedoc,' in *Juifs et Judaisme de Languedoc*, XIII siecle-debut XIV siecle, ed. Marie-Humbert Vicaire and Bernhard Blumenkranz (*Cahiers de Fanjeaux*, vol 12) (Toulouse, 1977), pp 363-86.

166 A.Pannekoek: *A History of Astronomy;* George Allen and Unwin Ltd; London; 1961. p.184.

167 A. Mieli: *La Science Arabe et son role dans l'evolution scientifique mondiale.* Leiden; E.J. Brill, 1966; p. 219. Constantine the African and `Ali ibn al-Magusti: *The Pantegni* and related texts, eds C. Burnett and D. Jacquard, Leiden, 1994.

168 See M.C. Welborn: Lotharingia; op cit; J. W. Thompson: Introduction of Arabic science; op cit;

169 W. Heyd: *Geschichte des Levantehandels im Mittelalter; 2 vols;* 1879;
Fr edition: W.Heyd: *Histoire du commerce du Levant au Moyen Age;* Leipzig; 1885-6; reedited: Amsterdam 1967.

him to North Africa precisely for such purpose, i.e learning the Muslim system of reckoning.[170] And the same impacts occurred, precisely on the same lines in relation to the crusades, the crusaders bringing from the East what they had acquired there (castle fortifications, windmills, etc); or in the south of France, the region thriving precisely in what it acquired from Islam, medical learning, primarily.

It is also, and precisely, whenever the West made contact with Islam, that it experienced change. And no period experienced as many changes in the West as that of the 12th –13th century. And no period brought the West closer to Islam than that period. Indeed, three major events took place then that brought Western Christendom in closest contact with Islam:
-The Crusades (which went on from the late 11th (1095) to the late 13th (1291).
-The re-conquest of Islamic territories, Sicily (late 11th), Spain (Toledo 1085; Cordova: 1236; Valencia: 1238; and Seville 1248.)
-The 12th century descent of Western scholars on Toledo to make translations of scientific works from Arabic.
And with hardly any exception, and `coincidently' (as mainstream history would tell us), most changes in every science or manifestation of learning and civilisation (technological advance, construction techniques, beginning of universities, hospitals, new forms of poetry, sciences...) took place in the West over that period: 12th-13th centuries. It was an age, Haskins notes, of fresh and vigorous life; witnessing the rise of towns, of the earliest bureaucratic states of the West, the culmination of Romanesque art and the beginning of Gothic; the emergence of vernacular literature; beginning of universities, etc.[171] It was also in 1200 that the Arabic numerals were first used in Europe by notaries charged with drawing up commercial contracts for use in the Islamic world.[172]Windmills also belong to the same period, the first sign of them, a French act of 1105 granting a religious community the right to establish one of them, called *molendinam ad ventum* (moulin a vent in French: windmill in English).[173] The first paper mill to fall in Christian hands was after Valencia was retaken from the Muslims in 1238;

---

[170] C. Singer: *The Earliest Chemical Industry*; The Folio Society; London; 1958. pp. 84-5.
[171] C.H. Haskins: The Renaissance; op cit; preface; p. vi.
[172] D. Abulafia: The Role of Trade in Muslim Christian contact during the Middle Ages; in *The Arab Influence in Medieval Europe*; ed D.A.Agius and R. Hitchcok; Reading; 1994; pp. 1-24; pp. 4-5.
[173] Cited in *Magasin Pittoresque*, t. XX, 1852, p. 50. In Baron Carra de Vaux: *Les Penseurs de l'Islam*; Geuthner; Paris; 1921; Vol 2; p. 190.

and the first paper mill was established in Bologna in 1293.[174] And one of the first, if not the first hospital in the Christian West, the asylum and hospital `Les Quinze Vingt' was founded in Paris by Louis IX (St Louis) after his return from his unhappy crusade in 1254-60, an institution first intended for three hundred poor blind men.[175] And so were many of the first castles, and other impressive constructions also founded following the return of the first crusaders (early years of the 12th). And countless more Western breakthroughs in that period as part three of this work will show. Also, with rare exceptions (Gerbert, John of Gorze…) all the first men, who set up the foundations of learning of the West also belong to that period: Adelard of Bath (fl first half of 12th); Aquinas (d 1272); Fibonacci (fl.1204); Alfonso X (d. 1288), Robert Grosseteste (1168-1253); Roger Bacon (1220-1294), Albertus Magnus (1206-1280)…[176] And of course, all early institutions of higher learning: Salerno, Bologna, Paris, Montpellier, Oxford, etc, came into existence around the same time, too.

From this outline, there seems to be plenty to support the Islamic source of impact on the West, or at least enough to engage into an intellectual consideration of such a role. Not the case at all with mainstream Western history, though. Modern history, in particular, chose to do away with such an Islamic impact.[177] This is noted by Dawson, who notes how `at a time when the rest of Western Europe was just emerging from the depths of barbarism,' the culture of Muslim Spain had attained complete maturity, surpassing the Christian East in genius and originality; the cities of Muslim Spain the richest and most populous, filled with public libraries and public baths, which contrast with `miserable groups of wooden hovels which were growing up in medieval Europe under the shelter of an abbey or a feudal stronghold…'[178] `And yet, this brilliant development of culture is ignored by the ordinary student of medieval European history. It is as though it were a lost world which had no more to do with history of our

---

[174] D. Hunter: *Papermaking: the History and technique of an ancient craft*; Pleiades Books; London; 1943; 1947; p. 474.

[175] M. Meyerhof: Science and medicine, in The Legacy of Islam; op cit; pp 349-50.

[176] See Dictionary of Scientific Biography for the lives of these and other pioneering men of learning of the West.

[177] Unlike the bulk of modern historians, older Western historians, and some of today's historians, even if they constitute a minority, have imposed on themselves high standards of impartiality and excellence. And thanks to their erudition, primarily, however much this author disagrees with their views on Islam, this work is possible.

[178] C. Dawson: Medieval Essays; op cit; p 220.

past than the vanished Kingdom of Atlantis. And yet, not only did it lie at the very doors of the Christian world: it was actually mingled with it.'[179]

Briffault goes even further:

`That a brilliant and energetic civilisation full of creative energy should have existed side by side and in constant relation with populations sunk in barbarism, without exercising a profound and vital influence upon their development, would be manifest anomaly. That no such suspension of natural law was involved in the relation between Islam and Europe, is abundantly attested in spite of the conspiring of every circumstance to suppress, deform and obliterate the records of that relation. Its extent and importance have been beyond doubt far greater than it is today possible to demonstrate in detail. Like the geological record of extinct life, our knowledge in the matter is derived from the scattered and accidentally preserved fragments of evidence which have been spared by forces universally tending to blot them out.'[180]

This blotting out of Islamic impact on the rise of the West has, indeed, remained one of the constants of modern history. It is examined now.

[179] Ibid.

[180] R. Briffault, The making of Humanity, op cit, pp. 189-90.

2. SIDELINING THE ISLAMIC ROLE

The denial of the Islamic impact on Western civilisation has been raised by many, some such as Draper, for instance, who speaks of:
`the systematic manner in which the literature of Europe has contrived to put out of sight our scientific obligations to the Muhammadans…'[181]
Or Watt, who observes: `For our indebtedness to Islam, we Europeans have a blind spot. We sometimes belittle the extent and importance of Islamic influence in our heritage, and sometimes overlook it altogether.'[182]
Or Lopez, who insists that `scholars have sought to minimise the role played by the Orient and even the South of Europe in the upsurge of Western Europe.'[183]
What Draper, Watt, Lopez, just as others, have failed to do is to look at the precise manner this denial is put into effect, and also the reasons behind the Western denial of the Islamic role in the rise of modern science and civilisation. Both these matters are considered in succession in this chapter.

1. Techniques and Forms of Denial:

The suppression of the Muslim role in the rise of modern science and civilisation is done through two principal techniques. The first consists in the over-focus on the Greek role, whilst lessening that of the Muslims. The other consists in a systematic removal of any Islamic link with any change that took place in Western Christendom in the medieval period. These two techniques are examined in turn.

a. Over-Inflating the Greek Role:

Western history, generally, holds that Greek learning, which thrived in the Classical period (up to the mid 5th century), is the foundation of the 16th–17th century `Renaissance', when such learning was recovered in Western Christendom to set the foundations for our modern science

---

[181] J.W. Draper: A *History*; op cit; Vol 2; p. 42.
[182] W. Montgomery Watt: *The Influence of Islam on Medieval Europe*, Edinburgh, 1972. p.2.
[183] R Lopez: Les Influences orientales; op cit; p. 608.

and civilisation. The period in between (5th -15th) is deemed to be that of `Dark Ages.' Garrison calls the first half of it (500-900 AD): The Age of Ignorance.[184] Somehow, the picture that has prevailed in Western history was that Europe went from the brilliance of antiquity prior to the 5th century, a period dominated by Greece, straight into ten centuries of darkness (5th-15th), and then suddenly, into the Revival (16th –17th); the very Revival that engendered Western power and supremacy prevailing today. In other words, Greek learning, dormant for ten centuries (during the dark ages), was one day recovered, for no obvious reason, and the West blossomed again. According to this dominant view, somehow, the mathematics, the astronomy, the optics, the medicine, etc, left by the Greeks being absolutely the same, untouched in ten centuries, and forming the foundation of the science we have today. The indebtedness of Western Christendom to Muslim civilisation, as a result, is systematically played down, if not completely denied.[185] A tradition was built up, by censorship and propaganda, Glubb says, that `the Muslim imperialists had been mere barbarians' and that the rebirth of learning in the West was derived directly from Roman and Greek sources alone, without any Islamic intervention.[186]A main proponent of such a view is one of the leading figures of Western history of science, Duhem, who says:

`The revelations of Greek thought on the nature of the exterior world ended with the `Almagest" (by Ptolemy) which appeared about A.D. 145, and then began the decline of ancient learning. Those of its works that escaped the fires kindled by Mohammedan warriors were subjected to the barren interpretations of Mussulman commentators and, like parched seed, awaited the time when Latin Christianity would furnish a favourable soil in which they could once more flourish and bring forth fruit.'[187]

Duhem's view, is not just backed by mainstream historians, but is also vulgarised for the sake of the millions, such as by the late 1960s classic programme on the rise of civilisation, entitled, understandably, Civilisation, shown on British television, and dealing with the cultural and intellectual heritage of Europe. According to this programme, Greece was the sole source of knowledge and culture, and no other

---

[184] Chapter IV in F.H. Garrison: *Contributions to the History of Medicine*, Library of Congress Catalogue, New York, 1966.

[185] J Glubb: *A Short History of the Arab Peoples*; Hodder and Stoughton, 1969. p.289.

[186] Ibid.

[187] P. Duhem: Medieval Physics, in R. Palter edition: *Toward Modern Science*; The Noonday Press; New York; 1961; Vol 1; pp 141-159; Quote at p. 141; This article is a reprint from `Physics, history of," *Catholic Encyclopaedia*, XII (1911), pp 47-52.

society or culture came within the purview of this description.[188] More recently, the BBC's `The Greeks' pursued on the same theme that modern civilisation owes all to Greece.[189] Another fairly recent instance had a prominent `scholarly' guest openly, and confidently, stating that science was a manifestation of Western civilisation alone.[190] At a recent conference attended by this author in Manchester, one contributor put the Greek contribution to science and learning to over 90%, and the remaining 10% divided between the rest (Muslims, Chinese, Hindus, etc).[191] Ancient Greece, since the Renaissance, being `revered as the true source of Western civilization, especially in its secular aspects and more particularly in its ideal of rational knowledge,' notes Palter.[192] A `Classical prejudice' according to which the Greeks and the Romans, the Judeo-Christian tradition and the Revival were alone the sources of all knowledge, adds Garaudy.[193] Or as observed by Selin:

`Reference works on other cultures tend either to omit science completely or pay little attention to it, and those on the history of science almost always start with the Greeks, with perhaps a mention of the Islamic world as a translator of Greek scientific works.'[194]

The Chinese, despite Needham's voluminous work to demonstrate their crucial role in the birth of modern science[195] are generally ignored; so are the Hindu, whose contribution is only acknowledged against the Islamic.

The Islamic contribution to the birth of modern science and civilisation is generally reduced to their guardianship of Greek learning, that was supposedly lost in Latin Christendom, until it was recovered to trigger the 16th century Renaissance. Thus, Selin notes how:

`in confrontation with medieval historians centred on Europe, it was not easy to reclaim the scientific heritage for the Muslims for this heritage was primarily seen as that of the ancient Greeks whose works had been translated into Arabic; and since these works, some centuries later, were

---

188 G. Gheverghese Joseph: *The Crest of the Peacock;* Penguin Books; London; 1991. p.346.

189 BBC2, Saturdays, January 2001, 8pm.

190 ITV: 2000 years charting the history of Christianity; 5 September 1999.

191 Manchester Metropolitan University; 27 October 01.

192 R. Palter edition: *Toward Modern Science*; op cit; vol 1; Preface; p.viii.

193 R. Garaudy: *Comment l'Homme devint Humain*, Editions J.A, 1978; Introduction.

194 H. Selin Editor: *Encyclopaedia of the History of Science, Technology, and Medicine in Non Western Cultures*. Kluwer Academic Publishers. Dordrecht/Boston/London, 1997. (p xi).

195 J. Needham: *Science and Civilization in China*; Cambridge University Press, 1954 onwards.

again translated from Arabic into Latin, the Arabs apparently were assigned the humble role of transmitters only like the merchants in an import-export business.'[196]

Selin refers to Renan, the late 19th century French ideologue, for whom the cultural role of Islam was actually limited to the preservation of ancient culture, which it then passed to Western Christendom, which revived it. Renan's views echoed by the overwhelming majority of Western scholarship, such as by Sherwood Taylor:

`The new discoveries of the Arabic world were few: the Arabs must be looked on as preservers of knowledge rather than originators of it. They absorbed foreign ideas with astonishing readiness and their assimilation of Greek culture was a fine achievement; none the less they originated no single great conception.'[197]

Muslim geographers, for instance, as Perroy says:

`All or nearly all, follow the practice of plagiarism of the Middle Ages, inspiring themselves for more than half of the works of Ptolemy, whose text they copied.'[198]

The Christian missionary-scholar, Zoerner, referring to Servier, denies outright any Islamic contribution to modern science.[199]Islam, he says, has had a paralysing influence on culture. Referring to Revd E.J. Bolus, he admits a certain legacy, but `of doubtful value'.[200]Zoerner further refers to De Lacy O'leary[201] to say, that rather of an Islamic legacy, it was the transmission of a particular type of Hellenistic culture, Muslim culture being essentially a part of the Hellenistic-Roman material, even the theology of Islam being formulated and developed from Hellenistic sources.[202] He concludes that:

-Debt is not to Islam but to Hellenised Muslims.

-That the Muslims' main contribution was transmission of Greek learning.

---

196 H. Selin: Encyclopaedia; op cit; p. 862.

197 F. Sherwood Taylor: *A Short History of Science*; William Heinemann Ltd, London, 1939.p.77.

198 E. Perroy: Encore Mahomet et Charlemagne in *Bedeutung Und Rolle des Islam Beim ubergang Vom Altertum Zum Mittelalter*, ed by P. Egon Hubinger; Darmstadt, 1968. pp. 266-275. p.271.

199 A. Servier: Islam and the Psychology of the Musulman; p. 271 in W.A. Zoerner: Has Western culture a debt to Islam: *The Muslim World*; Vol 27; pp 28-43; (Reprinted from the United Church Review of India).

200 W.A. Zoerner: Has Western culture; p.30.

201 De Lacy O'Leary: Arabic Thought and its place in History, p. 295; in W.A. Zoerner: Has Western culture; p.30.

202 De Lacy O'Leary: Arabic; op cit; p. vi.

-That the Islamic contribution was not indispensable to Western culture.[203]

An increasing majority of Western historians, today, go as far as asserting that had the Muslims not transmitted such Greek learning, it would have been recovered by Western genius anyway.[204]

Even amongst Western historians who give some role to the Muslims in the rise of modern science and civilisation, such Muslim role is cut to the minimum. Thus, when dealing with the history of Islamic civilisation, their focus is always on the translation of Greek works executed by early 8th-9th century Muslim translators and scientists (Hunayn Ibn Ishaq, Thabit Ibn Qurrah, etc). Such is the focus on such early period that it is always the most developed part of all writing on Islamic science and civilisation. This phase, in reality, was minimal in its duration, in the region of half a century, and concerning mainly the works of four authors: Galen, Ptolemy, Aristotle, and Euclid.[205] And yet, this phase in most outlines on Islamic civilisation takes the lion's share, so much so one might think one is reading an outline on Greek science rather than on the Islamic. Then, by some oddity, the centuries of Islamic independent brilliance and accomplishments (9th-13th) are generally muted, even if they include thousands of scientific works.[206] The period of passage of Islamic science to the Christian West (12th - $13^{th)}$ is briefly covered, most often completely suppressed. Besides, to accentuate the Greek influence and minimise to the maximum the Islamic role, every effort is spent associating any Islamic achievement with the Greek, as by Wiet et al, where the Greek element is found when it has absolutely nothing to do with the Islamic subject or science being discussed.[207]The expressions Neo-Platonism, Neo-Aristotelian, Neo Galen are always appended to the Islamic breakthrough, even in the case, such as Ibn al-Haytham's optics, when the Muslim breakthrough is in complete opposition to the Greek predecessor.

These are some dominant forms by which the Islamic influence is demeaned through inflating the Greek role; others will be considered in

---

203 W.A. Zoerner: Has Western culture; op cit; p.42.
204 As in conference Metropolitan University 27 October 01.
205 See, for instance, G. Sarton: Introduction; op cit;
206 See, for instance,
-H. Suter: *Die Mathematiker und Astronomen der Araber*, 1900.
-F.Wustenfeld: *Geschichte der arabischen Aerzte*; Gottingen; 1840.
207 G. Wiet et al: *History of Mankind*; Vol III: The Great Medieval Civilisations; Translated from the French; George Allen &Unwin Ltd; UNESCO; 1975; at pp.647-8.

chapter three of this part when the exaggerated role of Greece in the rise of modern science and civilisation is refuted.

There is another form by which the role of Islam in the rise of modern science and civilisation is distorted: it consists in the systematic suppression of facts showing such Islamic role.

b. Systematic Suppression of the Islamic Role:

The suppression of the Islamic role in the rise of modern science and civilisation from mainstream history is systematic. In astronomy, for instance, Krisciunas' opening statement of chapter two goes as follows:

`It is a common misconception that astronomical research fell into a dazed slumber following Ptolemy, not to reawaken until the time of Copernicus. I have briefly sketched in the previous chapter the efforts on the part of various Greeks in preserving their astronomical science. These efforts continued up to the time of the conquest of Egypt by the Arabs, who were not the book burning fanatics that some have made them out to be. Those who think that these Arabs made no contributions of their own have not investigated the subject.'[208]

Krisciunas then points out that during the Middle Ages the principal astronomers were Muslims, Jews, and some Christians, and what they had in common was that they wrote in Arabic. `This was the principal language of astronomy of the ninth through the eleventh centuries, just as English is today.'[209]

Countless examples can be mentioned to support Krisciunas' point. Thus, the two guiding lights of Western history of astronomy, Neugebauer[210] and Delambre,[211] both find nothing to report about Islamic astronomy. J.P. Verdet in *A History of Astronomy*,[212] manages to jump from Ptolemy to Copernicus, skipping nearly 1500 years, as if in his whole lifetime, he never came across one single work dealing with Muslim astronomy.

Browsing through our modern means of communication, the web, as was done by this author in the first two years of the new Millennium, also gives the impression that the Muslims never looked at the sky, or wrote on the subject. Thus at

---

208 K. Krisciunas: *Astronomical Centers of the World*; Cambridge University Press, Cambridge, 1988; at p. 23.

209 Ibid.

210 *Astronomy and History*; Verlag, 1983.

211 *Histoire de l'Astronomie Ancienne;* Johnson Reprint Collection; New York, 1965.

212 J. P. Verdet: *Une Histoire de l'Astronomie*, Le Seuil, Paris, 1990:

http://w3.restena.lu/al/pub/indivs/wagnjean/astronomy.htm#medieval all one finds is that Greek astronomy was transmitted to `the Arabs;' and although `compiling new star catalogues, and developing tables of planetary motion, the Arabs made few useful contributions;' and that the Arabic translations of Ptolemy' *Almagest* filtered into Europe. And that's all. Anybody without sufficient knowledge would believe that Ptolemy's *Almagest* was the only work translated from Arabic into Latin, which is wrong, for the *Almagest* was one of countless translations from Arabic into Latin in the 12th-13th centuries. These translations from Arabic included astronomical works by Al-Khwarizmi, Al-Battani, Al-Farghani, Mash'Allah, Al-Zarqali, Al-Bitruji, Jabir Ibn Aflah, and so on.

Another site: http://dmoz.org/Science/Astronomy/History/ out of the so many astronomical topics it lists, not a single reference is made to Muslim astronomy.

Another site http://homepages.tcp.co.uk/~carling/astrhis.html, and nothing, again. The author just jumps from Ptolemy to Copernicus, skipping 1500 years. One would search in vain for a paragraph on the Muslims, or the Chinese. The author, however, laments the burning at the stake of Giordano Bruno for adopting Copernican beliefs that were viewed with hostility by the Church.

The site of the International Astronomical Union (IAU) at: http://www.astro.uni-bonn.de/~pbrosche/iaucomm41/ reveals that such a union was founded in 1919 with the aim of `promoting the science of astronomy through international cooperation.' Commission 41 of such a union and devoted to the History of Astronomy was created at the 1948 General Assembly. From a look at the activities of such an organisation, its conferences, and also the membership of current officers (years: 2000-3), there is nothing whatsoever regarding Islamic astronomy.

The same suppression of the Islamic role is generalised to every science.

In mathematics, O'connor and Robertson observe:

`There is a widely held view that, after a brilliant period for mathematics when the Greeks laid the foundations for modern mathematics, there was a period of stagnation before the Europeans took over where the Greeks left off at the beginning of the sixteenth century. The common perception of the period of 1000 years or so between the ancient Greeks and the European Renaissance is that little happened in the world of mathematics except that some Arabic translations of Greek

texts were made which preserved the Greek learning so that it was available to the Europeans at the beginning of the sixteenth century.'[213]
The authors pursue:
`That such views should be generally held is of no surprise. Many leading historians of mathematics have contributed to the perception by either omitting any mention of Arabic/Islamic mathematics in the historical development of the subject.'
Recent research, however, the authors add, is painting a very different picture of the debt that we owe to Arabic/Islamic mathematics, as modern mathematics is closer to Muslim mathematics than the Greek; many previously thought brilliant new conceptions of the 16th and 17th centuries thought to be due to European mathematicians have in fact been developed by Muslim mathematicians around four centuries earlier.[214]

In the development of agriculture, Cherbonneau holds:
`It is admitted with difficulty that a nation in majority of nomads could have had known any form of agricultural techniques other than sowing wheat and barley. The misconceptions come from the rarity of works on the subject... If we took the bother to open up and consult the old manuscripts, so many views will be changed, so many prejudices will be destroyed.'[215]

Equally, in his `*History of Dams*,' Norman Smith states:
`Historians of civil engineering have almost totally ignored the Moslem period, and in particular historians of dam building, such as there have been, either make no reference to Moslem work at all or, even worse, claim that during Umayyad and Abbasid times dam building, irrigation and other engineering activities suffered sharp decline and eventual extinction. Such view is both unjust and untrue.'[216]
A similar point is raised by Pacey, who notes that it is often said that hydraulic engineering `made little progress under the Muslim,' and that the latter's achievements hardly evolved beyond the Greek or Roman's. Pacey corrects this view, pointing out that the Islamic civilisation adapted ancient techniques `to serve the needs of a new age,' and that the Muslims extended the application of mechanical and hydraulic technology enormously.[217]

---

[213] J. J O'Connor and E. F Robertson: Arabic Mathematics: a forgotten brilliance at: http://www-history.mcs.st-andrews.ac.uk/history/index.html
[214] Ibid.
[215] A. Cherbonneau: *Kitab al-Filaha; op cit;* p. 130.
[216] N. Smith: *A History of Dams,* The Chaucer Press, London,1971. p.75.
[217] A.Pacey: *Technology in World Civilization,* op cit; at p.8.

Equally, from the onset in one of his articles, Hill makes the observation, that of all the fields in which the Muslims made significant contributions to the progress of civilization, that of mechanical technology, has been the least studied, and so, historians studying the technologies of Europe and the Far East have been seriously handicapped by an inability to make comparisons with scholarly material on the Middle East.[218] Even more serious, he points out, `a damaging belief has taken root, both in the West and in the Arab countries, that modern technology is solely a Western achievement and that its products, for better or worse, are alien imports throughout the rest of the world. This false notion has had incalculable social and political effects on the ways in which peoples of these areas view one another.'[219]

And the same point is made by Janet Abu Lughod on the subject of trade, observing how:

`Too often, European writings view the medieval Italian maritime states as `active' agents operating on a `passive' Islamic society. The Italians are credited with introducing enormous and innovative mechanism for transport and trade into presumably a less competent region. The argument, however, illustrates some of the fallacies, namely, reasoning backward from outcomes and failing to discount perspective in evaluating narratives. Although it is true that the West eventually `won', it should not be assumed that it did so because it was more advanced in either capitalistic theory or practice. Islamic society needed no teachers in these matters.'[220]

And the same can be found with respect to every single science, or manner and form of civilisation,[221] thus helping reach the conclusion on the systematic and institutionalised suppression of the Islamic role.

---

[218] D.R. Hill: Mechanical Technology, in *The Genius of Arab Civilisation; Source of Renaissance*; ed J.R. Hayes; Phaidon, Oxford, 1976, pp 175-187 at p. 175

[219] Ibid.

[220] Janet L. Abu Lughod: *Before European Hegemony;* Oxford University Press; 1989. p.216.

[221] See for instance:

D. Talbot Rice: *Islamic Art*; op cit; throughout the work raises matters of misrepresentation of Muslim art and architecture, Turkish, most particularly.

J.B. Harley and D. Woodward ed: *The History of Cartography*; op cit; in their preface stress the suppression of the Islamic role in map making.

Or the neglect of Muslim mechanical engineering as noted by R.B. Winder: Al-Jazari, in *The Genius of Arab Civilisation; op cit;* p. 188.

This generalised suppression goes back a long way, involving even the destruction of concrete forms of Islamic impact, as Scott, in a lengthy tirade, here summed up for the sake of convenience, says:
`In the land illuminated by his genius and enriched by his industry, the Spanish Muslim is forgotten or absolutely unknown to the majority of the people The effects and the influence of his civilization are disputed or depreciated; his sites mutilated or entirely destroyed; his palaces transformed into the squalid haunts of mendicity and vice; while the leather-clad shepherd watches his flock on the once famous site of gardens adorned with magnificent villas and beautiful with all the luxuriant and fanciful horticulture of the East. Barbaric violence has annihilated the palaces, which lined the Guadalquevir, and whose richness and beauty were the admiration of the world. Ecclesiastical malignity has demolished to their very foundations or sedulously effaced the characteristics of the innumerable mosques, from the seven hundred mosques required for worship in the Cordova, but one has survived. `Diligent antiquarian research has failed to establish even the sites of all but three or four of the remainder, of whose existence and splendour both history and tradition afford abundant and indisputable evidence.' [222]
The same in Sicily, where, as Scott pursues, `the unrelenting hostility of the See of Rome to everything connected with Islam may account for the total disappearance of the superb architectural monuments which history informs us abounded during Muslim rule. The sumptuous edifices which abounded in every city have disappeared or have been mutilated almost beyond recognition. Ignorance and prejudice of successive generations, in addition to the above named destructive agencies, contributing their share, and no unimportant one, to the obliteration of these memorials of Muslim `taste and ingenuity.'[223]

The suppression of the Muslim (or non Western) role is also generalised in historical teaching. Hence, at http://www.man.ac.uk/Science_Engineering/CHSTM/bshs/bshscour.htm#warb as seen in 2001-2002, can be found a list of universities that offer courses in the history of science in the UK. In the introduction to the site, it is asserted that many of the staff listed in the brochure are `leading figures in their fields.' It is also said they are `active in promoting new ways of thinking about science.' `A student can investigate Ancient Greek culture, the impact of Victorian railways,

---

[222] S.P. Scott: *History; op cit;* Vol II; pp. 537; 553; 557-8.
[223] Ibid.

natural history collecting, the origins of the National Health Service, the relations between science and literature, or the philosophy of quantum physics.' `They (the scholars) aim,' it is also said `is to understand how science, medicine and technology operated in the past and how they have come to play such prominent roles in modern society. Studies range from the earliest recorded periods of human life to the most recent laboratory science.'

There are so many contradictions and misleading statements in these brief extracts. The courses that are offered, for instance, precisely highlight the problem. They, again, jump from the Greeks to modern times, as usual, ignoring over ten centuries of history, as if nothing happened in those centuries, stressing the ridiculous notion of spontaneous recovery of learning and of the `Renaissance.' Another problem is the focus on British modern history of science (Victorian changes, the National Health Service, etc..) as if nothing happened elsewhere, a teaching of history of science which completely leaves students and learners as ignorant as ever before, in fact legitimising their ignorance. Then is the assertion of `scholars' looking at all periods in history, which proves to be completely false when one looks at the content of such courses. Besides, with rare exceptions, the so called `scholars' add absolutely nothing of worth to the understanding of how science, medicine, and technology operated at certain times in history, the Middle Ages in particular, ignoring whole chunks of such history.[224] Finally, it is claimed that scholars are universal in their approach, whilst there is not a single word on the history of Chinese science, or anything on the beginnings of modern mathematics, or the transfer of science and ideas between cultures, and so on and so forth. `Scholars' who have no idea about China, Islam, India, or the African role, yet seek to explain how paper, printing, the compass, algebra, the numerals, etc, (which have origins in such civilisations) came into being and developed. Amongst the handful of exceptions noted in 2002, Belfast and the Warburg Institute (London) give some place to the non Western Middle Ages.

Elsewhere, in one of the universities, this author is acquainted with, the one and only person lecturing, supervising, and controlling both department and library of the `Department of History of Science,' literally cleansed his course from anything non Eurocentric. The list of subjects in his course makes an abysmal reading for any person acquainted with the subject.

---

[224] Aberdeen University does goes back to the 13th, but only a 13th century collection from Aberdeen Bestiary.

The suppression of the Islamic role is accompanied by the suppression, accidental or premeditated, of the sources that highlight such a role from bibliographies. A fairly recent author, Swanson, writes on the twelfth century renaissance, but finds no place for the main work on medieval science: Sarton's *Introduction to the History of Science*.[225] Not a single reference either to Needham, who thoroughly demonstrated the Chinese role;[226]and no reference to Millas Vallicrosa,[227]Mieli,[228]or even Haskins' most important work on the subject,[229] nor to Sedillot,[230] Singer,[231] Diercks,[232] Farmer,[233]Draper; Ferrand,[234] Castro,[235] Leclerc,[236] Wiedemann,[237] all major authorities on medieval sciences who also demonstrated the Islamic impact on that period. There is nothing either on Spain, Lorraine, the south of France, Sicily, Salerno, and the Middle East, whilst their role in the 12th century renaissance was decisive. Not even a reference to Southern's masterly *Western Views of Islam in the Middle Ages*,[238]in which Southern expands on the Islamic influence on Western Christendom. With such omissions of fundamental sources, it is the whole perception of the age which is altered, and fundamentally. And this is common to nearly all modern historians who erase sources

[225] R.N. Swanson: *The Twelfth Century Renaissance*, Manchester University Press, 1999. Swanson justifies his omission of material on the limits of his university library.

[226] J. Needham: Science and Civilization in China; op cit.

[227] J.M. Millas Vallicrosa: `Translations of Oriental Scientific Works to the end of the Thirteenth Century,' in *The Evolution of Science*, ed. Guy S. Metraux and Francois Crouzet, New York, 1963, pp 128-67.

[228]A.Mieli: *La Science Arabe et son role dans l'evolution scientifique mondiale*. Leiden: E.J. Brill. 1938.

[229] C.H. Haskins: Studies; op cit.

[230] L.A.Sedillot: *Histoire Generale des Arabes*, 2 Vols, Paris 1877.

[231] C. Singer ed: *Studies in the History and Method of Science*, Oxford, 1921.

[232] G.Diercks: *Die Araber in Mittelater und ihr einfluss auf die kultur Europa's*. Leipzig: Wigand, 1882.

[233] H.G.Farmer: Clues for the Arabian Influence on European Musical Theory', *JRAS*, 1925/1, pp 61-80.

[234] G.Ferrand: *Instructions Nautiques et Routiers Arabes et Portugais des XV et XVI Siecles*, 3 Vols, Paris, 1921-8.

[235]A.Castro: *The Structure of Spanish History*, English translation with revisions and modifications by E.A.King. Princeton: Princeton University Press, 1954.

[236] N.L. Leclerc: *Histoire de la medecine Arabe*. 2 vols, Paris, 1876.

[237] -E. Wiedemann:

-*Beitrage zur Geschichte der Natur-wissenschaften. X. Zur Technik bei den Arabern*. Erlangen, 1906.

-`Zur mechanik und technik bei der Arabern' in *Sitzungsherichte der physikalisch-medizinischen Sorietat in Erlangen* (38), 1906.

[238] In R.W. Southern: *Western Views of Islam in the Middle Ages*, Harvard University Press, 1978.

that are not fundamentally Eurocentric. Grattan Guiness, in the fairly recent Fontana History of the mathematical sciences,[239] in his extensive bibliography, with hundreds of names and sources, still passes over fundamental works on Islamic mathematics.[240]He even ignores Al-Khwarizmi the inventor of a whole science. Paul J. Gans, in his site on the history of technology, at http://scholar.chem.nyu.edu/~tekpages.html sidelines Wiedemann and Hill's (Islamic science and engineering) who wrote much more on Islamic technical achievements than acknowledged by the site. The site, instead, lends too much attention to the usual duo of Eurocentrics: Lynn White Jr[241] and Gimpel.[242] Hill, Pacey and Needham, already cited, and Singer[243] show that Gimpel's, White's and their followers' theories on technology being a wholly Western phenomenon are completely devoid of any credibility. And Gans' effort, it must be pointed out, is one of the better ones, which tells of the standards pursued by others.

It is even increasingly harder to find old Western historical sources and works, which bear the best information on Islamic science; works such as by Heyd[244] and Lombard[245] for trade and commerce, Sedillot for astronomy,[246] Ribera for education and learning,[247] Steinschneider,[248]

---

[239] I. Grattan-Guiness: *The Fontana History of the Mathematical Sciences*, Fontana Press, 1997.

[240] Including

- R. Rashed: *The Development of Arabic Mathematics*, Kluwer Academic Publishing, London, 1994.

-H. Suter: *Die Mathematiker und Astronomen der Araber und ihre Werke*; APA, Oriental Press, Amsterdam, 1982 (originally dated 1900.)

-A. Youschkevitch: *Les Mathématiques arabes* (VIIe-XVe siècles). Paris: J. Vrin, 1976.

-S.Zeki: *A History of Arabic Mathematics*: 2 Vols; Istanbul, 1929.

-F.Sezgin: *Geschichte des arabischen Schrifttums*. Leiden: E.J. Brill, 1967-.

-G.Z.Hieronymus: *Geschichte der mathematik in Altertum und Mittelalter* French translation by jean Mascart. Copenhagen, 1896.

-A. Von Braunmuhl: *Vorlesungen Uber Geschichte der trigonometrie*, 2 vols, Leipzig, Teubner; 1900-3.

[241] Lynn White Jr: technology in the Middle Ages: pp 66-79, in *Technology in Western civilisation*, Vol 1, edited by M. Kranzberg and C.W. Pursell Jr, Oxford University Press, 1967.

[242] J. Gimpel: *The Medieval Machine*, Pimlico, London, 1976.

[243] C. Singer et al edition: *A History of Technology;*5 Vols; Oxford at The Clarendon Press, 1956.

[244] W. Heyd: *Histoire du commerce; op cit*.

[245] M.Lombard: *The Golden Age of Islam*; tr J. Spencer; North Holland Publishers; 1975.

[246] L.Sedillot: Memoire sur les instruments astronomique des Arabes, *Memoires de l'Academie Royale des Inscriptions et Belles Lettres de l'Institut de France* 1: 1-229; Reprinted Frankfurt, 1985.

Bensaude,[249] for nautical sciences, Leclerc[250] for medicine, Wiedemann for physics and mechanics,[251] and so on and so forth. This means, that as time goes, Islamic science finds itself amputated, and very often for good, of substantial facts that are not found in modern history.

Adding to the problem is the fact that leading Western historians of science, such as Duhem, who have the widest influence on generations of historians, champion both suppression of Islamic role and the spread historical inaccuracies in every subject. Duhem, as Mieli notes, `often shows a sectarian attitude, which drives him to distort truth, which he does with an unusual expertise, using omissions, and reservations.'[252]In nautical sciences, for instance, Duhem, holds that the use of the baculus was introduced among the Portuguese navigators by the German scientist Behaim towards the end of the 15th century,[253] whilst Bensaude had amply demonstrated with irrefutable evidence that the baculus was known in Portugal long before the time of Behaim.[254]Dreyer points out how Duhem quotes Bensaude in a footnote without noticing that it demolishes what he had just stated in the text. Also contrary to assertions made by Duhem, that scientific revival began in France, the studies of Bensaude have shown that `the scientific light spread by the Arabs in Spain and Portugal had never been put out,' which amongst others things impacted considerably on navigation to the Indies and the New World.[255]Duhem is also misleading (deliberately or not) in regard to the history of mathematics, as noted by O'cconor and Robertson, distorting and demeaning considerably the Islamic contribution, when evidence points to the contrary.[256] He does the same with regard to

---

[247] J. Ribera: *Dissertaciones y opusculos*, 2 vols, Madrid, 1928.
[248]M. Steinschneider:
Etudes sur Zarkali; *Bulletino Boncompagni*; vol 20.
Notice sur les tables astronomiques attribuees a pierre III d'Aragon, Rome, 1881.
Vite dei mathematici arabi; Roma, 1874.
Die europaischen Ubersetzungen aus dem Arabischen bis Mitte des 17. Jahrhundert (1904-5), repr.
[249] J. Bensaude: *L'Astronomie Nautique au Portugal*, Meridian Publishing, Amsterdam, 1967.
[250] N.L. Leclerc: *Histoire de la medecine Arabe*; 2 vols; Paris; 1876.
[251] E. Wiedemann: Zur mechanik; op cit; etc.
[252] A. Mieli: La Science Arabe; op cit; p. 310.
[253] P. Duhem: *Le Systeme du Monde*; Paris; 1914-1919; Volume iv, p. 40.
[254] J. Bensaude: *L'Astronomie Nautique;* op cit.
[255] J.L. E. Dreyer: Mediaeval Astronomy; In *Toward Modern Science (Palter ed) op cit.* p. 256.
[256] J. J O'connor and E. F Robertson: Arabic Mathematics; op cit.

Muslim astronomy, reducing it to a pale imitation of Ptolemy's astronomy,[257] when as to be seen further on, Muslim astronomy refuted Ptolemy's. Duhem is also responsible for major confusions in the history of physics as Moody notes, two such confusions affecting considerably the history of the subject, notably in his (Duhem's) assertion that the new developments of 14th century mechanics were based on a liberation inspired by Christian supernaturalism, which they were not, and in his assertion of Aristotle Law of motion, which Aristotle never implied or stated, but which Ibn Baja (Avempace) did.[258]

The place of Islamic science in the medieval awakening is further dented by the excessive role attributed to Latin Christian scholars. Amongst these scholars, can be cited Grosseteste, Bacon, Thomas Aquinas, the scholars of Chartres, etc. So many changes are built around such names, and every sign of Islamic influence on them removed, hence giving the impression their creative labours were devoid of any Islamic influence. Yet, again, closer scrutiny, as will be lengthily expanded in the third part, will show a very strong Islamic influence on all of them. Briefly here, Aquinas (13th century) a southern Italian, was born in the highly Islamic influenced Campania, and received his first education in Monte Cassino and Naples,[259] two strongholds of Islamic learning. He was himself directly, and strongly influenced by Al-Farabi and Ibn Rushd, in particular.[260] In the same vein, the school of Chartres in France, which, in every single work on the Middle Ages, is hailed as the departing point for Western scholastic tradition, was founded by one of Gerbert's students at Rheims: Fulbert,[261] who mastered Arabic.[262] One of the earliest and most important translators of Islamic science, Hermann of Carinthia, was a pupil at that same school. Equally, William of Conches, one of the most important learned men of Chartres, had a vast Islamic learning, which he acquired primarily from the translations

---

[257] See J.L. Dreyer: Medieval Astronomy; in *Studies in the history and Method of Science*, ed by C. Singer; vol 2; Oxford at the Clarendon Press; 1921; pp. 102-20; at pp. 102-3.

[258] E. Moody: Galileo and Avempace: The Dynamics of the Leaning Tower Experiment; in *Studies in Medieval Philosophy, Science and Logic;* Center for medieval and Renaissance Studies; University of California; Los Angeles; 1975; pp.203-86; at p.284.

[259] G. Sarton: Introduction; Vol II, op cit; p.735:

[260] See for instance:
-E. Gilson: *History of Christian Philosophy in the Middle Ages*; New York; 1955; p.187.
-R. Hammond: *The Philosophy of al-Farabi and its Influence on Medieval Thought*; New York; The Hobson Book Press; 1947.

[261] L. Cochrane: *Adelard of Bath*. British Museum Press. 1994.p.6

[262] C.Pfister: De Fulberti Carnotensis episcopi; Nancy; 1885. in M. C. Welborn: `Lotharingia; op cit; p. 192.

of Constantine the African.[263]Chartres was also very much acquainted with the early translations of medical writings from Arabic.[264]

c. Effects of Multiple Suppressions:

Once facts related to the Islamic influence, or sources on such Islamic influence have been suppressed, it becomes easier to build the changes of medieval Western Christendom on supposedly internal factors. Which is in direct conflict with the line followed by the majority of earlier historians of science. Amongst such historians is Haskins, who considered the 12th century decisive in the European scientific revival,[265]and who saw the growth of science in this century in terms of transfer, translation, and assimilation alone. He displaced the centre of gravity from Europe itself to various points of contact with the Muslim world: Syria, Sicily, and Toledo; and also Byzantine Constantinople; thus a renaissance from outside.[266] Similarly, Briffault holds:

`It was under the influence of the Arabs and the Moorish revival of culture, and not in the 15th Century that a real renaissance took place. Spain, not Italy, was the cradle of the re-birth of Europe.'[267]

Briffault, in fact, devotes a whole chapter (Chapter VII) attacking the myth of the Renaissance of the 16th began in the North of Italy.[268]

Sarton, Owen,[269] Mieli, and other older generation historians already cited, also see the source of Western revival from outside the Western sphere, during the Middle Ages.

Modern historians, on the other hand, and with rare exceptions (Castro, Menocal, Metzliki, for instance),[270] have shifted this 12th century revolution to from within the Christian West.[271] Eurocentrists, the likes

---

263 G. Sarton: Introduction; Vol 2; op cit; p. 197.

264 C.H. Haskins: Studies; p. 92.

265 C.H. Haskins: Studies; op cit; and C.H. Haskins: The Twelfth Century Renaissance; op cit.

266 B. Stock: Science, technology, and Economic Progress in the Early Middle Ages: in Science in the Middle Ages (Lindberg ed) op cit; pp. 1-51; at p. 39.

267 R. Briffault: *The Making of Humanity,* op cit; pp 188-9.

268 Chapter VII, pp 223-33: The Soi-Disant Renaissance.

269 J. Owen: *The Skeptics of the Italian Renaissance;* Swan Sonnenschein &Co; London; 1908.

270 D. Metlitzki: *The Matter of Araby in Medieval England,* Yale University press, 1977.

271 See more on this:

-R. Benson, Giles Constable ed: *Renaissance and Renewal in the 12th C.* Cambridge, mass: Harvard University Press; 1984.

-C. Brooke: *The 12th Century Renaissance*; London, 1969.

of Lynn White, Duhem, Butterfield, Clagett, etc, have all focused on a revival from within; any change, amongst the many which shaped Western society in every field, attributed to a variety of reasons having nothing to do with Islam. One of the more recent works by Swanson, taken here as an instance, explains that the 12th century renaissance of Western Christendom is due to economic transformations between 1050 and 1250; the rise of agricultural production, proceeding at the same time as population increase, growing urbanisation, trade expansion as `the Mediterranean became increasingly a Christian lake,'[272]the relative peace; `peace, which reduced fear, and thereby encouraged freedom of movement.'[273]The new governmental structures (enhanced by the general cultural shift `from memory to written record,' he tells us, `encouraged administrative development at all levels of society) created a demand for administrators and clerks, provided employments opportunities for those with the requisite skills. Enhanced prospects encouraged people to take advantage of the novel developments which characterise the period.'[274] Thus, internal factors accounting for the 12th century renaissance. Which is fine until one begins to ask, what is the link between these changes and the new mathematics, astronomy, construction techniques, the construction of windmills, the birth of universities, etc.. These are not spontaneous outcomes of changes in agriculture, or population growth as Swanson asserts. And Swanson himself does not show the link between say the new astronomy, or mathematics, and the social factors he says are the sources for the 12th century renaissance. The reason: there are none.

Generally, one find odd origins for such changes in sciences, construction techniques, technology, arts, etc, such as by Compayre, for instance, who asserts that:

`The universities sprang from a spontaneous movement of the human mind.'[275]

This new history, which relies on the suppression of facts linking Islam with the Western awakening in science, other than destroying scholarly credibility, and suppressing vital chunks of historical knowledge, also

---

-H. Butterfield: *The Origins of Modern Science, 1300-1800*.Rev.ed, New York: Free Press; 1957.

-M. Clagett, Gaines Post, and R. Reynolds, ed: *Twelfth Century Europe and the Foundation of Modern Society*. Madison, University of Wisconsin Press; 1966.

272 R.N. Swanson: *The Twelfth Century Renaissance*, op cit; pp.7-8.

273 Ibid. p.8.

274 Ibid. p.9.

275 G. Compayre: *Abelard and the Origin and Early History of Universities*, London 1893, p. 26.

leads to the horrific, unscientific concept: Sudden scientific breakthroughs and civilisation out of nothing. Hence, from the midst of darkness, and from within a society dead intellectually for centuries, suddenly, and spontaneously, erupted every single manifestation of science and civilisation. This sudden outburst out of darkness is `explained' by historians, who, knowledgeable in their particular subject, can cite a number of causes. Having suppressed Islamic sources, they replace them with elements proper to their own field, or subject, an infinity of details poached left and right, which might look credible. All such changes separately looked at seem, indeed, to follow no particular link with anything other than purely Western internal evolution. However, once one brings together all such changes in all sciences and aspects of civilisation, one finds two major deficiencies with such new history:

First, one finds that all such changes emerge in roughly the same centuries 12th-13th, and roughly on the same line (following translations from Arabic), and following contacts with regions under Islamic influence: Spain, Sicily, the South of France, the crusades etc. All such changes also bear similarities with the same Islamic sciences or aspects of civilisation. One also discovers that all men behind them, without one single exception, were imbued with Islamic learning, and that any region, which first evolved was precisely the one with contacts with Islam, and it evolved precisely in the science or aspect of civilisation it borrowed from Islam, and that the first two Western powers to emerge the strongest were Spain and Portugal, by some odd coincidence, the two places where Muslims stayed the longest, and so on and so forth.

Secondly, and more fundamentally, one finds that, as each historian in his (her) subject erases the Islamic influence, and comes out with a set of explanations for the changes in his or her subject in the 12th and 13th century, we end up with a plethora of causes, often conflicting with each other, as any observer can conclude from an overall reading on the many medieval changes in Western Christendom by such Eurocentric historians.[276]

---

[276] As can be gathered by consulting the following:

-A. B. Cobban: *The Medieval Universities: Their Organisation and Their Development.* London. Methuen; 1975.

-R. Benson, Giles Constable ed: *Renaissance and Renewal; op cit.*

-H. Butterfield: *The Origins of Modern Science,* op cit.

-M. Clagett et al: *Twelfth Century Europe; op cit.*

-M.Clagett: *The Science of Mechanics in the Middle Ages*; Madison University of Wisconsin Press; 1959.

It is impossible to accept such history scientifically, for when something repeats itself on and on, on the same patterns, in the same places, and above all at the same time (12th-13th centuries) it is hardly the fruit of coincidence, or of odd, diverging causes, but the result instead of similar link(s). Phrased differently, it is impossible for causes, different and even at odds with each other, suddenly, for no reason, to come to work together exactly in the same places, exactly in the same pattern, and exactly at the same time, and produce the same effects.

Indeed, university learning, new architecture, hospitals, windmills, advances in particular sciences, the compass, paper, new farming techniques, etc, all appeared or took place, at once, and in the 12th – early 13th centuries, thus soon after the Christian West came into direct contact with Islam, and anywhere contact was made with Islam, and most of all, all such changes bore distinct and powerful Islamic features (which will be amply demonstrated in part three of this work).[277] Besides, as a rule, learning and civilisation, at all times, and in all places proceed by borrowing from the superior civilisation, and exactly preceding the Western Christian revival, between the 9th and the 11th century (three full centuries), was when Islamic science reigned `supreme.'[278] Which hence completely undermines the fallacy of a Western revolution of science and learning from within, devoid of an Islamic link.

2. Foundations of, and Reasons for Denial:

According to Watt:

`When one keeps hold of all the facets of the medieval confrontation of Christianity and Islam, it is clear that the influence of Islam on Western Christendom is greater than is usually realised. Not only did Islam share with Western Europe many materials products and technological discoveries; not only did it stimulate Europe intellectually in the fields of science and philosophy, but it provoked Europe into forming a new image of itself. But, Because Europe was reacting against Islam, it

---

277 Or, see, for instance:
H. Prutz: *Kulturgeschichte der kreuzzuge*; Berlin, 1883. C.H. Haskins: The Twelfth century Renaissance; op cit. M.R. Menocal: The Role; op cit; C. Burnett: The Introduction of Arabic learning; op cit.

278 G. Sarton: Introduction; Volume III. p.20.

belittled the influence of the Saracens and exaggerated its dependence on its Greek and Roman heritage.'[279]

Hostility, and hostility leading to adverse perception and depiction of the Islamic role in civilisation have remained the two principal reasons for the denial of such a role.

a. The Enduring Hostility to Islam:

The culture of hostility to Islam goes back to the Middle Ages, and has remained since. Here is a brief outline of how hostile depictions of Islam and Muslims evolved through the centuries.

Polemics against Islam from the early stages to the end of the Middle Ages:

According to Christian tradition, the Muslims practice polytheism, and worship statues and representations of the Prophet (PBUH).[280] Fulk of Chartres who took part in the first crusade and lived in Jerusalem for over a quarter of a century asserts that in the Dome of the Rock the Muslims `used to pray to an idol made in the name of Mahumet.'[281] In the Song of Roland, the Muslims were said to worship three Gods: `Tervagan, Mahomet, and Apollo,'[282]the polemists insisting that the Muslims adore an idol of Aphrodite.[283] Pagans and Muslims were linked together in the *Ars Fidei Catholicoe* of Alanus de Insulis (b.ca 1128), where he has a section `*contra paganos seu Mohometanos*',[284] whilst Jacques de Vitry wrote: 'as often as the followers of Mohammed possess the Temple of Solomon, they set up his statue in the Temple and permit no Christian to enter.'[285]When the Byzantine emperor, Manuel I

[279] W. Montgomery Watt: L'Influence de l'Islam; op cit; pp. 155-6.

[280] C. Pellat, `L'idée de Dieu chez les «Sarrasins» des chansons de geste', *Studia Islamica*, 22, (1965), 5-24.

[281] Fulcheri Carnotensis…in B. Z. Kedar: *Crusade and Mission*; Princeton University Press; 1984; at p. 89.

[282] See Paul Bancourt: *Les Musulmans dans les chansons de geste du cycle du roi;* 2 Vols; Aix. 1982.

[283] M.T. D'Alverny: La Connaissance de l'Islam en occident du IXe au XIIe siecle; in *Settimane di studio… Spoleto: 2-8 Aprile 1964*; Vol ii; Spoleto 1965. pp. 577-602. in M.T. D'Alverny: *La Connaissance de l'Islam dans l'Occident Medieval*; ed by C. Burnett. Variorum; 1994; p. 583.

[284]J.W. Sweetman: *Islam and Christian Theology*; Lutterworth Press; London; 1955; Vol I; Part II. P. 66.

[285] D.C. Munro: The Western attitude toward Islam during the period of the Crusades; *Speculum* Vol 6 No 4, pp. 329-43; pp 331-2..

Comnenus (1143-80), sought to show that it is inaccurate to equate Islam with idolatry he became stuck in controversy with the ecclesiastical hierarchy.[286]Even prominent figures, such as the Bolognese professor of civil law Azo (1150-1230) wrote a commentary on the Code of Justinian that holds that `the pagans, that is the Saracens, worship innumerable gods, goddesses, and indeed demons.'[287] The Prophet is also said to have made himself adored as an idol, and even as a God. Thus, in the Chronicle of the false Turpin, an immense idol of the Prophet dominates, whilst the *Gesta Francorum* speaks of gods, and of oaths taken by Muhammad as a god; and reported Corboran (Kerbogha, a Turkish army leader who fought the Crusades) as swearing 'by Mohammed and all the gods,' and his account was widely copied and served as the basis for the histories written by Robert, Baldric, Guibert and others who repeated its statement.[288] For Sigebert of Gembloux (d.1112), `this is the Muhammad to whom the Gentiles, hitherto offer the worship of a deity.'[289] In an official report sent to Pope Innocent III from Acre in 1204, the patriarch of Jerusalem and the Grand master of the Knights Hospitaliers and Templars state categorically that the Muslims daily visit and adore their `God magometh, just as the Christians worship Christ in their Churches.'[290]

Things reach apocalyptic proportions with the English historian Mathew Paris:

`A sort of infernal lightning, which, however, descended from the skies, had suddenly set fire to and destroyed the temple of Mahomet, together with his statue; and that again a second explosion similar to the first, had reduced the said temple to small bits; and that a third had, as we believed, thrust the ruins into an abyss in the earth. After this, he said, this fire, which burned with a most devouring heat, though it did not give a bright light, crept along under the earth, like the fire of hell, consuming even rocks in its way, and could not even yet be extinguished. And thus the whole city of Mecca, and the country in its vicinity, were consumed with inextinguishable fire.'[291]

---

[286]G.L. Hanson: Manuel I Comnenus and the `God of Muhammad' A Study in Byzantine Ecclesiastical politics; in J. V. Tolan. Ed: *Medieval Christian Perceptions of Islam*; Routledge; London; 1996; pp. 55-84.

[287] Azo: Summa Aurea, to Cod.1.11; Lyons; 1557; col 7a; in B. Z. Kedar: *Crusade*; op cit; p. 88.

[288] In D.C. Munro: The Western attitude; op cit at p.331-2.

[289] Sigebert of Gembloux, quoted in B.Z. Kedar: Crusade; op cit; p. 86.

[290] *Ryccardi de S. Germano Chronica*, ed. C.A. Garufi (1936-8); in B. Z. Kedar: Crusade; op cit; p. 90.

[291] Mathew Paris' English History, vol III, p.231 in J. Dahmus: *Seven Medieval Historians*, Nelson-Hall, Chicago, 1982; p.172.

It is needless to dwell in refuting this matter of idols, every person being aware that Islam's most important summon is never to adore idols in any shape or form, and the first act of the Prophet once entering Mecca was to destroy the idols, the pre-Islamic Gods. Yet, as Smith notes, the Prophet, the `destroyer of idols' was transformed into `an idol of God, and a servant of the devil.'[292]

It is also worth noting, that Tancred (a crusade leader) was heard in 1099 to have found a silver idol of the Prophet in the Temple of `the Lord.' This fable, although the result of a misunderstanding and mistranslation of the chronicler Fulcher of Chartres, Munro points out, was even taken up by today's scholars.[293]

In Western polemics, Muslims were also sexually perverse. Hence, according to Guibert (of Nogent) (d. ca 1124-30), the Prophet `removed the restraints on all shamefulness for his followers." Guibert says that all Mohammed ordered his followers to commit all kinds of turpitude in order to seduce them to follow him:

'. . .The more they abandoned themselves in all ways, as if authorized by heaven itself, to all kinds of excess in these permitted vices, the more they covered up the wickedness of it, in praising the grace of God, who accorded, in his indulgence, these loose times. All the severity of Christianity was condemned and given over to public insults; the teachings of honesty and virtue which had been laid down by the Evangels were accused of being hard, of being cruel; and on the contrary those that the cow had brought were called the teachings of generosity and were recognized as the only ones in accord with the liberty instituted by God himself. ... But since they did not place any restraint on the indulgence of the senses, one soon saw them giving themselves up to vices that even the ignorant animals ignore entirely and that are not even decent to mention…'[294]

Islam, in Western depiction, also promotes sodomy,[295] and the associated vision of the Muslim is that of as a figure of extremes-excessive in zeal, in cruelty, and in sensuality, a picture enduring for centuries.[296]

Daniel points out that these hostile identifications seek to justify in Christian minds Islam's great appeal, an appeal, which they say, owes to

---

[292] R.B. Smith: *Mohammed and Mohammedanism*; London; Smith Elder; 1874 1st ed p. 75 fwd.

[293] D.C. Munro: The Western: Op cit; pp 331-2.

[294] Ibid. p.334.

[295] N. Daniel: *The Cultural Barrier*, Edinburgh University Press, 1975.p.166.

[296] John Sweetman: *The Oriental Obsession:* Cambridge University Press, 1987. p.6.

nothing else `than to its corruption of souls, offering people sensuous pleasures Christianity would never contemplate to even address. Christianity since its early days,' Daniel reminds, `had stressed the value of total sexual continence in a way that was foreign to Islam.'[297]

Islam has also been identified as nothing but a heresy. In his treatise on Heresies about the life of Mohammed, the Eastern Christian, John of Damascus wrote that arose among the Arabs a man named mamed, who became acquainted with the Old and New Testaments, and later, after discoursing with an Arian monk, `established his own sect', which he imagined to be a new religion.[298] Another version on how the Prophet acquired his teaching is by Gauthier de Compiègne who wrote in the 12th century, telling of Mohammed as a poor child, but raised by a baron who made his fortune in Persia, India and Ethiopia, and whose trust Mohammed wins, before a Christian hermit teaches him about the Old and New Testaments.[299]Another story presents Mohammed as a renegade cardinal who, out of pique at having been passed over in a papal election, went off to Arabia and started a rival religion.[300] Before then, it was a monk who becomes a cardinal named Nicolas, who to take revenge on his attackers, makes of the Prophet the instrument of his revenge. Then Nicolas becomes the Prophet himself, hence Mohammed was initially in Rome, celebrated and adulated, but because angry for not having been elected pope, founds a new rival religion.[301] The Prophet, according to d'Alverny, thus, becomes the agent of `Perverse Jews,' and also heretic Christians: Nestorians, Jacobites, Arians, etc, depending on who makes the attack on Islam.[302]

Mohammed (PBUH) is also depicted as a sorcerer as in *The History of Charles the Great and Orlando,* whereby the pseudo-Turpin says that `the Saracens had a tradition that the idol Mahomet, which they worshipped, was made by himself in his lifetime; and that by the help of

---

[297] N. Daniel: *The Arabs and Medieval Europe*; Longman Librarie du Liban; 1975. p.230.
[298] John of Damascus: *De haeresibus*, *Patrologia Graeca*, vol. 94, 761-71; in G. Von Grunebaum: *Medieval Islam* The Chicago University Press; 1969. p. 43.
[299] Gauthier de Compiègne. *Otia Machometi. In* E. Edelstand du Méril, *Poesies populaires latines du moyen âge* (Paris, 1977).
[300] B. Lewis: *Cultures in Conflict*; Oxford University Press; 1995. p. 30.
[301] E. Doutte: Mahomet Cardinal, in *Memoires de la societe d'agriculture... sciences et arts de la Marne*; Second serie; Vol 1; 2nd part; Chalons; 1899. pp 233-43.
[302] M. T. D'Alverny: Pierre le Venerable et la Legende de Mahomet: *A Cluny, Congres Scientifique*... 9-11 July 1949; CNRS; 1950; pp 161-170; at p. 163. in M.T. D'Alverny: *La Connaissance; op cit.*

a legion devils it was by magic art endued with such irresistible strength that it could not be broken. If any Christian approached it he was exposed to great danger; but when the Saracens came to appease Mahomet, and make their supplications to him, they returned safely. The birds that chanced to light upon it were immediately struck dead.'[303] Vincent de Beauvais in his *Speculum Historiale* portrays Mohammed as a magus skilled in sorcery and black magic.[304] Hidlebert of Lemans (d.1133) archbishop of Tours (France), describes the Prophet trying to prove his divine mission in the eyes of the people by the apparent miracle that `a terrifying bull, secretly tamed and trained by the `impostor,' kneels before him at his bidding.'[305]Andrea Dandolo (d. 1354,) the Doge of Venice in the years 1343-54, talks of a white dove which had been `taught by Mohammed to settle on his shoulder and to pick grains of corn inside his ear: The people took the dove for the heavenly messenger through whom the Lord would communicate with the self styled prophet.'[306]

Southern has explained how a fictionalised image of `Mahomet as Sorcerer and Antichrist grew up in Europe in this period, and was elaborated and exaggerated according to expectations as to how such an enemy of Christendom might behave.'[307]

Hence, when Guibert of Nogent spoke about the Prophet in his *Gesta Dei per Francos*,[308] he may have garbled his name and pushed him a few centuries forward in time, and could neither separate fact from fiction, still he concluded:

`It is safe to speak of evil of one whose malignity exceeds whatever ill can be spoken.'[309]

Davenport also notes the repeated assertion that the Prophet was subject to epileptic fits, `to impute that morbid affection to the apostle of a novel creed as a stain upon his moral character.'[310]

---

[303] In D.C. Munro: The Western ; op cit; at p.331-2.

[304] Vincent de Beauvauis: *Speculum Historiale*, *Bibliotheca Mundi* (Douai, 1624), vol. 3, Lib. XXIII.

[305] H. Prutz: *Kulturgeschichte der kreuzzuge* (Berlin, 1883), p 81.

[306] Ibid.

[307]R.W. Southern: Western; in J Sweetman: The Oriental Obsession; op cit; p.6.

[308] *Gesta Dei per Francos*, bk.1, caput 3 in patrologia latina, ed. J.P. Migne; Paris, 1853; Vol 156; col.689.

[309] In R.W. Southern: *Western Views of Islam; op cit;* p. 31.

[310]J Davenport: *An Apology for Mohammed and the Koran;* J. Davy and Sons; London; 1869. p. 14.

Just as the Messenger, the message, the Qur'an, equally, faced onslaught on the part of Christian polemists. According to Guilbert of Nogent, it was a book of law which appeared by a false miracle on the horns of a cow (or bull or ox).[311] And Sura 29, which says:

`The likeness of those who take other patrons besides God is as the likeness of the spider, which maketh to herself a house: but the weakest of all houses surely is the house of the spider.' This became in Christian polemics:

`He (the Prophet) made up a story of spiders and mousetraps to catch flies.'[312]

The Qur'an, according to one of the so-called Cordova martyrs, Eulogio (who was executed for insulting the Prophet in 859, in Cordova,) has for Mary the worst of thoughts. Eulogio says that:

`he will say nothing about the horrible sacrilege about Mary (in the text).'[313]

Which, of course, can be easily disproved by any reading of the text of the Qur'an.

Sweetman notes how the ignorance of Islam persisted, and misconceptions about it have remained profound.[314]Very often, Daniel, adds, Islam suffered untrue accounts which are deliberate, malicious misrepresentations, absurd, based on pure fantasy.[315] Which, however, transferred to the following period.

The `Renaissance' (Late 15th-17th):

Schwoebel holds that Crusade views of Islam in the Middle Ages were carried over and perpetuated even `after the main lines of the medieval world view had crumbled.'[316] Daniel observes that the Europeans inherited from their mediaeval fathers a large and persistent body of ideas about Islam;[317]the same accounts of Islam recurring monotonously, and even travellers who felt bound to describe Muslim doctrine with authority of their experience, still just repeated statements

---

[311] In N. Daniel: The Arabs, op cit, p. 233.
[312] Ibid. p.40.
[313] N. Daniel: The Arabs, op cit; p.41.
[314] J.W. Sweetman: Islam and Christian Theology; op cit; P. 63.
[315] N. Daniel: The Arabs; op cit; p.232.
[316] R. Schwoebel: *The Shadow of the Crescent: The Renaissance image of the Turk*; Nieuwkoop; 1967. p. 147.
[317]N. Daniel: *Islam, Europe and Empire,* University Press, Edinburgh, 1966. Preface: xiii:

which had been, or might have been, lifted straight out of medieval accounts.[318] Martino also notes that the representation of the Orient in tragedy in that period reproduced the usual stereotypes:

`the imbecile cruelty of the rulers; the power of the Imams, and the rushed credulity of the Muslims.'[319]

The technique of rejection could hardly be faulted, Daniel observes.[320] `The dogmatic filter,' he adds, `excluded every Islamic idea, except deformed to `prove' a Christian argument.'[321] Hence, in the *Castillo inexpugnable de la fe*,[322] written at the behest of Charles V, Geary explains, Arredondo (the author) espoused many of the standards medieval stereotypes of Islam. And that many Renaissance authors, taking their cue from a long list of medievals, resorted to caricature and distortion in their accounts of Islamic religious ideas.[323] *The Castillo* is one important `early modern extension' of a medieval tradition in which particular perceptions and misrepresentations about the Prophet and Quranic revelations are rooted in the theological conception of Christian unity.[324]

European envoys to the Muslim land hardly altered the misrepresentations of Islam. Gunny focuses on Herbert, the attaché to the British Embassy in Persia;[325]one of Herbert's claims was that:

`some men keep a lock on top of the head by which Muhammad may distinguish them from Christians on Judgement day and by which he will lift them to paradise....'[326]

About Mohammed, Herbert stated that it was from his parents that the Prophet: `sucked knowledge of both religions'. Obviously Herbert was blinded to the fact that the Prophet was orphan. Herbert also held that the Prophet, although circumcised, was baptized by Sergius, a `Sabeeian heretic who denied the Trinity'. With such `help' the Prophet

---

[318] Ibid. pp. 23-4.

[319] As in the play *Roxelane*; 1643; in P.Martino: *l'Orient dans la Literature Francaise au 17em et 18em siecles*; Librarie Hachette; Paris; 1906. p. 193.

[320] N. Daniel: The Cultural Barrier; op cit; p.165-6.

[321] Ibid. p. 166.

[322] Published on June 23; 1528 by J de Junta; in J.S. Geary: Arredondo's *Castillo inexpugnable de la fee*: Anti Islamic propaganda in the Age of Charles V. in J. V.Tolan. Ed: *Medieval Christian Perceptions of Islam*; Routledge; London; 1996. pp 291-311: at p. 292..

[323] J.S. Geary: Arredondo's *Castillo;* op cit; p. 292.

[324] Ibid. *p 292.*

[325] A. Gunny: *Images of Islam in Eighteenth Century Writing*; Grey Seal, London, 1996.p.11.

[326] Ibid.

`concocted' the Qur'an and by money and force subjected the rest of his followers.[327] Herbert adds that all Muslims invoke the Prophet four times a day, and expect his coming patiently.[328] Of course, none of this is accurate in Islam.

One usual theme of polemics remains the supposed Muslim `sexual perversion.' Sex became, according to Sardar and Davies, one of the dominant themes, and sexual perversity was seen to be intrinsic in the teachings of Islam.[329]Hence, George Lengherand, mayor of Mons in Hainault, who visited Palestine and Egypt in 1486, stated that:
`Muslims believed blessedness consisted of food, drink, luxuries, and in all sensualities, and pleasures which excite the body, even sodomy. Mohammed decreed that those who did not live in such pleasures would perish... and His Alcoran was full of errors. I believe it is the greatest horror in the world.'[330]

Holt, through the writing of Prideaux, analyses the techniques used to distort Islam. Prideaux (d. 1724), Dean of Norwich, compiled his work on the Prophet: *The True Nature of imposture etc,* completed in 1697.[331]Holt looks at the sources Prideaux uses, and also his methodology. Prideaux presents a well documented work in appearance, so that he `may not be thought to draw this Life of Mahomet, with design to set forth his imposture in the foulest of colours the better to make it serve (his) present purpose.'[332] In his account Prideaux lists 36 Arab authors or works, and makes great display of their names in his footnotes. This, of course, aims to give his work great legitimacy. However, as Holt observes, upon examination, it becomes clear that his knowledge of them was from second hand, either from translations or quotations in the works of Orientalists. Together with these `Arabic' sources, Prideaux uses the writings of anti Muslim controversialists. Thus, as Holt notes, the resulting biography is a combination of Muslim tradition and Christian legend, `inspired by a sour animosity towards its

---

[327] Ibid.
[328] Ibid.
[329] Z. Sardar; M-W. Davies: *Distorted Imagination*; Grey Seal, London;1990. p.41.
[330] *Voyage de George Lengherand*, edt Charles Denys, Mons, 1861, pp. 181-2.
[331] P.M. Holt: The Treatment of Arab History by Prideaux; Ockley and Sale. In *Historians of the Middle East*; Ed by B. Lewis and P.M. Holt; Oxford University Press; London; 1962; pp. 290-302. pp. 291-4.
[332] Ibid. p. 293.

subject.'[333] And commenting on Prideaux's work, Daniel holds that it `outdoes almost any medieval writer in its virulence.'[334]

The 18th century:

18th century's minds, supposedly enlightened, without an exception, though, tell facts about Islam that are contradicted by reality.

In his letter 67 (of his work *Lettres Persannes*), Montesquieu holds that:

`Mohammedan faith deprives women of their freedom,... and Mohammedanism locked women behind bars... and had that religion conquered the earth, women would have been imprisoned everywhere.'[335]

Then, in letter 24, he asserts that this religion (Islam) is so much `discriminating against women, that they are not just forbidden to read the scriptures, but also that they were not to ender paradise because of their sex.'[336]

Obviously, Montesquieu shows little awareness of the Qur'an. Sura XLIII; verses 69-71 gives a good place for women in paradise, as it says:

`(Ye) who believed Our revelations and were self surrendered.
Enter the Garden, ye and your wives, to be made glad.
Therein are brought round for them trays of gold and goblets, and therein is all that souls desire and eyes find sweet. And ye are immortal therein.'

Herbelot in *Bibliotheque Orientale,*[337] for instance, claims that when Muslims `refer to the Trinity, they easily accept that the first person-the father-is the essence of God, the second person-the Son-is wisdom and that the third-the Holy Ghost-is life.'[338] This is utterly wrong, for one of the main dividing lines between Islam and Christianity is the matter of Trinity, as in Islam the Oneness of God is absolute, and Mohammed, as Jesus, is only a Prophet.

---

[333] Ibid. p. 294.
[334] N. Daniel: *Islam and the West*; Oneworld; Oxford; 1993. p. 309.
[335] Montesquieu; Pensees; p. 508; 1622. in Pauline Kra: *Religion in Montesquieu's Lettres Persanes*; Institut et Musee Voltaire; Geneve; 1970; p. 113.
[336] Montesquieu: Letter 24; in p. Kra: Religion, op cit; p. 114.
[337] B. Herbelot: *Bibliotheque Orientale*; Paris; 1697; The Hague; 1777.
[338] In A. Gunny: Images; op cit; p. 52.

In the same vein, Herbelot also holds that `Muslims believe that most mad people are saints and that some wisdom resides in madness.'[339] Where does Herbelot find this remains a mystery, for in Islam, there is no sainthood, and mad people are not even allowed in mosques; tolerated, looked after, surely, but not listened to for their wisdom.

Boulanger in 1766 writes[340]that everything took place on the tenth day of Muharram for the Persians: the floods, the same day the Qur'an was sent from heaven, and Hussein, Ali's son was killed at Kerbala by Omar's followers.[341] All of this, of course, has no true foundation in history, for neither was Hussein killed by Omar or his followers, but instead was killed during the Umayyad rule (which began in 661, whilst Omar died in 644), and even more importantly, the Qur'an was not revealed in one day but in phases during the Prophet's life in Mecca and Medina.

Montesquieu, again, states that Turkish `despotism' excluded all rights to the possession of private property, to succession, and inheritance from families, from females and wives. Montesquieu even denied the existence of any civil law among the `Turks.'[342] Yet, Sura iv shows amply how succession and inheritance are precisely fixed and regulated, and beyond the powers of the Sultan to change; and that women are not forgotten in their share for inheritance.

Volnay wrote *Voyage in Egypt and Syria,*[343] where he asserts categorically that Islam fails to fix the obligations or rights of individuals, groups and classes.[344]Of course, anyone consulting the Qur'an will find that this `erudite' mind has completely missed a substantial part of it, and that legislation (obligations and rights) form some of the most detailed verses of the text. Just the index on legislation in one of the translations of the Qur'an includes matters such as bequests; arbitration, blood-money, bribery, charity, contracts, children etc…[345]

---

339 Ibid.

340 N.A. Boulanger: *L'Antiquite Devoilee par ses Usages*; Amsterdam; 1766.

341 In A. Gunny: Images; op cit; p.99.

342 Montesquieu; in A Gunny: Images; op cit; at p. 24.

343 C. Chasseboeuf (Volnay): *Voyage en Egypte et en Syrie;* Paris, Mouton and Co; 1959 edt.

344 Ibid. p. 372.

345 M.M. Pickthall: *The Meaning of the Glorious Qu'ran;* Ta ha Publishers; London; 1930; p. 463.

From the 19th to the present:

According to the French writer Chateaubriand, in the Qur'an, which he calls `The Book of Mahomet':
`There is no principle of civilisation, nothing that elevates the minds and souls. This book preaches neither hostility to tyranny nor love for freedom.'[346]
For Scott, an otherwise fervent admirer of Islamic civilisation, the Qur'an is a sum of Jewish and Christian `legends; rules for the ceremonial of Islam.'[347] `Mohammed,' Scott adds, `having derived his idea of heaven indirectly from the Chaldean accounts of the garden of Eden, and that of the devil from the dualism of Persian mythology, borrowed the name and description of the place of torment from the Jews, who denominated hell Ge-Hinnom, literally, the `Vale of Hinom.'[348]
W.St Clair Tisdall (1859-1928), Head of Mission at Bombay 1888 onwards, then secretary of Persia mission (1892-94), and then from 1912 until his death, associate editor of the missionary organ, *The Moslem World*, holds that Islam `is a Jewish heresy mixed with ideas derived from apocryphal Christian books and even from Zoroastrianism and other eastern sources.'[349]
The same for J.D. Bate (1836-1923) who served as a missionary in India (1865-1897), and who also contributed many articles to the Missionary Herald and the Baptist Magazine, who saw:
`The credit for founding Islam is Muhammad's alone… its distinctive peculiarities are all his own. He alone is responsible for its faults and he alone is entitled to all the credit, whatever it may be, of being its sole founder.'[350]
Montgomery Watt, more `conciliatory' towards Islam, writes, that whilst it is divine, the Qur'an includes errors:
`What other believers in God would hope for would be that Muslims would find a way of maintaining the general truth of the Qur'an, but without denying that in some secondary matters there were slight errors…'[351]

---

346 Chateaubriand, Itineraire… p.908. in C.Grossir: *L'Islam des Romantiques*; Maisonneuve; Larose; Paris, 1984. p. 56.
347 S.P. Scott: History: vol 1; p. 106.
348 Ibid. p.109.
349 W.St Clair Tisdall: *India, its history, Darkness and Dawn;* London; Student Volunteer Missionary Mission; 1901. p. 78.
350 J.D. Bate: *The Claims of Ishmael*; London; W. Allen; 1884; p. 43.
351 W.M. Watt: *Muslim Christian Encounters*; Routledge; London; 1991. p. 137.

Just as in the past, in Western perception, Islam still remains a corrupt, sensual faith. Thus, E.A. Freeman, judged `the West to be progressive, monogamous and Christian,' the East as `stationary, arbitrary, polygamous and Mahometan.'[352] Which is also the point by J.D. Bate, who insists that `Islam succeeded by corrupting its followers. Men had even converted to Islam, according to him to indulge their `brutal appetites for sexual pleasure… the great Arabian reformer made permanent provisions for the flesh.'[353]

Being sexually lax hardly prevents Islam from enslaving women, a contradictory view, which is still found in the writings and paintings of the Romantics movement. The woman becomes for the fanaticised, brutal Muslim a prize of war and piracy; the Muslim prowling upon her, and ravaging her.[354] Thus Helena, heroine of a poem by Alfred de Vigny, is violated brutally by the Turks; an act de Vigny dwells upon in every single, morbid detail. As for her women folk, in the *Orientales* of Victor Hugo, they are all prisoners at the Seraglio, and are offered to the beastly delectation of the Sultan. Of course, all these women are young and virgin.[355] The victims of Turkish beastly desires are generally convent girls kidnapped by pirates (Muslims), and taken to the Harem of the Sultan.[356]
The painters go further in reconciling this contradiction of Muslim sexual depravity and enslavement of women by paintings the slave market, where naked women are sold. Kabbani goes through a number of such paintings.[357] John Faed's 'Bedouin exchanging a slave for armour', dating from 1857, shows the Bedouin with an almost entirely naked slave-girl exhibited in the stall of a sword merchant. The girl's body is inspected in such meticulous, very searching manner, her worth assessed in armour. Her expression, Kabbani notes, `is a piteous one... completely helpless; naked, bound, female, and a slave.' The Muslim, on the other hand, is predatory, lecherous, gross, and loathsome.
Another slave-market scene is Gérôme's 'Le Marché d'Esclaves,' where the slave girl is in the midst of would be purchaser men. The girl, again, is naked, offered to the gaze of her captors and would be buyers. The

---

[352] E.A. Freeman: *The History and Conquests of the Saracens;* Oxford: John Henry and James Parker; 1856; London Mc Millan 1876; 3rd ed. pp; i.4.
[353] J.D. Bate: *The Claims of Ishmael*; London; W.H. Allen; 1884; pp. 285; 253.
[354] C. Grossir: L' Islam; op cit; p. 99 fwd.
[355] V. Hugo: Les Orientales; 1964; Les Tetes du Serail; IV; pp. 602-3.
[356] Ibid. Chanson de Pirates; p. 619.
[357] R. Kabbani: *Europe's Myths of the Orient*; Mc Millan; 1986. pp. 78-9.

Muslim owner, holding her head veil is `a ghoulish-looking man,' just as Muslims are always depicted: frightening with their gross, dark complexions, their hairy faces, big, bulging eyes, thickened lips… Four other victims await their turns for inspection, still buddled in their veils.[358]

It is needless here to reproduce the modern hysteria related to the veil. It is the symbol of Islam oppression of women par excellence. All that is needed here is the extract from the back cover of a book, which captures in a few lines the horrors that the veil represents, and the oppression of Muslim women.[359] From the title of the book: *Le Voile contre l'Ecole,* (the Veil against the school), the veil becomes an attire that hinders Muslim women's social progress, and even deprives them of education. Which is remarkably odd, for veiled Muslim women do not just attend colleges and universities in huge masses, but also exert functions of surgeons, journalists, high officers in the administration, ministers, can own and operate businesses, and so on and so forth.

Concluding words:

A dark picture was painted of Islam, such as every crime imaginable was popularly associated with the Prophet, concludes Smith.[360] Daniel, too, summing up the Western view of Islam, has concluded that nonsense was accepted, and sound sense was distorted.[361] Attacks on Islam, which Daniel notes, are `most divorced from reality, and most remote from any contact with Islam.'[362] Bucaille, equally, has concluded that the erroneous statements made about Islam in the West are just the result of systematic denigration.[363]Whilst Van Ess, has re-currently pointed out to the anti Islamic clichés, which lay deep in the subconscious and meet with unanimous approval.[364]
These very anti Islamic clichés transfer straight to the manner in dealing with Islamic civilisation.

---

358 Ibid.
359 E Altschull: *Le Voile Contre l'Ecole*; Le Seuil; Paris; 1995.
360 R. B. Smith in C. Bennett: *Victorian Images of Islam;* Grey Seal; London; 1992. p. 77.
361 N. Daniel: Islam and the West; op cit p.302.
362 Ibid. p.232.
363 M Bucaille: *The Bible, The Quran and Science*, Translated from French by A.D. Pannell & the author. 7th edition (revised). Publisher Seghers; Paris (1993). p. 1.
364 J. Van Ess: Islamic Perspectives; in H. Kung et. al: *Christianity and the World Religions*; Doubleday; London, 1986; P. 6.

b. From Hostility to Islam to Hostility of Islamic Civilisation:

Glubb makes a good link between hostility to Islam as faith and to its civilisation:
`If knowledge of the history of the period from the 7th to the 12th centuries is vital to the comprehension of the development of Europe, why, it may be asked, had it never been taught?' he asks, before giving his own explanation:
`Throughout these five hundred years, Christendom lived in constant fear of Muslim conquest. From the 12th to the 15th centuries, Islam and Christendom were equally balanced. The West was overtaking and gradually surpassing the Muslim countries in power.... But throughout the Renaissance period in Europe, fear of the Muslims was still strong and hostility, political and commercial as much as religious, was intense. Doubtless as a result of these factors, the indebtedness of Western Christendom to Arab civilisation was systematically played down, if not completely denied.'[365]
This is fairly the same conclusion reached by Daniel,[366] Sardar and Davies,[367] Southern,[368] and Smith.[369] And like much else, the origins of this go back to the Middle Ages.

Throughout the Middle Ages, Tolan explains, `both as a rival religion and as a rival civilization, Islam was tremendously successful. It was hence appealing, intriguing, and frightening. The attraction of Muslim learning, Muslim culture, and Muslim sophistication was extremely strong... But the more Christians were attracted to Islam, the stronger others felt the need to condemn it-for it was this attraction, more than the might of Muslim armies, that was most threatening to Christendom.'[370]
Daniel, just as Tolan, note, that as many conversions to Islam were taking place, the Christian presentation of Islam had to be what it was, so as to deter Christians who might be curious about it.[371] The image

[365] Sir John Glubb: *A Short History; op cit;* p.289.
[366] N. Daniel: *The Arabs; op cit; p.* 1975.
[367] Z. Sardar; M-W. Davies: *Distorted Imagination*; Grey Seal Books; London, 1990.
[368] In R.W. Southern: *Western Views; op cit.*
[369] R.B. Smith: *Mohammed; op cit;.*
[370] J.V. Tolan ed: *Medieval; op cit;* pp. xix-xx.
[371] N. Daniel: *The Cultural Barrier*, op cit; p.158.

that was created of Islam, Watt, equally notes, was that Christians were fighting forces of darkness, something that was necessary to compensate for Western Christendom's feeling of inferiority.[372]Savage, too, observes, how ecclesiastical and university administrators were quite conscious of it in medieval days. Muslim learning was dreaded as disturbing to the curriculum of the medieval university and the pattern of thought taught therein.[373] Thus, what was taught at Muslim Cordova and Palermo, Scott notes, inspired audacious medieval reformers, who were far in advance of their age, but only for their aspirations for intellectual and religious liberty to be `promptly and mercilessly extinguished at the stake and the scaffold.'[374]

One of the earliest such transmitters, Gerbert of Aurillac (future Pope Silvestre II) (d. 1003), seeking to introduce Muslim science that he had learnt in Spain into Christian Europe, was not able to set up the schools that institutionalised the sciences `so dear to him'.[375] Muslim mathematics, which he brought north was deemed a `dangerous Saracen magic.'[376]
Nearly a century after him (late 11thcentury), Constantine the African, who had inaugurated the birth of higher learning in Europe through his transfer of medical knowledge from Tunisia to Salerno[377] `at a time when Islam was thoroughly hated in Christendom,' under clerical pressures being brought to bear on him, Constantine had to suppress the name of Muslim authors whose works he produced Latin versions of.[378] It was not that Constantine, as nearly all historians of science accuse him of, sought to plagiarise the Islamic works, he was forced to do so. Even amongst the translators of the 12thcentury, whose translations from Arabic were to serve as foundations of Western learning, in no single case did the dependence on Islamic sources or writers, stimulate in any Latin writer `a kindly or a tolerant thought' for Islam or its culture,[379]Daniel notes. Indeed, then was born the practice, replicated today in history writing, that whilst taking learning from the Muslims', such learning was still disguised as a recovery of Ancient learning.

---

[372] M.W. Watt: l'Influence de l' Islam in *Revue des Etudes Islamiques*, Vol 41; p. 154
[373] H.L. Savage: Fourteenth Century Jerusalem; op cit; p.199.
[374] S.P. Scott: History; op cit; Vol 3: p. 3.
[375] M.L. Colish: *Medieval Foundations of the Western Intellectual Tradition 400-1400*: yale University Press; 1997; p. 164.
[376] William of Malmesbury, History of the kings of England, tr. Revd John Sharpe (London, 1815), P. 199, in L. Cochrane: *Adelard of Bath*, British Museum Press, 1994, p. 43
[377] On Constantine, see: C. Burnett and D. Jacqart: *Constantine the African*, Brill, 1994.
[378] D. Campbell: *Arabian Medicine, op cit;* pp.123-4.
[379] N. Daniel: *The Cultural; op cit;* p. 171.

If today this trick of feeding from one source and labelling it another is used in the misrepresentation of the role and place of Islam in the rise of modern science and civilisation, at the time it was a way of survival. The fear of Islamic `heresy' was such, Durant notes, that the Church saw heretics as traitors who undermined the unity of Christendom in its gigantic conflict with Islam.[380] In the South of France, the Islamic influence was very strong, and it caused the Church to feel threatened; worse symbols of such threat were the hostility to images, distaste for priests, and a secret doubt as to the divine origin and support of the Christian Church.[381]These led to the Albigensian (Southern French) crusade of the early 13th century with its thousands of victims.

The so called Humanist movement of the late Middle Ages, had a peculiar aversion for the Islamic tendency of the age.[382]The humanists' purpose following Petrarca was to resurrect Greek knowledge and to clean it of medieval Islamic additions; love of Greece and Rome nourished by hatred of Islam.[383] The campaign of the medical humanists against the medieval and Islamic writers led, for instance, to the replacement of Ibn Sina by Latin translations from the Greek text of Galen.[384]At the end of the 14th century, the Florentine, Niccolo Falcucci, in his *sermones medicinales* proclaimed Galen's infallibility.[385]The Frenchman, Champier's medical books, with the exception of the mirror of apothecaries, written in Latin, were devoted to Galenic commentaries and controversies, and to the defence of Greek against Muslim medicine.[386]Champier's attempts were to reconcile Plato with Aristotle, and Galen with Hippocrates, and to reconcile all the Greeks against `the Arabic barbarians.'[387]This strength of hostility, however, only suggests that Islamic influences were very strong permeating both science and philosophy.[388]

Humanist hostility to Islamic science, and a longing for the Classical heritage, whilst feeding from the Islamic source is very well expressed by Viete. François Viète (1540-1603) in his *In artem analyticem isagoge* of 1591, clearly expressed his humanistic desire to purge

---

380 W. Durant: The Age of Faith, op cit; p.777.
381 Ibid; p.769.
382 C. Singer: *Short History of Scientific Ideas to 1900*, op cit; p. 196:
383 G. Sarton: *The Appreciation of Ancient and Medieval Science during the Renaissance (1450-1600)*, University of Pennsylvania Press, 1955. p.44.
384 D. Campbell: Arabian Medicine, op cit; p. 192.
385 G. Sarton: The Appreciation of Ancient; op cit. p.20
386 Ibid. p.23.
387 Ibid. p.23.
388 G. Sarton: Introduction; vol III; op cit; p. 509.

algebra of its Islamic `corruptions and to return it to a more pristine state inspired by the classical Greeks.' He bade his readers:
`Behold, the art which I present is new, but in truth so old, so spoiled and defiled by the barbarians, that I considered it necessary, in order to introduce an entirely new form into it, to think out and publish a new vocabulary, having gotten rid of all its pseudo-technical terms lest it should retain its filth and continue to stink in the old way, but since till now ears have been little accustomed to them, it will be hardly avoidable that many will be offended and frightened away at the very threshold. And yet underneath the Algebra or *Almucabala* which they lauded and called "the great art", all Mathematicians recognized that incomparable gold lay hidden, though they used to find little ... our art [i.e., the analytical art of algebra] is the surest finder of all things mathematical.'[389]

Hostility to symbols of Islam (before they were subsequently adopted) spreads to a variety of essentials. Money changers in the 13th–14th century were summoned not to use Arabic numerals in their transactions and keep with the methods of the ancients.[390]The true explanation of the resistance to the numerals is that they were considered an integral part of the Arabic script, whereas the Roman ones were inseparable from the Latin script.[391] In Spain, hostility extended to inanimate objects, which bore marks of Islamic skills, and `which were at once suggestive of heresy.'[392]The use of private and public baths in that country, symbol of Islamic faith, were banned, and measures were passed to that effect, all baths being forthwith destroyed, commencing with those of the king.[393]

From the 17th century forward, a new strategy was devised: to assert domination over Islam through the use of academic studies of Islam, the aim of which, in the expression by Kabbani was to `devise and rule.'[394] Or as seen by Sardar and Davies to dominate Islam, to ridicule it, abuse it and demonstrate its inferiority, and, `once raped, to envelop it within

---

[389] F. Viète: Introduction to the analytic art, trans. by Rev. J. Winfree Smith, in Jacob Klein: *Greek Mathematical Thought and the Origin of Algebra* (Cambridge, 1968), 318-19. In K.H. Parshall: The Art of Algebra from Al-Khwarizmi to Viete: A Study in the Natural selection of Ideas; *History of Science*, Vol. 26, No. 72, pp.129-164. p. 129.
[390] D.J. Struik: The Prohibition of the use of Arabic Numerals in Florence: *Archives Internationales d'Histoire des Sciences* Vol 21 pp 291-294. p. 294:
[391] G. Sarton: Introduction; op cit; vol iii. P.127.
[392] S.P. Scott: History; Vol ii; op cit; p.576.
[393] H.C. Lea: A History of the Inquisition in Spain; p.336
[394] R. Kabbani: Europe's Myths; op cit; p. 138.

Western civilization and to turn Muslims into nice, docile, subject people, an extension of the West.'[395]
Thus, Sir William Jones, a servant of the East India Company, inaugurated Orientalist studies in order `to increase Europe's acquaintance with the peoples it would exert control upon.'[396]Whilst William Bedwell, instrumental in establishing the Chair of Oriental studies at Cambridge, aimed amongst others at `enlarging the borders of the Church, and propagation of the Christian religion to them who now sit in darkness'.[397]

Which, of course, was useful in the age of imperialism and missionary activity in the 18th –19th century. Hitti explains how Arabic studies were conditioned by missionary activity and interest and by world politics, and how such studies were carried either to convert Muslims or to further imperialistic interests. In this `Western chauvinism, religious zeal and sheer ignorance played their part,' and Islamic society was painted dark and its inferior character overemphasised.[398]
Which brings us to the next point.

Colonisation, and the myths of inferior people:

Joseph notes how in the history of mathematics, for instance, Western writing deliberately passes scientific knowledge from the Greeks into a period of Dark ages, then a re-discovery of Greek learning leading to the Renaissance, completely setting aside the contribution of the colonised people, so as to maintain the image of their inferiority and ease their subjugation and domination.[399] Thus, the 19th century Frenchman Renan insists:
`It is the Aryan spirit which has created everything from political life, art, literature etc. `the Semitic peoples have nothing of it, apart from some poetry-above all science and philosophy. In these matters, `we are entirely Greek.' Even the so-called Arabic sciences were a continuation of Greek sciences... Christianity, too, in its developed form is the work of Europe.'

---

395 Z. Sardar and M. W. Davies: Distorted Imagination; op cit; p. 41.
396 *Ibid.* p. 43.
397 Quoted by J.D. Latham in Z. Sardar and M.W. Davies: Distorted Imagination; op cit; p. 42.
398 P.K. Hitti: America and the Arab Heritage; in *The Arab heritage*, op cit; 1-24: pp.9 and 14.
399 G.G. Joseph: *The Crest of the Peacock*; Penguin Books; 1991; at p 4.

`The Semitic spirit has produced monotheism, and Christianity and Islam have conquered the world, but it can produce nothing else-no myths, therefore no higher literature or art, because of the terrible simplicity of the Semitic spirit, closing the human brain to every subtle idea, to every fine sentiment, to all rational research, in order to confront it with an eternal tautology: God is God,'[400]

In his Caliphate, Muir, who was in charge of the North Western Frontier region of India, concluded:

`Islam kept Muslim nations `in a backward and in some respects barbarian state.'[401]

The coloniser, thus, saw himself, according to Fontana, a missionary of new times who proposed `to teach primitive peoples the true path of intellectual and material progress.'[402]

Engels wrote in 1848 in an article in the Northern Star, that:

`The French victory over Emir Abd el Kader (in Algeria) was finally a good thing for the progress of civilisation, as the Bedouin are barbarous thieves preying on the sedentary populations, whose supposed noble liberty can only appear admirable from the distance'[403]

Communists of Western nations with colonies were the most ardent defenders of such views. `From their perspective,' Rodinson wrote, `the Muslims remained culturally backward because of the strength of fanaticism, which these Western Marxists saw as intrinsic part of Islam.'[404] And to ascertain their enlightenment, which might take some time, though, `the revolutionary role, in Muslim countries,' had to belong to the European elite.[405]

The Europeans saw themselves as educators and guides, condemning Islam and the Ottomans for their lack of capacity to insert themselves in the march for progress.[406]

Shaler, thus, writes:

`true civilisation could only come about by a transfer of responsibility into the hands of Christian nations who would favour agriculture,

---

[400] E. Renan: De la Part des peoples semitiques dans l'histoire de la civilisation in *Oeuvres Completes*, Paris, Calmann-Levy, 1947, Vol II; p. 333.

[401] W. Muir: *The Caliphate*; Smith and Elder and Co; London; 1883. p. 599.

[402] J. Fontana: *The Distorted Past*, Blackwell, 1995. p.130.

[403] Quoted by W. Bouzar: *Le Mouvement et la Pause*; Algiers; 1983; vol 1; pp 216-7.

[404] M. Rodinson: *Europe and the Mystique of Islam*; trans: R. Veinus; I.B. Tauris and Co Ltd; London; 1988. p.74.

[405] Ibid. p 74.

[406] C. Grossir: Islam; op cit; p. 160.

industry and commerce and thus civilise the region. The `primitive' was incapable of progressing by his own unaided efforts.'[407]

Abbe Raynal saw that the North Africans, who cannot civilise themselves, must be taken in hand by the Europeans.[408]

`Political domination and economic exploitation needed the cosmetic cant of *mission civilisatrice* to seem fully commendatory,' Kabbani explains. `The image of the European coloniser had to remain an honourable one: he did not come as exploiter, but as enlightener. He was not seeking mere profit, but was fulfilling his duty to his maker and his sovereign, whilst aiding those less fortunate to rise toward his lofty level. This was the white man's burden, that reputable colonial *malaise*, that sanctioned the subjugating of entire continents.'[409]

Colonisation was far from being the humane, noble, deed given by its apologists, though. The French following their arrival in Algeria (1830) slaughtered hundreds of thousands of people, and devastated towns, cities, crops, livestock, besides looting wealth and property.[410]An official report, for instance, stated:

`We have tortured people just on suspecting them; we have desecrated tombs, and temples and houses; have robed people of their wealth, have massacred people carrying safe conducts, slaughtered whole populations, who were guilty of nothing; have tried local leaders because they dared oppose us, have imprisoned tribe leaders, have decorated dishonest intermediaries, turned shameful acts into diplomacy... in words have beaten in barbarism barbarians we had come to civilise.'[411]

But writing to the Minister of war, Soult, General Bugeaud held:

`that rigorous methods had to be applied to submit the country, without which there would be no colonisation, administration, or civilisation.'[412]

Such misdeeds had to be justified, indeed; and so the colonial authorities identified the colonised with semi barbarians, whose casualties were part of a rectifying process; such losses necessary for `the advancement of civilisation.'

---

[407] W. Shaller: *Sketches of Algiers*; Boston; 1826. p.56.

[408] Abbe Raynal: *Histoire philosophique et politique des etablissements et du commerce des Europeans dans l'Afrique*; Paris; 1826;

[409] R. Kabbani: Europe's Myths; op cit; p.6.

[410] C. Ageron: *Modern Algeria*, trslted by M. Brett, Hurst and Company, London, 9th edt, 1990; p. 11:

[411] *Proces Verbaux et rapports de la commission nommee par le roi le 7 Juillet 1833*; Paris, 1834.

[412] H Alleg et al: *La Guerre d'Algerie; 3* vols, Temps Actuels, Paris, 1981. pp.66; 69.

Obviously independence from colonial powers eventually took place; but, as Chejne explains, cliches have changed, of course, but the basic attitude remains the same. `As in medieval times, whether referred to as Muslim, Arab, Saracen or Moro, he is a member of a degraded race. Unfortunately, this has affected Western judgement and led to ambivalence, and to unwillingness to acknowledge any merit in the Muslim's past or present.'[413]

Derogatory impressions which can be found expressed by Garrison, for instance, here depicting Islamic civilisation:

`During the long period of Moslem domination (711-1276) (of Spain), there was constant warfare, but the intervals of peace were far more frequent… and in these intervals, Christian, Moslem and Jew managed to subsist side by side without any apparent friction, like the wild animals in railhead Uganda. The Unitarian, standardizing mania of Islam was, in theory, at least, a species of theological Sovietism. But the real object of the emirs was conquest as a pathway to pleasure, with monotheism as a stalking horse. The Arabs themselves were sceptical, materialistic, indifferent, pleasure loving, polygamous, sometimes atheistic, and fonder of music, dancing and erotic poetry than orthodoxy and devotion. Like all converts to a creed or a social code, the Berbers and other North African tribesmen were inevitably more fanatical than those born and bred in the faith…. Apart from the mathematics and polite literature, the Moslems were assimilators and transmitters rather than innovators. Their architecture (domes and decorated flat surfaces) derived from Byzantium. The patio or enclosed court of their houses came from Rome. Their medicine was but a diluted or debased strain of Greek medicine.'[414]

And little deviation from this approach on the part of leading figures of modern history of science such as Duhem, Lynn White Jr, Lawn, Rashdall, etc,[415]and their countless followers exerting today, whose

---

[413]A Chejne: The Role of al-Andalus in the movement of ideas between Islam and the West, In *Islam and the Medieval West*, K. Semaan Ed; State University of New York Press/Albany, 1980, pp 110-33: at p. 117.

[414] F.H. Garrison: *Contributions to the History of medicine*, Library of Congress Catalogue, New York, 1966. pp. 208-9.

[415] Lynn White Jr: `Technology in the Middle Ages,' in *Technology in Western civilisation*, Vol 1, ed by M. Kranzberg and C.W. Pursell Jr, Oxford University Press, 1967, pp 66-79.

L White Jr: Cultural Climates and Technological Advance in the Middle Ages; *Viator*; 2; pp 171-201.

L White Jr: The Act of invention; *Technology and Culture,* Vol 3; pp 486-500.

P. Duhem: *Le System du Monde*; Paris; 1914.

M.Clagett: *The Science of Mechanics in the Middle Ages*; op cit.

B. Lawn: *The Salernitan Questions*, Oxford at the Clarendon press, 1963.

mindset has remained frozen, holding by, and perpetuating the same image of the inept Muslim.

All such derogatory perceptions and depictions are based upon, or rely upon, a distorted history, which lends the barbaric to the Muslims, and suppresses anything in their favour. This history, which uses the techniques looked at above, and which is now refuted.

H. Rashdall: *The Universities of Europe in the Middle Ages*, ed F.M Powicke and A.G. Emden, 3 Vols, Oxford University Press, 1936.

3. REFUTING MAINSTREAM HISTORY

This chapter looks at, and counters the three fundamental manners by which the Islamic role in the rise of science and civilisation is demeaned or suppressed in mainstream Western history. It first counters the fallacies around which the Greek argument as foundation of modern science and civilisation is built. Then, it shows, and in great detail, how a fallacious history of science and civilisation is built by systematic suppression of facts. Then, finally, it exposes the myths and fallacies related to the so-called 16th-17th Renaissance, out of which, supposedly, our modern science and civilisation originate.

1. The Fallacies Surrounding the Greek Legacy:

Europe, Joseph explains, bypassed her Arab and non European heritage and `homed in on Greece and Rome,' Greece thereby becoming the fount of the Western intellectual and cultural heritage.[416] The history of the last five hundreds years has tended to strengthen these ties, partly as a consequence of European dominance and partly under the pressure of `classical' scholarship, much of which regards Greece as the sole source of knowledge and culture.[417] As a result, science and civilisation are kept securely within the realm of the Western entity alone: Classical Europe, and then Renaissance Europe, and then modern civilisation, all based on Greece and its legacy alone. This version of history is based on a series of historical fallacies.

a. The Flawed Over Focus on the Greek Element:

Most historians hardly, if ever, refer to Muslim or Arabic science, but use the expression: `Greco-Arabic science.' This approach also consists in putting a Greek name as soon as the Muslim work or scientific theory is cited. Thus, whatever the Muslim breakthrough is, it has to be either a continuation of, or inspired by, or a response to something Greek. Any resemblance, however minute, often a hint, is sufficient to assert the Greek link. Quite often, even when there is no connection of any sort,

---

[416] G. Gheverghese Joseph: *The Crest of the Peacock;* op cit; p.345.
[417] Ibid. pp.345-6.

expressions such as: Neo-Ptolemaic, Neo-Platonism, Neo-Aristotelian, Neo Galen are used and repeated in relation to the Islamic work or Islamic breakthrough. At times such linkage reaches a ridiculous level as can be found in Wiet et al,[418] where there is not a single mention of anything Islamic without a Greek addition. This highlights the point made by Multhauf[419] on the authors' competence in relation to Greek learning, and yet, their large ignorance of the Islamic. It also highlights a determined, even obsessive Western scholarly urge to trace the Western origin of every breakthrough anywhere. In Armesto's words:

`No reader can have had any difficulty in interpreting them as an allusion to the doctrine that: ``Western society' derives, by unbroken tradition, from Greco-Roman origins. The doctrine may not be true; the terms in which it is commonly expressed may be misleading. Yet its influence is such that it forms part of the self perception of almost every educated person in Europe and the Americas and much of the rest of the world today. Studies of periods of crisis in the transmission of the supposed legacy-in late antiquity of the early middle ages, when rival cultural traditions were received, or in the `age of expansion' when Western society is thought to have broken out of its heartlands- have concentrated, like Theseus in the labyrinth, on following as if it were a lifeline this single, tenuous thread.''[420]

This obsession with the Greek source of every achievement often reaches ludicrous dimensions, that such Greek influence is even found when the Muslim scientist demolishes the Greek theory; asserting its direct opposite. Thus is the case with Ibn al-Haytham, for instance, who completely deconstructs Greek optics,[421]still historians assert such Greek linkage. Dijksterhuis, for instance, tells us that all Western 13th century optics was a return to Greek sources, which the `Arab' authors have only followed or adopted.[422] Bernal in his `authoritative' four volume work on science in history, and on the particular matter of origins of Western science, insists

---

418 G. Wiet et al: *History of mankind*; op cit.

419 R.P. Multhauf: *The Origins of chemistry*; Gordon and Breach Science Publishers; London, 1993. p.1.

420 Felipe Fernandez Armesto: *Before Columbus:* Mac Millan Education; London, 1987; p.1

421 See for instance:

D. C. Lindberg: The science of optics. In *Science in the Middle Ages*; ed D.C. Lindberg. The University of Chicago Press. Chicago and London. 1978 pp 338-68.

G.A. Russel: Emergence of Physiological Optics, in *Encyclopaedia of the History of Arabic Science* 3 Vols.Ed by R Rashed; Routledge, London and New York: 1996. pp 672-715.

422 E.J. Dijksterhuis: *The Mechanisation of the World Picture;* trans by C.Dikshoorn; Oxford at the Clarendon Press; 1961; pp. 145-52.

that Muslim scientists accepted and codified classical sciences, and that, in his words:

`They had little ambition to improve it and none to revolutionise it. As al-Biruni (973-1048) put it: We ought to confine ourselves to what the Ancients have dealt with and perfect what can be perfected.'[423]

Which is remarkable, for Al-Biruni's science is spent exactly demolishing the Greeks. In his famed *Al-Is'ilah wa'l ajwab* (Questions and answers) with Ibn Sina, to which he refers in his *Chronology,* Al-Biruni questions fundamental Aristotelian theories such as:

-Aristotle has no sound reason for his supposition that the Heavens are neither heavy nor light.

-Aristotle's method of seeking support for his theories in the opinions of former thinkers (in respect of the idea that the universe had no beginning) is improper.

-Aristotle reasons for rejecting the atomic theory are not sound and his own theory of the infinite divisibility of matter is no less open to objection.

-Aristotle is not justified in denying the possibility of the existence of other universes besides our own.

-Aristotle is not justified in saying that the Heavens move from the east, as the east is the right side. Right and left are merely relative terms.[424]

In *The Book of the Demarcation of the Limits of the Areas* Al-Biruni insists on correcting Ptolemy location of places.[425] And the same refutation of Greek science can be found in any work by this scientist, whether in relation to the measurements of the earth circumference, or the planets, or the measurement of densities of metals, or in geology, or in any area, as can easily be checked by anyone consulting Al-Biruni's works.[426]

---

[423] J.D. Bernal: *Science in History;* in four volumes; Ca. Watts and Co Ltd; London; 1969; Vol 1; p.273.

[424] H M. Said; A. Z. Khan: *Al-Biruni: His Times, Life and Works;* Hamdard Foundation, Pakistan, 1981.; pp. 105-6.

[425] In N. Ahmad, *Muslim contribution to Geography* Lahore: M. Ashraf, 1947, p 35.

[426] *Alberuni's India*, Edward C. Sachau, trans. (1888), abridged in Ainslie T. Embree, ed., Alberuni's India (1971);

-*Tahdid Nihayat al- Amakin*' Pavel G. Bulgakov, ed. (1962), trans. by Jamil 'Ali as *The Determination of the Coordinates of Positions for the Correction of Distances Between Cities* (1967), commentary by Edward S. Kennedy, *A Commentary upon Biruni's Kitab Tahdid al-Amakin* (1973);

-*Al-Qanun al- Mas'udi*, complete Arabic edition, 3 vols. (1954-1956), abstract in English in Edward S. Kennedy *A Survey of Islamic Astronomical Tables* (1956) 157-159, English table of contents by Kennedy, "Al-Biruni's Masudi Canon," in *Al-Abhath*, 24 (1971);

It is generally asserted that all Muslim science consists of is to be found in Ptolemy's *Geography* and *Almagest* and Galen's medical works. Ptolemy's *Almagest*, most particularly, it is generally held, is a very good case of Muslim `plagiarism.'[427] Thus, Dreyer tells us, that:

`Though Europe owes a debt of gratitude to the Arabs for keeping alive the flame of science for many centuries and for taking observations, some of which are still of value, it cannot be denied that they left astronomy much as they found it.'[428]

And:

`When the Europeans again began to occupy themselves with sciences, they found astronomy practically in the same state in which Ptolemy had left it in the second century.'[429]

This view, common to the overwhelming majority of writing on the history of astronomy,[430]is, in fact, a big distortion of truth. Suter, who had made an early comprehensive study of medieval astronomy, finds that the number of Muslim astronomers was not just in the hundreds,[431]but also that nearly all of them corrected Ptolemy, and even more importantly, that they dealt with a vaster array of subjects Ptolemy never contemplated, all subjects today the realm of modern astronomy. A simple comparative exercise between Muslim astronomers and Ptolemy will show that it is not in Ptolemy that one finds trigonometrical calculations,[432] or the use of planetary observation for scientific purposes as the Muslims did,[433] or the

---

-W. Hartner and M. Schramm, "Al-Biruni and the Theory of the Solar Apogee: An Example of Originality in Arabic Science," in *Scientific Change: Symposium on the History of Science*, Alistair C. Crombie, ed., Oxford, 1961 (1963);

-Edward S. Kennedy, *The Exhaustive Treatise on Shadows* (1976).

[427] See G. Wiet et al: History; op cit; O.Pedersen: Early Physics; op cit; A.Crombie: science; op cit. etc.

[428] J.L. E. Dreyer: *A History of Astronomy from Thales to Kepler;* Dover Publications Inc; New York; 1953; p.249

[429] J.L. E. Dreyer: *A History of Astronomy*; p.279-80.

[430] A theory held by many, such as:

J. P. Verdet: *Une Histoire de l'Astronomie*, Le Seuil, Paris, 1990.

O. Pedersen: *Early Physics and astronomy*, Cambridge University Press, 1974.

J.Delambre: *Histoire de l'Astronomie Ancienne;* Johnson Reprint Collection; New York, 1965.

[431] H. Suter: *Die mathematiker und Astronomen; op cit.*

[432]See: A.Nallino: *Albateni Opus Astronomicum* (Arabic text with Latin translation), 3 vols, Milan 1899-1907 reprinted Frankfurt 1969.

G. Sarton: Introduction; op cit; vol 2, most particularly.

[433] A Sayili: *The Observatory in Islam*, Turkish Historical Society, Ankara, 1960.

B. Hetherington: *A Chronicle of Pre-Telescopic Astronomy*; John Wiley and Sons; Chichester; 1996.

use of large instruments for observation.[434] It is not Ptolemy who constructed astronomical instruments as al-Zarqali, and literally hundreds of Muslims did.[435] Has Ptolemy devised or built the torquetom,[436] or the quadrant, or any armillary sphere such as al-Khazini's for instance, which shows the earth rotating?[437] Are Ptolemy's tables similar in precision and value to those of Al-Zarqali?[438] Has Ptolemy contributed the same as al-Bitruji did to Planetary theories?[439] And the list is endless. Any beginner astronomer can do such comparisons and realise how the argument that Muslim astronomers just plagiarised Ptolemy is wholly absurd in substance. Moreover, Muslim astronomers, in their entirety, refuted Ptolemy, and even ridiculed him.[440]For instance, contrary to Ptolemy, Muslim astronomers such as al-Sijzi (fl late 9th century) did conceive that the earth was moving in its own axis.[441] Which is further confirmed by another astronomer of the 13th century, Al-Harrani, who held `according to the geometers (or engineers) (muhandeseens), the earth is in constant circular motion, and what appears to be the motion of the heavens is actually due to the motion of the earth and not the stars.'[442]

In geography, it was also al-Istakhri, Al-Muqaddasi, Al-Idrisi and many other Muslim geographers, who did not just correct Ptolemy's geography, but also built the necessary knowledge upon which modern geography is

---

[434] L. Sedillot: Memoire sur les instruments astronomique des Arabes, *Memoires de l'Academie Royale des Inscriptions et Belles Lettres de l'Institut de France* 1: 1-229; Reprinted Frankfurt, 1985.

[435] A.L. Mayer: *Islamic Astrolabists*, Albert Kundig edition, Geneva, 1956.

[436] R.P. Lorch: The Astronomical Instruments of Jabir Ibn Aflah and the Torquetom; *Centaurus,* 1976; vol 20; pp 11-34.

[437] E. S. Smith: *Islamicate Celestial Globes*; Smithsonian Institute Press; Washington, D.C, 1985.

[438] M. Steinschneider:

Etudes sur Zarkali; *Bulletino Boncompagni*; vol 20.

Notice sur les tables astronomiques attribuees a pierre III d'Aragon, Rome, 1881.

[439] J. North: *Astronomy and Cosmology*; Fontana Press, London, 1994.

G.Saliba: Critiques of Ptolemaic Astronomy in Islamic Spain; in *Al-Qantara*, Vol 20, 1999; pp 3-25.

[440] See the following for an abridged outline of Islamic refutations of Ptolemy's astronomy by Al-Battani in P Benoit and F. Micheau: The Arab Intermediary; op cit; p. 203; by Al-Zarqali in P.K.Hitti: *History of the Arabs*, MacMillan, London, 1970 ed. p. 571; by Al-Bitruji in A. Djebbar: *Une Histoire de la Science Arabe*; Le Seuil; Paris; 2001. p.194; by Jabir Ibn Afllah in F.Braudel: *Grammaire des Civilisations*; Flammarion, 1987. p.113, and G. Sarton: Introduction; op cit;Vol II; p.18.

[441] G. Saliba: Al-Biruni; in *Religion, Learning and Science in the Abbasid Period;* Ed by M.J.L.Young; J.D. Latham; and R.B. Serjeant; Cambridge University Press; 1990; pp. 405-23; p. 413.

[442] A.B. H. Al-Harrani: *Kitab jami al-funun;* British Library; Ms Or..6299., fol. 64v.

based.[443] Al-Khwarizmi, for instance, substantially improved Ptolemy's geography in his *Face of the earth*, as regards to both text and the maps.[444] Al-Biruni insists on correcting Ptolemaic `Geography', where places in the east were to be found actually in the west, and vice versa.[445] And several other writers did the same.[446] Why, then, does one find the repeated assertion by the so many,[447]that Muslim geography is just a reproduction of `Ptolemaic' geography is impossible to comprehend.

The supposed Muslim plagiarism of Ptolemy's astronomy and geography extends to every subject, all Muslim medicine, for instance, supposedly that of Galen.[448] Which is again a ridiculous assertion, for the Muslims wrote works wholly devoted to his refutation. Al-Razi, for instance, based his medical theories nearly solely on his criticism of Galen in his *Fi'l-Shukuk ala jalinus* (Doubts about Galen);[449] and the same with Ibn al-Nafis, who reconstructed the theory of the lesser circulation of the blood exactly in refutation of Galen.[450]And absolutely no Muslim medical writer sets aside criticism of Galen as can be found in every single treatise on the subject.[451] As for the subjects dealt with by Muslim physicians and those dealt with by Galen, the field is free to compare and measure, and the conclusions for the neutral will be staggering; staggering because what they will find contradicts fundamentally what one reads in mainstream history that the Muslims hardly deviated from the Galenic line. It may, also, be noted in passing, as Rosenthal observes, that Galen's excursions

---

443 D.M. Dunlop: *Arab Civilisation to A.D. 1500*, Longman, Librairies du Liban, 1971, pp 150-71.
J. H. Kramers: Geography and Commerce, in *The Legacy of Islam*, edited by T. Arnold and A. Guillaume, Oxford University Press, first edition, 1931; pp 79-197;
-Baron Carra de Vaux: *Les Penseurs de l'Islam*; Geuthner; Paris; 1921; vol 2; pp.1-101.
444 G.H. Kimble: *Geography in the Middle Ages;* Methuen and Co; London; 1938. p. 49.
445 N. Ahmed: Muslim contribution; op cit; p. 35.
446 G.H.T. Kimble: *Geography in the Middle Ages*;op cit; p. 49.
447 Such as E. Perroy: Encore Mahomet et Charlemagne; op cit, who asserts that all the Muslims did was to plagiarise Ptolemy.
Or M.A. Tolmacheva: Geography and Cartography: Islamic; *Dictionary of the Middle Ages*; Vol 5; pp 391-5; at p. 394.
448 This argument can be found even amongst the most ardent defenders of Muslim civilisation.
449 For a specific criticism of Galen by Al-Razi, see:
S. Pines: Razi Critique Galien in *Studies in Arabic Versions of Greek Texts and in Mediaeval Science*, The Magnes Press, Brill, Leiden, 1986. pp 256-63.
450 M. Meyerhof: Ibn Nafis and his Theory of the Lesser Circulation. *ISIS* 23 (1935). Pp.100-20.
451 N.L. Leclerc: *Histoire de la Medecine Arabe*; 2 vols; Paris; 1876.

into fields other than medicine were at times severely criticised.[452] Al-Biruni blamed Galen for his excessive credulity when he reports the story of the snake queen whose sight or hiss caused immediate death: `I should like to know,' al-Biruni asks, `who could have told Galen about her habitat and qualities, if all who looked at her died.'[453]In fact, as Rosenthal notes, even among those Muslims who championed Ancient learning, the position of no classical authority was safe from attack.[454]

If this line of attributing every Islamic accomplishment to a Greek predecessor because of some supposed link was generalised to the whole study of the history of science, then, a Muslim name would have to be included in every paragraph, and maybe every three or four lines in any scientific writing of any sort. Anything on geography, especially if including maps, and the name of Al-Idrisi would have had to be mentioned (nobody before him made such an accurate representation of the world). Anything on medicine, and the names of Ibn Sina and al-Razi would have had to be added (for it was the translation of their works which laid the foundations of modern medicine, and they were relied upon until the late 18th century by Western scholarship.) Anything on optics and cameras, and reference to Ibn al Haytham should be obligatory. Anything on surgery, and al-Zahrawi would have to be referred to (as he pioneered in the design of modern surgical instruments). Anyone making any calculation of any sort, amongst the billions of operations which take place every day, and they would have to acknowledge al-Khwarizmi first, and then proceed. All history would have to acknowledge Ibn Khaldun; all physics should acknowledge al-Biruni and al-Khazini, all chemistry Jabir Ibn Hayyan, and so on and so forth. And so the whole depiction of modern science and civilisation will be peppered with such Muslim names just as is the history of Muslim civilisation is with Greek names. And at least the Muslim names, as will be amply shown in the subsequent parts, will deserve their place, for their impact on the sciences and accomplishments just cited and others, was not based on fictitious historical writing.

Whilst keen to graft the Greek link onto every single Muslim scientific breakthrough, however minimal, unproven, or even historically untrue, the same historians completely ignore the Islamic influence on their Western successors when such influence is not just glaring, but even when it is

---

[452] Cf. P. Kraus: Jabir Ibn Hayyan; 2. 328f. Cf. also *ISIS* 36 (1946). pp. 251-5; in F. Rosenthal: The Technique and Approach of Muslim Scholarship; *Analecta Orientalia;* 24; Roma; 1947. p. 55.

[453] Al-Biruni: Jamahir; p. 99 in F. Rosenthal: The Technique. p. 55.

[454] F. Rosenthal: The Technique. p. 54.

plagiarism pure and simple. There are some remarkable examples of this to be highlighted to some length in the last section of this chapter, such as Harvey's discovery centuries after Ibn al-Nafis of blood circulation; Witelo's nearly word by word re-writing of Ibn al-Haytham's *Kitab al-Manazir*, or Copernicus's planetary theory. Briefly here, on Harvey, first, Crombie, for instance, says:
`The discovery by Harvey of the circulation of the blood provided a fact that necessitated the reconstruction of the theory of the exchange of energy and matter by the engine of the body.'[455]
A point subscribed to by the BBC[456] stating that Harvey seized where Galen left off, and established the modern theory of blood circulation. In truth it was Ibn Al-Nafis (1210-1288) of Damascus, who, in a treatise written before 1241 challenged Galen's views on blood circulation, and built the theory, attributed to Harvey centuries later.[457]
The same goes for Copernicus, who plagiarised his Muslim predecessors.[458]Yet, many modern historians of astronomy, such as Pedersen, who whilst acknowledging the glaring similarities between Copernicus and his Muslim predecessors, still says:
`Copernicus-like al-Shatir- could well have calculated his parameters in such a way that the model gave the maximum and minimum equations known from the Almagest (Ptolemy's).'[459] (Hence, that Copernicus did not copy his Muslim predecessors, according to Pedersen, which is a plain fallacy as will be amply demonstrated further on).

There are historians of science who praise Muslim achievements, but then they devaluae such Muslim achievements in comparison with their Greek counterparts. Thus, when Mieli says that Al-Khazini wrote *Mizzan al-Hikma* which was a remarkable Arab work on weights, but remarkable amongst the Arabs,[460] he stipulates that any non-Arab work is much superior to it, whilst in truth, Al Khazini's work on measures of weights and densities surpasses his Greek predecessors', and stands to this day in

---

455 A.C Crombie: *Science, Optics and Music in Medieval and Early Modern Thought*; The Hambledon Press, London, 1990. pp. 175-6.
456 BBC September 1998.
457 A.Z. Iskandar: Ibn al-Nafis in *Dictionary of Scientific Biography*, vol. 9, pp. 602-6.
M. Meyerhof: Ibn Nafis; op cit.
E. Abouleish: Contribution of Islam to Medicine, in *Islamic Perspective in Medicine,* S Athar ed; American Trust Publications, Indianapolis, 1993; pp. 15-43.
458 A Gingerich: A Tusi Couple from Shoner's de Revolutionibus? see *Journal for the History of Astronomy*, Vol 15 (1984); pp 128-32.
459 Such as O. Pedersen: *Early Physics and Astronomy*, Cambridge University Press, 1974. p.273.
460 A.Mieli: La Science Arabe; op cit; p.154.

accuracy and in the manner the measurements were effected.[461] And when Mieli says that Al-Jazari's work is the best to help us understand the development of Greek mechanics in Islamic countries,[462] again he undervalues the Islamic role. Now that al-Jazari's work is available in its English version, it is also available for comparative purposes with preceding Greek works, and one finds in Al-Jazari a majority of mechanical devices not known in Greek works.[463]
Mieli's observations are, however, benign when compared to most others, such as by Garrison, for instance, who informs us that:
`Apart from mathematics and polite literature, the Moslems were assimilators and transmitters rather than innovators. Their architecture (domes and decorated flat surfaces) derived from Byzantium. The patio or enclosed court of their houses came from Rome; Their medicine was but a diluted or debased strain of Greek medicine.'[464] Picking the latter point for argument here, if anyone compared Galen's medicine with his Muslim successors, it will show the vast superiority of all the latter, who do not just deal with more subjects, diseases, and cures,[465] but also, as noted above, refute him thoroughly and convincingly.

The most derogatory approach to the history of Islamic science and civilisation found amongst nearly every single Western writer or historian, however `favourable' to the Islamic side, is their ranking less than ten figures of Classical Greece (Euclid, Ptolemy, Galen, Aristotle, Archimedes,...) higher in accomplishments than all Muslim scholarship, i.e thousands of scholarly figures.[466]Incidentally, this manner of depicting Islamic accomplishments is shared amongst all Western historians dealing with any subject, military historians, for instance, always rank Muslim military successes as victories accomplished by hordes of Muslim armies against handfuls of crusaders, or Mongols, etc. With regard to the ranking of ten or so Greek figures higher than the thousands of Muslim scholars, any consultation of any bibliographical work will show that matters

---

[461] E. Wiedemann: *Beitrage zur Geschichte; op cit;* `Zur mechanik und technik; op cit; M Rozhanskaya (in collaboration with I.S. Levinova) Statics, in Encyclopaedia of the History of Arabic Science (Rashed ed), vol 3, op cit; pp 614-42.
[462] A.Mieli: La Science Arabe; op cit; p.155.
[463] D. R. Hill, *The Book of Knowledge of Ingenious Mechanical Devices*, Dordrecht, Boston, 1974.
[464] F.H. Garrison: *Contributions to the History of Medicine,* op cit; p. 209.
[465] See the numerous examples of this in D. Campbell: Arabian Medicine; op cit; M. Leclerc: Histoire; op cit; etc.
[466] It is, indeed, impossible to list all the names of Muslim scholars of that period. Al-Fihrist by Ibn Nadim lists thousands of them up to the last decade of the tenth century. George Sarton wrote on more than a thousand Muslim scientists.

addressed by Muslim science are not just wider in terms of volume, but also deal with more complex issues, and bring us to modern science more than the Greek works do. If Ptolemy's geography is taken as an instance, any closer scrutiny of works that have looked at Muslim geography more extensively, such as Miquel,[467] Kratchokovsky[468] or Sarton,[469] will show that Ptolemy's geography covers no more than the most minute percentage of subjects dealt with by Muslim geographers. Muslim travellers alone in their writing on China, Scandinavia, India, Africa, tell us thousands of facts none of which is found in Ptolemy.[470] Muslim nautical science, as the last part will explore, gives us the whole foundation of nautical science, which is not found in Ptolemy.[471] Muslim economic geographers, equally, go into economic systems of diverse regions in such detail as one never finds in Ptolemy.[472] Muslims geographers, moreover, as already noted, without one single exception, corrected Ptolemy. And, when one looks at crucial breakthroughs in other aspects of science and civilisation, i.e, manufacturing of paper, the use of the magnetic needle in navigation, the numerals, trade mechanisms, irrigation techniques, etc… one finds nothing Greek in them, but instead all relate to Muslim science (also to China and India.) Moreover, many modern sciences are not Greek in origin, most notably nautical sciences, arithmetic, trigonometry, etc, but are instead the fruit of medieval, Islamic accomplishment.

---

[467] A. Miquel: *La Geographie Humaine du Monde Musulman*, Vol 4, Ecole des Hautes Etudes en Sciences Sociales, Paris, 1988.

[468] I.J. Krckovskij: *Izbrannye Socinenja* (chosen works); Vol 4, Moscow, 1957.

[469] G. Sarton: Introduction; op cit.

[470] G. Ferrand: *Relations de Voyages et textes geographiques Arabes, Persans and Turks relatifs a l'Extreme Orient du VIIem au XVIIIem Siecles*; Ernest Leroux, Paris, 1913-4

G. Ferrand: trans and ed: *Voyage du marchand Arabe Sulayman en Inde et en Chine redige en 851…* Paris; Edition Bossard; Vol vii; Les Classiques de l'Orient.

J.T. Reinaud: *Relations de voyages faites par les Arabes et les Persans dans l'Inde et la Chine*; Paris; Imprimerie Royale; 2 Vols; 1845.

C.de La Ronciere: *La Decouverte de l'Afrique au Moyen Age;op cit.*

Harris Birkeland: Nordens hidstorie I middelalderen etter arabiskenkilder, *Norske Videnskaps-Akademi i Oslo, Skrifter, Hist.-Filos.* Klasse, 2 Scriffer, 1954, 2 (1954).

[471] G.Ferrand. *Instructions Nautiques et Routiers Arabes et Portugais des XV et XVI Siecles*, 3 Vols, Paris, 1921-

H.Grosset-Grange: La Science Nautique Arabe', *Jeune Marine,* 1977-9, 16-29 (except 22).

----- (1993) *Glossaire nautique Arabe ancien et moderne de l'Ocean Indien,* Paris.

G.F. Hourani: *Arab Seafaring in the Indian Ocean in Ancient and Early Medieval Times*, Princeton, 1971.

G. Tibbetts: *Arab Navigation in the Indian Ocean Before the Coming of the Portuguese,* London. 1971

[472] A.Miquel: *La Geography Humaine du Monde Musulman;op cit.*

Very often, the obsession in demeaning the Muslim contribution to mere reproduction of Greek science locks its authors in incongruous situations, for there is a conflict between what they assert, and what they themselves come across in their brief focus on Muslim science. The issue is raised by Watt, who refers to one such historian, who began his summing up of one particular history of science asserting that:

`we cannot expect to find with the Arabs the same powerful genius, the same gift of scientific imagination, the same enthusiasm, the same originality of thought as with the Greeks. The Arabs are before anything else, the pupils of the Greeks; the children of Greeks; their science is only a continuation of the Greek science, which they have preserved, cultivated...'[473]

However, further on, Watt notes, the same author states:

`The Arabs have truly accomplished great things in the scientific domain. They have taught the use of numbers although they did not invent them, and they founded arithmetic of daily life; made algebra an exact science, and developed it considerably; they also set up the foundations of analytical geometry and spherical trigonometry etc...'[474]

This contradictory approach is generalised amongst the many, such as Pannekoek, here taken at random, who writes:

`The Muslims did not go beyond Ptolemy, and when they did, it was from preference to Aristotle.'[475]

And:

`There was a brilliant rise in Arabian astronomy, but no significant progress. After some centuries it died down.'[476]

And then, remarkably, the same author goes on to say:

`European Christendom now began to raise itself spiritually with the help of Arabic science…'[477]

`A century after Gerbert, Adelard of Bath went to Spain to study Arabic wisdom…

Arabic words have remained in use as technical terms: azimuth, zenith, nadir, and the names of stars: Betelgeuse, Algol, etc.'[478]

And:

Western Christians carried planetary observations with instruments `borrowed mostly from Arabic writings.'[479]

---

[473] W. Montgomery Watt: l'Influence de L'Islam; op cit; part II; pp 297-327; at p.297-8.

[474] Ibid.

[475] *A.* Pannekoek*: A History of Astronomy;* Allen and Unwin Ltd; London; 1961; p. 170.

[476] Ibid.

[477] Ibid. p.174.

[478] Ibid.

[479] Ibid. p.179.

And:

`The Iberian peoples, first the Catalans and the Portuguese and the Spaniards as seafarers and discoverers, opened up the routes across the oceans. They made use of the astronomical knowledge handed down from Arabian science.'[480]

Then, even more remarkably, Pannekoek concludes his short outline, saying that:

`Arabian scientists certainly observed diligently; they constructed new instruments, and in astronomy they seem to have displayed more practical activity than did the Greeks. Also the accuracy of their work often surpasses the results of Antiquity. Their aim, however, was not to further the progress of science-this idea was lacking throughout-but to continue and to verify the work of their predecessors.'[481]

b. The Fallacy Surrounding `Lost' Greek Learning:

As already noted, the view is that the Muslims only acted as mere guardians of Greek learning at the time it was lost in the West, until Western Christendom recovered such learning, ten or so centuries later, to begin the Renaissance. This view of Greek learning lost to the Christian West for more than ten centuries, until it was recovered from the Muslims is generalised amongst nearly all Western historians dealing with Islamic science and civilisation.[482] Fletcher's back cover on the history of Spain, for instance, reads: the scientific and philosophical scholarship of the Greeks and Persians had been lost to the West but was re-introduced to European intellectual life via the Islamic world in Spain.[483] For Duhem, by far one of the principal sources of influence on modern Western history of science,[484] after Ptolemy (AD 145), learning declined, and the Greek books which escaped burning by the Muslims `awaited the time when Latin Christianity would furnish a favourable soil in which they could once more flourish and bring forth fruit.'[485]

---

[480] Ibid. p.184.

[481] Ibid. p.169.

[482] Such as the SOAS historian appearing on the BBC program: An Islamic History of Europe, Broadcast on BBC4, 10 April; 2005; 8.30 p.m, seen by this author.

[483] R. Fletcher: *Moorish Spain;* Phoenix; London; 1992; back-cover.

[484] P.Duhem: *Le System du Monde;* Paris; 1914.

[485] P. Duhem: Medieval Physics, in *Toward Modern Science*; (R. Palter ed); op cit; pp 141-59; Quote at p. 141.

It is very difficult, if not impossible, to reconcile the inherent contradictions found in Duhem's statement, and that of his hordes of followers, that the Muslims were both burners of Greek science and its guardians at once. It is either one or the other. For the story, the burning of the Alexandria library (to which Duhem refers) was the work of Christian zealots centuries before the Muslims arrived in Egypt.[486]

Nevertheless, Duhem's and his followers' central argument remains that modern science and civilisation arose only after the recovery of the formerly lost Greek learning was accomplished; a loss which explains why Western Christendom remained in darkness for centuries, and a recovery from Arabic of such previously lost Greek heritage which explains the `Renaissance' and the Classical foundation of modern science and civilisation. Yet, these two arguments are based on two huge fallacies, themselves built on secondary fallacies.

First, the recovery of `Greek learning' took place in the 12th century (not in the 16th-17th century,) as studies of the medieval period agree,[487]and as will be expanded upon further on.

Secondly, this recovery of `Greek learning' from Arabic, in former Islamic lands, and from Islamic sources, is said to be due to the fact that such Greek learning was lost in the West. This is historically untrue for two fundamental reasons:

First: such recovery of `Greek learning' was done from Arabic, and in regions once under Islamic control (Spain, Sicily, South of France..), and most particularly in the Spanish town of Toledo some decades after it was retaken from the Muslims (1085).[488]The obvious question to ask is: Why fetch such Greek learning from Islamic sources, from a complicated language, Arabic, and not from the source itself: today's Greece or Byzantium, from a language, Greek, easily translatable into Latin?

Indeed, with the rarest of exceptions, hardly any 12th-13th century Western scholar travelled to Byzantium, Athens, or any Greek centre of learning to acquire any scientific book. Those who made the journey can be counted on the fingers of one hand; included amongst these

---

486 E. Gibbon: *History Of The Decline And Fall Of The Roman Empire* Vol. 5; 1782; Chapter LI: Conquests By The Arabs. Part VII. 1923 ed; pp 452-4.

487 See works on 12th century or medieval Renaissance, those cited, and others such as M.L. Colish: *Medieval Foundations of the Western Intellectual Tradition 400-1400*: Yale University Press; 1997.
E. Grant: *A Source book of Medieval Science*. Cambridge, Mass.: Harvard University Press; 1974.

488 Jose M. Millas Vallicrosa: *Estudios sobre historia de la ciencia espanola*, Barcelona, 1949. N. Daniel: *The Arabs and Medieval Europe*; op cit.C.Haskins: Studies; op cit; etc.

Burgundio Pisano (c.1110-1193), who translated the Aphorisms of Hypocrates; some works by Galen, and extracts from John of Damascus; and Jacobus Clericus of Venezia, who translated many parts of the Organon of Aristotle.[489] A movement which fizzled out soon after it came to life.[490] The rest, the translators who had the real impact on the birth and rise of Western science, whether Gerard of Cremona, Robert of Chester or Michael Scot etc, all went to former Islamic lands. Just like the earlier learning, it came almost entirely through Muslim channels and not from Greek sources.[491]

No Western historian has discussed this matter, all accepting that every single translator translated Greek science from the Muslims, from Arabic, without asking why it was not taken from the source itself (Greece-Byzantium). This is all the more baffling, as Greek learning was at reach. `The existence of the Greek text,' Multhauf says, `testifies to the importance of Byzantium as an archive of ancient records'.[492]Scores of sources can be used to show how Byzantium and Greek civilisation thrived during the whole of the so called `Dark Ages.'[493] At the beginning of the 11th century the Greek Empire, through the arms and statemanship of Isaurian and Macedonian dynasties, had reached again the power, wealth, and culture of its zenith under Justinian.... Greek art and literature were enjoying a Macedonian renaissance; the 9th and 10th centuries witnessing a remarkable revival of letters and arts.[494] Education was completely Greek, and nearly every free male, many women, even many slaves, received some education. The University of Constantinople was restored in the 9th century, and attained high repute for its courses in philology, philosophy, theology, astronomy, mathematics, biology, music, and literature. Tuition was largely free to qualified students, and the teachers were paid by the state. Libraries, public and private, were numerous, and still preserved those classic masterpieces which had been forgotten in the disordered West.[495]

If, thus, it was Greek learning that was the source of our modern civilisation, why go to Toledo instead of Athens or Constantinople to get it. Why wait until the Muslim foe was defeated to raid his `Greek'

---

[489] A. Mieli: La Science Arabe; op cit; pp. 218-9.
[490] Ibid.
[491] W.R. Lethaby: Medieval Architecture: in *The Legacy of the Middle Ages,* ed by C.G. Crump and E.F Jacob: Oxford at the Clarendon Press, 1969, pp 59-93. at p. 63-4.
[492] R.P. Multhauf: The Origins of Chemistry; op cit; p.119
[493] See D.J. Geanakoplos: Medieval Western Civilisation, op cit; G. Sarton: Introduction; op cit; C. H. Haskins: Studies; op cit; W. Durant: the Age of Faith; op cit.
[494] P. Boissonade: Life and Work in Medieval Europe, p. 56 in W. Durant The Age of Faith; op cit; pp. 431-2.
[495] W. Durant: The Age; p. 437.

scientific works. Why wait centuries in darkness to recover what was next door in Constantinople, Athens, or Byzantine territories in the Christian West (parts of Italy, for instance). Constantinople itself was under Latin rule for more than half a century (1204-1261), thus why is there no sign of a burst of scientific accomplishments in the Christian West following that rule, or learning travelling from East to West during that period.

Besides, in the early stages, the Muslims themselves sought Greek learning from Byzantium. Witness, in the 9th century, Caliph Al-Mamun (813-33) sent a deputation to the Byzantine emperor, Leo the Isaurian to obtain scientific works of Aristotle, Ptolemy, Galen, Archimedes, and some others were accordingly translated into Arabic.[496]Al-Mamun even asked Emperor Leo to lend him scientific manuscripts to translate into Arabic, or face war if he refused.[497] In the following century the Emperor of Constantinople offered a copy of Dioscoride (1st century) *treatise on plants* to the Caliph of Cordova Abd Errahman III.[498] It was in fact frequent that Byzantine emperors sent valuable Greek manuscripts as gifts to the caliphs,[499] and more importantly, all of the Greek works translated by the Muslims would have been available from Byzantium in the original Greek.[500] Constantinople kept alive the knowledge of the ancient world, notes Sherwood Taylor;[501]whilst Hill, points out, that Greek manuscripts `were preserved in Byzantium.[502]

Thus, the notion that Greek learning had been extinguished, and was only available through the Muslims is a fallacy, for the Christian West could have obtained such learning from Byzantium very easily.

Second: Even if admitting that for some reason, Western scholars of the Middle Ages could not go to today's Greece, at the time, it must be remembered, still free and prosperous, or Constantinople in Byzantium (also free and prosperous), and both places open to the Latin, still, why should they get such Greek learning from the Muslims, and in Arabic, and going through the tiring efforts of translation from Arabic, whilst it was

---

496 F. Sherwood Taylor: *A Short History of Science*; William Heinemann Ltd, London, 1939.p.76.

497 A. Djebbar: *Une Histoire de la Science Arabe*; Le Seuil; Paris; 2001. pp 111.

498 Ibid. pp 111; 115.

499F. Reichmann: *The Sources of Western Literacy;* Greenwood Press; London; 1980. p.201.

500 Ibid.

501 F. Sherwood Taylor: A Short History of Science; op cit; p.88.

502 D.R. Hill: Mathematics and applied science: in *Religion, Learning and Science in the Abbasid Period*; ed M.J. L. Young, J.D. Latham and R.B. Serjeant. Cambridge University Press, 1990: pp 248-273: p.248.

available in Latin translations,[503] and available in Western Christendom itself. Indeed, much of Italy was under Byzantine rule throughout all the Middle Ages, and could have been an excellent centre of passage of Greek learning. In truth, not a single Italian city under Byzantine rule played even the most minute role in translations. Even Salerno, under Byzantine influence, only played a role in translation of scientific works but of Islamic origin, works brought by Constantine the African from Al-Qayrawan (Tunisia), as to be seen further on.
Moreover, plenty of evidence shows that Greek learning was available in all centres of Western Christendom. A French contemporary scholar concluded from his catalogue that the York library, in the 8th century, had owned books in Greek, Hebrew, and Arabic:

There shalt thou find the volumes that contain
All of the ancient fathers who remain;
There all the Latin writers make their home
With those that Glorious Greece transferred to Rome.'[504]

Artz admits, that thanks to the Carolingian Renaissance, many of the Latin classics survived; over ninety per cent of the writings of ancient Rome that have come down to us exist in their oldest form in a Carolingian copy.[505]Greek works have also been translated very early into Latin. Dioscorides' *De materia medica,* held by many to be the foundation of Islamic pharmacy, was translated into Latin before the 6th century. This translation is found in Munich Ms (CLM 337) and Paris Bibliotheque Nationale lot MS 9332 fols 243-321v.[506] The work of Dioscorides on herbs appears in the catalogue of Saint Amand, Durham and Peterborough.[507] Greek writings on medicine such as by Hippocrates appear catalogued at Sant Angelo at Capua, Saint Amand, Durham, in the medieval library of Bishop Bruno of Hildesheim, and elsewhere, whilst writings of Galen are mentioned in the catalogues of Reichenau, Saint Amand, Durham, Salzburg, Hildesheim, and other collections.[508] Also available were Plato's *Timaeus*, works by Aristotle (usually as translated by Boethius (ca.480-ca.525), or accessible via his

---

503 See W. Durant: The Age; op cit; C.H. Haskins: Studies; op cit; G. Sarton: Introduction; op cit; etc.
504 The metrical catalogue of the library at York as translated by A.F. West: *Alcuin and the Rise of the Christian Schools;* New York; 1892; p. 34; in D. Metlitzki: *The Matter of Araby in Medieval England,* Yale University Press, 1977; p.15.
505 F.B. Artz: The Mind; op cit; p. 198.
506 J.M. Riddle: Theory and practice in medieval medicine: *Viator*: 5:pp 157-184; p. 162.
507 J.S. Beddie: Libraries in the Twelfth Century; *Anniversary Essays in Medieval History by Students of C.H. Haskins*; Boughton Mifflin Company; Boston; 1929; pp. 1-23; p. 14.
508 Ibid. p. 14.

commentaries), and Cicero's *Topics*.[509] In general, the logical works of Aristotle and Porphyry, accompanied by the commentaries of Boethius, appeared in numbers in the monastery libraries.[510] Aristotle was more popular in the Middle Ages and his works were better preserved; his *Categories* can be found in the catalogues of Bobbio, Montier en Der, St Emmeram's, Hamersleven, Pfaffers, Reichenau, Wessobrun, Saint Amand, Anchin, Arras, Reischbach, and with the rest of *The Organon*, at Canterbury and Rochester, whilst the *De interpretatione* was listed at St Emmeram's, Pfaffers, Salzburg, Anchin, Arras, and Fleury.[511] And such Greek learning was available in one of the earliest, and the most important centres of Western learning, in Chartres. Grant, for instance, notes:

`The increasing concern for intellectual pursuits brought with it a greater interest in works of antiquity. Plato's Timaeus, for example, was studied intensively and used to explain the structure of the universe by the Neoplatonists at Chartres.[512]

Crombie also holds that:

`Some intellectual need to produce some kind of quantified conceptualisation of physics can be seen as early as the twelfth century, for example, in the Chartres school. The sources of this are a form of Neo-Platonic philosophy derived from St Augustine and from Plato's *Timaeus*, and such scriptural texts as that from the Wisdom of Solomon stating that God had ordered all things in measure and number and weight.'[513]

And examples can be multiplied. Thus, stating that Greek or Classical learning was lost, and was recovered from its Muslim guardians, as is generally asserted, is one of the biggest and longest fallacies to crown history.

The fundamental reason, however, why historians tell us that Greek learning was lost and was recovered from the Muslims in Arabic is to justify their assertion that the mass translations from Arabic in the 12th – 13th century, which triggered the beginnings of modern science, were of Greek science. These translations cannot be denied to have taken place as they were the largest of the sort that ever took place, the whole of Christendom descending upon the Islamic centres of learning. Scholars from all `the lands of the Holy Roman Empire' swarming to Toledo to

---

509 R.N. Swanson: *The Twelfth Century Renaissance*, op cit; p.46.

510 J.S. Beddie: Libraries; op cit; p. 14.

511 Ibid. p. 13.

512 E. Grant: *Physical Science in the Middle Ages*; John Wiley and Sons, London, 1971. p.15.

513 A.C Crombie: Science, Optics; op cit;. p. 75.

participate in `the salvaging of these unprecedented treasures of learning,' says Burckhardt.[514] Busily flocking,[515]; in waves throughout the 12$^{th}$ and even 13$^{th}$ century. An influx into Spain, from Italy, Germany, England and elsewhere, which drew from all lands those who `thirsted for knowledge,' says Rose;[516] `to seize on the wondrous secrets of the world of thought,' constituting an impressive sight reckon Wiet et al.[517] Translations from Arabic which as Meyerhof saw `descended on the barren scientific soil of Europe,' having the effect `of fertilizing rain.'[518] Translations, which for Grant, were to constitute `one of the true turning points in the history of Western science and intellectual history in general.'[519]

Which brings to the matter debated here: had such historians admitted these translations were of Islamic works, it would have defeated the whole argument of Greek science being the foundation of modern science and civilisation; it would have been the biggest proof of all that it was the translations of Islamic scientific works, which led to the revival and re-birth of the West. This being anathema, such translations had to be, thus, of Greek science. And for this to be the case, such Greek learning had to be **Unavailable** in Latin, and unavailable in short; lost to, and lost in the Christian West. And early Christian scholars had, thus, to be playing the part of recovering such learning from its Muslim guardians. For this theory to stand, though, it required another crucial ingredient: that the translations of the 12th-13th centuries had to be of Greek learning. Which leads to the next point.

c. The Fallacies Surrounding the Translations of the 12th Century:

For the previous fallacy to stand, and to explain the Western revival and modern science based on Greek learning through the decisive role of translations, historians simply resort to the usual techniques of exaggerating the place of Greek works and suppress reference to the translations of Islamic works. Hence, according to Pedersen, Gerard of Cremona (the main translator), with his collaborators translated 90 writings by Aristotle, Themistios, Ptolemy, and others.[520] Whether the

---

[514] T. Burckhardt: *Moorish Culture in Spain,* George Allen & Unwin, London. 1972; p. 162.
[515] D. Metlitzki: The Matter; op cit; p.6.
[516] V. Rose: `Ptolemaus und die Schule von Toledo' in *Hermes*, viii. 327; (1874); in C.H. Haskins: Studies, op cit, p. 12.
[517] G. Wiet et al: A History; op cit; p.465.
[518] M. Meyerhof: Science and Medicine, in *The Legacy of Islam*, op cit; pp 311-55, at p. 351.
[519] E. Grant: Physical science; op cit; p.15.
[520] O. Pedersen: *Early Physics and Astronomy*; Cambridge University Press, 1974; p.339.

Muslims are amongst the others, Pedersen would not care to tell us. For anyone not learned in Islamic history, as is the case amongst the majority of people, they would believe Gerard of Cremona translated only Greek works, just as Pedersen and others hold. Had Pedersen been more honest, or just read the entry on Gerard of Cremona in the Dictionary of Scientific Biography, for instance, he would have read that Gerard translated mostly Islamic works, and preferred to stay in Toledo, and keep translating, even when his health was failing, and even until his death, because he sought to translate the vast number of Islamic books into Latin, for `he felt sorry for the Europeans who needed them.'[521]

Just like Pedersen, another historian, taken at random, Jaques Paul, claims that Christianity received a vast amount of knowledge via translations, then he states that Gerard of Cremona and Alfred of Sarachel translated Aristotle; Herman The Dalmatian translated scientific works (no mention which);[522] and most important was the translation of Euclid's optics, and Plato, Ptolemy etc; Paul making not a single mention of any Muslim work except Ibn Sina in a note.[523]

Ganshof, for his part, says:

`In the course of the twelfth and thirteenth centuries, in Italy and in Spain, translations were made from the Greek and Arabic of hitherto unknown, or little known, works of Aristotle on physics, astronomy, metaphysics, zoology, and ethics; while scholars at the court of Frederick II, or at the translating centre set up in Toledo by its bishop, or elsewhere, also translated the Arab commentators, notably Averroes. The Aristotleian system, revealed in its entirety, exercised an extraordinary fascination on men's minds.'[524]

Then, Ganshof devotes the entirety of his writing to the impact the translation of Aristotle had. Again, no mention of translations of Muslim works. And it seems, indeed, the translation of Aristotle alone revolutionised modern science.

And the same with Grant:

`Without the earlier translations, however, which furnished a full blown and well articulate body of theoretical science to Western Europe, great scientific revolutionaries such as Copernicus, Galileo, Kepler, Descartes, and Newton would have had little to reflect upon and reject, little that could focus their attention on significant physical problems. Many of the

---

[521] N. Daniel: *The Cultural Barrier*, Edinburgh University Press, 1975; p169.

[522] J Paul: *Histoire Intellectuelle de l'Occident Medieval*. Armand Colin, Paris, 1973.pp 156-7.

[523] Ibid. pp 156-7.

[524] F.L. Ganshof: The Middle Ages; in *The European Inheritance*, Ed: Sir. E. Barker, G. Clark, and P. Vaucher, Vol I, Oxford, at the Clarendon Press, 1954; p. 413.

burning issues and vexing scientific problems that were resolved in the 17th century entered Western Europe with the translations or were brought forth by medieval authors, who systematically commented upon that body of knowledge. Of this mass of science and learning, the physical works of Aristotle were fundamental...'[525]

Grant, just like Ganshof, and just like the overwhelming majority of historians, then proceeds to attribute the rise of the whole modern science to the translation of Aristotle.

In the same vein, explaining the developments that led to the maritime discoveries of the late 15th, one of the main authorities on the matter, Chaunu, writes:

`All this unconscious preparation for discovery resulted with the amazing intellectual changes which took place at the end of the 12th century. It followed from the rediscovery of ancient science and then its outstripping by the use of Aristotelian method.'[526]

Yet, all this exaggerated role of Aristotle is historically untenable. Aristotle (384-322 BC) was available to the West for fifteen centuries, in Greek, in Latin, and even some other tongues, and yet the West was sunk in barbarism. Besides, had he been the source of all scientific knowledge, why did no awakening take place in Greece or Byzantium his lands of birth and availability respectively? And why did neither today's Greece nor old Byzantium make the maritime discoveries Chaunu refers to if Aristotle was the key? Why, if Chaunu and others are talking sense, did not the West understand the earth was round by just reading Aristotle in any century (fifteen of them) before he was translated from Arabic. Why did the West wait until Aristotle was discovered in formerly Islamic lands (Toledo and Sicily) and in translations from Arabic in the 12th century to understand this. And why did Western Christendom have to discover Aristotle in Arabic to understand all about philosophy, optics, physics, etc. Arabic must have magical scientific properties one never knew about, indeed.

In truth, the learning that was available in the hands of the Muslims surely had plenty of Greek in it, which the Muslims, or this author, never denied. A Greek learning, which was one of the many and diverse foundations of Islamic science and learning. But the learning the Christian West found in the 12th century, and that was translated, as any person can check by going to the original sources of the translators themselves (Gerard of Gremona, Robert of Chester, Plato of Tivoli, John of Seville,

---

525 E. Grant: *Physical Science*; op cit; pp.18-9.

526 P. Chaunu: *European Expansion in the Later Middle Ages;* trans by K. Bertram; North Holland Publishing Company; Amsterdam; 1979. pp 84-5.

etc) was mainly of Islamic science and Islamic scientists, namely: Ibn Sina, Al-Khwarizmi; Al-Battani; Al-Farghani; Al-Zarqali; Al-Zahrawi etc.[527] Besides, as will be demonstrated under the next heading, the translated 12th century learning bears little relation with the one left by the Greeks centuries before. Modern historians who tell us such 12th century learning is Greek expose themselves and their institutions to ridicule as this aberration can be demolished by any first year university student, who, instead of taking their assertion at face value, would lend just an hour of his/her time to check any Greek work, especially those by Aristotle, on any subject, with its equivalent available in the 12th century, and see whether the mathematics, medicine, optics, chemistry, geography, etc, `recovered' by the Christian West in the 12th is that left by the Greeks (including Aristotle).

d. The Fallacies of Modern Science Being Greek:

Setting aside all that has already been said, let us for a moment, side with modern `historians' and admit that the recovery of learning accomplished by Western Christendom at whichever Renaissance (in the Renaissance of the 16th-17th centuries for the haters of the Middle Ages) (in the Renaissance of the 12th-13th centuries according to the lovers of the Middle Ages), was of Greek learning, and solely Greek learning. Thus, admitting, that after the barbarian invasions (5th century), Greek learning was lost for centuries (over ten) until it was recovered for Western Christendom to begin its scientific revival in either of the two Renaissances. And supposing one also believes, that learning/science in the 12th-13th or 15th-16th is absolutely the same as the Greeks left it; untouched for over ten centuries. As one begins to go through such learning with good focus, however, one finds absolutely no relation of the remotest sort between Greek learning and that recovered in the 12th and subsequent centuries. Far, very far from this, in fact, as the following shows.

In mathematics, for instance, one agrees with O'connor and Robertson, who have concluded that modern mathematics is closer to Muslim mathematics than the Greek. Many of the ideas, previously thought to have been brilliant new conceptions of European mathematicians of the

---

[527] See Appropriate entries in Dictionary of Scientific Biography; op cit; or G. Sarton: Introduction; op cit; or C.H. Haskins: Studies; op cit; etc

16th through to the 18th century, have been developed by Islamic mathematicians centuries earlier.[528] Many mathematical innovations, such as algebra, the decimal system, modern trigonometry, etc, date from the Middle Ages. Sarton notes that Arithmetic was a medieval novelty, very different from the arithmetic of the Greeks, and from the crazy numerology of the Neo-Platonists and their followers.[529] Sabra also reflects on how Muslim mathematicians were able to use, formulate and solve new problems in the very Greek field of excellence: geometry.[530] Muslim mathematicians searched for ever better solutions, both formulating and proving non Euclidean theorems.[531]

In astronomy, the view held by most historians, as expressed here by Crombie, holds no ground. Crombie goes:

`Until the seventeenth century, astronomy was far ahead of all other theoretical sciences in the extent to which it was accurately and systematically quantified with actual measurements. For the medieval astronomers, Ptolemy's writings provided an example not only of quantified mathematical theory and procedures but also of systematic numerical observational data.'[532]

Crombie is telling a major fallacy. Ptolemy (just like Galen, Euclid and other Greeks, for that matter) was repeatedly, and utterly, refuted by Islamic scientists. Relying on measurements made at the court of al-Mamun (9th century), for instance, Al-Farghani (fl.861) made many corrections to Ptolemy.[533] His improved tables of the sun and the moon helped him discover that the direction of the sun's eccentric as recorded by Ptolemy was changing, which, in modern astronomy means the earth moving in varying ellipse.[534] From the second half of the 9th century al-Battani (d.929) made a commentary on Ptolemy's *Almagest*, which he also corrected and completed by relying on new observations.[535] Al-Zarqali (1029-1087) also amended Ptolemy's exaggerated estimate of the length of the Mediterranean Sea from 62° to nearer to its correct value of 42°.[536] Al-

---

[528] J O'connor and Robertson: Arabic Mathematics; op cit.

[529] G. Sarton: *The Appreciation of Ancient and Medieval Science during the Renaissance (1450-1600)*, University of Pennsylvania Press, 1955. p.151

[530] A.I Sabra: The Scientific Enterprise, in *Islam and the Arab World*; ed B. Lewis; London; 1976; pp. 181-92. p. 185.

[531] Ibid.

[532] A.C Crombie: Science, Optics; op cit; p.86:

[533] R. Morelon: Eastern Arabic Astronomy, in *Encyclopaedia of the History of Arabic Science*, op cit; pp 20-57; at p. 24.

[534] C. Singer: *A short History of Scientific Ideas to 1900*; op cit; p. 151.

[535] P Benoit and F. Micheau: The Arab Intermediary; op cit; p. 203.

[536] P.K. Hitti: History, op cit; p. 571.

Bitruji (d. c 1204) modified Ptolemy's system of planetary motions.[537] And so did Jabir Ibn Aflah and nearly every other Islamic astronomer of renown. Muslim scholars, most particularly, used their perfected instruments to correct the glaring errors of Ptolemy.[538] And contrary to what Crombie and most historians hold, modern astronomy, as will be shown in part two, is based on these Muslim scholars findings rather than Ptolemy's data.

Besides, again contrary to what Crombie holds, it was Jabir Ibn Aflah's astronomical treatise *Islah al-Majisti* (*Refutation of the Almagest*) which was valued for centuries in its Latin and Hebrew versions by both Christians and Jews.[539]And, it was not from Ptolemy that medieval and post medieval Western scholarship took over but from his Muslim critics. It was al-Zarqali's tables for the meridian of Toledo, for instance, that were used as source of reference whether by Raymond of Marseilles (in 1140), Walcher of Malvern (fl. late 11th century), or Roger of Hereford; the meridian of Toledo remaining for centuries the standard of computation for the West.[540]In 1178, for instance, Roger of Hereford adapted the astronomical tables that existed for Toledo and Marseilles (based on Toledan tables) to the meridian of the city of Hereford, only using the Christian calendar `because the years of the Arabs and their months are difficult to our people who are not accustomed to them.'.[541]Moreover, Raymond of Marseilles, decades earlier, in 1140, says `that students of astronomy were compelled to have recourse to worthless writings going under the name of Ptolemy and therefore blindly followed; that the heavens were never examined, and that any phenomena not agreeing with such books were simply denied.'[542] He, Raymond, therefore decided to transform the astronomical tables of al-Zarqali, which were computed for the meridian of Toledo and adapted to Muslim years, so as to arrange them for the meridian of his native city and according to years dated from the birth `of our Lord.'[543]The work of Ptolemy was in fact so much refuted and discussed that the end result was the origin of Copernicus' conception of the planets.[544]

---

[537] A. Djebbar: Une Histoire; op cit; p.194.
[538] F.Braudel: Grammaire; op cit; p.113.
[539] G. Sarton: Introduction; Vol II, op cit; p. 123.
[540] C.H. Haskins: Studies; op cit; P. 18.
[541] D. Metlitzki: The Matter of Araby; op cit; p.38.
[542] J.L. E. Dreyer: Mediaeval Astronomy; in *Toward Modern Science*; op cit; pp 235-56; p.243.
[543] Ibid.
[544] P Benoit and F. Micheau: The Arab Intermediary; op cit; p. 203.

It is the same in pharmacology, which the Muslims considerably developed by adding hundreds of new drugs.[545]The Muslims also adapted the transmitted material in varying ways, some writers emphasising the botanical description of the drugs, others their potency, their mode of operation, their composition, and the forms which the medicaments took (that is to say, preparations like pastes, solutions, tinctures, etc.), and also synonyms for drugs.[546] Dietrich refers to Meyerhof who noted how the Muslims appended to each name its synonyms in other languages so as to arrive in this way at as unambiguous a definition of the drugs as possible.[547] Meyerhof has also been able to trace about a hundred and ten Muslim writers who worked on the subject, approximately a quarter of whose works are probably extant but very little of it printed, most of it in manuscript form in libraries, especially those of the East,[548]which dwarfs the dominant Greek figure in the field, Dioscorides. The Islamic legacy, more importantly, is in introducing experimentation and laboratory work within the science, and thus setting the very modern foundations of this science.[549]

When it comes to medicine, and en par with Garrison,[550]and others, Dietrich, mistakenly, holds:
`The Muslims did not advance the state of knowledge in the subject (medicine) beyond this (Hippocrates and Galen); their own contribution was the comprehensive systematisation of the transmitted heritage, and the description of a few diseases like small pox which were not known to the Greeks.'[551]
Yet, again, any student in medicine can compare both sets of medical writing (the Greek and the Muslim) and check for themselves the truthfulness of Dietrich's (just as Garrison's and others') writing. Besides, there are good, old sources, Campbell[552]and Leclerc,[553] for instance, which could have proved wrong Dietrich, Garrison, and the so many holding the

---

[545]Alexander Tschich, ed: *Handbuch der Pharmakognosis*, 3 vols, ed.2. (Leipzig, 19) 1.2 pp. 594-615 In J.M. Riddle: Theory and Practice in Medieval Medicine: *Viator*: 5; pp 157-84. p. 174.
[546] A. Dietrich: Islamic Sciences and the Medieval West, Pharmacology: in *Islam and the medieval West:* (K. I. Semaan; ed); op cit; pp 50-63; p.50.
[547] Ibid. p.52.
[548] Ibid.
[549] S.K. Hamarneh: The Life Sciences; in *The Genius of Arab Civilisation*, op cit; p. 156.
[550] F.H. Garrison: *Contributions*, op cit;
[551] A Dietrich: Islamic Sciences; op cit; p.50.
[552] D. Campbell: *Arabian Medicine,op cit.*
[553] N.L. Leclerc: *Histoire de la Medecine Arabe*; 2 vols; Paris; 1876.

same absurd views. It is not just that the Muslims addressed and dealt with diseases and their cures, which the Greeks never considered, the Muslims even had to rebuild the whole subject to give us our modern medicine. As instances, Al-Razi (d. 925), in his encyclopaedic work *Al-Hawi* (The Continens) rejected the works of Hippocrates and Galen through experiments and observations.[554] In fact, Al-Razi compiled his work as a response to all inconsistencies and shortcomings of Hippocrates, whom he also found obscure and disorderly.[555] A Disciple of Al-Razi, Abu `Ali Ibn al-Abbas al-Majussi (d.995 A.D) composed a medical treatise: *al-Kitab al-Malaki* which also attacks Hippocrates as obscure and too concise.[556] Ibn al-Nafis (d.1288) attacks Galen and his `anatomy' of the heart, and the same with al-Baghdadi who also corrects many observations of the Greeks.[557]

More importantly, without the Muslims, medicine would have remained for much longer in Western Christendom a wholly folkloric matter, relying on saints relics and witchcraft for cure, as seen in the first chapter. Sherwood Taylor also notes how medical works written in Western Europe from the end of Greek science to the beginning of the revival of Medicine in the 12th and 13th centuries being of poor scientific value.[558]The first person to introduce medicine to the West, Constantine the African, brought his stock of works from Al-Qayrawan (Tunisia), translations of which led to the blossoming of both medicine and Salerno, which became the first medical faculty in Europe.[559] Constantine, in a letter to Abbot Desiderius of Monte Cassino, revealed his concern that so few he found considered medicine a science.[560]

In physiological optics, Al-Razi refuted the texts of the *De Demonstrationes*; exposing with supporting arguments Galen's inadequate theory of vision.[561] Galen considered that `the eye emits a light which transmutes in its own nature the air between the subject who sees and the object of vision; and it is by the means of that air that's transformed, and which is conceived as capable of sensation and similar to the animal spirit contained by shallow conducts with the name of optic nerves, that vision

---

[554] C. Bouamrane-L. Gardet: *Panorama de la Pensee Islamique,* Sindbad; Paris, 1984; p. 231.

[555] Ibid.

[556] Ibid.

[557] Ibid.p. 233.

[558] F. Sherwood Taylor: A Short History; op cit; p.87.

[559] D. Campbell: Arabian Medicine; op cit.
Constantine the African and `Ali ibn al-Magusti: *The Pantegni* and related texts, eds C. Burnett and D. Jacquard, Leiden, 1994.

[560] J.M. Riddle: Theory and Practice; op cit; p. 177.

[561] S. Pines: *Studies in Arabic; op cit;* p. 261.

is exercised.'[562] This notion of air having the faculty of sensation had already troubled the earlier Muslim scientist Hunain Ibn Ishaq, who fought it, but had supposed that Galen had put it forward in deference for the people of his time.[563] An excuse which did not hold according to Al-Razi, for the whole of Galen's theory of vision was based on this notion; Al-Razi citing a passage of *De Demonstrationes* where the human body (and most particularly after the context, the brain and the eyes) are assimilated to light.[564]

Having just mentioned optics, Aristotle's optics, based on the so-called intromission theory, was the principal reason why Greek optics, and optics in general, remained a dead science for over ten centuries until the time of Ibn al-Haytham (965-1039), who via experiment, both demolished Aristotelian (and Euclidian) optics to set up the modern foundation for this science.[565] Ibn al-Haytham, combining geometry and physics, argued that objects are seen by means of reflected rays passing toward the eye, and not vice versa, as the Greeks had assumed.[566]In fact, Ibn al-Haytham was the first scientist to unlock optical science after centuries of Greek cogitation around their main conflicting theories of intromission, something entering the eyes representative of the object, and of `emission,' vision occurring when rays emanate from the eyes and are intercepted by visual objects.[567]

As Sayili observes, Greek `science,' expressed in Aristotelian physics, Ptolemaic astronomy, and Hippocratic or Galenic medicine, caused scientific knowledge to become `static, conservative, and dogmatic.'[568]The same also noted by Garaudy, who explains that the major reason for the loss of originality in Ibn Rushd's philosophy was due to Aristotle's influence.[569]Kimble notes the same defects with regard to Ptolemaic geography, for once his work was rendered accessible in Latin, and it won the allegiance of Western Christendom, it retarded the growth of accurate geographical concepts.[570]

---

[562] Ibid.
[563] Ibid.
[564] Ibid.
[565] See for instance D.C. Lindberg: *Studies in the History of Medieval Optic*s; London, Variorum; 1983.
[566] B. Stock: Science, Technology, and Economic Progress in the Early Middle Ages; in *Science in the Middle Ages* D. C. Lindberg ed; Chicago. 1978: pp. 1-51: p. 21
[567] See for details: D.C. Lindberg: *Studies in the History; op cit.*
[568] A. Sayili: *The Observatory in Islam*; Publications of the Turkish Historical Society, Series VII, No 38, Ankara, 1960. p.410.
[569] R. Garaudy: *Comment l'Homme devint Humain,* Editions J.A, 1978. p.216.
[570] G.H.T. Kimble: Geography; op cit; p. 62.

And one of, if not the principal, reason for such lack of progress, whether with respect to Aristotle's physics, or other Greek sciences, was the making of postulates without one single experiment being ever carried out.[571] Around A.D. 830, already, Al-Jahiz had observed `the curiosity that is, that the Greeks are interested in theory but do not bother with practice, whereas the Chinese are very interested in practice and do not bother with theory.'[572]

The transplantation of classical scholarship into Muslim soil, Rosenthal observes, caused the awakening of a critical scholarly spirit amongst the Muslims, who asserted that `A scholar should not make any unproven statements.'[573] Thus, al-Kindi (b. 803) is rightly angry at a Greek author, who was his main source in one of his treatises on optical problems, because he did not heed this rule.[574]

`The Greeks,' as Briffault puts it, `systematised, generalised and theorised, but the patient ways of investigation, the accumulation of positive knowledge, the minute method of science, detailed and prolonged observations and experimental enquiry were altogether alien to the Greek temperament.... What we call science arose in Europe as a result of a new spirit of enquiry, of new methods of experiment, observation, measurement, of the development of mathematics, in a form unknown to the Greeks. That spirit and those methods were introduced in the European world by the Arabs.'[575]

`The Greeks,' Mathe observes, `were abstract intellectuals, and the Arabs ingenious practitioners,' and `it was to take another thousand years for our European Middle Ages to reach that stage of scientific experimentation.'[576] Aristotle or Ptolemy only cared for generalisation and theory, and neglected and were careless of facts.[577]This is well illustrated in optics, for instance, whereby the principal reason that delayed progress in the science under the Greeks was their incapacity, unlike their Muslim successors, to experiment.[578] Ptolemy did carry out experiment in fact but only to support already held views; experiment succeeding the

---

[571] R. Briffault: The Making, op cit, pp 193-4.
[572] J.M. Riddle: Theory and Practice; op cit; p. 184.
[573] CF. Islamic Culture 16. 464 f. 1942 in F. Rosenthal: The Technique; op cit; p. 53.
[574] Ibid.
[575] R. Briffault, The Making of Humanity, op cit, p. 191.
[576] J Mathe: *The Civilisation of Islam*, tr. David Macrae, Crescent Books, New York. p 120.
[577] R. Briffault: The Making, op cit, pp 192-4.
[578] D.R. Hill: Islamic Science, op cit, pp 72-3.

findings, rather than the other way round.[579]Ibn al-Haytham, on the other hand, made repeated experiments to test his theory.[580]

Speculation by one and experimentation by the other having different outcomes on science. Hill remarks, for instance, how Aristotle speculative physics, and reverence to him had `a stultifying effect upon creative thought.'[581] Greek physics reasoned and deduced but hardly ever calculated, observes Benoit; calculation, he adds, being the essential foundation not only of the sciences but also of technology and economic activity.[582] The experimental path taken by Islamic scientists, on the other hand, constituted not just a breakthrough of considerable implication for physical investigations, but also freed scientific thought.[583] Al-Biruni and Al-Khazini (d. 1123), for instance, pioneered in determining specific weights.[584] And so accurate were Al-Khazini's tabulation of specific gravities they are in near total agreement with those we have today.[585]The same holds in medicine and anatomy, whereby the opinions of Hippocrates and Galen were often rejected by Muslim physicians, who, from experience, or though logical reasoning recognised their fallacy.[586] Fallacies such as Aristotle's that men had more teeth than women, or Galen's assertion that the lower jaw consists of two bones.[587] It took good clinical observation on the part of the Muslims to change things.[588] Ibn al-Nafis using dissection, for instance, declared Galen wrong. [589]To mention all available instances, Rosenthal concludes, would mean `to write a complete history of Arabic medicine.'[590]

It was Islamic learning, and not Greek learning, which remained central to Western awakening as parts two and three of this work will amply show. Briefly, here, in philosophy, it was not Aristotle, but Islamic commentaries and also writing, which had the pre-eminence. The influence of the Mu'tazilah, Ibn Sina, al-Ghazali, and Ibn Rushd went, indeed, far beyond the role of mere transmitters of garbled Aristotelianism

---

579 Ibid.

580 See S.B. Omar: *Ibn al-Haytham's Optics*: Bibliotheca Islamica; Chicago, 1977.

581 D.R. Hill: *Islamic Science; op cit;* p 58.

582 P. Benoit: Algebra, Commerce and Calculation: in A history of Scientific Thought; op cit; pp 246-79; at p.246.

583 D.R. Hill: Islamic Science; op cit; p. 58.

584 A. Mieli: *La Science Arabe; op cit;* p. 101. Mieli considers the determination of specific weights by al-Biruni and al-Khazini as outstanding manifestations in experimental physics

585 D.R. Hill: Islamic Science; op cit; p. 66.

586 F. Rosenthal: The Technique and Approach; op cit; p. 56.

587 R. Briffault: The Making: op cit; 192-4.

588 C. Bouamrane, L. Gardet: Panorama, op cit, pp. 231-2.

589 I.R and L. Al-Faruqui: The Cultural; op cit; p. 322.

590 F. Rosenthal: The Technique and Approach; op cit; p. 56.

generally attributed to them.[591] Despite the Church's opposition to Ibn Rushd' writing, it remained alive in Europe until the 16th century; Dante, for one, acknowledging his pre-eminence.[592] In medical science, again, against established wisdom, and from the 12th century onwards until the 17th century, it was the works of Al-Razi, Ibn Sina, Al-Zahrawi; Ibn Zuhr; Ibn Rushd, etc, which received more attention than those of Hyppocrates and Galen, while Ibn Serabion and Massawayh al-Maridini of Baghdad and Cairo, became the foundation of the New Pharmacy.[593] Osler mentions the textbook of Ferrari (1471), which quotes Ibn Sina 3,000 times, Al-Razi 1000, and Hypocrates only 140 times.[594] Equally all early Western scholars, whether Bacon, Aquinas, Chaulliac, Witelo, etc, were learned in Arabic, not Greek. Bacon, for instance, was thoroughly conversant in both Hebrew and Arabic.[595]The knowledge of Greek was rare in Italy in the year 1360; Petrarch in this year being able to name only ten men of learning in Italy who were acquainted with it.[596] And leading figures of Western learning, from Aquinas, Bacon, Chauliac, Witelo, Lull, etc, up to the 15th century, and many for centuries after, until the late 17th century, had Islamic learning as the basis of theirs as their works show.[597]

The very concept of learning in its essential purposes: spreading knowledge for practical, that is economic and social reasons, was removed from the Greek notion of learning. `The capriciousness of mathematical development,' Sarton says, `cannot be emphasised too much. Why were the early Greeks so interested in the theory of numbers, and so little in plain arithmetic? The latter was highly needed. Every reason of economic necessity should have caused the development of arithmetic, and

[591] John P. Dolan: Medieval Christian Tolerance and the Muslim World: *The Muslim World.* Vol 51: 1961; pp 280-7. p.280.
[592] E. A. Myers: *Arabic Thought and the Western World.* Frederick Ungar Publishing, New York, 1964: p.48.
[593] D. Campbell: Arabian Medicine, op cit; p.167.
[594] Ibid. p.201.
[595] S.P. Scott: History; op cit; vol 3; p.496.
[596] G. Voight: *Die Wiedebelebung des classischen Altherthums;* Berlin, 1881, ii, 107 in D.Campbell: Arabian medicine, op cit; p. 120.
[597] For those not wishing to do so, they can always check this in:
-G. Sarton: Introduction to the History; op cit.
-J. Vernet: *Ce que la culture doit aux Arabes d'Espagne*, tr by G Martinez Gros, 1985, Paris.
-A.Mieli: *La Science Arabe; op cit.*
-H.R. Turner: *Science in Medieval Islam*, Austin Texas, 1997.
-E. Myers: *Arabic Thought; op cit.*

discouraged as a luxury the growth of fanciful ideas on the properties of numbers...'[598]
It was the Arabic numerals, on the other hand, that revolutionised the whole function of exchange; and Muslim mathematical knowledge, via the son of a trader, Fibonacci, who studied in North Africa, which became the crucial step for the introduction of arithmetic into Western Christendom.[599]
On the social front, there is not a single piece of evidence showing learning being delivered on an organised, universal form under the Greeks. In Islam, knowledge was diffused in mosques, hospitals, observatories, and specialised madrasas.[600] Besides, as Farukh observes, we find a surprising fact that the Greeks had rifled libraries, schools and treasuries of books, but collected these books and stored them away in catacombs and caves to keep them away from scholars and to deprive students of their truth.[601]Which is exactly the very opposite of what can be found under Islam, where was born the very concept of our modern public libraries: spreading the knowledge through books to as many as possible.[602]

Finally, to refute comprehensively the notion that Greece is the centre of modern civilisation, any exploration of most aspects of modern science and civilisation shows no Greek antecedent of any sort. In Civil engineering, for instance, there is no Greek antecedent in dam construction, or bridge building. One wonders where is the Greek influence in relation to the invention of paper, or the compass, or any sort of Greek antecedent in the geography of travel. One cannot find a single Greek traveller who described mysterious lands, except in the imagination of Homerus. Surely, there is no sign of Greek nautical information of any sort that impacted on the maritime discoveries of the later Middle Ages. What impact did the Greeks have on the development of banking, or

---

[598] G. Sarton: *The Study of the History of Mathematics:* Harvard University press, 1936. p.18.

[599] W. M. Watt: *The Influence of Islam; op cit.* pp. 63-4.

-R. Rashed: Fibonacci et les Mathematiques Arabes, in Science at the court of Frederick II; *Nature, Sciences and Medieval Societies*, II. Brepols, 1994; pp 145-60.

-Dictionary of Scientific Biography for entry on Fibonacci.

[600] B. Dodge: *Muslim Education in Medieval Times*; The Middle East Institute, Washington D.C, 1962.

J. Pedersen: *The Arabic Book*; tr by G. French; Princeton University; 1984.

F. Rosenthal: *Knowledge Triumphant: the concept of Knowledge in Medieval Islam*, Leiden; E.J. Brill, 1970,

[601] O.A. Farukh: *The Arab Genius in Science and Philosophy*; American Council of Learned Societies, Washington, D.C, 1954. p.6.

[602] On this, see, most particularly:

R.S. Mackensen: Background of the History of Muslim Libraries.' *The American Journal of Semitic Languages and Literatures* 51; pp.114-125; 52; pp. 22-33, and pp. 104-10.

money, bills of credit and other trade mechanisms. None is the answer. Where is the Greek influence in relation to farming, irrigation techniques, crop rotation, plant diffusion and so on and so forth. One would also look very hard for a Greek observatory, precursor to the Islamic, or to a Greek madrasa, and a Greek precedent to universal learning, organised by the state or built around institutions that were funded by state or individuals. One would seek in Greek science a trace of the chemical laboratory, and would look in vain for one sole example of Greek experiment in any science. And one would look in great vain for Greek architectural influence in the birth of the Gothic, or castles and fortifications; or one single Greek historiographer who informs us of anything of value the way Ibn Khaliqan, or al-Maqari do. Have the Greeks legated anything that approaches the value of what others, Muslims and non Muslims legated, such as the Arabic numerals, surgical instruments (as constructed by Al-Zahrawi), gardens, flowers, book making, workshops and industrial mills, etc. Not at all. Thus, the notion that our modern civilisation evolves from Greece is a ridiculous notion conveyed by `historians' with hardly any grasp of the origins of science, learning and civilisation.

Final Words:

To resolve this Greek question, and see where did the revival of science and civilisation arise from, it is necessary to compare the like by the like, for ex:

-Galen/Hippocrates and Ibn Sinna and Al-Razi (medicine).
-Greek optics, and Ibn Al-Haytham's optics.
-Euclid's mathematics and Al-Khwarizmi's.
-Ptolemy's geography, vs Muslim's geography.
-Aristotle's science vs Islamic science.
-Greek astronomy and Muslim astronomy

And so on and so forth... and in the end assert which of Greek or Muslim science is:

-nearest to modern science.
-has a wider reach in terms of facts, subjects, and scientific breakthroughs.

The concluding words are left to Le Bon:

`As Pascal said: `All the follow up of men, for all the centuries, must be seen as if the same man who survives always and who learns continuously.' Each generation benefits first from the treasure accumulated from those which have preceded it, then, if capable, increases it in its turn.

No people has escaped this rule, and it cannot be said one single one can escape it. In recent times, when the origins of Greek civilisation were totally unknown, it was considered for certain that they owed nothing to any other people; recent study, however, has shown that Greek art had its origins with the Assyrians and the Egyptians. The latter, themselves, must have borrowed from other people more ancient; and if all rings of the chain which relate us to the origins of humanity were not lost, we can gradually progress towards the distant origins of prehistory, when man could hardly be differentiated from animals who have preceded him.'[603]

Indeed, this author does not claim the Greeks had no contribution; they did. Not the one Western history attributes to them, though. They did to the level from where the Muslims took over, not to the level the West took over. Thus, the Western view that modern science and civilisation are Greek, and such Greek science was taken over by Westerners need to be corrected as follows:
The Muslims took elements of science and civilisation from Greek, Hindu, Chinese, African, Pre Islamic Middle Eastern, and Roman civilisations. Such elements were fertilised and developed by the Muslims to the levels Western Christendom took over in the 12th–13th century (although many aspects were passed a little earlier or later than that.) Western Christendom, in turn, gradually developed them to give us our modern science and civilisation.

2. Suppressing Facts Related to the Islamic Role in the Middle-Ages and their Distorting Effect:

Selective omission of historical facts so as to rebuild a different history has been noted already, and Hartner,[604] Mieli,[605] Daumas,[606] Tout,[607] and others have in their own ways highlighted its distorting effects. Halpern, with the specific instance of Muslim science, has raised the issue that

[603] G. Le Bon: La Civilisation des Arabes; op cit; p.396:
[604] W. Hartner: Essay Review of O. Neugebauer op cit. at p. 201.
[605] A. Mieli: la Science Arabe; op cit; p.310.
[606] M. Daumas: The history of technology: Its limits; its methods; trans into English and notes by A. Rupert hall; in *History of Technology*, 1976; pp 85-112; p.91.
[607] T.F. Tout: The Place of the Middle Ages in the Teaching of History, *History*, New series, Vol 8 (1923-4); pp 1-18; at p.2.

many of the once great achievements of Muslim civilisation are taken away from the Muslims one after the other. [608]The dominant practice has been for modern historians to complement each other in the suppression of the Islamic legacy established by earlier authorities. Hence, the eighteenth century historian Gibbon declared that the science of chemistry owes its origin and importance to the industry of `the Saracens': "They first invented and named the alembic for the purpose of distillation, analysed the substances of the three kingdoms of nature, tried the distinction and affinities of alcalis and acids, and converted the poisonous minerals into soft and salutary medicines."[609] Yet a century after Gibbon the originality of the Muslims in all these respects had been considerably diminished, Berthelot (and his countless followers) denied to them any significant contribution in this field, ascribing rather to Western alchemists whatever advances were made in the Middle Ages.[610] Equally, the Gothic style was amply demonstrated by Christopher Wren in the 17th century to be of Muslim authorship, at a time, when Gothic was identified with the barbaric, [611] and yet, today, hardly any modern historian sees anything Islamic in such a style. The same with regard to the Arabic numerals, once shunned,[612] regarded even as a symbol of `Saracen magic,'[613]then, as they became the foundation of modern civilisation, and by a gradual re-working by modern historians, these numerals are no longer Arabic, hardly any modern historian failing to call them Hindu, or even attribute their origins to Western sources.[614] Experimentation, and the experimental method, viewed in the Western Middle Ages as dabbling with the occult; any person who performed experiments or made astronomical observations soon incurring the suspicion that he carried on the forbidden intercourse with the world of demons.[615] Gradually, again, in modern historian interpretations, experimentation becomes a purely

---

608 L. Halpern: *l'Essor de l'Europe (XI-XIII Siecles);* Presses Universitaires de France; Paris; 1941; p. 101.

609 In C.H. Haskins: *The Renaissance of the Twelfth century;* op cit. pp. 319-20.

610 C.H. Haskins: *The Renaissance*. p. 320.

611 J. Sweetman: *The Oriental Obsession;* Cambridge University Press, 1987. p.6.

612 D.J. Struik: The Prohibition of the use of Arabic numerals in Florence: *Archives Internationales d'Histoire des Sciences* Vol 21 pp 291-294.P. 294:

613 William of Malmesbury: History of the kings of England, in L. Cochrane: *Adelard of Bath,* British Museum Press, 1994. p. 43.

614 See H.P. Lattin: The Origin of our present system of notation according to the theories of Nicholas Bubnov. In *ISIS*; XIX; pp. 181-94; at p. 182.

615 E.J. Dijksterhuis: *The Mechanization of the World Picture*; Oxford at the Clarendon Press; 1961: p.104.

Western creation, regardless of evidence.[616] Another crucial matter for the rise of modern science, the use of reason against authority, one of the early Western scientists, Adelard of Bath, its promoter, attributing his inspiration to his `masters' the Arabs as will be lengthily highlighted in the following chapter. Here, briefly, Adelard in his *Quaestiones naturales*, praises the learning and rational method of Arab teachers, and says, explicitly:

`a magistris Arabicis ratione duce didici'[617]

Yet, modern historians, overwhelmingly, question Adelard's affirmation itself, one such modern historians, Brian Lawn, stressing that Adelard did not mean `Arab,' his inspiration being Classical thought, instead.[618] Jolivet, on the other hand, clearly demonstrates how `reason, at any rate in scientific matters, is according to Adelard not to be found in the Western world but among `the Arabs.'[619]Jolivet also shows that Adelard's position was shared by all of his 12th century contemporaries who translated Muslim works.[620]These translators also, without one single exception, stated that their dearest wish was to acquire the science of `the Arabs,' and to transmit it to the West, as the chapter on translations will amply show. Gerard of Cremona, the leading figure amongst such translators, in front of the `multitude' of Arabic books in every field, `pitied the poverty of the Latin.'[621] Modern history, however, and overwhelmingly, as shown above, insists that such translators aimed at the recuperation of `Greek' learning. Another modern historian: Hamilton Gibb, again, questions the wisdom of his predecessors, declaring even dubious some parts of the Legacy of Islam,[622]and proceeding to cut away such Islamic influence.[623] And the list can go on endlessly, showing how each modern historian, building on his predecessor, removes more traces of the Islamic role, until such Islamic role is fundamentally erased, and a new version of history is established.

---

616 A.C Crombie: *Robert Grossesteste and the Origins of the Experimental Science,* Oxford, 1953.

617 *Quaestiones Naturales*, ed. M. Muller; BGPTM xxxi (1934) ii; quotation in J. Jolivet: The Arabic Inheritance; in *A History of Twelfth Century Western Philosophy;* Ed by P. Dronke; Cambridge University Press; 1988; pp.113-48. p. 113.

618 B. Lawn: *The Salernitan Questions*; Oxford at the Clarendon Press; 1963; pp. 21-2.

619 J. Joliver: The Arabic Inheritance; op cit; note 69; p. 134.

620 Ibid.

621 C.H. Haskins: *Studies in the History of Mediaeval Science*. Frederick Ungar Publishing Co. New York. 1967 ed. p. 14.

622 T. Arnold and A. Guillaume: The Legacy of Islam; op cit.

623 H. Gibb: The Influence of Islamic Culture on Medieval Europe; in *Change in Medieval Society*; ed S. Thrupp; Appleton Century Crofts; New York; 1964; pp. 155-67.

The major result of this concerted effort which suppresses the Islamic links in relation to all scientific and other changes is that it gives rise to completely disconnected, contradictory explanations for the changes that took place in the medieval period. These changes took place during the same period of the middle ages (12th-13th centuries), along the same pattern, in the same places, in contact with the same agents, bearing the same substance and content, and yet are attributed by modern historians to different, even contradictory origins. Which hardly stands to close scrutiny, especially if seen from a wide perspective. Menocal,[624] Ribera,[625] Dawson,[626] and few others, have noted this technique consisting in setting aside the evidence which favours the Islamic origin of breakthroughs, and building new theories and explanations for them, even if such explanations are untenable on closer scrutiny. A closer scrutiny which follows, and which shows the techniques followed in cleansing out the Islamic role by the selective suppression of facts, and also by misattributing scientific breakthroughs of Islamic origin.

a. Selective Suppression of Facts:

The suppression of facts supporting the Islamic sources of modern science and civilisation is generalised amongst Western historians as illustrated by random instances here. Beginning with Pernoud, who says:
`It was in the High Middle Ages that we have the spread of the book in the form as we know it nowadays, the *codex*, instrument of culture, which henceforth replaces the *volumen*, the Antiquity roll; printing can only render the services it did thanks to that invention: the book.'[627]
One agrees on the crucial role of the book, but there are two fallacies here. The true time of the beginning of the book was centuries earlier than the High Middle Ages, and it is by no means Latin as Pernoud holds, but definitely Islamic. It was the introduction of paper and its industrial manufacturing in the early 800s in Baghdad, then other parts of the Muslims East,[628] which led to the profession of Warrak (warraq: paper), who both sold paper, and manufactured books in such large numbers as to

---

[624] M.R. Menocal: The Arabic Role; op cit; p. 1 fwd.
[625] J. Ribera: *Dissertaciones y opusculos*, 2 vols, Madrid, 1928.
[626] C. Dawson: *Medieval Essays; op cit;* the last chapter most particularly; pp. 215 fwd..
[627] R Pernoud: *Pour en Finir avec le Moyen Age*: Editions du Seuil, Paris, 1977; p.44.
[628] D. Hunter: *Papermaking:The History and Technique of an Ancient craft*; Pleiades Books; London; 1943.

trigger the first mass book production, and the true revolution in learning.[629]

Another historian, Sherwood Taylor, with more suppressions of crucial fact, as he says:
`One great mathematician, Leonardo of Pisa (also called Fibonacci), lived in this age. In 1202 he published his great work, the *Liber Abacci* or *Book of the Counting Board.* He was a merchant and had travelled widely and studied the methods of computing used in different parts of the world.'[630]
In three lines, Sherwood Taylor suppressed many decisive pieces of information. First that Leonardo learnt his mathematics amongst Muslim teachers in today's Algerian city of Bejaia.[631] That his *Liber Abacci* was mainly based on Islamic precedents, concerning the types of problems addressed; the methods for their solution; terminology, and even symbolism;[632]and not only in arithmetic, but also in algebra and in the theory of numbers, as carried by Islamic mathematics of the first period, that of the 9th-10th centuries.[633]And *Liber Abacci* was the first, most decisive breakthrough in modern mathematics, `the first monument of European mathematics,' according to Sarton;[634]thus, modern mathematics based principally on Islamic sources.
Anyone unaware of the points just made would have never understood or seen the Islamic foundation of modern mathematics by relying on Sherwood Taylor's and similar accounts. Besides, had a similar work of a Muslim scholar borne the slightest Greek influence, as already noted above, Sherwood Taylor would have dwelt on it at length.

A historian of great repute, Chaunu, outlining the findings of yet another historian of great repute, Beaujouan, writes:
`The astrolabe, first appeared in the eleventh century. It became a scientific instrument at Chartres in the twelfth, and at Oxford especially in the thirteenth century. These later more complicated astrolabes were not so much measuring instruments as machines for calculating the

---

[629] See, for instance:
J. Pedersen; The Arabic Book, op cit.
O. Pinto: `The Libraries of the Arabs during the time of the Abbasids,' in *Islamic Culture* 3 (1929), pp. 211-43.
[630] F. Sherwood Taylor: A Short History; op cit. p.102.
[631] W. Montgomery Watt: The Influence; op cit; pp. 63-4.
[632] A. Djebbar: *Une Histoire; op cit;* p.146.
[633] R. Rashed: Fibonacci et les Mathematiques Arabes; op cit; p.146.
[634] G. Sarton, Introduction, op cit, vol 3; p.7

stars' courses.[635] Detailed measurements of angle were made in the Middle Ages, as at the time of Tycho Brahe, using very large quadrants, but these instruments had been improved.[636] The turquet appeared round 1280. In 1342 Levi Gerson introduced the Jacob staff probably invented in the thirteenth century by Jacob Ben Mahir. These measurements led to the compiling of tables, starting with the Toledo tables. During the eleventh to thirteenth century these were followed by the Marseilles tables in 1140, Robert de Retinus Canons and the London tables. The very superior Alfonsine tables appeared in Paris in 1296.'[637]

In this paragraph, not a single reference to anything Islamic playing any part. This omission will be addressed after one fundamental glaring error is raised, first. This concerns Chaunu's assertion that `these measurements (taking place in the 12th, 13th and 14th centuries) led to the compiling of tables starting with the Toledo tables.' This is historically false, for tables were compiled already in the 9th century, tables by Al-Khwarizmi, for instance.[638] As for the Toledo tables, if he refers to those by Al-Zarqali, they date from 1084,[639] and, thus, cannot be the result of events which took place centuries after. With regard to Chaunu's omissions, beginning with the matter of tables, and quoting him `the very superior Alfonsine tables,' in reality, these tables were prepared by Jewish scholars, and were based on Al-Zarqali's tables already mentioned.[640] The Alfonsine tables were, indeed, by King Alfonso of Seville who based them on preceding Muslim tables.[641] Chaunu also fails to tell us that the Muslims are behind the astrolabe as is known to us,[642] that its first usage in Western Christendom goes back to contacts made by Christian scholars with Catalonia and carrying from there the first elements of knowledge about the instrument.[643] The astrolabe was not used just for astrology, but was also used for hundreds of other problem solving matters, including surveying,

---

[635] G. Beaujouan: In Histoire Generale des sciences; i. 521; 547 in P. Chaunu: *European Expansion in the Later Middle Ages;* Tr by K. Bertram; North Holland Publishing Company; Amsterdam; 1979; p.257.

[636] G. Beaujouan: In Histoire Generale; i. 547-8 in P. Chaunu: *European Expansion*; p.257.

[637] G. Beaujouan: Histoire Generale; i. 548 in P. Chaunu: *European Expansion*; p.257.

[638] G. Sarton, Vol I; op cit; p. 545.

[639] M. Steinschneider: Etudes sur Zarkali; *Bulletino Boncompagni*; vol 20.

[640] E. Rybka: Mouvement des Planetes dans l'Astronomie des Peuples de l'Islam; in *Convegno Internationale: Oriente e occidente Nel Medioevo Filosofia E Scienze;* 9-15 Aprile 1969; Academia Nationale Dei Lincei; Roma; 1971; pp. 579-93; p. 591.

[641] C.H. Haskins: *Studies; op cit;* p. 18.

[642] A.L. Mayer: *Islamic Astrolabists*, Albert Kundig edition, Geneva, 1956.

[643] J. W. Thompson: Introduction of Arabic Science; op cit; M. C. Welborn: `Lotharingia as a Center; op cit;.

calculating of heights, etc.[644] Equally the use of quadrants preceded Tycho Brahe by centuries.[645] The turqet which appeared in the year 1280 was in fact Jabir Ibn Aflah's work. [646] And many other omissions by Chaunu, which end up completely distorting historical reality.

Another historian of great repute, Parry, who says:
`Thanks to Sacrobosco (John of Holywood), it was at least common knowledge among educated people in the fifteenth century that the world was round.'[647]
Which completely distorts the picture of the true authorship of this idea, for, any scrutiny of John of Holywood's work, will instead reveal that his famed *Tractatus de Sphaera, or Sphaera Mundi,* completed in 1233, is nearly a word by word reproduction of al-Farghani and al-Battani.[648]As Singer insists, it contains nothing new or original that is not derived from the translations of Islamic works.[649]

Crombie, again:
`The development of modern trigonometry dates from mathematical work done in Oxford and France in the fourteenth century in connection with astronomy.'[650]
Which is false, for modern trigonometry was at least four-five centuries older than Crombie's supposed beginnings, principally owing to the pioneering works by al-Battani (d.929). Al-Battani Sabian tables (al-Zij al-Sabi), which had great impact on his successors, Muslim and Christian, in equal measure,[651]included a trigonometrical summary wherein not only sines, but tangents and cotangents, are regularly used.[652] It also contains a table of cotangents by degrees and a theorem equivalent to our formula giving the cosine of a side of a spherical triangle in function of the cosine of the opposite angle and of the sines and cosines of the other sides.[653]Von Braunmuhl, on the steady Growth of trigonometry, also

---

644 W. Hartner: The Principle and Use of the Astrolabe, in W. Hartner, *Oriens-Occidens*, Hildesheim, 1968, pp. 287-318; and J.D. North: The Astrolabe, *Scientific American* 230, No 1, 1974, pp 96-106.
645 L. Sedillot: Memoire sur les Instruments; op cit.
646 D.E. Smith: *History of Mathematics*; Dover Publications; New York; 1958; p. 206.
647 J.H. Parry: *The Age of Reconnaissance;* Weidenfeld and Nicholson; London; 1966; p.11.
648 A. Mieli: La Science Arabe; op cit; p. 241.
649 C. Singer: *A Short History of Scientific Ideas;* op cit; p.173.
650 A.C. Crombie: Science, Optics; op cit; p. 86.
651 R. Morelon: Eastern Arabic Astronomy, op cit; pp. 46-7.
652 G. Sarton: Introduction, vol I, op cit; p.585.
653 Ibid.

explains that the tangent and cotangent functions were introduced by Abu'l Wafa in the 10th century, and rather slowly made their way into European trigonometry via translators such as Adelard of Bath.[654] Sarton, equally, notes that Hasan al-Marrakushi's *al-Jami al-mabadi wal ghayat* (1229), includes a mathematical part, and trigonometrical tables, not only of sines but also of versed sines, arc sines, and arc cotangents. `Thus while the Christian mathematicians were opening new paths, the Muslims were continuing along the trigonometrical road which they had made so conspicuously their own.'[655]

Crombie, again, but on another distinct matter, holds:
`Adelard of Bath,[656] translator of Euclid's Elements of geometry from Arabic into Latin, demanded for reason precedence over authority.'[657]
Crombie's two lines are misleading on many accounts. First, Adelard was not just the translator of Euclid, his medieval fame owes to his translations of al-Khwarizmi and above all Abu al-Ma'Shar.[658] Adelard is mostly famed for being the one scholar who championed Arabism in all its manifestations;[659] spending seven years in study and travel in order `to investigate the learning of the Arabs as best as he could,'[660] and bringing back a unique enthusiasm for *Arabum studia.*[661] Adelard's *Questiones Naturales*, which preaches the use of reason, is based wholly on Islamic learning, Adelard praising both Islamic learning and the use of reason. He says:
"from the Arabic masters I have learned one thing, led by reason, while you are caught by the image of authority, and led by another halter. For what is an authority to be called, but a halter? As the brute beasts, indeed, are led anywhere by the halter, and have no idea by what they are led or why, but only follow the rope that holds them, so the authority

---

[654] Von Braunmuhl, in I. Grattan-Guiness: *The Fontana History of the Mathematical Sciences*, Fontana Press, 1997; pp 162-65: at p. 163.
[655] G Sarton: Introduction; Vol II; op cit. pp. 505-6.
[656] Adelardus Von Bath, *Die Quaestiones Naturales*, c.6, ed. M. Muller (*Beitrage zur Geschichte der Philosophie des Mittelalters*, xxxi.2; Munster, 1923; L. Thorndike: *A History of Magic and Experimental Science*, ii (New York, 1923) 28-9.
[657] A.C Crombie: *Science, Optics; op cit;* p.31.
[658] See: L. Cochrane: *Adelard of Bath,* op cit.
-C. Burnett: *Adelard of Bath*, Warburg, London, 1987.
-B.G. Dickey: *Adelard of Bath*, unpublished Thesis, University of Toronto, 1982.
[659] Ibid.
[660] Die Quastiones Naturales des Adelardus von Bath; ed. M.Mueller; p. 1; lines 6-11; in D.Metlitzki: The Matter of Araby; op cit; Chapter 2: p.13.
[661] D. Metlitzki: The Matter of Araby; op cit; Chapter 2: p.13.

of writers leads not a few of you into danger, tied and bound by brutish credulity."[662]
One such Muslim preaching the pre-eminence of reason, al-Maqdisi (fl 966), says:
`He (the learned) should not yield to bad habits or permit himself to be led astray by vicious tendencies. Nor must he turn his eyes from truth's depth. He should discriminate between the doubtful and the certain, between genuine and spurious, and should always stand firm by the clear light of reason.'[663]
Thus, Adelard was not the first medieval preacher of the use of reason, as Crombie holds, but that, instead, he was preceded and inspired by his Muslim masters.

Writing on the leading role of the southern Italian city of Salerno, Lawn holds:
`It has long been known that Salerno was the birth place and nursery of what has been called the scientific renaissance; that the masters there were the first, in the Latin West, to make use of the newly translated Aristotelian books, the *libri naturales*, in scientific and medical writings; and that, particularly during the twelfth century, *the civitas Hippocratica* became a centre for the diffusion of philosophical and scientific doctrines, as well as a school renowned far and wide for its medical teaching.'[664]
Lawn completely sets aside the most determining element of the rise of Salerno: the Islamic element. Salerno became the first institution of higher learning in the Christian West, not before, but precisely when Constantine the African (died.c.1087) made the translations into Latin of the works he had brought with him from Tunisia.[665] Born in Tunisia, whether Carthage or Al-Qayrawan, Constantine travelled with a cargo of medical books from Al-Qayrawan, and settled in Salerno and Monte Casino, where he made translations into Latin of such books,[666] works that included Hunayn and his son Ishaq, and the *Kitab Kamil as-sin'a at-tibbiya* (the `perfect' book on medical art') of `Ali ibn Abbas al-Majusti (*The Pantegni;*) and several works by doctors in Qayrawan on diets, the stomach, melancholy, forgetfulness and sexual intercourse.[667] These had Latin translations such

---

662 N. Daniel: The Arabs and Mediaeval Europe; op cit; p. 265-6: *Questiones*, ch vi, on why man must use reason with which he is endowed (Muller ed).
663 Mutahhr b. Tahir al-Maqdisi (fl 966) *Livre de la Creation et de l'Histoire*, ed. and trans. C. Huart (Paris, 1899-1910) I,, I: 5-6.
664 B. Lawn: *The Salernitan Questions*, op cit; p. xi
665 D. Campbell: Arabian Medicine, op cit; p. 123.
666 For more on Constantine see M. Mc Vaugh: Constantine the African,' *Dictionary of Scientific Biography*, vol 3, pp. 393-5.
667 C. Burnett: The Introduction of Arabic Learning; p. 23.

as *Chirurgia, `prognostica,' `De pulsibus,' `De instrumentis,' `practica'* (in xii books), *`Liber graduum,' De Stomachi et instestinorum infirmitatibus,' `Liber de urina,'*.[668] It was not, thus, Aristotle, but the works from Al-Qayrawan which were, indeed, the foundation of the revival. Aristotle and the Classics were available for centuries and had no impact, impact which occurred only after Constantine made his translations, and then Salerno came to play its prominent part. What is baffling, is that Lawn himself recognises that the classical heritage has always been available in Salerno prior to Constantine without having any decisive impact:

`Long before Salerno had achieved fame as the foremost school of medicine in western Europe,' he says, `traditional questions, dealing with the sciences and medicine, had been available in the Latin West: questions in which were reserved and kept alive many ideas, stemming from the rich heritage and Roman culture; until the advent of what has been called the scientific renaissance in the twelfth century, fresh channels were opened up.'[669]

Which contradicts, and fundamentally, Lawn's theory of Western revival based on Greek learning without the Islamic primary role. To refute further Lawn and others making similar assertions, one will add that it was in Salerno, where Constantine worked, and nowhere else where Greek learning was also available for centuries, that the revival in medical learning took place, and where the first faculty of higher learning was established. And it happened exactly soon after Constantine's translations, not before, even if classical learning was available all along in Salerno, which it must be reminded was in Byzantine hands for centuries. Why, thus, should this Greek learning, ineffective for centuries, only become effective when there is an Islamic link, neither Lawn nor other historians has so far managed to explain. From Salerno medical and higher learning spread, and its offshoots reached other parts of Italy, especially the first universities of Palermo and Padua, and from there further north.[670]Thus, Constantine's translations supplied the basic foundation of medical literature on which the West would build for several centuries.[671]Which is the central element, but completely set aside, or hardly acknowledged by Lawn and the countless others making similar argument.

---

668 D. Campbell: Arabian Medicine; op cit; p. 123.

669 B. Lawn: The Salernitan Questions, , p. 1.

670 P.O.Kristeller: `The School of Salerno: Its development and its contribution to the History of learning,' *Bulletin of the History of Medicine* 17 (1945): 151-7.
W. Durant: The Age of Faith; op cit; P. 457.

671 D. C. Lindberg: The Transmission of Greek and Arabic learning to the West: in Science in the Middle Ages (Lindberg ed) op cit; pp 52-90, p. 62.

On the matter of Sicilian impact, Lawn says:
`Perhaps here originated the custom of sending abroad lists of difficult questions for solution. One such collection, dealing with rather abstract, philosophical matters, the so-called *Sicilian Questions*, was sent by the emperor, c. 1237-42, to several Eastern philosophers, before being finally answered by the Spaniard, Ibn Sab'in. Other sets of questions dealing this time with the mathematical sciences, geometry, astronomy, and optics, were sent to places as far a field as Mosul, Toledo, and Egypt.'[672]
Here Lawn omits some crucial details. By Emperor, he means Frederick II, who was the ruler most imbued with Islamic learning in Western Christendom; so much so he was declared a heretic by the papacy.[673] By saying East, Lawn seeks to cover the true destination of Frederick II's correspondences, which was precisely with the Muslim world, and Egypt most particularly (both points made clear by Haskins, but Lawn, mischievously suppresses them; a good case of a modern historian cleansing old history).[674] As for Toledo, it was the Muslim centre of learning from where most science passed into Western Christendom as touched upon briefly already, and to be expanded in greater detail in the following part.

On the crucial role of scientific translations, Swanson holds (p.51) that during the seizure of Constantinople (in 1204), some of those who went east returned with Greek volumes, yet Swanson provides not one single instance of a scientific work brought back (the only work he cites, p. 54, being a theological work). In fact, all historical evidence shows that the Latin passage in Constantinople rather than acquiring learning was one of the most barbaric acts against civilisation. The crusaders engaged in an orgy of destruction, looting, rape and slaughter; also destroying the most priceless treasures of arts and civilisation in Constantinople.[675] And instead of bringing back books, the Latin destroyed learning, including that of Aristotle.[676] In Constantinople, in 1204, Draper informs, whilst the bronzes were melted into coins, thousands of manuscripts and parchments were burned, and from that time the works of many ancient authors disappeared altogether.[677]

---

[672] B. Lawn: The Salernitan Questions, op cit; p. 75.
[673] M.R. Menocal: The Arabic Role; op cit; p.63.
[674] C.H. Haskins: Studies, op cit, p. 253 and p. 265.
[675] G Le Bon: La Civilisation; op cit; p.256.
[676] W. Durant: The Age of faith, op cit; pp.604-5.
[677] J.W. Draper: A History; op cit; vol 2; p. 57.

Swanson then (p.51) says that translations of Greek works came via Hungary, before he tells four lines down: `the scale of this Hungarian activity and its Western impact remains obscure.'

Swanson moves to Sicily (p.51), saying that translations were of Greek works, mostly by Euclid, Ptolemy's Almagest, and one or two other Greek. Again, anyone consulting the role of the island in the awakening of Western civilisation will find instead a very strong Islamic influence, including translations; that of al-Bitruji's *On the Sphere*, most particularly, being decisive in impact. Besides, Frederick II established a policy of translation of all Islamic works, and of borrowing and exchanges with Muslim princes and scholars of the East.[678] And it was to Sicily, after it was taken by the Normans (late 11th), as Haskins, Sarton, and above all Amari, have shown, that learned men travelled to acquire Islamic science.[679] It is also from Sicily that arrived Qaid (Thomas) Brown, the Muslim exile playing the decisive role in the growth of the English Exchequer as Haskins amply demonstrated.[680]On this particular point, Swanson's explanation, whereby `a shift to written record from memory' is the result of such development, is yet another of the countless, obscure, explanations given for the medieval changes, changes, which happened in medieval Christendom, oddly enough, and by coincidence, following contact with Islam in any particular area; the English exchequer evolving precisely soon after the arrival of Qaid (Thomas) Brown, and not before.

In dealing with Adelard of Bath, (pp.53-4), Swanson reduces his contribution to the translations of `Arabic astrology' with the possible help of Petrus Alfonsi, `sometimes physician to King Henry I.' Which is misleading, again. Adelard did not just translate astrology, but did much more as already explained above, and as in the words of Cochrane:

`what we must be grateful for is that among a number of scholars who brought scientific information to the attention of the Latin West Adelard took the initiative not only in translating Arabic works but in recording their usefulness and developing the reasoning on which they were based'.[681]

And finally, Swanson, in page 53, first, tells us:

`Important as they were individually, and as evidence of intellectual curiosity, the overall impact of the translations was variable. Knowledge of

---

678 R. Briffault: The Making, op cit, p. 213.

679 G. Sarton: Introduction; op cit; C.H. Haskins: Studies; op cit; A. Amari: *La Storia dei Musulmani di Sicilia,* 3 vols, (1933-9) Revised 2nd edition by C.A. Nallino, Rome.

680 See: C.H. Haskins: England and Sicily in the 12th century; *The English Historical Review*: Vol XXVI (1911) pp 433-447 and 641-665.

681 L. Cochrane: Adelard of Bath; op cit; p. 108

their existence was often limited; their manuscript tradition is often weak; evidence of their use is patchy.'

Then, in page 54, he insists:

`The translation movement was one of the most important cultural trends in the long twelfth century. It certainly stimulated enquiry; once the scale of the material available was appreciated, the work gained a momentum of its own... Without these labours the intellectual transitions of the long twelfth century could not have been achieved.'

b. Misattribution of Scientific Breakthroughs:

Scores of Islamic breakthroughs are misattributed to their successors. Many will be seen as this work progresses. Here, two instances are examined: the origins of experimentation, and the use of modern instruments.

The Experimental Method:

Whilst Lynn White (already cited) champions every form of absurdity with regard to the history of technology, with respect to the matter of scientific experimentation, Crombie remains the true master. Here is one instance how Crombie makes his point:

`I have argued at length elsewhere that the contribution of Grosseteste and Roger Bacon and their successors to the scientific tradition of their time was to formulate, from the theoretical empiricism of the twelfth century and the deductive form of scientific explanation learnt from Euclid and from Aristotle's logic, a conception of science that was experimental, mathematical and deductive. From one point of view we can see their work as an attempt to combine the form of scientific thought imposed by Greek geometry and expounded by Plato with the empirical requirements insisted upon by the other great tradition of Greek methodology, that of medicine and of Aristotle.'[682]

Crombie echoed by one of his devotees, Beaujouan, who writes:

`Robert Grosseteste, for instance, did not break with the Platonic and Augustinian tradition: his cosmology of light led him to give first place among the natural sciences to geometrical optics and to the mathematical concepts connected with it. His conception of experimental science owed

---

[682] A.C Crombie: Science, Optics; op cit;. p.143.

much to Aristotle, but retained its independence. He was thus in the forefront of a scientific revival[683] of which the most illustrious exponent was Roger Bacon and of which the most brilliant success was the more or less accurate explanation of the rainbow by Dietrich of Freiberg.'[684]
Crombie, in fact, devotes a whole book attributing the birth of experimental science to Grosseteste.[685] A labour of historical fallacies, though.

Before dealing with Crombie, first a quotation from Briffault who outlines the scope of the problem:
`Discussions as to who was the originator of the experimental method, like the fostering of every Arab discovery or invention on the first European who happens to mention it, such as the invention of the compass to a fabulous Flavio Gioja or Amalfi, of alcohol to Arnold of Villeneuve, of lenses and gun-powder to Bacon or Shwartz, are part of the colossal misrepresentation of the origins of European civilisation. The experimental method of the Arabs was by Bacon's time widespread and eagerly cultivated throughout Europe.'[686]
Thus, the Muslim pioneering role in experimentation being suppressed from knowledge is hardly an isolated case.

With regard to Crombie's inane attribution of the experimental method to Grosseteste, and his contemporaries, it ought to be remembered, that centuries before, the Muslims made experimentation a central requirement of their science. Thus, Jabir Ibn Hayyan (722-815) said:
`The first essential in chemistry is that thou shouldest perform practical work and conduct experiments, for he who performs not practical work nor makes experiments will never attain to the least degree of mastery. But thou, O my son, do thou experiment so that thou mayest acquire knowledge.
Scientists delight not in abundance of material; they rejoice only in the excellence of their experimental methods.'[687]
Jabir, Sherwood Taylor notes, by describing chemical operations very clearly and practically, deserves `honour as one of the few medieval writers who soiled his hands in a laboratory.'[688]

---

683 A.C Crombie: *Robert Grossesteste; op cit*.
684 Guy Beaujouan: Motives and opportunities for Science in *Scientific Change*; Edited by A.C. Crombie:, Heinemann, London, 1963; pp 219-36.p. 226.
685 A.C Crombie: Robert Grossesteste; op cit.
686 R. Briffault: The Making, op cit, at p. 201.
687 E.J. Holmyard: *Makers of Chemistry*; Oxford at the Clarendon Press, 1931. p. 60.
688 F. Sherwood Taylor: A Short History; op cit; pp.113-4.

And so did al-Razi, who built the first chemical laboratory in the modern sense.[689]
Experimentation was also carried by Ibn al-Haytham, who was able to determine optical rules through experimentation rather than the speculative exercise current before him.[690] Ibn al-Haytham, who, according to Sarton, was the best embodiment of the experimental spirit of the middle ages.[691]Muslim astronomers, too, defined their findings, and devised astronomical tables through observations and calculations, and using for the first time sophisticated apparatuses for such operations.[692]Very early, Briffault notes, the Muslims compiled new sets of planetary tables, and obtained more accurate values for the obliquity of the ecliptic and procession of equinoxes, that were checked by two independent measurements of a meridian the estimates of the size of the earth.[693] One highlights here the two expressions: checking and reliance upon independent measurements.

Experimentation is in fact a fundamental of Islam and Islamic culture. Garaudy observes:
`The importance granted to the sensitive perception of beings, who are visible symbols of the invisible God, allows the focus to be put on the experimental method, as against the lowly deductive speculations of the Greeks, of whom we saw none, in Athens, who was interested in the sciences of nature, practised in Asia Minor, and in Alexandria.'[694]
Al-Faruqi explain that the Muslims built knowledge on *istidlal* (calling for evidence), seeking through evidence to make the unknown known. *Istidlal* meant observing the data and their examination through experimentation, measurement and more observation.[695] Jabir had a special name for scientific experiment, al-Tadrib; and Ibn al-Haytham called it *al-Itibar*.[696] Ibn al-Haytham's conclusions only reflected the evidence, and he was quite prepared to modify or even reject a hypothesis if it conflicted with

---

689 D.R. Hill: *Islamic Science; op cit*; at p. 84.
690 See the multiple experiments carried by Ibn al-Haytham in S.B. Omar: *Ibn al-Haytham's Optics*: Bibliotheca Islamica; Chicago, 1977.
691 G Sarton: Introduction; vol I, op cit; p.694.
692 See for instance:
L. Sedillot: Memoire sur les instruments astronomique des Arabes, op cit.
B. Hetherington: *A Chronicle of Pre-Telescopic Astronomy*; John Wiley and Sons; Chichester; 1996.
R.P. Lorch: The Astronomical Instruments of Jabir Ibn Aflah and the Torquetom; *Centaurus,* 1976; vol 20; pp 11-34.
693 R. Briffault: The Making, op. cit, p. 193.
694 R. Garaudy: Comment l'Homme; op cit. p.208.
695 I. R. and L L al-Faruqi: *The Cultural Atlas; op cit;* p. 322.
696 Ibid.

experimental results.[697] Al-Biruni refused any statement without testing it in experience and confirming it by examination.[698] The vulgar sense of experimentation is well expressed in the Arabic proverb: `*Is'al mujarrib la tas'al tabib*' meaning `Ask the experimenter (or the experienced person) don't ask the physician.'[699]

The Islamic renaissance is also evidenced by the publication of collections of experimental facts, e.g., the *Mujarrabat* of Abu-l-Ala Zuhr of Cordova (Ibn Zuhr's father); the *Mujarrabat* of the Baghdadite Christian, Ibn al-Tidlmidh; the *Mujarrabat* of the two Egyptian Jews, ibn al-Mudawwar and Ibn al-Naqid. All these books were significantly called *Mujarrabat*, meaning *experiments*.[700] In medical sciences, Al-Razi advised medical students that they should compare the symptoms they came across in practice with those they found in textbooks.[701] As did Ibn Sina, who indicated that theory and practice were interdependent.[702] Thanks to practice and observation, Benoit and Micheau observe, the precise descriptions of smallpox and of measles were made by al-Razi, and the discovery of the lymphatic system by Ibn al-Nafis at the end of the 13th century.[703] The constant progress in the anatomy and physiology of vision was also the product of a thought which had its bases first of all in practice and observation.[704] And Al-Biruni travelled forty years to collect mineralogical specimen; whilst Ibn Al-Baytar collected botanical specimen from the whole Muslim world and compared them with those of Greece and Spain.[705] The astronomers of Islam, too, had a strong feeling for precision. They were not satisfied with rough and approximate results, but aimed at exploiting thoroughly the advantage of utilising the mathematical tools at their disposal; and they insisted on the need for basing their results on as accurate observational data as possible.[706]

---

697 D.R. Hill: Islamic Science, op cit, pp 72-3.
698 I.R; and L. Faruqi: The Cultural; op cit; p. 322.
699 G. Sarton: Introduction; Volume III; op cit; p.17.
700 Ibid, Vol II, p.94.
701 I.B. Syed: Medicine and medical Education in Islamic History in *Islamic perspective in Medicine*, ed S. Athar, American Trust publication, Indianapolis; 1993; pp 45-56, p. 45.
702 In *Liber Canonis* (Venice 1555), Book 1, preface, fol. 3r; book 2, fen 3, chap.1, fol. 56r. B. Stock: Science, op cit, p. 21.
703 P Benoit and F. Micheau: The Arab Intermediary; op cit; p. 209.
704 Ibid.
705 J. Scarborough: Herbals: Byzantine and Arabic; Dictionary of Middle Ages; op cit; vol 6; p 179.
706 A. Sayili: The Observatory in Islam; op cit; p.312.

It is also remarkable, as Garaudy notes, that the precursor of the methods of observation and experimentation in the West, Roger Bacon (1214-1294), had studied Arabic, and had written that the knowledge of Arabic and Islamic science were for his contemporaries, the only means of access to true knowledge.[707] Roger Bacon derived a great deal from Islamic sources, and also indirectly from the Arabist Robert Grosseteste, in particular.[708]

And so, contrary to what Crombie holds, it was not through the Greeks, who loathed experiment, but through Islamic science and techniques in their practice, as Garaudy insists, [709] and as just demonstrated, that the scientific revival took place. And had Crombie and his hundreds of followers consulted Sarton, for instance, they would have read the complete opposite of what they held. Sarton, commenting on the more practical recipes of al-Razi, says:

`Unfortunately the full value of the latter could only be appreciated by those who were prepared to follow humbly in al-Razi's footsteps, and ready to make dirty and disgusting experiments. With but too few exceptions the Latin schoolmen were still more eager to discuss these matters in the abstract than to test the validity of the facts in the only possible way. That way, the experimental way, had hardly dawned upon them.'[710]

And whilst Sarton relies on historical facts to make his point, Crombie and his hordes of modern followers rely on the suppression of crucial facts to make theirs. Just as is the case for the next topic.

On The Use of Instruments:

Crombie, again, asserts the following:

`Practical demands forced an attention to numerical measurement and calculation and led to the development of instruments and mathematical techniques. Surveying methods were being taught in the *quadrivium* by the twelfth century, and in the whole practical quantification of space scholarly mathematics played an essential part in supplying mathematical procedures to the empirical methods of mariners, instrument makers, and other craftsmen. One example will suffice. In the sixteenth century the compass charts of *portolani* used in navigation gave two essential pieces of

---

[707] R. Garaudy: Comment l'Homme; op cit. p.208.
[708] D.Campbell: Arabian Medicine, op cit; p.175.
[709] R. Garaudy: Comment l'Homme; op cit;. p.208.
[710] G. Sarton: Introduction; Vol II, p.33.

information: the route to follow and the angle it must make with the North-South axis as given by a magnetized needle; and the distance to run in the direction thus determined. Ideally the navigator went on a line at a constant angle from the line of the magnetized needle until he reached his destination.'[711]

Again, had Crombie taken evidence from history, he would have found that the development of instruments (i.e the astrolabe, quadrants, sundials, armillary spheres etc) and their practical use, in calculating heights of walls, construction, surveying, sea travel etc, was an Islamic manifestation, centuries earlier than the Western origins he gives; and such uses were widespread.[712]Thus, Stock informs, that in Islam, the dependence on well made apparatuses did not just mean that theory and practice were brought closer together, but also that scientists such as al-Battani were also expert makers of instruments, which enhanced their powers of observation and calculation.[713]Al-Biruni (973-1050) was well-versed in *ilm-al-alah* (knowledge of instruments), using them to illustrate his theories, and also making them. One such instrument was the hydrostatic balance which helped him measure the correct densities of eighteen substances.[714] The other was a new type of astrolabe called *al-Ustawani* which helped him measure the height of heavenly bodies, their apogees, and time; and also to measure depth of wells or rivers and heights of walls, towers and hills which were inaccessible otherwise.[715] Al-Zahrawi (B. 936. D. 1013) devised and made his own instruments for surgery,[716] whilst Al-Razi set up a laboratory with all requisites to conduct chemical experiments common to modern laboratories.[717]Ibn al-Haytham, too, took great care in the construction and assembly of equipment for his experiments. He made `the radical innovation' of including dimensions as an integral part of his specifications, which was crucial to experiment and major improvements in instrument design.[718]

---

711 A.C Crombie: Science, optics; op cit; p. 87.

712 See for instance:

L. Sedillot: Memoire sur les instruments; op cit.

W. Hartner: The Principle and use of the astrolabe, op cit.

713 B. Stock: Science, Technology, op cit; p. 21.

714 A. Mieli: *La Science Arabe; op cit;* p. 101.M. M.Rozhanskaya (in collaboration with I.S. Levinova) Statics, in Encyclopaedia of the History of Arabic Science (Rashed ed) ; op cit; pp 614-42. at. pp. 638-9.

715 H. M. Said; A. Z. Khan: *Al-Biruni: His Times, Life and Works*; Hamdard Foundation, Pakistan, 1981. pp.147-8.

716 M.S. Spink and G.L.Lewis: *Abulcasis on Surgery and Instruments*; The Wellcome Institute, London, 1973.

717 For abridged description of Al-Razi's laboratory, see C. Singer: *The Earliest Chemical Industry*; The Folio Society; London; 1958. p. 50.

718 D.R. Hill: Islamic Science, op cit, pp 73-4.

In astronomy, the construction of astrolabes evolved in sophistication to make measurement minutely precise.[719] Al-Zarqali perfected the astrolabe so much it revolutionised scientific advance.[720] In devising astronomical tables and calculations, the Muslims used sophisticated apparatuses and instruments, some of them gigantic.[721] The importance Islamic astronomers attached to precision and accuracy of observation and measurement, and the care they exercised in the construction of elaborate instruments are clear witnesses of their strong empirical tendency.[722] Such instruments even exceeded in accuracy those developed in Germany in the 15th century.[723]

As for Portulans, contrary to what Crombie says, they were used much earlier than the 16th century for navigation; the 10th century Muslim geographer al-Muqaddasi speaks of nautical maps in substantial detail.[724] And the magnetic needle was also used much earlier for such navigation purpose.[725]

Concluding Words:

By suppressing crucial facts that link changes of the Middle Ages with Islamic sources, and by misattributing major developments of science, mainstream modern Western history has not just distorted history, much worse, it has created oddities of the first order, such as, that suddenly, the Christian West, hitherto sank into utmost barbarism, discovered everything, and at once. Such sudden upsurges sink the birth of modern science and civilisation into contradictory explanations, and also give answers to such changes which are devoid of logic or historical veracity.

On the first point, i.e contradictory explanations for changes, contrast, for instance, the sudden, and different times of the Western Renaissance, the

---

719 W. Hartner: The Principle and use of the astrolabe, op cit.
720 Ibid.
721 See for instance:
L. Sedillot: Memoire sur les instruments; op cit.
B. Hetherington: *A Chronicle; op cit.*
R.P. Lorch: The Astronomical Instruments; op cit;.
A. Sayili: The Observatory in Islam; op cit.
722 A. Sayili: The Observatory in Islam; op cit. p.318,
723 R. Briffault: The Making, op. cit, p. 193.
724 Al-Muqaddasi: *Ahsan at-taqasim; op cit; p. 10.*
725 See M. Watt: The Influence of Islam; op cit; pp. 19-21.
J. Bensaude: *L'Astronomie Nautique au Portugal*, Meridian Publishing, Amsterdam, 1967.
D. Howse: Navigation and Astronomy the first three thousand years; in *Journal of Renaissance and Modern Studies*, vol 30; pp 60-86;

famed one in the 16th-17th centuries, and then here, another, by Revd Carlyle, who says:
`The new intellectual movement came very suddenly in the last years of the eleventh century; why it should have come then is hard to determine, but it seems reasonable to say that it represents the re-awakening of the desire for knowledge which had been in abeyance during the stormy centuries after the fall of the Roman Empire in the West, when men had little leisure for anything but the constant labour to secure a little decent order and peace....'[726]
And another Renaissance courtesy of Crombie, who holds that the scientific tradition was virtually lost in the West between the 6th and 12th, and then science thrived in the 13th and 14th centuries, after `it had been recovered.'[727]

The second major problem is that, if the Islamic link with medieval changes is suppressed, then, we have the untenable logic that the scientific transformations of Western Europe are the result of conditions and factors which have been in existence for centuries before, and yet nothing changed until suddenly in the 12th –13th century everything spontaneously happened. Greek learning, for instance, is said to be one such main source of change, whilst it has been available for over ten centuries, and never impacted positively in any way. And how could it be the influence of Greek learning when the so many changes that affected Western Christendom in the 12th-13th centuries, such as the appearance of windmills, paper, the numerals, the compass, the exchequer, new construction techniques etc, have no Greek link or origin. And why did no region of Greece/Byzantium, whether in the east or in the Latin West, build on its Classical heritage between the 6th and 12th century to emerge as the leading region or power? If such Classical learning was the source of the scientific revival absolutely nothing could have prevented such rise, or even the continuity of Greek civilisation, uninterrupted from the classical times to our day. Instead, absolutely no region under Greek influence achieved any scientific breakthrough of any sort until contact was made with Islam. All changes took place, at once in the 12th–early 13th centuries, exactly, and soon after the Christian West came into direct contact with Islam, that is after Sicily was taken from the Muslims (end of the 11th), soon after translations were made in Toledo (12th century),[728] and soon

---

[726] Rev A.J. Carlyle: Progress in the Middle Ages, in *Progress and History*; F.S. Marvin editor; Oxford University Press, 1916.pp 72-95. p. 85.
[727] A.C. Crombie edition: *Scientific Change*, Heinemann, London, 1963; p.317.
[728] J.M. Millas Vallicrosa: Translations of Oriental Scientific Works to the end of the Thirteenth Century, in *The Evolution of Science*, ed. G.S. Metraux and F. Crouzet, New

after the Crusaders went East, and then returned to the Christian West (12th century).[729]Nothing happened before or anywhere on such a scale as happened when and where direct contact was made with Islam. In fact, when any other change took place at a different time, i.e the entry of early mathematics, astronomy, and knowledge of the astrolabe into Western Christendom, in the late 10th early 11th century, it did exactly when contact was made with Catalonia, where precisely knowledge of Islamic mathematics, astronomy and the astrolabe had become known.[730]And if any part of Western Christendom showed a sign of scientific development, it was again, soon after it made contact with the land of Islam (i.e Lorraine, for instance) and not before.[731]Moreover, any region or country developed in precisely the subject or area it borrowed, or was in contact through, with Islam. The Development of Western medicine, for instance, took place precisely via Salerno, precisely soon after Constantine brought there and translated Islamic medical learning in the 11th century.[732] Lorraine made the breakthrough in mathematics and astronomy precisely the two subjects it brought from Muslim Spain.[733] The South of France advanced in medicine, that is precisely what Jewish doctors sought and brought from Muslim Spain.[734] The Italian cities, which made commercial advances (Pisa, Florence, Venice..) were precisely those which had commercial link with Islam.[735] England's exchequer follows precisely contacts with the Islamic administrative organisation of Sicily.[736] It is precisely the crusading regions of Western Christendom, which developed castle fortifications, and precisely after the return of their first crusaders.[737] Fibonacci developed the numeral system, and again, precisely because that was what he went to learn in the Algerian city of Bejaia.[738] And the

---

York, 1963, pp 128-67. G. Thery: *Tolede Grande Ville de la Renaissance Medievale*; Oran; 1944.

729 H. Prutz: *Kulturgeschichte der kreuzzuge*; Berlin, 1883.

730 J. W. Thompson: Introduction; op cit; M. C. Welborn: Lotharingia as a center; op cit.

731 J. W. Thompson: Introduction; op cit.

732 C. Burnett and D. Jacqart: *Constantine the African*, Brill, 1994; E.G. Browne: *Arabian Medicine*; Cambridge University Press, 1962. M. Mc Vaugh: Constantine the African,' op cit.

733 M. C. Welborn: Lotharingia as a center; op cit.

734 G. Sarton: Introduction; op cit; relevant sections on Jewish science.

735 M.L. de Mas Latrie: *Traites de Paix et de Commerce, et Documents Divers, Concernant les Relations des Chretiens avec les Arabes de l'Afrique Septentrionale au Moyen Age*, Burt Franklin, New York, Originally Published in Paris, 1866.

736 C.H. Haskins: England and Sicily; op cit.

737 J. Harvey: The Development of Architecture, in *The Flowering of the Middle Ages*; ed J. Evans; Thames and Hudson; pp. 85-105; M. S. Briggs: Architecture, in *The Legacy of Islam,* op cit; pp 155-79.

738 C. Singer: *The Earliest Chemical Industry*; The Folio Society; London; 1958. p.85.

instances can be multiplied at infinitum, showing that each region, each place, developed according to, and precisely in, what it borrowed from Islam, or was in contact through with Islam, and nothing else. Supposing it was not the Islamic link that was in operation, but other factors, whether the Classical heritage, or specific internal conditions within Western Christendom, which were at the origin of such changes, in such situation, every region could have erupted into breakthroughs other than in matters it received from Islam. Salerno, for instance, could have delivered mathematics or Aristotelian philosophy rather than medicine. French towns could have led in commercial techniques. Lorraine could have given us medicine, or optics. And so on and so forth. But that, in the tens, or hundreds, of instances of changes, was at no single time the case. And finally, here, as will be amply demonstrated in part three, every single new manifestation of science and civilisation that appeared in the medieval Christian West also bore distinct and powerful Islamic resemblance and substance.

If the preceding points are removed from medieval history, as is mostly the case, this leaves many unanswered questions:
-Why did Western Christendom wait until the 12th century to initiate its revival?
-Why did the first men of European science suddenly, and overwhelmingly, emerge in the 12th century and after?
-Why did such learning take place in all subjects, and at once, over that short period?
-How was it done out of a state of Barbarism?
-Why did it happen just after the Christian West came into direct contact with Islamic learning?
-Why did Western Christendom wait until the 12th century to recover Greek learning when it had been in contact with such Greek learning for over ten centuries?
-Why take Greek learning from Arabic instead of directly taking it from Latin or Greek, easily accessible, and easier to use?
-And can developments and changes that took place in Western Christendom that have no Greek origin: paper, the compass, windmills, numerals, etc, be explained?
-So where do they come from?
-And if they belong to the Western heritage, other than the Greek, why wait for the 12th–13th for them to be revived again. For the sake of argument, one might give ground to the theory that Greek learning could only be recovered from Arabic through translations; but how about the rest (universities, paper, numerals..); have they been lost, too?

Hence, unless these matters are answered satisfactorily, there is no logic in the history of science and civilisation as it stands at the moment in the majority of writing and in the majority of institutions of learning. Any neutral historian looking at the matter closely reaches the same conclusion as reached by Sarton, who says that `Medieval historians, who have neglected to consider Arabic literature, have thus given us not only an incomplete, but an entirely false view of their subject.'[739]

Or Glubb, who observes that:

`These four hundred years (900-1200) had completely changed the history of the world. The omission of the whole period from our history books has removed a vital link from the history of human development, making the subsequent story of the rise of Europe largely incomprehensible.'[740]

3. Refuting the Myths of the 16th Century Renaissance

The 16th century Renaissance, Geanakoplos says, is based on the assumption that the Middle Ages (the Dark Ages) in the West ended rather abruptly and distinctly during the middle or latter part of the 15th century, when, Italy, under the influence of rediscovered writings of classical antiquity, discarded the civilisation of the `moribund' Middle Ages and experienced a rebirth or `Renaissance' of ancient culture that resulted in the emergence of new institutions, new social and cultural values.[741]

The term Renaissance (Rinascita), itself, Pernoud explains, was used for the first time by Vasari in the middle of the 16th century; `The arts and letters, which seemed to have perished in the same sinking as Roman society, seemed to re-flourish after ten centuries of darkness, to shine with a new splendour;' this is how it was stated in 1872 by the *Dictionnaire General des Lettres*,[742] one of the many encyclopaedia of the 19th, which caught the general opinion of the time and its cultural standards.[743]

---

[739] G. Sarton: Introduction;, vol I, op cit; p.30.

[740] J. Glubb: A Short History; op cit; p.135.

[741] D. J. Geanakoplos: Medieval Western; op cit; pp. 417-8.

[742] Bachelet and Dezobry, published by Delagrave, 1872. The authors surrounded themselves for the redaction of their articles with a large collaboration of the intelligentsia of the time.

[743] R Pernoud: *Pour en finir avec le Moyen Age*: Editions du Seuil, Paris, 1977; p.17.

Zealous fondness for the Renaissance was the child of the hostile reaction to the precedent era, the Middle Ages. The term Middle Ages was first used, derogatorily, by Italian humanists of the late 14th-early 15th centuries, for whom the entire thousand-year period preceding their own age of the Renaissance was `a long step backward, a Dark Age, for in their view Western culture had lost the chief ingredient necessary for cultural validity: Greco-Roman thought and learning,' Geanakoplos notes.[744] The Middle Ages, also, Daniel notes, do coincide with the period of Muslim greatness,[745] thus a twin reason for dislike of the period. Petrarca (1304-74) leading the humanist movement, indeed, loathed the present and the more immediate (mediaeval) past; setting his goal in classical antiquity; eager to restore Roman culture.[746] He loathed the Middle Ages, and the Renaissance of the 12th and 13th centuries, which under Islamic stimulation, was a scientific renaissance.[747] His, and the movement interests being instead in the literary, and a peculiar aversion for the Islamic tendency of the age that they were leaving behind.[748] His hostility to both science and Arabism `comparable to the form of modern anti Semitism associating Jewishness with radicalism,' according to Sarton;[749] Christian rationalism against everything suggesting Islamic influences.[750] Thus, the subsequent campaign of the medical humanists against the Islamic writers aimed at replacing Ibn Sina by Latin translations from the Greek text of Galen.[751] To study geometry became to study Euclid; Geography was Ptolemy's; and so on and so forth. The arts themselves were inspired by classical models; this was sometimes true even in the case of religious paintings, for the artists would easily mix the symbols of paganism with those of Christendom.[752]

The tradition set down by Petrarca was gradually built upon in the interpretation and writing of history in the West. Hence Shramm points to the prejudices which have been accumulated by Renaissance scholars, and which barred the way to a correct evaluation of medieval

---

[744] D. J. Geanakoplos: Medieval; op cit; p.13.
[745] N. Daniel: The Arabs; op cit; p.319.
[746] G. Sarton: Introduction; op cit; Vol 3; p. 505.
[747] Ibid. p. 508.
[748] C. Singer: *Short History of Scientific Ideas; op cit* p. 196:
[749] G. Sarton: Introduction; vol III; op cit; p. 508; and p. 178.
[750] Ibid. p. 178.
[751] D.Campbell: Arabian Medicine, op cit; p. 192.
[752] G. Sarton: The Appreciation; op cit; p.171.

science.[753]A good expression of this, the 16th century *Scholae mathematicae* of Pierre de la Ramee[754] gives, in the first three books, a detailed historical account of the development of the mathematical sciences, but what is striking, is that the author almost ignores the work done by medieval scholars, and jumps from Greek antiquity straight into the period during which took place the `revival of the sciences.'[755]
A practice which has endured to our day, Singer notes, the Middle Ages being even substantially omitted and the narrative passing almost direct from Greek to modern times.[756] This has become the norm in the bulk of the writing of modern history, two great periods: the Classical (Prior to 5thcentury Ad,) and the Renaissance (16th-17th centuries), and between the two (5th-15th), `a middle age' an intermediary period, a uniform bloc, `vulgar centuries' and `obscure times'.[757] Somehow, as Douglas puts it, many saw the Middle Ages `as a waste land separating the twin peaks of classical achievements,' when `a thousand years of diverse development are summed up far too frequently in a few facile phrases of praise or blame.'[758]The common opinion was that science, in the usual modern sense, was almost entirely absent in the Middle Ages, and that our scientific system is essentially an outgrowth of classical antiquity.[759]For four hundred years there has been a widespread educational attempt to represent our entire civilization as the continuation of that of Greece and Rome.[760] Eminent figures from amongst the most prominent learning institutions to this day holding that the 17th was the century of the scientific revolution; doing away with the `dark centuries' in the middle.[761]

Such interpretation in the end, legitimises the view that civilisation is a Western product, passing from Classical civilisation (up to the 5th century AD) into ten centuries or so of Darkness (5th-15th century), and into the Renaissance (16th century); thus, that modern science and civilisation never departed from within the Western realm.

---

753 M. Schramm: Steps towards the idea of function: A comparison between Eastern and Western science of the Middle Ages; in *History of Science*, Vol 4; 1965; pp 70-112; p.70
754 Petrus Ramus: *Scholarum mathematicarum libri unus et triginta*; Basileae: per Eusebium Episcopium; 1569.
755 M. Schramm: Steps towards; op cit; p.70
756 C. Singer: Science; in *Medieval contributions to Modern Civilisation*; edited by F.J. C. Hearnshaw; Dawsons of Pall Mall; London; reprint, 1967; p. 107.
757 R Pernoud: Pour en finir; op cit; p.17.
758 D.C. Douglas: The Importance of Medieval Studies in the Teaching of History: *HISTORY* (new series) Vol 23 (1938-9) pp 97-107; p. 99.
759 C. Singer: Science; op cit; p. 106.
760 Ibid.
761 As seen on Newsnight (BBC2) 20 July 1999.

This view, of course, is historically false. As lengthily expanded above, the science of the 16th-17th century (as any first year student taking one hour to check it by comparing with the Greek, and in respect to every subject) is not the science left by the Greeks.

The 16th-17th century Renaissance is also based on historical fallacies of the first order, fallacies, which are discussed along two lines herein:
First, the concept of Renaissance is based on major historical myths and fallacies. The period was far from being a Renaissance except in some artistic/literary aspects; and even bore some of the darkest moments of Western history. This myth also relies on the removal of between ten and fifteen centuries of scientific achievements, which are deemed dark ages.
Second, this myth of the Renaissance ignores the crucial fact that most of the breakthroughs made in the 16th century onwards, either have foundations in the centuries before, or are simply breakthroughs made in the Middle Ages by the Muslims, and falsely attributed afterwards.

a. The Myths of the 16th-17th Century Renaissance:

The Myth of the Concept of Renaissance:

A very succinct look at the life and work of Galileo, highlighted by Pernoud, offers good illustrations of some of the folkloric myths built around the Renaissance and the preceding Dark Ages.[762]Someone who thought that Galileo was burnt alive in the Middle Ages for having said that the earth was a sphere will be mistaken on three grounds. Galileo did not discover that the earth was a sphere: this was known four centuries before him. He was not burnt alive either, but only put in prison. And that did not happen in the Middle Ages: Galileo belonged to the Classical period, born in 1564 and died 1642, and was a contemporary of Descartes.[763]

`Renaissance, it is decadence' said Henri Matisse.[764]A decadence, indeed, in each and every respect. First it marked a decline for sciences. Haskins, and above all Sarton, saw such Renaissance as a regressive episode.[765]It

---

[762] R Pernoud: Pour en finir; op cit; p.101.
[763] Ibid.
[764] Ibid. p.17.
[765]In N.F. Cantor: *Inventing the Middle Ages,* The Lutterworth Press, Cambridge, 1991. p.433.

substituted, or more properly it prioritised the arts and literary forms against the scientific advances made in previous centuries. For Briffault:
`The Greeks had been concerned with ideas, the Arabs and Arabists with facts, the pedants of the Renaissance were concerned with words.'[766]
Indeed, what was born, or more properly `reborn' in the 16th century are the arts and the classical letters.[767] And in Sarton's words:
`It was golden age of learning, art, music and letters. Science had hardly won its independence; whatever prestige it obtained, it could obtain it only as a form of learning.'[768]
And this supposed age of pure reason was not in reality. Newton, Fontana notes, was seen `not the first of the age of reason; he was the last of the magicians: he was deeply involved in alchemy and in prophecies, and wrote a book that announced the imminent fall of the papacy and placed the end of the world at about 1867.[769]

On further myths of the Renaissance, Fontana, again:
`Brought up in a culture born out of that secular crusade, we have got used to accepting all its myths as truths. These are the myths which set modern Renaissance brilliance against medieval obscurantism, the religious Reformation (and the Counter Reformation) against superstition and witchcraft, the rationality of science against the senselessness of magic and courtly refinement against rustic coarseness.'[770]
The attraction of witchcraft, and its bloody repression, increased immensely in the 16th century. Jean Bodin, prosecutor for the king of France, and Nicolas Remy, judge and general prosecutor of Loraine, both wrote on demons, the latter sending to the stake, as a judge, about three thousand sorcerers and sorceresses.[771] Between 1590 and 1597, 1500 women were executed for Witchcraft in Scotland alone.[772] By the 17th century, the number of trials for witchcraft increased to mad proportions.[773] There was hardly any region in France, where cannot be evoked famous trials whether Loundun, Louviers, Nancy, in Normandy etc.[774] And the same in most parts of the continent, with the mass exterminations of `witches' that resulted.

---

766 R. Briffault: The Making; op cit; p. 225.
767 R Pernoud: Pour en finir; op cit; p.17.
768 G. Sarton: The Appreciation ; op cit;. p.171.
769 J. Fontana: *The Distorted Past*, Blackwell, 1995. p.106.
770 Ibid.
771 R Pernoud: Pour en finir; op cit; 103.
772 Channel Four; 9-10 Pm; 30 January 03.
773 R Pernoud: Pour en finir; op cit; p.103.
774 For a summary on this see: Jean Palou: *La Sorcellerie,* Edition Que sais je?, no 756, 5ed, 1975, notably.

`The Renaissance was an intolerant age, disgraced by persecutions and by religious wars,' also reminds Sarton.[775] Needless to dwell here on the bloody episodes of the Thirty Year War (1619-49), The St Bartholomew Massacre, the tens of thousands of Muslims burnt at the stake by the Spanish Inquisition,[776] and so on and so forth. And needless, either, to go into the widespread extinction of the Indians in the Americas, one of the bloodiest events in history, which also happened in those Renaissance centuries (16th-17th centuries).[777] Nor would one go into the early intrusion into Africa, the beginning of the mass slave trade, and the extinction of whole ethnic groups in the Canaries and western Africa, also taking place in the great Renaissance times.[778] Far, indeed, from the notion that the 16th and 17th was an age of light, splendour, and above all the foundation of the good of our modern civilisation.

The Myth of the Dark Ages:

Haskins, writing on the Renaissance of the 12th century held:
`The title of this book will appear to many to contain a flagrant contradiction. A renaissance in the twelfth century! Do not the Middle Ages, that epoch of ignorance, stagnation, and gloom, stand in the sharpest contrast to the light and progress and freedom of the Italian Renaissance which followed? How could there be a renaissance in the Middle Ages when men had no eye for the joy and beauty and knowledge of this passing world, their gaze ever fixed on the terrors of the world to come?.'[779] The conception of bright Middle Ages, he pursues, `runs counter to ideas widely prevalent not only among the unlearned but among many who ought to know better. To these the Middle Ages are synonymous with all that is uniform, static, and un-progressive.'[780]
An erroneous view institutionalised, again, via higher learning. Thus, Whipple notes how students of medical history and medical science have been informed that the Middle Ages, or `Dark Ages', imply a period of regression, of endless controversy, of fruitless arguments, and even the mere mention of this period is met with disinterest if not

---

775 G. Sarton: The Appreciation; op cit; p.171.
776 H C Lea: *A History of the Inquisition in Spain,* The MacMillan Company, New York, 1907.
777 D E. Stannard: "Genocide in The Americas" in *The Nation*, October 19, 1992; pp. 430-4;
R. Garaudy: *Comment l'Homme devient Humain*. Editions J.A, 1978.
778 W. Howitt: *Colonisation and Christianity*: Longman; London; 1838.
779 C.H. Haskins: The Renaissance; op cit; Preface: pp.v-vi:
780 Ibid. p. 4.

antagonism.[781] Equally observed by Palter, who notes how students of physics were brought up to believe that modern physics was born in `the fertile brain of Galileo.'[782]And not just physics and cosmology, but also chemistry, and medicine.[783] A similar point raised by Rvd Carlyle, who blames `the ignorance and perversity of the men of the Renaissance' for the `notion that the civilisation of the Middle Ages was fixed and un-progressive.'[784]

To make this 16th century Renaissance theory stand, between ten and fifteen centuries were removed from the whole history of science and civilisation; stipulating nothing happened in those centuries. Ten centuries of Islamic and Latin Middle Ages that play an essential role in the emergence of European science, suppressed.[785] They had to be, because, for the concept of the 16th-17th century Renaissance to prevail, that of the Dark Ages (5-15th century), had to prevail, too. The solution, thus, was to qualify ten centuries as Dark Ages, and remove them.
These centuries were, however, anything but dark.

First and foremost, whilst it might have been very dark in the Christian West, it was much less so in the East. Considering things from the standpoint of the history of technology, Lynn White Jr observes, the so-called Dark Ages was only applicable to the western portion of the Roman Empire.[786] In Western Asia and North Africa, it was a period of wealth, progress and enlightenment, adds Glubb.[787]A point reaffirmed by Le Bon, who insists, that at the time the Christian West was `sank in Barbarism' the Muslim Orient had a brilliant civilisation.[788]Geanakoplos notes, how modern medieval historians whilst being too often oriented exclusively towards the West, forgot or neglected the significance of developments in both Christian East and the Islamic world.[789]

Picking the instance of one science, astronomy, illustrates both facts, that the Middle Ages were an age of great discoveries, and that they took place in the land of Islam. Heinrich Suter, in 1900, counted over 500 Muslim

---

781 A. Whipple: *The Role of the Nestorians and Muslims in the History of Medicine.* University Microfilms International, Ann Arbor, Michigan, U.S.A. 1977, p.1.
782 R. M. Palter: Toward Modern Science, Vol 1, op cit; p.ix.
783 Ibid.
784 Rev A.J. Carlyle: Progress in the Middle Ages, op cit; pp 72-95.
785 P. Benoit and F. Micheau: The Arab Intermediary; op cit; p. 191
786 Lynn White Jr: Technology in the Middle Ages, op cit; p. 66.
787 J. Glubb: A Short History; op cit; p.136.
788 G. Le Bon: La Civilisation; op cit; p.256.
789 D. J. Geanakoplos: Medieval; op cit; p.12,

astronomers and mathematicians, giving for each enough information to highlight their originality and impact on subsequent developments affecting the subject.[790]There is more information on such astronomers and their works provided by Sezgin[791], Sarton.[792], Sedillot[793]and Nalino.[794]

In greater detail, the Islamic achievements in the science are vast, diverse, and had a considerable impact on modern astronomy. Thus, Al-Battani (d.929) timed the new moons, calculated the length of the solar and sideral year, and wrote on the phenomenon of parallax.[795]He also popularised if not discovered the first notions of trigonometrical ratios used today;[796]his Sabian tables (al-Zij al-Sabi) remained influential centuries after him.[797]Al-Sufi (903-986) made observations on the obliquity of the ecliptic and the motion of the sun (or the length of the solar year.)[798] He also observed and described the stars, setting out his results constellation by constellation, discussing the stars positions, their magnitudes and their colour, and for each constellation providing two drawings from the outside of a celestial globe, and from the inside.[799] Al-Biruni (973-1050) was the first to claim that the earth rotated around its own axis,[800] besides calculating extremely accurately, and in the most effective manner the earth circumference.[801] Ibn Yunus (d 1009) made observations for nearly thirty years (977-1003) pioneering in the use of large instruments, such as an astrolabe of nearly 1.4 m in diameter. He was also famed for determining more than 10,000 entries of the sun's position throughout the years.[802] Al-Farghani explained for subsequent users the mathematical theory behind the astrolabe.[803] His most famous book *Kitab fi Harakat Al-Samawiyah wa Jaamai Ilm al-Nujum* on cosmography contains thirty chapters including a description of

---

[790] H. Suter: *Die Mathematiker und Astronomen; op cit;*.

[791] F.Sezgin: *Geschichte des arabischen Schrifttums* (vol vi for astronomy); 1978.

[792] G. Sarton: Introduction; op cit.

[793] L.A. Sedillot: *Traite des Instruments astronomiques des Arabes*; Paris, 1834.

[794] C.A. Nallino: *Raccolta di scritti Editi e Inediti*, Roma, 1944.

[795] G.M Wickens: The Middle East as a world centre of science and medicine; in *Introduction to Islamic Civilisation*, ed by R.M. Savory; Cambridge University Press, Cambridge, 1976; pp 111-8.

[796] P.K. Hitti: *History of the Arabs*, Mac Millan St Martin's Press, 1970, at p. 572.

[797] R Morelon: Eastern Arabic Astronomy, op cit; 46-7.

[798] Ibid. p. 50.

[799] C. A. Ronan: The Arabian Science; in *The Cambridge Illustrated History of the World's Science;* Cambridge University Press. Newness Books, 1983; pp 201-44. p. 213.

[800] M. A. Kettani: Science and Technology in Islam: The underlying value system, in Z. Sardar ed: *The Touch of Midas; Science, Values, and Environment in Islam and the West*; Manchester University Press, 1984, pp 66-90; at p. 76.

[801] R. Morelon: Eastern Arabic, op cit, p. 52.

[802] C. Ronan: The Arabian Science, op cit p. 214.

[803] Ibid. p. 207.

the inhabited part of the earth, its size, the distances of the heavenly bodies from the earth and their sizes, as well as other phenomena.[804] Al-Zarqali (Arzachel) (1029-1087) perfected the astrolabe to make it the first sophisticated instrument to enable calculations on land and sea. He also prepared the Toledan Tables, upon which subsequent tables in the Christian West were based.[805] Jabir Ibn Aflah (d. 1145) was the first to design a portable celestial sphere to measure and explain the movements of celestial objects, besides contributing to the advance of spherical trigonometry. Al-Bitruji (d. c.1204) wrote *Kitab-al-Hay'ah*', which was translated by the Sicilian based Michael Scot, and bore considerable influence thereafter, in fact opening the way to the most decisive breakthroughs in the subject.[806]

Islamic breakthroughs in nautical astronomy opened the way to the great maritime discoveries as well elaborated upon by Steinschneider.[807] Bensaude[808] has particularly highlighted the fact that the scientific impact of the Muslims in Spain and Portugal has prevailed, and contributed very decisively to the advance of navigation to the Indies and the New World.[809] Dreyer has also highlighted the otherwise obscured fact about the spherical shape of the earth, a notion which until the modern times led its authors in Western Christendom to the stake, whilst in the world of Islam, there was no record of any Muslim being persecuted for stating that the earth was a sphere that was capable of being inhabited all over; and that it was also very small compared to the size of the universe.[810]

The notion that Western astronomy was born in the Renaissance with Copernicus, principally, rests on the neglect of a crucial element: the passage of Islamic astronomy to the West centuries earlier. This obscured phase will be developed further in the next chapters, but briefly here, it was from Catalonia, Spain, that the early treatises on the astrolabe went North of the Pyrenees, via John of Gorze, who took them to Lorraine, which, in turn triggered astronomical advances in other parts of the Christian West, England, most notably.[811] Further input of Muslim astronomy was the fruit

---

[804] R. Morelon: Eastern Arabic astronomy, op cit, p. 24.
[805] Carra de Vaux: Astronomy and Mathematics, in the Legacy of Islam ; op cit; p. 394.
[806] E. J. Dijksterhuis: *The Mechanisation of the World Picture*; op cit; p. 212.
[807] M. Steinschneider: Etudes sur Zarkali; op cit; *Die europaischen; op cit etc.*
[808] J. Bensaude: *L'Astronomie Nautique au Portugal*, op cit.
[809] In J.L. E. Dreyer: Mediaeval Astronomy; *Toward Modern Science*, Vol I, op cit; pp 235-56; p. 256.
[810] J.L.E. Dreyer: *A History of Astronomy from Thales to Kepler*; Dover Publications Inc, New York, 1953, at p. 249.
[811] J. W. Thompson: Introduction of Arabic; op cit; M. C. Welborn: Lotharingia; op cit.

of Gerbert of Aurillac (later Pope Silvester II), who brought to the West early knowledge about the astrolabe (as well as Muslim mathematics) (see next chapter). To England arrived in 1091 from Lotharingia (modern day Lorraine) Walcher of Malvern, who had come into possession of the astrolabe, and who, for the first time, in Latin Europe, on 18 October 1092, used such instrument to determine the time of lunar eclipse that he had observed in Italy.[812]Petrus Alphonsi was another learned, who popularised Muslim astronomy in the English court.[813]It was also to Toledo, after its recapture from the Muslims, where flocked in the 12thcentury, in particular, scholars from all Christian lands to translate Muslim science, including astronomy. Translations which included the Toledan tables of al-Zarqali and Jabir ibn Aflah's *Islah al Majisti* (refutation of the *Almagest;*) astronomical works of al-Battani, Thabit ibn Qurra, al-Qabisi, and al-Majriti; the astronomical tables of Al-Khwarizmi, as revised by Maslama at Cordoba etc. It was also, and above all, at Cracow, where Copernicus studied, that Islamic astronomical studies were most popular, and for generations before and during his studies there.[814]

By suppressing the centuries of the so called Dark Ages the supporters of the 16th-17th century renaissance, thus suppress all these facts. And these facts are absolutely crucial for the understanding of the development of astronomy between Classical Greece and the modern times. Rybka puts it perfectly when he states that `There is little on Muslim astronomy, and yet, a study of such astronomy will help understand the development of modern astronomy, from Peuerbach and Regiomontanus by Copernicus, Tycho Brahe down to Kepler.'[815]

And the same holds for every science and manifestation of civilisation (architecture, arts, higher learning, finance, trade, etc..). Thus, obscuring centuries when so many decisive changes took place, other than being fallacious, makes history absolutely impossible to understand. Without such centuries, with their so many changes and transfers, as just seen in

---

[812] O. Pedersen: Astronomy, in *Science in the Middle Ages*, ed D.C. Lindberg; op cit; pp 303-37; at p. 312.

[813] C. Burnett: *The Introduction of Arabic Learning into England*; The Panizzi Lectures, 1996; The British Library; 1997.

[814] A. Birkenmajer: Coup d'oeil sur l'histoire des sciences exactes en Pologne; in Studia Copernicana; 4; 1972; pp. 3-4. in J.B. Korolec: La Premiere Reception de la Philosophie Islamique a l'Universite de Cracovie; in *The Introduction of Arabic Philosophy into Europe*; C.E. Butterworth and B.A Kessel ed; Brill; Leiden; 1994; pp. 112-30 at p. 114.

[815] E. Rybka: Mouvement des Planetes dans l'Astronomie des Peuples de l'Islam; in *Convegno Internationale: Oriente e occidente Nel Medioevo Filosofia E Scienze;* 9-15 Aprile 1969; Academia Nationale Dei Lincei; Roma; 1971; pp. 579-93; p. 592.

respect to astronomy, how is it possible to understand that what is not found in Greek science suddenly surfaces from nowhere in 16th–17th century Western Christendom? The particular, omission from history books of the Islamic centuries, which as Glubb notes, have completely changed the history of the world, and which has indeed `removed a vital link from the history of human development, making the subsequent story of the rise of Europe largely incomprehensible.'[816] Or as Tout observes, the Middle Ages form an integral part of the advance of science and civilisation, and unless `you make allowance for them, you see modern history all askew.'[817] It is indeed, from the Middle Ages that our civilisation proceeds. And if we sought to understand our modern civilisation, as Tout held, we cannot make a fresh start a hundred or a hundred and fifty years ago.[818]

b. The Medieval Origins of Modern Sciences:

T.F. Tout finds it painful that people hop straight from the `Periclean or the Augustan ages to the times of the Medici and Louis XIV.'[819]

Continuity of history rejects such sharp and violent contrasts between successive periods, as Haskins rightly observes.[820] Both continuity and change are characteristic of the Middle Ages, as indeed of all great epochs of history;[821] as he elaborates:

`Once re-quickened, intellectual life did not slacken or abruptly change its character. The fourteenth century grows out of the thirteenth as the thirteenth grows out of the twelfth, so that there is no real break between the medieval renaissance and the Quattrocento. Dante, an undergraduate once declared `stands with one foot in the Middle Ages while with the other he saluted the rising star of the Renaissance".[822]

The early `Renaissance' era of the 14th and 15th centuries was, indeed, a period of transition from medieval to modern times, explains Geanakoplos: `the twilight of one era, the medieval, and the dawn of another.'[823] Sarton surmises:

---

816 J. Glubb: A Short History; op cit; p.135.
817 T.F. Tout: The Place; op cit; p.8.
818 Ibid. p. 7.
819 Ibid. p.8.
820 C.H. Haskins: The Renaissance; op cit; pp.v-vi:
821 Ibid. p.3.
822 Ibid. p.9.
823 D.J. Geanakoplos: Medieval Western Civilisation, op cit;pp.417-8.

`It does not follow, as so many ignorant persons think, that the mediaeval activities were sterile. It would be `just as foolish as to consider a pregnant woman sterile as long as the fruit of her womb was unborn. The Middle Ages were pregnant with many ideas which could not be delivered until much later. Modern science, we might say, was the fruition of mediaeval immaturity. Vesalius, Copernicus, Galileo, Newton were the happy inheritors who cashed in.'[824]

Some of the most important specific developments and characteristics of modern life and institutions are a direct or indirect outgrowth of medieval times. These include the development of vernacular languages, and the origins of parliament and city councils.[825] Also included the rise of towns, of the earliest bureaucratic states of the West, the culmination of Romanesque art and the beginning of Gothic; the emergence of vernacular literature; beginning of universities, etc.[826] `The mediaeval groping,' in the words of Sarton, is the source of the so-called Galilean physics, and Newtonian fluxions and gravitation have mediaeval roots, too.[827]Palter, equally traces modern physics and cosmology to the same Middle Ages.[828]And so did others, each in their field, demonstrating the crucial role of the Middle Ages.[829] Emeagwali, for her part, asks that if the birth of science is granted to the 17th century, how can such science be conceived without the Arabic numerals, the concept of zero and algebraic notions, the optics of Ibn al-Haytham and al-Kindi, or how to conceive Galileo without the pendulum.[830]Besides, she notes, the Chinese contribution of printing (the first printed text is dated from 868 found in the China Gobi Desert) gunpowder, the compass, paper money, the mechanical clock, helicopter tops, the parachute, deep drilling, etc all appeared in the same non Western Middle Ages. She also points to the stirrup, the sternpost rudder, the lateen sail, the abacus, the pendulum, the axle, the bow drill, the chisel, and the wedge, all of them of non European origin; and so can be added the windmill and

---

[824] G. Sarton: Introduction; op cit; Volume III. p.15.
[825] D.J. Geanakoplos: Medieval; op cit; p.11.
[826] C.H. Haskins: The Renaissance; op cit; preface; p. vi.
[827] G. Sarton: Introduction to the History of Science. Op cit; Volume III; p.14.
[828] R. M. Palter, Toward Modern Science, op cit; p.ix.
[829] Such as
E. Grant: *A Source Book of Medieval Science*; Cambridge, Mass.: Harvard University Press; 1974.
P. O. Long. 1985: *Science and Technology in Medieval Society*. New York Academy of Sciences. 1985.
[830] G.T. Emeagwali: *Eurocentrism and the History of Science and Technology* at: http://members.aol.com/Sekglo/racism.htm.

watermill, the predecessors of the modern water turbines, glass, cement, enamel, porcelain, the nail and saw, the cheque, etc, all of which appeared during those so called `Dark Ages.'[831]

Even more, as the following instances show, decisive breakthroughs, which are generally attributed to the Western 16th-17th century Renaissance, are in fact Islamic medieval breakthroughs.

Observation of the Sky:

In one of the so many programmes on science devoted to spatial observation on British television, `scientists and historians' gathered for the occasion asserted that Galileo was the first person to make observations of the sky, and that all changes and developments in observation happened after him.[832]Another channel, and we hear the same, that the first observations of the sky, and even the whole science of astronomy began with Galileo and the Europeans.[833]It is needless to go into the long list of writings (some already seen), which carry the same errors.

Yet, again, Hetherington charted observation throughout history,[834]and through exceptional evidence has shown that by the time Galileo began to observe the sky, this has been ongoing for centuries before him in the East. Observation in the world of Islam has been expertly studied by both Sayili[835]and Sedillot.[836]And, the Muslims pioneered in the use of instruments for the purpose as here outlined by Benoit and Micheau:

`Islam appeared as a world of observation, from the simple quadrant to the princely observatory. This is attested by the number of treatises on the astrolabe and the number of instruments surviving into our own day. The astrolabe wasn't used to observe the heavens but to interpret them, and its manufacture required a thorough knowledge of the stars and of their apparent movement. It was made up of a circular plate against which there turned another disc, mostly cut away, resembling a spider. The plate bore a projection of the earth from a particular place, while the spider was a map of the sky with the principal fixed stars, among them the sun. It allowed

---

831 Ibid.

832 10 August 1999, on BBC2.

833 On Channel IV on 15 November 1999.

834 B. Hetherington: *A Chronicle*. Op cit.

835 A. Sayili: *The Observatory in Islam*, op cit.

836 L. Sedillot: Memoire sur les Instruments; op cit.

the determination of the azimuth and the hours of sunrise and sunset, the position of the stars on the horizon and much other information.'[837]

The use of gigantic instruments was generalised in Islam since the early stages (9th century), and they remained in use throughout the subsequent centuries as Hartner demonstrated, and not just in the very late (14th – 15th) stages as held by Neugebauer.[838]

Prolonged and continuous observation, required by modern observation, also took place in the earliest observatories (9th-11th) of Baghdad, Cairo and Damascus, and the later ones, i.e Samarqand (15th.)[839] Kruiscinas has noted that at Samarqand, observation of any part of the sky required ten or fifteen continuous years because certain conditions suited to the determination of matters pertaining to the planets do not obtain within a single year, so that observations cannot be made in one year, and might last up to twelve-fifteen years, which is, of course, the dominant feature of planetary observation today.[840] As Hartner concluded, it was only in the 17th century, thanks to Brahe that high standards of Islamic observation were reached by the Europeans.[841]

Copernicus' Planetary theory:

Copernicus' planetary models are identical to those of his Muslim predecessors, especially Ibn Shatir and other contemporaries.[842] Ibn Shatir had assumed the heliocentric theory of the earth, ie earth's elliptical orbit around the sun, centuries before Copernicus.[843]The resemblance between the treatises and procedure being such, that Swerdlow did not question the `borrowing', but only when and where did Copernicus do it.[844] Copernicus' indebtedness to his predecessors, according to Hill, `lies not only in the fact that he uses the same theorems to build his own models, but that he also uses them at the identical points in the models where they were used by the Muslim astronomers.'[845]

---

[837] P Benoit and F. Micheau: The Arab Intermediary; op cit; p. 205.
[838] Essay review by W. Hartner of O. Neugebauer; op cit; p. 202.
[839] R.Briffault: The Making, op. cit, p. 193.
[840] K. Krisciunas: *Astronomical Centers of the World*, at http://www.ukans.edu/~ibetext/texts/paksoy-2/cam6.html
[841] Essay Review by Hartner; op cit; p. 211, note 20.
[842] N. Swerdlow and O. Neugebauer: Mathematical Astronomy in Copernicus' *De revolutionibus*, New York: Springer Verlag, 1984, p. 46. D.R. Hill: Islamic, op cit, p. 46.
[843] D. Hill: Islamic Science; op cit; p. 46.
[844]N. Swerdlow and O. Neugebauer: Mathematical, op cit , p. 46.
[845] D.R. Hill: Islamic Science, op cit, p. 46.

Modern Western historians, in their majority, however, refute the idea that Copernicus borrowed from his Muslim predecessors. Pedersen, thus, says:

`Copernicus' work resembles that of the late Arabic astronomers Nasir al-Din al-Tusi and Ibn Shatir, who tried to stress the principle of uniform, circular motion more consistently than Ptolemy cared to do.'[846]

Pedersen goes on:

`A comparison with the lunar theory of Ibn Shatir (of Copernicus lunar theory) shows that not only is the general structure of the two models the same, but the geometrical parameters are also identical. It would be very tempting to explain this agreement on the assumption of direct influences. If this is true, the line of transmission is unknown, but it is not impossible that an account of Ibn Shatir's work might have reached the West, though there is no other evidence to support such an assumption. The hypothesis is not even necessary, for Copernicus-like al-Shatir-could well have calculated his parameters in such a way that the model gave the maximum and minimum equations known from the Almagest (Ptolemy's).'[847]

This line of transmission, strange to Pedersen, was, however, clarified by North, who explains that Greek and Latin materials that made use of Islamic device were circulating in Italy at about the time Copernicus studied there.[848] Hill, equally, explains how Copernicus came across these two theorems; the evidence in a Byzantine Greek manuscript that came to the Vatican Collection after the fall of Constantinople in 1453. On one page of the manuscript, Hill observes, `there is a clear representation of the Tusi's Lunar model as well as a diagram demonstrating the adaptation of the Tusi couple to a configuration of solid bodies.'[849] These results reached Italy, where Copernicus resided for a few years, and Copernicus could read Greek (the language used in the manuscript.). Saliba elaborates in great detail on the manner Copernicus used his Muslim predecessors' work at http://www.columbia.edu/~gas1/project/visions/case1/sci.1.html

Ibn al-Haytham, Witelo and others:

Another Muslim breakthrough, in optics, and yet more misappropriations, as by Wiet et al, who write:

---

[846] O. Pedersen: Early Physics and Astronomy; op cit; p.277.

[847] Ibid. p.273.

[848] J. North: *Astronomy and Cosmology*; Fontana Press, London, 1994; at p. 195.

[849] D. Hill: Islamic Science; op cit; p. 46.

`The passionate preoccupation of Grosseteste and Bacon with optics sprang from the influence of neo Platonism.'[850]

And:

`The scientific spirit was more clearly seen in the work of the Pole, Witelo (born c.1230), who determined experimentally new values for the angles of refraction of light passing through air, water, and glass, and succeeded in producing the colours of the spectrum by passing light through a hexagonal crystal.'[851]

And yet, here is what Duhem (by no means warm to anything Islamic) admits:

`Alhazen's (Ibn al-Haytham) treatise on perspective was read thoroughly by Roger Bacon and his contemporaries, John Peckham (1228-91), the English Franciscan, giving a summary of it.'[852]

Duhem adds, though:

`About 1270 Witelo composed an exhaustive ten volume treatise on optics, which remained a classic until the time of Kepler, who wrote a commentary on it.'[853]

Duhem, who, corrects Wiet and his group's fallacy, adds a twin distortion, though:

First, Witelo, who is supposed to have initiated the greatest advances in optics went extremely far in his `borrowings' from Ibn al-Haytham's *Kitab al-Manazir* (book of optics), which was translated as *perspectiva and De aspectibus*. As Lindberg says:

`I have discovered no explicit reference by Witelo to Alhazen or to `auctor perspective' as he was often cited in the 13th but such citations are quite unnecessary for a demonstration of Witelo's close reliance on the Muslim scientist. The best demonstration is simply to follow the cross-references between Al-Hazen and Witelo in the Pisner edition of their works: one quickly learns that for the most part Witelo treats the same topics in the same fashion, and sometimes in even the same words. Occasionally Witelo omits a topic, and sometimes he seeks to clarify Alhazen's points by further elaboration on a tightening of the argument, but seldom does he depart from this his principal source.'[854]

Then, contrary to what Duhem, Wiet et al, and the majority of modern Western historians hold, as Sherwood Taylor points out:

---

[850] G. Wiet et al: History of Mankind; op cit; p.671.

[851] Ibid.

[852] P. Duhem: Medieval Physics; op cit;.p.152.

[853] Ibid. p.152.

[854] Introduction by D.C. Lindberg: *Optica Thesaurus: Alhazen and Witelo*; editor: H. Woolf. Johnson Reprint Corporation, New York, London, 1972. pp v-xxxiv At p. xiii:

`In optics, too, much progress was made by Al-Hazen (965-1020) who worked out the theory of spherical and parabolic mirrors, and also studied lenses. He treated optics mathematically, and the Latin translation of his works remained the standard optical textbook in Western Europe until the 17th century.'[855]
And this can easily be checked through a comparison of Ibn al-Haytham's work with his successors' such as Descartes, Kepler, etc.

Ibn al-Nafis and his Successors:

The discovery of pulmonary circulation has generally been attributed to Harvey (17th century).[856]This is given substance by Mowry, who holds that Galen's theory persisted unchanged and unchallenged down to the Renaissance, when Vesalius and Columbus at last, corrected it.[857] Wilson adds that the breakthroughs made in the 16th century by Servetus and Colombo were independently made, both inspired by Galen.[858]For Crombie, it seems that:
`The discovery by Harvey of the circulation of the blood provided a fact that necessitated the reconstruction of the theory of the exchange of energy and matter by the engine of the body.'[859]
Prior to this, and in the same book, the same Crombie held:
`This Egyptian (Ibn al-Nafis) commentator on Avicenna's Canon was the first to state the theory which Harvey was to generalise into his theory of the general circulation of the blood, thereby laying the foundations of modern physiology.' [860]
Ibn al-Nafis, indeed, who, in 1241, challenged Galen's views on blood circulation, and rejected his view that the heart had three ventricles.[861] Ibn al-Nafis discovered the lesser circulation of the blood before 1288, anticipating the Spaniard Miguel Servetus (1511-53) by more than 265

---

855 F. Sherwood Taylor: *A Short History of Science*; William Heinemann Ltd, London, 1939. p.82.
856 BBC2 September 1998.
857 B. Mowry: From Galen's (Galen AD 130-200) Theory to William Harvey's Theory: A case study in the rationality of scientific theory: *Studies in History and Philosophy of Science*: Vol 16; pp 49-82; p.51.
858 L. G. Wilson: The Problem of the discovery of the pulmonary circulation; *Journal of History of Medicine*; Vol 17 (1962) pp 229-44.
859 A. Crombie: Science, Optics; op cit; p. 176.
860 Ibid. pp. 104-5.
861 E. Abouleish: Contribution of Islam to Medicine, in Islamic Perspective, op cit; pp. 15-43, at p. 38.

years.[862] Unlike Servetus, who hid his discovery in a theological treatise, as Sarton notes, Ibn al-Nafis published his right where it belonged, in a commentary on Ibn Sina's anatomy.[863]

Three centuries after the discovery of the pulmonary circulation by Ibn al-Nafis, others: Michael Servetus, of course, but also Realdus Columbus, Carlo Ruini, Andrea Cesalpino, and Francois Rabelais claimed the same results.[864]These authors might have obtained their knowledge from the manuscripts in Arabic widely available then. We know that Ibn al-Nafis had been translated into Latin at the beginning of the 16th century in Damascus by the Italian ambassador/scholar, Alpago. The latter translated directly from Arabic the commentary of Ibn al Nafis, and the text was published in Venice in 1547 under: `*Ebenefis philosophi ac medici expositio super quintum Canonem Avicennae ab Andrea Alpago Bellunensi ex.ar.in lat.versa*, Venetiae 1547'.[865] Crombie acknowledges that a few years after 1547, the same theory was published by a Spaniard, Miguel Serveto (1553), and by a pupil of Vesalius, the Paduan physiologist Realdo Colombo (1559), who supported it by experiments.[866]However, citing Bayon, Crombie adds, that `There is at present no evidence that either of these two writers knew of Ibn al-Nafis manuscripts.'[867]Which is odd, for as Crombie himself accepts, this theory of pulmonary circulation seems to have been forgotten until the 16th century,[868]only to come to life again in the Christian West (in 1553 and 1559), precisely after Ibn al-Nafis' commentary was first published in the West (1547).[869]Thus, a theory forgotten in the Christian West for over fifteen centuries, suddenly, by chance, it seems according to Crombie, coming back to life, and by coincidence, soon after the translation of Ibn Al-Nafis (in 1547), and simultaneously appropriated by four different Latin authors, in the space of a few years (1547-59). This idea that such four authors made an independent discovery in such a short space of time, just then, makes no sense at all. Binet and Herpin, contrary to Crombie and mainstream historians, insist that Servetus could have known of the work of Ibn al-Nafis.[870] He could have well borrowed from

---

862 G. Sarton: Introduction; op cit; Volume III. p. 267.

863 *Christianismi restitutio*, Vienne, Dauphine 1553.

864 M. Meyerhof: Ibn Nafis and his Theory of the Lesser Circulation. *ISIS* 23. pp. 100-20.

865 A K Chehade: *Ibn an-Nafis*, Institut Francais, Damascus, 1955; p.47

866 A. Crombie: Science, Optics; op cit; p. 104-5.

867 See. H.P. Bayon: William Harvey, physician and biologist: his precursors, opponents and successors. Part III.' *Annals of Science* (London), III, 1938; 448; part IV; Ibid. IV; 1939; 88.

868 A. Crombie: Science, Optics; op cit; p. 104-5.

869 Brunet; Mieli.... in A. Sayili: The Observatory in Islam; op cit; p.382.

870 L. Binet and A.Herpin referred to by A K Chehade: Ibn an-Nafis, op cit; p.47.

Ibn al-Nafis without indicating his source, for at that time, there was little care of detail, and so for about four centuries he was rewarded as the inventor of the pulmonary circulation.[871] Meyerhof had in fact noted:

`what struck me in reading the first passage relative to this matter in the Arabic commentary of Ibn Nafis was the extraordinary resemblance with some crucial extracts in Servetus. All happens as if the extract of the Arabic work had been freely translated into Latin.'[872]

Also noted by Mieli, who observes how Ibn Nafis' description of lesser circulation reminds strangely (word by word) of that of Servetus three centuries later in his *Christianismi restitutio*.[873]

---

[871] Ibid.

[872] M. Meyerhof: Ibn Nafis; op cit.

[873] A. Mieli: La Science Arabe, op cit; pp.164-6.

Part Two

SOURCES OF ISLAMIC IMPACT

This part looks at the agents, the geographical sources, and the forms and manners of diffusion of Islamic science and civilisation in the Christian West. It first deals with the role of travellers, scholars, crusaders, monarchs, and the Jewish intermediaries. In the second chapter will be considered the role played by some regions in such diffusion, not just the customary Sicily and Spain, but also Lorraine, the South of France, and Salerno. The third chapter looks at the role of translations in the subsequent Western outburst of scientific learning.

Brought together, these elements will highlight, once more, that all developments in Western science and civilisation were the result of a wide concourse of events related to Islam, and hardly the fruit of a recovery of an old heritage, nor the result of coincidences, or of spontaneous outbursts of the `Western mind.' This link with Islam, which is not obvious if any change was dealt with separately, as has been mostly the case with most studies on the subject, will show much more easily once changes and developments of the crucial period (12th-13th century) are brought together. The main merit of this work is in bringing all these elements together, and showing that what seems a coincidence, or can be attributed to specific causes, if dealt with in isolation, once seen with other simultaneous developments, proves that there is, instead, a very visible uniform pattern, that each and everything that happened in the 12th-13th century and led to the rise of science and civilisation in the Christian West relates to the same Islamic link.

In its effort to focus on the main picture, this work will not address each and everything in its deserved length. Reasons for this are simple: it is not, first, the object of this work to do this. Many have dealt with matters of specific influences (medicine, architecture, learning, etc) and with Spain, Sicily, Salerno etc. They have offered, for most, much better facts than this work does. What they have not done is to look at all matters together. Seeking to present an overall picture of Islamic influence forbids dwelling on any particular matter, for this will dilute the main argument into too many details, and make it very difficult to understand the central element considered here, which is that all agents of diffusion of learning in the Christian West in the middle Ages, whatever their nature, all go back to the same Islamic source.

1. SCHOLARS, MONARCHS, AND OTHERS

During the Middle Ages, Lethaby says, what filled the minds of makers and listeners in Western Christendom, were `Caliphs and Emirs, Arabs, Turks, and Saracens who had nothing white but their teeth; Spain, Africa, Egypt, Persia; Cordova; Toledo; Seville; Palermo; Babylon, and Alexandria with its harbours and ships; silk from Alexandria, gold from Arabia, embroideries, `olifants' and ivory chairs, helmets and swords ornamented with carbuncles; saddles covered with gold and gems, painted shields, bright gofalons.''[874]

Gabrieli also states that when the two religions and political worlds (Muslim and Christian) began to have contacts other than those of war, the West became aware of the high level of culture and learning achieved by the `Saracens.' Envoys, travellers, and pilgrims were the first to bring news to Europe of the existence of Muslim culture and science; and most of all, the collective contact between Muslim and Christian communities in the areas of mixed population on the borders between the two worlds, `that revealed to Christendom the wealth of cultural attainments of which the Arabs were now the depositories, the promoters and the transmitters.'[875]

Diplomats, traders, travellers and pilgrims, and also Jews and scholars saw, gleaned, and brought back and spread most of what they had come across in the land of Islam. Crusaders, monarchs, and religious figures also conveyed whatever impressed them in the land of the foe.

1. Early Men of Western Medieval Science

All first precursors of Medieval Western sciences acquired their scientific knowledge from Islamic sources, and all of them spread it widely through Western Christendom.

---

[874] W.R. Lethaby: Medieval Architecture: in *The legacy of the Middle Ages*, edited by C.G. Crump and E.F Jacob: Oxford at the Clarendon Press, 1969 ed; pp 59-93. p. 63.

[875] F. Gabrieli: The Transmission of Learning and Literary Influences to Western Europe, in *The Cambridge History of Islam*, vol 2, edt P.M. Holt, A.K.S. Lambton, and B. Lewis, Cambridge University Press, 1970, pp 851-89, at p 851.

Credit for early introduction of the new mathematics and astronomy in the Christian West goes to the man who at the beginning of the new millennium was to become Pope Sylvestre II, Gerbert of Aurillac (930-1003). While a scholar in the Abbey of Aurillac, he attracted the attention of his superiors, among others the Count of Barcelona, who took him to Spain. Gerbert spent three years in Catalonia (967-70) where he studied mathematics and astronomy.[876] Catalonia was the immediate neighbour of Muslim Cordova, and the collection at the Ripoll monastery at the time `partook of the riches of Andalusian writings on these subjects.' [877] During those three years (967-970) Gerbert studied mathematics in the Spanish March under Bishop Atto of Vich.[878] The fact that Gerbert went to Catalonia to study mathematics, Lindberg argues, shows that he was intent on making contact with Muslim learning, which throughout his career remained his high interest.[879] Draper also notes that he spoke Arabic with fluency, which (with his desire to learn Islamic science,) made him proficient in the mathematics, astronomy, and physics of the Muslim schools.[880] Watt, however, points out, that although there is no suggestion Gerbert knew Arabic, the monastery of Ripoll had a relatively good library that included translations of Muslim sciences.[881] There is also a legend that he visited Cordoba, studied `the forbidden sciences' under a `Saracen' teacher, and stole his books.[882] Draper notes, however, that having resided in Cordova, in his subsequent residence in Rome, he found an inconceivable `ignorance and immorality,' which where not lost upon his future life, driving him immensely to promote such learning he had acquired in Spain.[883] After his studies, Pope John XII (pope 955-64), struck with Gerbert's knowledge, pointed him out to Emperor Otto I, who employed Gerbert to teach the young men of the Emperor's suite.[884]

---

876 W.M. Watt: *The Influence of Islam on Medieval Europe*, Edinburgh University Press, 1972, p. 58.
877 M. R. Menocal: *The Arabic Role; op cit;* p.28.
878 S. C. McCluskey: *Astronomies and Cultures in Early Medieval Europe;* Cambridge University Press; 1998; p. 175.
879 D.C.Lindberg: The Transmission of Greek and Arabic Learning to the West, in Science in the Middle Ages D.C. (Lindberg ed:) op cit, pp 52-90, at p. 60.
880 J. Draper: History; op cit; Vol II; p.4.
881 W.M. Watt: The Influence, op cit, p. 59.
882 Ibid.
883 J. Draper: History; op cit; Vol II; p.4.
884 R. Allen: Gerbert Pope Sylvester II; *The English Historical Review*: Year 1892: pp 625-68; p. 628.

Gerbert contributed to three areas of great interest: the abacus, the algorism and the astrolabe.[885] Allen notes that he was also the first to introduce into the schools instruments as an assistance to the study of arithmetic, astronomy, and geometry, in arithmetic, for instance, he was the first to introduce the abacus.[886]The abacus as it was then used in Spain exerted a great fascination upon Western Christendom.[887]The abacus, Stock describes, was `a polished board divided into thirty equal columns. Through a system of semi circular arcs groups of three columns were united, and thus, even using Roman numerals, the operations of addition, subtraction and multiplication could be performed.'[888] To Gerbert's influence may also be attributed the early introduction into Europe of the Arabic numerals.[889] He was the first northern European to see the advantage of such numeral system.[890] The system was not adopted at this time in the Christian West. With respect to the astrolabe, Hill asserts, the earliest Latin treatises were produced towards the end of the 10th-and early 11th Century in the Abbey of Ripoll in Catalonia (where Gerbert had spent three years,) and from where he probably took copies of the treatises with him to France.[891] Cochrane, for her part, states that before Gerbert time, there were occasional relations between Saxon Germany and Muslim Spain (see next chapter); and this is how he became acquainted with the astrolabe.[892]
By all such contribution, Stock says, Gerbert `exemplified the growth of scientific culture in the North,' and in him as in Hermann Contractus, `one feels the pragmatic bent of the Western intellectual taking its first genuine steps towards science.'[893]

Gerbert's role is a lot greater as a teacher, for he was, according to Millas Vallicrosa, `the first ambassador who carried this new (Islamic) science across the Pyrenees' to which he owed his reputation, and which he taught his many disciples, especially at Rheims, and who themselves introduced it to the learned circles of Lorraine.[894] In a spell of ten year at

---

[885] B. Stock: Science, Technology and Economic Progress in the Early Middle Ages, in *Science in the Middle Ages,* D. C. Lindberg ed; op cit; pp 1-51, p. 37
[886] R. Allen: Gerbert Pope Sylvester II; op cit; pp 630-1.
[887] B. Stock: Science; op cit; at p. 37.
[888] Ibid.
[889] G. Wiet et al: History; op cit; p.206.
[890] M.R. Menocal: The Arabic; op cit; p.28.
[891] D.R. Hill, Islamic Science, op cit, p. 221.
[892] L. Cochrane: Adelard of Bath, op cit, p. 6.
[893] B. Stock: Science; op cit; p. 37.
[894]J.M. Millas Vallicrosa: `Translations of Oriental Scientific Works to the end of the Thirteenth Century,' in *The Evolution of Science*, ed. G.S. Metraux and F. Crouzet, New

the school at Rheims (beginning in 972), which he had established, he taught logic, music and astronomy.[895] He also taught mathematics, and not just as merely an abstraction, but clearly extended into astronomical measurements, which he saw as the key for comparing `theoretical and actual measurements of the sky.'[896]Gerbert emphasised mathematics and astronomy, laying stress on visual aids, and explaining how to construct a sphere to represent the heavens.[897]He actually made one which simulated the motions of the constellations, using wires fixed on the surface of the sphere to outline the stellar configurations.[898]At Magdeburg, between 994 and 995, he constructed an oralogium, either a sundial or an astrolabe, for which he took the altitude of the pole star.[899] He also collected a splendid library, copying books, introducing new methods of study, inventing ingenious instruments.[900] With their minds well trained, his pupils, according to Allen, `advanced to the higher arts of the quadrivium-arithmetic, music, astronomy, and geometry.'[901] However, there was a secondary and wider secondary impact as Grant explains: `Deeply impressed with his ingenuity and dedication, his pupils went forth with great enthusiasm' to continue and extend his teachings, emphasising science as an integral part of the liberal arts.[902] Many of the cathedral schools that rose to prominence and replaced the monastic schools as centres of learning in the 11th and 12th were founded, or at least revived, by his pupils, the most eminent of whom being Adalberon of Laon, John of Auxerre, and especially Fulbert of Chartres (ca.960-1028).[903] Among the cathedral schools whose beginnings or maturity are associated with his pupils are Cologne, Ultrecht, Sens, Cambrai, Chartres, Laon, Auxerre, and Rouen; and until the emergence of the universities in the late 12th century, these schools were the most important centres of learning in the West.[904]

York, 1963, pp 128-67, at p. 143; cited in D.C. Lindberg: The Transmission, op cit, p. 61.

895 J. Draper: History; op cit; Vol II; p.4.

896 Gerbert: *Letters*; pp. 3-20. *Constantino suo Gerbertus scolasticus*, in Gerbert: *Opera mathematica*; pp. 6-8; cf. Gerbert: *Letters*; Letter 7; pp. 45-7; in S. C. McCluskey: *Astronomies; op cit*; pp. 175-6.

897 E. Grant: *Physical Science in the Middle Ages;* John Wiley and Sons, London, 1971: p.14.

898 Ibid.

899 D.J. Struik: Gerbert; in Dictionary of Scientific Biography; op cit; vol v; pp. 364-7; at p. 365.

900 R. Allen: Gerber; op cit; p. 629.

901 Ibid. pp 630-1.

902 E. Grant: Physical; op cit; p.14.

903 Ibid.

904 Ibid.

It is in great part thanks to one of Gerbert's students, Fulbert of Chartres, the noted master of the schools and later (1006-1028) bishop of that city, that Knowledge of the astrolabe spread widely during the first part of the 11th century. He composed a brief mnemonic rhyme placing eight of the astrolabe stars (with their Arabic names) within the familiar zodiacal constellations.[905] A list of the same eight `stars of the hours' appears in the De *horologio secundum alkoram*, a treatise on the astrolabe that had also been quoted by the anonymous Reichenau compiler.[906] Fulbert clearly selected these stars for actual observation: all but two are first magnitude stars and they are well distributed around the zodiac so several will be above the horizon at any time:

Aldeberan stands out in Taurus, Menke and Rigel in Gemini,
And Frons and bright Cabalazet in Leo
Scorpio, you have Calbalgharab; and you Capricorn, Deneb,
You, Bantalhaut, are alone enough for Pisces.[907]

(note here such Arabic words: Calbalgharab (the Crow's heart); or Bantalhaut (the fish daughter.); Rigel (men), etc.

Fulbert also prepared a brief glossary giving the equivalent Arabic and Latin names of the parts of the astrolabe.[908]

Possibly one of the reasons why Western Christendom failed to make the decisive scientific strides in the 11th century, as it was to do in the subsequent centuries, might have owed to the slow, and initial hostile reception of such Islamic learning (Islam, as outlined in the second chapter of the first part, was both main foe, and great source of fear for the Christian West). Gerbert was also far ahead of any Christian scholar of the time,[909] so far ahead of his compatriots `who did not cultivate the knowledge of Al-Andalus.'[910] And so astonishing was his skill, that people were bewildered, and no sooner was he dead a tradition sprang up that such powers could have no source but the devil.[911] His science, as already noted, was seen as a `Saracen magic;' Gerbert dying poisoned, just as his patron Otto was.[912]But his impact, especially

[905]S.C. McCluskey: *Astronomies; op cit;* p. 177.
[906] Ibid.
[907] Frederick Behrends; ed: *The Letters and Poems of Fulbert of Chartres;* Oxford; Clarendon Press; 1976; pp. xvi; xxvii-xxviii; 260-1; Frederick Behrends and M.Mc Vaugh: Fulbert of Chartres; notes on Arabic astronomy; *Manuscripta*; 15; 1971; 172-7.
[908] S. C. McCluskey: *Astronomies; op cit;* p. 177.
[909] W.M. Watt: The Influence, op cit, p. 59.
[910] M.R. Menocal: The Arabic; op cit; p.28.
[911] R. Allen: Gerbert; op cit; pp 630-1.
[912] J. Draper: History; op cit. vol 2; p. 7.

through his students, was going to be ever lasting, putting the seeds for future revival.

Four subsequent figures had great role in acquainting Western Christendom with Islamic science: Walcher of Malvern, Petrus Alphonsi, Daniel of Morley, and, first, Hermann the Cripple.

Herman the Cripple (1013-54) was one of the earliest, most influential Western scientists.[913] Hermann was born in Reichenau in Switzerland, and spent his life at the Benedictine Abbey of Reichenau. He wrote many works on mathematics and astronomy, all of which displayed strong Islamic influence.[914] His two works on the use of the astrolabe *De mensura astrolabii; de utilitatibus astrolabiu* were both written before 1048.[915] Hermann's name is attached to the first account by a Latin of the use of the plane astrolabe as developed by the Muslims.[916]The principle of the plane astrolabe is stereographic projection, that is a way of plotting the surface of a sphere on a plane.[917] He also wrote an *opuscula musica,* Hermann introducing a curious notation to determine pitch, which was derived in all probability from Muslim models, for a pitch notation was already known to al-Kindi (b. ca 803).[918] Hermann's infirmities prevented him from travelling amongst `Arabian scholars of Spain and elsewhere,' but he managed to get such learning from the material he acquired from other wandering scholars such as Donnolo and *Alcandrius*.[919] Hermann's infirmity did not prevent him either from maintaining contacts with other scholars, Meinzo of Constance, for instance, came to Reichenau in 1048 and discussed mathematical questions with Hermann on the measurement of the circle.[920]It was he, Hermann, with Gebert, who first adapted and popularised the earliest works of Islamic learning on the stars and the astrolabe obtained from Catalonia.[921] Hermann's works were substantially used in the following century by Bernard Sylvestris.[922]

---

[913] D. Campbell: *Arabian Medicine, op cit*; p.117.

[914] C. Singer: Science in *Medieval Contributions to Modern Civilization*; ed by F.J.C. Hernshaw and E. Barker; Dawsons Publishers; London; 1921. pp. 107-48; at p. 120.

[915] G. Sarton: Introduction; op cit; vol 1; p.757.

[916] C. Singer: *A Short History of Scientific ideas to 1900;* op cit; p.157.

[917] *Ibid. p.*149.

[918] G. Sarton: Introduction; op cit; vol 1; p.757.

[919] D. Campbell: Arabian Medicine; op cit; 117.

[920] G. Sarton: Introduction; op cit; vol 1; p.757.

[921] C. Burnett: The Introduction of Arabic Learning into British Schools in *The Introduction of Arabic Philosophy into Europe*; C.E. Butterworth and B.A Kessel ed; Brill; Leiden; 1994; pp. 40-57; at p. 41. (Referred from now on as Arabic Learning at

Walcher, a Lotharingian scholar monk (further details later), came about the last decade of the 11th century to England.[923]He represents the earliest example of introduction of Muslim astronomy in England, an example, as Metlitzki points out, which casts its light far ahead into the future on two particularly significant landmarks in English literature and thought: Malvern the priory of William Langland, author of Piers Plowman, and Chaucer's treatise on the astrolabe.[924]Like Chaucer (14th century,) Walcher was both interested in astronomy, and possessed the major element of Muslim astronomy: the astrolabe, of whose use north of the Pyrenees, he was first to make in 1092.[925] Walcher had become interested in astronomical observations after experiencing the darkness of an eclipse in Italy and then discovering on his return to Malvern that the selfsame eclipse had been observed in his own monastery at a different time of the day.[926] Using the services of a converted Jew, Petrus Alphonsi, he made various observations using degrees, minutes and seconds. Walcher presented Petrus' values from the mean daily motion of the Sun, moon, and lunar modes, apparently derived from al-Khwarizmi's tables.[927]Walcher had already adopted the Islamic methods of astronomical calculation and has transposed them to the meridian of England.[928] Walcher's applying a new astronomical instrument to bring increased observational precision to familiar astronomical questions also provided one challenge to the inherited traditions of Latin astronomy.[929] These and further contributions of his, as highlighted further on, will constitute the first dominant strides of the science in the country.

Petrus Alphonsi, just named, was a Spanish Jew convert to Christianity. He was born in Huesca, Aragon, Spain, in 1062 or 1063, and lived in the learned court circle in the Muslim ruled cities of Huesca and Zaragoza, and received a good scholarly education.[930] When the Christians took Huesca in 1097 and Zaragoza in 1118, Petrus converted to Christianity,

---

British Schools to avoid confusion with the other work with the same title referred to already)

922 C. Singer: Science; op cit; p. 120.

923 M.C. Welborn: Lotharingia as a Center; op cit; p. 198.

924 D. Metlitzki: The Matter; op cit; pp. 17.

925 C. Burnett: Arabic Learning at British Schools; op cit; pp 44.

926 L. Cochrane: Adelard; op cit; p. 7.

927 S.C. McCluskey: *Astronomies; op cit;* p. 183.

928 D. Metlitzki: *The Matter*. Op cit; p.24.

929 S. C. McCluskey: *Astronomies; op cit;* p. 186.

930 L. G. Ballester: Introduction; in *Practical Medicine from Salerno to the Black Death*; ed L.G. Ballester et al; Cambridge University Press; 1994; pp.1-29; note 43 at p.13.

and from then onwards he had contacts with both England and the North of France.[931] Petrus introduced to the West knowledge completely unknown then; including astronomy; cosmology, cosmogony, elemental theory, meteorology, psychology, and medicine.[932] In this latter capacity, he was one of King Henry's physicians in England from 1112 to 1120. For Petrus, the ignorant had to be educated in Islamic science, and that he (Petrus) has laboured hard-`magno labore.... et summo studio' to translate Islamic works `for the benefit of the Latin.'[933] He even expressed a `sense of mission' in spreading Islamic astronomy among the Latin in the land of the Franks.[934] Evidence of the astronomical contributions of Petrus Alphonsi is contained in a treatise preserved in Oxford, where he put a set of chronological tables based upon Islamic ones, including a concordance of eras for the year 1115; also a series of tables for the various planets, and an explanation of the use of the chronological tables.[935] Most significantly, though, are the twelve dialogues (*Dialogus*) between Peter and one Moses, which reflect the Islamic astronomical learning, which Petrus was first to carry to the attention of the Western Christians on their own ground.[936] Petrus also shared Walcher's respect for real experience, dismissing the mere book learning of those who presumed that they could learn astronomy by reading Macrobius and other Classical sources.[937]

The same sense of mission in seeking to convey Islamic learning to the Christian West also gripped Daniel of Morley.[938] Like Adelard (of Bath), he emphatically relies on the Muslims against the antiquated authority of ancient Christian authors.[939] Nothing expresses this best than the dedication of his *Philosophia* to John of Oxford (Bishop of Norwich from 1175 to 1200).[940] In this dedication, already seen in great detail in part one, Daniel became disgusted with the bookishness, pretentious ignorance and deliberate obscurity of the professors at Paris

---

931 Ibid.

932 See J.H.L. Reuter: Petrus Alfonsi: an examination of his works; their scientific content, and their background.' Unpublished Ph.d thesis; Oxford; 1975. p. iii.

933 D. Metlitzki: The Matter; p.24-5.

934 Ibid. p. 24.

935 C.H. Haskins: Studies; op cit;. P.117.

936 D. Metlitzki: The Matter; op cit; 21.

937 Petrus Alfonsi: *Epistola*; trans in Hermes; *Petrus Alfonsi*; pp. 69-70; in S. C. McCluskey: *Astronomies; op cit;* p. 182-3.

938 On Daniel of Morley, see: T. Silverstein: Daniel of Morley; *Medieval Studies;* 10; 1948; pp. 179-96.

939 D. Metzliki: The Matter; op cit; p. 60.

940 In C. Burnett: *The Introduction of Arabic learning into England.* The Panizzi Lectures, 1996. The British Library, London, 1997. pp 61-62.

and left for Spain to hear the `wiser philosophers of the universe.'[941]It is to the bishop that he sings the praises of the Muslims, and of Toledo in particular where he hastened to hear `the teaching of the Arabs, which was famous in those days. In Paris, he had found `Asses, with grave figures, occupying university chairs, reading in strange tongues and words, which they did not understand, anyway; standing in their places like statues `because of their ignorance' but nevertheless wished to appear wise on account of that very silence. By 1180 Daniel of Morley had returned to England from Toledo convinced, with Abu Al Ma'ashar (Albumasar), that he who condemns astronomy destroys science.[942] Daniel of Morley's principal sources are Abu Al Ma'ashar, of course, and Al-Farghani who, between 1187 and 1199, appears in Neckham's *De naturis rerum* as well.[943] Most importantly, Daniel talks of the Islamic treatise amongst others he brought, that he submitted to the Bishop.[944] Daniel of Morley who it must be pointed out, was a direct disciple of Gerard of Cremona, the main translator of Islamic science in Toledo (see chapter on translations further on) in approximately between 1175 and 1185.[945] His *Philosophia* is a cosmology, which fits into the traditions of the Chartres school in France in keeping with Gerbert's presence there two centuries before Daniel.

Adelard of Bath (fl early 12th) championed Islamic learning more than any other early scientist. He was born in Bath, studied at Tours and taught at Laon. After leaving Laon he spent seven years in study and travel, and can be traced in Cicilia and Syria. He might have visited Spain, Sicily before 1116 and probably before 1109; and was by 1115 in Palestine. By 1126 he was back in the West, busy making the astronomy and geometry of the Muslims available to the Latin world.[946] Adelard could not endure the prejudice against modern science which in his time was synonymous with Islamic scholarship, especially after he had spent those seven years in study and travel in order `to investigate the learning of the Arabs as best as he could.'[947] He brought back a unique

[941] T. Silverstein: Daniel of Morley; op cit; p. 180.
[942] Daniels Von Morley Liber de naturis inferiorum et superiorum; ed Sudhoff; p. 32; in D. Metlitzki: The Matter; op cit; p. 60.
[943] D. Metzliki: The Matter; op cit; p. 60.
[944] See: C. Burnett: Introduction; L. Cochrane: Adelard; D. Metlitzki: The Matter etc..
[945] J.Puig: Arabic philosophy in Christian Spain; in *The Introduction of Arabic Philosophy into Europe (* Butterworth and Kessel ed) op cit; pp. 7-30; at p. 21.
[946] C.H. Haskins: *Studies*. op cit; pp 33-4.
[947] Adelard of Bath: Die Questiones Naturales des Alardus von Bath; ed. M. Mueller; p.4 in D. Metlitzki: The Matter of Araby; op cit; p.13.

enthusiasm for *Arabum studia,*[948] (on which more will be said in his dialogue with his fictional `Nephew'). Adelard was the first translator of the *Zij* (astronomical tables) of al-Khwarizmi, and was one of the first, if not the first, to provide Western Christendom with information about sines and trigonometry.[949] Just like Petrus (Alphonsi) Adelard became associated with the court of Henry I. Both men were important in the transmission of Islamic science in both court and kingdom as well as much of the West. Both worked on the *Zij* of al Khwarizmi, although whether this was separately done, or in cooperation, cannot be proved; but this might have happened after his return from his travels.[950] Adelard's work also includes translations of treatises by Abu Ma'ashar and Thabit Ibn Qurra. His masterpiece, however, is a collection of Natural Questions which gave him opportunity for publishing Islamic knowledge on a variety of subjects.

The *Quaestiones naturales* is in 76 chapters, each dealing with a scientific question, to explain the new knowledge which he had acquired from `his Arabs.' Adelard writes in the form of a dialogue with his nephew, who is rather aggressive in manner; a fictional device, whether in fact he existed or not.[951] The nephew symbolises a generation which refuses the ideas of the "moderns," representing those who stay at home, young men who resist the ideas of the travellers.[952] Adelard imputes the new ideas to the Muslims, the nephew asking for "something new in the way of Arabic studies."[953] Adelard tells his nephew that he does not want anyone to think that he is propounding something as his own opinion, when he is really offering the "judgement of the Arabic schools"—"I have known what happens to true teachers among the Ordinary people. That is why I am putting the case of the Arabs, not my own."[954]

The nephew replies aggressively:

"That really is clear to no one but the bleary-eyed and the shaven. Haven't those Saracens deceived you with subtle trifles? You shall never trick me into concealing your bogus and unintelligible reasons disguised by subtle untruth. What you are doing must be exposed. You argue something intelligible neither to me nor to you, in order that I shall get

---

948 D. Metlitzki: The Matter of Araby; p.13.
949 See: L. Cochrane: Adelard of Bath; op cit.
950 Ibid. p.42:
951 N. Daniel: The Arabs and Mediaeval Europe; p. 265.
952 Ibid. p. 265.
953 Ibid. pp. 265-6.
954 Ibid.

fed up and concede untruths to you. You do not know who you are talking to—but let us put it to the test."[955]
Adelard answers:
"from the Arabic masters I have learned one thing, led by reason, while you are caught by the image of authority, and led by another halter. For what is an authority to be called, but a halter? As the brute beasts, indeed, are led anywhere by the halter, and have no idea by what they are led or why, but only follow the rope that holds them, so the authority of writers leads not a few of you into danger, tied and bound by brutish credulity."[956]
Whilst Adelard praises the Muslims as his mentors, just like Daniel of Morley, he is contemptuous of knowledge found North of the Alps. He goes out of his way to attribute methods of rational investigation to the Muslims. In that, Daniel notes, he represents a tendency in contemporary opinion, the excitement at something new and the rejection of the old methods as inadequate.[957]
`What we must be grateful for' Cochrane concludes `is that among a number of scholars who brought scientific information to the attention of the Latin West, Adelard took the initiative not only in translating Arabic works but in recording their usefulness and developing the reasoning on which they were based.'[958] Adelard of Bath could also be regarded not just as one of the pioneers of 12th century translations, but also as `the greatest name in English science before Robert Grosseteste and Roger Bacon'.[959] His works `mark a significant stage in the history of ideas,' as he sets out to acquire and to pass on a broadly based understanding of Islamic science, mathematics and astronomy, in particular.[960]

Bacon and Grosseteste, just like Aquinas and Albertus Magnus, and their links with Islamic learning will come under another heading in the next part. Here, brief focus is on a group of other early learned men of the West, not just to highlight their connections with Islamic science, but also, and above all, common to all early men of science, how they diffused such learning far and wide.

---

[955] Ibid.
[956] Ibid. in *Questiones*, ch vi, on why man must use reason with which he is endowed.
[957] N. Daniel: *The Cultural Barrier*, Edinburgh University Press, 1975; p. 168.
[958] L. Cochrane, Adelard of Bath, op cit, p. 108.
[959] D. Wright: Biographia Britanica Literaria; London, 1846; ii. 94; in C.H. Haskins: Studies, op cit, p. 20.
[960] L. Cochrane, Adelard of Bath, op cit, p. 1.

Johann Hake of Cottingen, who studied in Montpellier, where Islamic learning (as to be shown to great length further on), practiced in Avignon, and was himself from Northern Europe.[961]Joseph Kaspi (b.1280) comes from Languedoc, but travelled extensively in Spain, Majorca, and North Africa.[962] Aldobrandin of Siena (d.1287 in Troyes, France), is a Tuscan physician, physician to Beatrice of Savoy, countess of Provence, and possibly to her son in law (St Louis), later. Aldobrandin wrote a medical treatise, *Le regime du corps*, which was based on Islamic medicine, at Beatrice's request, on the occasion of a journey which she undertook to visit her four daughters, the Queen of France, the Queen of England, the Queen of Germany, and the countess of Anjou (later Queen of Sicily).[963] Arnold of Villanova (d.1311), born near Valencia, c. 1234-1250, studied medicine at Naples (another sanctuary of Islamic learning, founded by the keen admirer of Islamic learning: Frederick II). He travelled and exerted in Paris, Montpellier, Barcelona, Roma, etc.[964]Amongst his professions was professorship at the University of Montpellier, and as physician-regular to three kings of Aragon and three popes,[965] including court physician to Pedro III of Aragon from at least 1281, intimate adviser to the King's sons, sois disant interpreter of the dreams of Jaime II of Aragon and Frederick II of Sicily.[966] Arnold was, thus, well placed to reflect and perhaps to influence the self perceptions of his masters: he retained the confidence of Jaime until about 1308 and of Frederick until his death.[967] He mastered Arabic, and in his enthusiasm for Islamic medicine translated a series of its important works into Latin, which include: Al-Kindi's *Risala fi maarifat quwa'l adwiya al-murakkaba (*De medicinarum compositarum gradibus); Qusta ibn Luqa: *de Physics ligatures*; Ibn Sina's *De viribus cordi;* Abu-l-Ala Zuhr's *De Conservatione corporis*

[961] G. Sarton: Introduction; Volume III.p.251

[962] Ibid.p.589.

[963] Ibid,.Vol II; pp 1083-4.

[964] See J.N. Hilgarth: *The Spanish Kingdoms*; 2 vols, Oxford, 1976-81; 1, p. 263

[965] R.I. Burns: Muslims in the Thirteenth Century Realms of Aragon: Interaction and Reaction, in *Muslims under Latin Rule, 1100-1300*, J.M. Powell, Editor: Princeton University Press, 1990. pp 57-102: at p.90-1.

[966] See most particularly: Luis Garcia Ballester, *La minoria musulmana y morisca*, vol i of his projected *Historia social de la medicina en la Espana de los siglos XIII al XVI;* Madrid, 1976, quotations from pp 12-18, 29, materials largely from chap.1, pp.15-65. Michael Mc Vaugh, who is editing Vilanova's Opera medica omnia, 2 vols, to date; Granada, 1975- does the entry `Arnald of Villanova' in *The Dictionary of Scientific Bibliography;* New York, 1970, 1: 289-91 (quotation) and in *The Dictionary of the Middle Ages*, ed. J.R. Strayer, 13 vols; New York, 1982-89; 1: 537-8.

[967] J.Carreras Artau: *Relaciones de Arnau de Vilanova con los reyes de la casa de Aragon;* Barcelona, 1955, pp 43-50.

et regimine sanitatis; Abu Salt's *Kitab al-adwiya al-mufrada.*[968]His seventy scientific works made him the first great figure of Western medicine, and its pioneer also in pharmaceutical advance.[969]

2. Travellers, Traders, Students and Pilgrims

Understandably, those who had the earliest contacts with the Islamic lands, whether East (Jerusalem) or West (Spain) were the pilgrims, as well as religious orders and other men of religion. The particular role of the pilgrims is highlighted by Sarton who explains that:
`Pilgrims were especially numerous because it was now a well established custom in Christendom to start on pilgrimage to obtain indulgences or the remission of sins. So many were the pilgrims that hospices were built to accommodate them, as on the Alpine and Pyrenean passes (some of these hospices were much older.) The influence of these pilgrims cannot be overestimated. The pilgrimage roads stand in the same relation to the intellectual and artistic development of Christendom as the commercial roads to its economic organisation.'[970]
Pilgrims to the East, Savage notes, were passing into Palestine by various routes, and in the majority of cases, returning to their homes- maybe to profit their souls, but most certainly, `to the enlightenment of their neighbours and to the general and gradual improvement, physical and mental, of medieval life.'[971]
Male cites the presence of monks at Cordova in the 9th century; Cluniac monasteries in Aragon; Castille and Leon, and even a French quarter in Toledo.[972] French and German monks obtained the textbooks of the new sciences; and they established many schools where Muslim science was both popularised and translated.[973] The Order of Cluny, one of the dominating facts of 11th century Western Christendom, contributed considerably to the transfer of Muslim construction skills, most

---

[968] G. Sarton: Introduction; op cit; Vol ii; p.893.
[969] R.I. Burns: Muslims in the Thirteenth Century; op cit. pp.90-1.
[970] G. Sarton: Introduction; Vol II, op cit; p.131.
[971] H.L. Savage: Fourteenth Century Jerusalem and Cairo; op cit; at pp.199-200.
[972] E. Male: l'Art et les artistes du Moyen Age; 1927; in J.W. Thompson: The Introduction of Arabic Science; op cit; p,193.
[973] R. Briffault: The Making, op cit, p. 200.

particularly through their constructions, propagating art forms, and enriching this art through borrowings from Mozarab (Christians living under Muslim rule in Spain) architectural motives.[974]

The Dominican St Peter Paschal was well acquainted with Islam, and his knowledge of Muslim theology and of Arabic literature, in particular, were very extensive; and he may have been one of the channels through which Islamic lore reached Dante.[975]Another religious figure of renown, Humbert of Romans, in 1265, rejoiced that it has been some time in Spain that the brothers have studied Arabic amongst the `Saracens', as by 1250 there were names of eight friars designated by the Provincial Chapter of Toledo to learn Arabic. This learning then took place in Tunisia and Murcie.[976]One friar: Dominicus Marrochini made the translation (in 1270 or 1271) of the work on ophthalmology the *Liber oculorum* of Ali ibn Isa (Jesu Haly) at the *Studium* of Murcia in southern Spain.[977]

Similar to Gerbert's example, is another scholar imbued with Islamic learning who also became pope, Petrus Hispanus, a Portuguese physician who became pope under the name Giovanni XXI; his writing showing very clearly a very strong Muslim influence.[978]

Patronage of learning by ecclesiastical figures, as Lindberg recognises, was also a factor of vital importance.[979] Hence, Michael, Bishop of Tarazona, became the patron of the translator Hugh of Santalla and others. John of Seville and Michael Scot secured patronage from two Toledo archbishops Raymond (who was the founder of the school of translation of Toledo) and Rodrigo Jimenez, respectively.[980] Monastic institutions also supported the translations from Arabic of Constantine the African and the collaborative efforts of Robert of Chester and Hermann the Dalmatian.[981] The Papal registers From 1224 to 1227 also show that Michael Scot had the active support of Pope Honorius III and his successor, Gregory IX.[982]

The missionary effort also contributed considerably to this effort as highlighted by Raymond Lull, who at about 1246, entered the personal

---

974 M. Defourneaux: *Les Francais en Espagne aux 11 et 12em siecles*; Presses Universitaires de France; Paris; 1949.p.17-8.
975 G. Sarton: Introduction; op cit; Vol II; p. 734.
976 J. Richard: l'Enseignement des Langues Orientales en Occident au Moyen Age: *Revue d'Etudes Islamiques*; Vol 44; 1976; pp 149-164; p.159.
977 D.C. Lindberg: The transmission; op cit; p.77.
978 A. Mieli: La Science Arabe; op cit; p.241.
979 D.C. Lindberg: The Transmission; op cit; at p.78.
980 Ibid.
981 Ibid.
982 C.H. Haskins, Studies, op cit, p.274.

service of James the Conqueror, king of Aragon, before becoming the tutor of the king's sons, Peter and James. From 1265 to 1274 he lived in Majorca, studying Arabic with a Muslim slave. After that he travelled considerably in Western Europe, to Montpellier in particular, and Rome, lecturing in universities, attending religious conferences, trying to interest popes and kings in his projects.[983]

The role of Spaniards caught on either side of the religious divide, whether Mozarabs (Christians under Muslim rule) or Muslims (Mudjedars) living under Christian rule, following the fortunes of misfortunes of war, has not been studied on its own merit, although many references to their impact were raised. The role of the Mozarabs, however extensive in the transmission of Islamic learning to the West, possibly even leaving traces in early England, according to Metlitzki, still eludes us.[984] Christian Spain welcomed the cultural influences, which came from the south (Islamic Spain) via these Mozarab intermediaries, who were fleeing from Islamic rule. They contribute amongst others to the restoration of monasteries, where many retired.[985] Their contribution is highly visible in architecture in particular, in the erection of churches in northern Spain at the end of the 10th century, and the beginning of the 11th.[986] Mozarab influences were particularly strong in Asturias and Leon, some churches, modest in conception, but showing Islamic characteristic in their horse-shoe arches, their capitals and, sometimes, their rubbed vaulting.[987]The role of the Mozarabs, mainly due to their good knowledge of Arabic and local Latin dialects, was to become particularly influential in the translation effort of Islamic sciences in the 12th century as to be seen in chapter three.[988] Gerard of Cremona, the most prolific of all translators could not have done all his translations without such assistance. He had the assistance of a Mozarab named Galippus, and many versions could not be Gerard's own work. Both Gerard and Gallipus also lectured on astronomy.[989]

Equally, Mudejar (Muslims living under Christian rule) influence was very strong, for instance in respect to the advances in medicine. Luis

---

[983]G. Sarton: Introduction; op cit; Vol II, p.900.

[984] D. Metlitzki: The Matter; op cit; p. 6.

[985] M. Defourneaux: Les Francais en Espagne; op cit; p.14.

[986] Ibid.

[987] G. Wiet et al: History; op cit; p.206.

[988] or see: M.T. D'Alverny: Deux Traduction Latines; op cit; D. Metlitzki: The Matter; op cit; p.6. V. Rose: `Ptolemaus und die Schule von Toledo' in *Hermes*, viii. 327; (1874); in C.H. Haskins: Studies, op cit, p. 12.

[989] See R. Lemay's entry on Gerard of Cremona in Dictionary of Scientific Biography (Vol 15); and C.H. Haskins: Studies, op cit, p. 12.

Garcia Ballester who has studied the phenomenon throughout Spain sees Valencian Mudejar medicine as enjoying `a brilliant and fugitive moment of splendour which persisted during the first fifty to seventy five years following the conquest.[990] Arnau de Vilanova himself represents this `frontier medicine,' the symbol according to Ballester of the Valencian mix of the three people (Christian-Jewish and Muslim) in its earliest stage, and the gift of Islam within that promising context.[991] Mudedjar influence will be particularly strong in the dissemination of crafts and skills of all sorts as the last part of this work will amply show.

In the search for, and diffusion of, learning and science, the roles in the medieval times were the complete reverse of what we have today; the place of Europe then corresponding to that of Islam today, and that of Islam then to that of the West today. From all parts of Western Christendom scores of students travelled to the `great Arab seats of learning in search of the light which only there was to be found,' and even Christian rulers entrusted the education of their sons to Muslim tutors.[992] Whipple explains that the principal cities of Spain, Cordova, Toledo, Seville, Malaga and Granada had academies that taught mathematics, astronomy, geography and medicine, and all were staffed not only with Muslim scholars, but Christians and Jews took part in the teaching.[993] The Jews, in particular, formed possibly, the greatest link between Islamic learning and the Christian West.[994]Of course better known is the impact of some teachers and students of repute. Gerbert of Aurillac who was master of the school at Rheims had as his pupil Fulbert who founded the school at Chartres,[995]a school, which was going to take a leading role in the development of learning in the Christian West. Amongst Gerbert's other students can also be included Robert, son of Hugh Capet (Later Robert II of France); Ardabold, later bishop of Utrecht; Richer of Saint Remy, who wrote Gerbert biography, and possibly, a certain Bernelius of Paris, the author of a *Liber Abaci*, that may represent Gerbert's teachings.[996]And so can be grasped a second generation of influential men, who disseminated Islamic learning even if their role does not form the core or focus of historical studies.

---

990 R.I. Burns: Muslims; op cit.p.90.
991 Luis Garcia Ballester, *La minoria musulmana y morisca*, vol I; op cit.
992 R. Briffault: The Making of Humanity, op cit; pp 198 and 202.
993 A. O. Whipple: *The role of the Nestorians and Muslims*. op cit; p.32:
994 Ibid.
995 L. Cochrane: Adelard of Bath; op cit; p.6.
996 D.J. Struik: Gerbert; op cit; p. 365.

The influences at work in the cathedral schools of the period especially those of Lorrraine and Spain (i,e Ripoll in Catalonia), was of paramount importance in accumulating and disseminating Islamic science and learning.[997] Menocal also explains that London, Paris, Bologna, and Sicily enjoyed very close relations with the centres of Islamic learning, and the science of Ibn Sina, Ibn Rushd and Islamic astronomers and mathematicians were spread quickly and efficiently by men whose lives were devoted to making such knowledge and texts known to other Europeans who, unlike themselves, were ignorant of Arabic.[998] No student at Paris, Bologna, or London, Menocal points out, would have ignored these works- they had been banned, after all- and since they were all Andalusian, or had come through al-Andalus, al-Andalus and `its prolific intellectual outpourings were at the very centre of the students' attention.'[999]

Contrary to a number of opinions (such as Pirenne's),[1000]the establishment of Islam entailed no curtailment of Muslim trading relations with the Christian West.[1001]Ganshof remarks, that the ports of the French southern Provence had not stopped their activity from the 8th to the 10th century.[1002] The Christian pilgrim Arculf, who, passing through Alexandria, thirty years after the Muslim took the city (7th century), met innumerable races taking on provisions.[1003] Equally, movements of goods between East and West were hardly affected, exchanges both appreciable and continuous after the Muslim arrival.[1004] Demand also continued in Europe for Muslim goods, as in the past, and Alexandria retained its prestige.[1005] By the high Middle Ages, there were also considerable links between North Africa and the Italian republics as has been well documented by Mas de Latrie.[1006] The Pisans, Florentines, Genoese, Venetians, Sicilians, Marseilles, Majorcans, Aragonese, and alongside the latter Languedoc and Roussillon and the county of

---

997 See C. Haskins: Studies; op cit; L. Cochrane: Adelard of Bath; op cit; etc.
998 M.R. Menocal: The Arabic role; op cit; p. 57.
999 Ibid. p.57.
1000 H. Pirenne: *Mohammed and Charlemagne*; F. Alcan; Paris-Bruxelles; 7th edition; 1937.
1001 Lopez quoted in G. Wiet et al: History; op cit; p.161.
1002 F.L. Ganshof, *Note sur les ports de Provence du viii au x siecle,* in *Revue Historique*, t. CLXXXIV, 1938, p. 28.
1003 In G. Wiet et al: History op cit; p.161.
1004 E. Sabbe: l'Exportation des tissus orientaux en Europe occidentale au haut Moyen Age, in *Revue Belge de Philologie et D'histoire* XIV (1935); 811-848 and 1261-1288.
1005 G. Wiet et al: History; op cit; p.161.
1006 M.L. de Mas Latrie: *Traites de Paix et de Commerce, op cit.*

Montpellier, all had trade establishments in the Maghrib; Christian funduqs (storage and trading establishments as well as hostels for traders) were principally located in Tunis, El-Mehdia, Tripoli, Bone, Bejaia, Ceuta, and Oran; the Pisans and Genoese disposing of further establishments in Gabes, Sfax, and Sale.[1007] Every funduq became `a part of Europe'.[1008]With the East, Haskins notes, the commercial republics of the Mediterranean (Venice, Genoa, Pisa etc) were the chief means of communication via their commercial quarters at Constantinople as well as in the principal Syrian cities.[1009]

With trade much else travels, Goiten phrasing it well, when he points that during the high middle ages, the Mediterranean resembled a free trade community, goods, money and books travelling far and almost without restrictions throughout the area.[1010] Thompson notes with respect to France, that although there is not much evidence of advanced intellectual relations between France and either Christian or Muslim Spain in the 9th and 10th century, ideas do follow trade and courier routes.[1011] The loose machinery of the Muslim state, the personal rather than territorial conception of law, and the liberal treatment of foreigners, Stock also observes, all promoted cultural interchange.[1012]And Haskins notes how `intercourse' with the Muslim East, although mainly concerned with the wares of commerce, `we must remember that ever since the Greek and Phoenician traders it has been impossible to separate the interchange of wares from the interchange of knowledge and ideas.'[1013] Documents from the medieval Jewish quarter of Cairo, the earliest that are known, reveal that artisans were instrumental in transferring techniques throughout the highly mobile Muslim world.[1014] Many such techniques will be looked at in great detail in the third chapter of the last part of this work, and include new methods of accounting and the use of the Arabic numerals in transactions. Interestingly, here, worth noting that Leonardo of Pisa, who was to revolutionise Western mathematics in the 13th century (via the *Liber Abacci* in 1202) studied mathematics in North Africa for commercial purposes. His father had before him discovered the superior Islamic

---

[1007] Ibid. vol 1; pp.88-92.

[1008] B.Rosenberger: La Pratique du Commerce in *Etats, Societes et Cultures du Monde Musulman Medieval*; J.C. Garcin et al ed; vo2; Presses Universitaires de France; Paris; 2000. pp 245-72; at pp. 271-2.

[1009] C.H. Haskins: The Renaissance; op cit; p. 64.

[1010] S. D. Goitein: A Mediterranean Society, Vol.1; Berkeley, 1967; p. 66.

[1011] J.W. Thompson: The Introduction; op cit; pp 186-7.

[1012] B. Stock: Science, op cit; at p31.

[1013] C.H. Haskins: The Renaissance; op cit; p. 64.

[1014] S. D. Goitein: A Mediterranean Society, op cit; p. 66.

techniques and had sent his son to learn them in the city of Bejaia (today's Algeria).[1015]Another interesting impact of trade on learning and culture is observed by Reichmann, who points out how Muslim prescriptions and spices were well known in Europe and enjoyed a large market.[1016]The European pharmacists also sold paper and ink, and in many localities participated in the book trade especially in Tuscany where the shop of the druggist was the city's main bookstore; and as he bought his spices from the East, he may have observed or was told of the flourishing book trade, and thus was encouraged to share in this type of business.[1017]And as Menocal comments, `the virtual invasion of the material wealth and luxury' that came from Muslim Andalusia and the rest of the Mediterranean fell on a Europe long deprived of much of that kind of wealth, enabling Europe to reap the benefits of many such acquisitions, as well as the innovations of Al-Andalus itself.[1018]

Emeagwali notes the contribution made by the pilgrims, trading columns, migrant craftsmen, and also that of spies and diplomatic missions who added to the know how.[1019] Early and significant contacts between Islam and Western Christendom were, indeed, diplomatic, one well known event bearing relation with learning is recorded in *Anales Fuldenses,* when in the year 807 Harun al-Rashid sent Charlemagne a clock that struck the hours, which bewildered the emperor and his entourage.[1020] A more significant development in diplomatic-cultural exchanges took place when John, a monk of Gorze, was sent by the German Emperor Otto I to Cordoba as ambassador in 954. In the course of his three years there, John had contacts with diverse aspects of Islamic learning, and very probably brought back manuscripts, which made Lorraine (further details to follow) one of the first centres for the diffusion of Islamic science.[1021]
Although Catalonia played a crucial role in the movement of ideas, it was Cordoba that captivated travellers and visitors of all sorts. Whether in peace or at war with its neighbours, Spain and its capital, was a scene

---

[1015] See:
-W. Montgomery Watt: The Influence of Islam; op cit; pp. 63-4.
-R. Rashed: Fibonacci et les Mathematiques Arabes, in Nature, Sciences and Medieval societies, op cit; pp 145-160.
[1016] F. Reichmann: *The Sources of Western Literacy;* Greenwood Press; London; 1980. p.210.
[1017] Ibid.
[1018] M. R. Menocal: The Arabic Role; op cit; pp.39-40.
[1019] G. Emeagwali: Eurocentrism; op cit.
[1020] G. Le Bon: La Civilisation; op cit; p.130.
[1021] G. Wiet et al: History; op cit; p.206

of `feverish diplomatic activities,' from Byzantium, Germany, North Africa, and the Christian states of the North.[1022] Visitors marvelled at its wealth, and at what seemed to them an extraordinary general prosperity; one could travel for ten miles by the light of street lamps, and along an uninterrupted series of buildings.[1023] Caliphs' residences, as opposed to those of their counterparts in Europe, `were embosomed in woods, and had overhanging orange gardens, courts with cascades of water.'[1024]The streets were paved and well lit, and the schools were open even to the children of the poor.[1025] Included amongst its libraries were the great mosque libraries which were open for anyone, included non Muslims.[1026] Cordova, Scott observes, destined to remain during Islamic rule, the literary centre of the Middle Ages, `the school of polite manners, the home of science and arts; to be regarded with awe by every Moslem, with affectionate veneration by every scholar, and with mingled feelings of wonder and apprehension by the turbulent barbarians of Western Europe.' [1027]

3. The Jewish Intermediaries

The Jews played a significant role in the diffusion of Muslim science in the Christian West.[1028] They became, according to Scott, the distributors of `the precious stores of Arab wisdom.'[1029]They had the advantage, Durant explains, not just of living in contact or

[1022] A. Chejne: `The Role of al-Andalus in the movement of ideas between Islam and the West,' in K. Semaan: *Islam and the Medieval West;* State University of New York Press. 1980, pp 110-33; p 115.

[1023] J.W. Thompson: Economic and Social History; p. 549; in W. Durant: the Age of Faith; op cit; p. 302.

[1024] J.W. Draper: A History, op cit, vol II, pp 30-1.

[1025] T. Burckhardt: *Moorish Culture in Spain,* George Allen & Unwin, London; 1972; p. 9.

[1026] F B. Artz: The Mind, op cit, at pp 148-150.

[1027] S.P. Scott: History of the Moorish Empire; op cit; Vol 1; p.271.

[1028] As can be found in:

-G. Sarton: Introduction; op cit; under the appropriate headings.

-D. C. Lindberg: The Transmission of Arabic; op cit, at pp. 67-70.

-B. R. Goldstein: The Heritage of Arabic Science in Hebrew, in the Encyclopaedia of Arabic Science, (Ed. R. Rashed,) op cit, vol 1, pp. 276-83.

D. Romano: `La Transmission des Sciences Arabes par les Juifs en Languedoc,' in *Juifs et Judaisme de Languedoc*, XIII siecle-debut XIV siecle, ed. M-H Vicaire and B Blumenkranz (*Cahiers de Fanjeaux*, vol 12) (Toulouse, 1977), pp. 363-86.

[1029] S.P. Scott: History; op cit; Vol II, p.165.

communication with Muslims, many also read Arabic, and `the whole rich world of medieval Islamic culture was open to them;' they took Islamic science, and by their mediation they aroused the mind of the Christian West.[1030] The discovery of America, courtesy of Christopher Columbus, and his nautical knowledge might have to do with the heritage derived from the Muslims by the Jews.[1031] Scott also says that `after the lapse of five centuries and at a distance of a thousand miles, the civilization of the Moslem empire in Spain produced, through the agency of an alien and exiled race (the Jews), the glorious revival of arts and letters in Italy.'[1032] That the Jews should be credited with the dissemination of Muslim science and literature, he goes on saying, is demonstrated by the fact that in whatever country, Jews of Spanish extraction, or their descendants, established themselves, the people of that country quickly experienced `an intellectual impulse unknown to others not exposed to similar associations.'[1033]

The Jews, scorned and regularly (and bloodily) repressed in diverse parts of Western and Eastern Christendom, found good place in the Islamic realm (albeit on rare occasions). It is needless to go on about the privileges they derived within Islam; one or two instances suffice. That the Jews were allowed by the Muslims to live and practise their religion in Jerusalem is acknowledged gratefully by a number of Jewish authorities, who contrast this happy state of affairs with their situation under Byzantine rule:
`The temple remained with Byzantium for 500 or so years and Israel were unable to enter Jerusalem; whoever did so and was found out, suffered death. Then when the Romans left it, by the grace of the God of Israel, and the kingdom of Ishmael was victorious, Israel was given leave to enter and take up residence and the courtyards of the house of God were handed over to them and they were praying there of a time.'[1034]
In Spain, having suffered the vexations and repressions of the Wisigoths for centuries, the Jews welcomed the arrival of the Muslims in the early 8th century, blessing the tolerance the Muslims had brought to the

---

1030 W. Durant: The Age of Faith, op cit; Chapter XVII; p.395.
1031 See for instance: J. Bensaude: *L'Astronomie Nautique au Portugal*, Meridian Publishing, Amsterdam, 1967.
1032 S.P. Scott: History; op cit; Vol II, p.160.
1033 Ibid.
1034 Thus Salman ben Yeruhim (wr.ca 950) in his Judaeo-Arabic commentary on psalm 30. in R.G. Hoyland: *Seeing Islam as Others Saw it*; The Darwin Press, Inc; Princeton; New Jersey; 1997. p 127.

land.[1035]`Muslims,' Lewis observes, `were willing to concede a certain place in society to other, approved religions ... There is no equivalent to this tolerance in Christendom until the Wars of religion finally convinced Christians that it was time to live and let live. During the eight centuries that Muslim ruled part of the Iberian Peninsula, Christians and Jews remained and even flourished.'[1036]

Isolated and scorned, the Jews of medieval Christendom, Durant says, took refuge in mysticism, superstition, and Messianic dreams; no situation could have favoured science less.[1037] On the other hand, Jewish science and philosophy in the Middle Ages were almost entirely domiciled in the Islamic land, Durant adds. The Jews studied philosophy and science with Muslims and became experts in such disciplines.[1038] It is also from Islamic books, and a flood of translation from Arabic into Hebrew, that Islamic science and philosophy spread through the Jewish communities of Europe, and broadened their intellectual life beyond purely rabbinical lore.[1039]All treatises in Arabic, of practical or scientific value were translated into Hebrew.[1040] Every synagogue had a school (*Beth ha midrash*-House of Study-the Arabic *madrasa*); besides private schools and personal tutors.[1041] Most probably, literacy rates were highest among the medieval Jews than among the Christians,[1042] though lower than among the Muslims.[1043] In Spain, the period between the 10th-13th centuries, constituted in fact, the golden age of Spanish Jewry, the happiest and most fruitful period in medieval Hebrew history.[1044] They held high positions within the Islamic realm. Hasdai ibn-Shaprut who had become a court physician to Abd-ar-Rahman III, was also a diplomat at the service of the Caliph; besides establishing in Spain a group of Talmudic scholars.[1045] In Cordova Moses Ben Chanoch (d. 965), one of the Bari *emigres*, organised with Hasdai's help an academy that soon acquired the intellectual leadership of the Jewish world; whilst

---

1035 J.J.Saunders: *A History of medieval Islam*; Routlege; London; 1965.p.88.
1036 B. Lewis: *Cultures in Conflict*; Oxford University Press; 1995. pp 16-7.
1037 W. Durant: The Age of Faith, op cit; p. 402
1038 W. Montgomery Watt: The Influence, op cit, p. 62.
1039 W. Durant: The Age of Faith, op cit; p. 403.
1040 S.P. Scott: History; op cit; Vol II, p.166.
1041 W. Durant: The Age of Faith, op cit; p.383.
1042 S.W. Baron: *Social and Religious History of the Jews*: Columbia University Press; 1937; 3 Vols. I; p. 288; and ii; p. 97.
1043 W. Durant: The Age; op cit; p.372.
1044 Ibid.
1045 W.M. Watt: The Influence; op cit;p.62.

similar schools were opened at Lucena, Toledo, Barcelona, Granada.[1046] Al-Mutamid of Seville invited to his court the astronomer Isaac Ben Barruch, gave him the title of Prince, and made him head Rabbi of all the Jewish congregations there.[1047] At Granada Samuel Halevi ibn Naghdela combined the study of the Talmud with that of Arabic literature, and also selling spices. King Habbus made him his secretary.[1048] Jacob Ibn Ezra held an important post in the government of the same King Habbus, his home a salon of literature and philosophy, whilst one of his sons, Joseph, rose to high office in the state.[1049] Maimonides for his part went east and became the personal physician to Salah Eddin el-Ayyubi. There were also countless numbers of Jews who ran hospitals or universities in the Islamic realm.

The Jews spread Muslim science across frontiers of the Christian West. They were equally at home in France, Spain, and Africa;[1050] having, thus, a foot in both camps: the Christian and the Muslim, freer and safer, it must be added, under the Muslims. And the two halves of the community were in very close contact; the Jewish communities in Lyons, Marseilles and Bordeaux of the 9th century and after were in commercial relations with Spain, Italy and the Orient. Agobard of Lyons (d. 840) in his polemical tract, *De insolentia Judaeorum* protested against the coming and going of Spanish Jews between Muslim Spain and the Frank kingdom.[1051] The tide of Hebrew emigration and trade rolled steadily into France, Portugal and Italy; whilst the states of Provence and Languedoc, under the Gothic name of Septimania, were long subject to Hebrew influence.[1052] The turbulent situation in Muslim Spain, beginning in the late 11th and accentuating in the 12th century, also led large numbers of Jews to desert Spain for the south of France and south Italy, where they took with them their Andalusian heritage.[1053] Jewish scholars obtained the textbooks of the new sciences and established many schools where Muslim science was both popularised and translated.[1054] The best medical books of Maimonides were written in Arabic and had to be translated into Hebrew to become available to

---

1046 W. Durant: The Age, op cit; p.372.
1047 D. Druck: Yehuda Halevy; p. 26; in W. Durant: The Age; op cit; p.371.
1048 W. Durant: The Age, op cit; p.371.
1049 Ibid. p.397.
1050 C. Dawson: Medieval Essays; op cit; p. 222.
1051 J.W. Thompson: The Introduction; op cit; p.192.
1052 S.P. Scott: History; op cit; Vol II, p.154.
1053 B.Z. Richler: Translations and Translators; Dictionary of Middle Ages; op cit; vol 12; pp. 133-6; p 133.
1054 R. Briffault: The Making, op cit, p. 200.

the Trans-Pyrenean Jews, and even to a growing number of Spanish ones.[1055] Abraham ibn Ezra, of Tuleda, during the years 1140-1167 visited the principal cities of Italy, France and England,[1056] and contributed immensely to the translations from Arabic into Hebrew for the Jewish communities of Provence and Languedoc.[1057] Bevenutus Grassus, a Jerusalem Jew, taught at Salerno and also at Montpellier, and his *Practica oculorum* (c.1250) was one of the most definitive treatise on diseases of the eye; one of the first books to be printed on its theme.[1058]

The Jewish communities, in the south of France in particular, stimulated the growth of Muslim science to a considerable extent.[1059] This may seem puzzling when one remembers that they were expelled from France in 1306, but happily for them `France' at that time did not yet include the county of Orange nor the whole of Provence and Languedoc; where large Jewish colonies had existed.[1060] The Ibn Tibbon family who came from Spain to Southern France created a nucleus of Jewish scholarship in the region. One member of the family, Jacob, translated from Arabic to Hebrew a number of works, including Ibn al-Haytham *Fi hai'at al-alam* (on the Configuration of the World,) and works by al-Ghazali, Ibn Rushd, Qusta ibn Luqa, al-Zarqali and Jabir.[1061] In the town of Arles (also south of France) resided one of the most prolific Jewish translator, Qalonymos ben Qalonymos, who amongst other translated Jabir's treatise on poisons, various works by al-Kindi and al-Farabi, and Ali ibn Ridwan's *Kitab al-umud fi usul al-tibb*. Moses Ben Joshua of Narbonne (d. 1362) is the author of *Orah hayyim* (Road of life), a medical treatise, written about 1350, is a collection of remedies for various diseases, and is arranged in similar method of the *Kitab al-Tasrif* of Abu-l-Qasim al-Zahrawi.[1062] Even as late as the late 13th-early 14th century, out of thirteen eminent Southern French scholars, nine were Jews, and only four Christians.[1063]

The Jews were according to Chejne mobile people, who also by choice or under compulsion, found themselves serving the Christian

---

1055 G. Sarton: Introduction', op cit; Volume III. p.254.
1056 G. Wiet et al: History; op cit; 277.
1057 The impact of his translations will be seen alongside others in the following chapter.
1058 W. Durant: The Age of Faith; op cit; p.403
1059 For details see, for instance: D. Romano: `La Transmission; op cit.
1060 G. Sarton: Introduction; op cit; Volume III. p.56.
1061 See B.Z. Richler: Translations and Translators; op cit.
1062 G. Sarton: Introduction; Volume III; p.607.
1063 Ibid. Vol II p.328.

rulers in their capacities of interpreters, translators, tax collectors, and administrators.[1064] And these functions, together with their mobility, and being the legates of Muslim science, played a vital role within courts, palaces, and amongst elites, who, so to say, `officialised,' such learning. Pedro Alfonso (Petrus Alphonsi) a Jew from Huesca, converted to Christianity in 1106, was the court physician to Alfonso VI, King of Castille, first, and then later to King Henry I of England. As Petrus became tutor to the young King Henry,[1065]his admonition addressed to Latin scholars (to acquire Islamic science) became part of the Western heritage, and was now being handed down to a young Englishman of royal blood.[1066]Many Jews also followed William of Normandy to England when he established Norman rule on the island (after 1066) enjoyed his protection, and established a school of science at Oxford, where, under their successors, Roger Bacon (one of the Latin West's most prominent early scientists) learned Arabic and Muslim science.[1067]

The Jews' knowledge of all principal languages: Arabic, Latin, and local dialects made them the ideal intermediary between cultures. This is quite obvious in Richler's outline on translations and translators in the Dictionary of the Middle Ages.[1068] Jewish scholars translated massively from Arabic into Hebrew, much of which, later, was turned into Latin, and also translated from Arabic into Latin, and into Castilian or Catalan and other local languages, from which some other scholar translated into Latin. John of Seville, whose original name could have been Solomon ben David, was possibly the second greatest translator of all times after Gerard of Cremona.[1069] Moses ibn Tibbon and Jacob Ben Mahir produced between them Qusta ibn Luqa's treatise on celestial spheres, Ibn al-Haytham's astronomy, treatises on the astrolabe by ibn al-Saffar and al-Zarqali, Jabir ibn Afflah's and al-Bitruji's astronomy, and the arithmetic and algebra of Muhammad ibn Hassar.[1070]Samuel Ibn Tibbon, whose Hebrew version of the *Dalalat al-Ha'rin* was to make him famous in the 13th century, completed at Beziers in 1199 his first translation of Ali ibn Ridwan's commentary on Galen's *Tegni,* whilst

---

[1064] A. Chejne: The Role of al Andalus; op cit; at pp. 118-19.
[1065] See: J.H.L. Reuter: Petrus Alfonsi: an examination of his works; op cit; C. Burnett: *The Introduction; op cit;* and C.H. Haskins: Studies; op cit.
[1066] D. Metlitzki: The Matter; op cit; p. 29.
[1067] R. Briffault: The Making; op cit; p.200.
[1068] B.Z. Richler: Translations and Translators; op cit; pp. 133-6.
[1069] See entry on John of Seville in Dictionary of Scientific Biography; op cit; vol 12.
[1070] G. Sarton: Introduction; op cit; vol 2; p. 752.

Isaac ben Pulqar (fl 1307-30), completed in 1307 the translation of al-Ghazali's *maqasid al-falasifa* (the third part on physics), began by Isaac Albalag under the title of *Tiqqun ha filusufim. Albalag* (logic metaphysics).[1071] Moses ben Joshua of Narbonne (d. 1362) learned Arabic in Spain, and was well acquainted with Latin and Catalan, and his work *Orah hayyim* (Road of life), is a medical treatise, which gives technical terms in Arabic and Latin as well as in Hebrew.[1072] The encyclopaedia of Islamic medicine, *Tasrif* of al-Zahrawi, was translated into Hebrew at least twice, by Shem-Tob ibn Ishaq and by Meshullam ben Jonah; a third translation of it ascribed to Nathan ha Me-ati; and a part was translated from Hebrew into Latin by Abraham ben Shem-Tob.[1073] The first two books of Ibn Sina's *Qanun* were put into Hebrew by Zarahiah Gracian, and the whole of it by Nathan ha Me'ati (Rome 1279). And the list of such Jewish translations is extremely long as will be highlighted in the third chapter.

The Jews in Toledo, as in other places, also acted as intermediaries for Christian scholars, who would not have achieved as much without such Jewish role. Adelard, for instance, whom it is not certain visited Spain, most certainly benefited from the assistance of Petrus Alphonsi, and perhaps other Arabic speaking Jews or former Jews who collaborated with him and his circle.[1074]Abraham bar-Hiyya (Savasorda), who spent most of his life in Barcelona, was essential to Plato of Tivoli (the main translator of Muslim algebra), and the two of them translated books on astronomy, astrology and mathematics, especially works by al-Battani and al-Imrani.[1075] As for John of Seville (a Jewish convert to Christianity), amongst those he assisted was Gundisalvo, the archdeacon of Segovia, author of many scientific translations. John of Brescia worked with Jacob Ben Mahir to translate al-Zarqali's treatise on the astrolabe, from the Arabic, and Armengaud son of Blaise collaborated with the same Jacob to translate the latter's treatise on the quadrant, from the Hebrew.[1076] The Jews like the Mozarabs, often translated into a vulgar lingua, which then the clerk turned into good Latin; such as with Ibn Sina's De Anima, which was translated in Toledo between 1152-1166 with the assistance of Avendauth, a Jewish philosopher refugee

[1071] Ibid. Volume III; p.693
[1072] Ibid. p.607.
[1073]See chapter on translations further on.
[1074] D. Metlitzki: The Matter; op cit; 29.
[1075] B.Z. Richler: Translations and Translators; op cit; p. 135.
[1076] G. Sarton: Introduction; op cit; vol II; p.748.

from Cordova.[1077] In the end, even after most of Islamic literature was available already to Westerners, they still found themselves in need of Jewish assistance. It was always simpler for Jews to study the Arabic originals; even if they had forgotten their Arabic it was a good deal easier for them than for the Latin to learn or relearn it.[1078] All in all, without the Jews, according to Burckardt `who were equally at home in both worlds,' Toledo (where most translations of Islamic learning were made), could hardly have played the part of intermediary in the dissemination of Islamic culture.[1079]

The Jews also spread Muslim science through their own works.[1080] Maimonides is one such figures, but also others, such as Abraham Bar Hiya of Barcelona, who incorporated Islamic learning in his Hebrew works.[1081] Also briefly cited here are Isaac ben Baruch, who was one of the most learned and accomplished mathematicians of his time; just as were astronomers like Ben Chia; geographers like Isaac Latef; Physicians like Charizi; travellers like Benjamin of Tudela; natural philosophers like Ben Gabirol; Ben Ezra, and so on.[1082]

Muslims were gradually eliminated in Europe under Christian rule, but as Lacroix points out, although: `the light of science emanated chiefly from `Saracen' schools in Spain,' it was not extinguished when the Muslims were eliminated; and more importantly, `when reviving civilisation was once more threatened with an invasion of barbarism,' it was the Jews, who picked up the scattered fragments of `the sacred arts of science, and divided them between the various countries of Europe.'[1083]

Hence, at the court of the King of Castile, Alfonso X, the Jews translated most often from Arabic into the current Spanish idiom, which the Christian translator then turned into Latin.[1084] In 1313, King James II of Aragon paid a fee to a Jewish physician of Barcelona, Yehuda Bonsenyor for the translation of a medical work, probably *The Surgery*

[1077] F. Micheau: La Transmisison a l'Occident Chretien: Traductions Medievales de l'Arabe au Latin; in *Etats, Societes et Cultures (*J.C. Garcin et al ed); op cit; pp. 399-420. at p. 406.

[1078] G. Sarton: Introduction, op cit; Vol II, p.787.

[1079] T. Burckhardt: Moorish Culture; op cit; p. 162.

[1080] C. Burnett: The Introduction; op cit; p. 40.

[1081] B.Z. Richler: Translations and Translators; op cit; p. 133.

[1082] S.P. Scott: History; op cit; Vol II, p.141.

[1083] P. Lacroix: *Science and Literature in the Middle Ages*, Frederick Ungar, New York, 1964.p.110:

[1084] C.H. Haskins: Studies, op cit, p. 18.

of Abulcasis (Al-Zahrawi), from Arabic to Catalan.[1085] And the same in Sicily, where the translation of al-Razi's *al-Hawi* (the Compendium) was done for the Angevin court of Sicily by Faraj ben Salim (Moses Farachi or Faragut etc) in 1279 (that is roughly two centuries after Muslim rule ended on the island.)[1086]

Scattered throughout Europe, the Jews, Scott says, preserved for future generations the precious heritage of Muslim science and culture; and had they not proved capable of retaining and transmitting it, `the discoveries of Moorish genius, banished with those who made them, would have been lost to posterity.'[1087]

4. Courts and Monarchs

Menocal makes the point that early Western Christian scientists, Adelard of Bath, Robert of Ketton, and Michael Scot were important and prestigious, and not just because of the technical knowledge of Arabic culture they imparted through translations.... but also because `their unrecorded accounts and retellings of the world they knew so well, the anecdotes and insights of such world travellers, would have held notable attractions.... We can hardly suppose that at such times and in such courts they would have been the only stories from the Arabic world to fascinate and intrigue the members of the courts of northern Europe.'[1088]

Many such courts and monarchies fought the Islamic foe very fiercely, and yet literally exhibited a near thorough Islamic outlook (with the exception of the faith, of course). And not just that, they were going to act as the main agents for the dissemination of Islamic knowledge, maybe more than any other force, for, obviously, they had the power and authority to do it. `Arabized monarchs,' Menocal holds, presided over courts where the patronage of poetry and advanced intellectual pursuits was part of the very definition of a monarch's role.[1089]They turned sponsors of Islamic culture, and its dissemination amongst their own people, and also throughout the rest of the continent. Playing such leading parts were the Carolingian court of Charles the Bald; of Roger,

---

1085 Jose Cardoner in D.C. Lindberg: The Transmission, op cit, p. 70.
1086 F. Micheau: La Transmission; op cit; p. 411.
1087 S.P. Scott: History; op cit; Vol II, p.154.
1088 M.R. Menocal: The Arabic Role; op cit; p.50.
1089 Ibid. p. 54.

Frederick II and Manfred in Sicily; the Angevin court in Naples; and the courts of Alfonso X in Castile and James II in Aragon.[1090]

In Spain, the court of Alfonso VI was according to Trend `as much imbued with Muslim civilisation' as the court of Frederick II at Palermo nearly two centuries later, and Alfonso even declared himself `Emperor of the two Religions.'[1091] The role of Alfonso X in the transfer of Islamic learning to the Christian West is particularly important. During his reign (1252-1284) was established a school of translation in Toledo with scholars from all three monotheist religions, commissioning works of history and science of Islamic origin.[1092]The Jews and Mozarabs played the major part, translating from Arabic into Castilian, then his clerks transcribed everything into Latin.[1093]During the reign of Alfonso was also produced a collection of treatises on astronomy, the famed Alfonsine tables, and writings on instruments mostly based on known Muslim works. These were elaborated, reconciled, systematized, regrouped, and often rewritten at Alfonso's command.[1094]Such endeavours were to form the core of much astronomical knowledge and developments, as well as the development of instruments of science in the subsequent centuries.[1095] It was the so called Alfonsine tables, compiled in Toledo in the 13th century, which constituted an important link between Islamic and Western Christian astronomy.[1096] Their name came from the fact that they were compiled at the instigation of Alfonso, in the second half of the 13th century.[1097] Jewish intermediaries such as Jehuda Ben Mose Cohen, and Isaak Ben Said Hassan compiled these tables based on those of Muslim astronomers, the tables of Al-Zarqali's Toledan tables serving as models.[1098] The Alfonsine tables took into account the theory of trepidation, by then largely accepted in the Christian West.[1099] The Alfonsine tables, widely disseminated throughout Europe in the 14th century, were composed in Paris in 1320,

---

[1090] D.C. Lindberg: The Transmission, op cit, p. 78.

[1091] J.B. Trend: Spain and Portugal, op cit, p. 28.

[1092] P.F. Kennedy: The Muslim Sources of Dante? in *The Arab Influence in Medieval Europe*, ed D.A. Agius and R. Hitchcock, Ithaca Press, 1994, pp. 63-82 p. 72.

[1093] F. Micheau: La Transmission; op cit; p. 411.

[1094] C.H. Haskins: Studies; op cit; P. 16.

[1095] E. Procter: *Alfonso X of Castile*; Oxford; 1951.

[1096] E. Rybka: Mouvement des Planetes dans l'Astronomie des Peuples de l'Islam; in *Convegno Internationale: Oriente e occidente Nel Medioevo Filosofia E Scienze;* 9-15 Aprile 1969; Academia Nationale Dei Lincei; Roma; 1971; pp. 579-93; p. 591.

[1097] Ibid.

[1098] Ibid.

[1099] E. Zinner: *Die Geschichte der Sternkunde;* Berlin; 1931; p. 287.

and were one of the first works purchased by Copernicus when he studied in Cracow.[1100] Alfonso el-Sabio also contributed widely to the rise of higher learning in the Christian West, incorporating the University of Salamanca in 1254, and in the same year establishing the Latin and Arabic college of Seville.[1101] A title of his famous code (*las siete partdas*) defines universities and explains their duties, privileges and administration.[1102]

The Sicilian monarchs played an even greater role in the sponsorship and diffusion of Islamic learning in the Christian West. When in the middle of the 11th century, the Normans took Sicily and the southern portion of Italy from the Muslims, they granted the medical school founded by the latter a thorough protection.[1103] Roger I, who was the first to rule the island after the Muslims in 1091, and taking the risk of being considered a Muslim, `encouraged them to cultivate their gifts.'[1104] Roger I kept the Muslim system of administration and his kingdom presented the `unique spectacle' of a Christian kingdom in which Muslims held some of the highest positions.[1105] His successor, Roger II (1111-1154), count of Sicily, duke of Calabria, since 1101, was the most enlightened monarch of his time, and patron of science and art.[1106] He allowed religious freedom and cultural autonomy to the Muslims, and himself wore Muslim garb; living as a Latin king in an Oriental court.[1107] His kingdom for a generation was considered `the richest and most civilised state in Europe'.[1108] A tradition kept by his grand son, Frederick II (1194-1250), whose court also bore a very strong Muslim influence, even stronger after his visit to the East (1220s), and maintained by the political and commercial relations with Muslim lands.[1109] It was under his rule, Briffault explains, that Muslim culture on the island reached its height and had `a great and far reaching civilising influence over barbaric Europe.'[1110] In his preference to be surrounded by Muslim rather than Christian influence, he was half

---

[1100] E. Rybka: Mouvement des Planetes; op cit; p. 591.
[1101] G. Sarton: Introduction; op cit; p.726.
[1102] Ibid.
[1103] G. Le Bon: *La Civilisation; op cit;* p.391
[1104] A.H. Miranda: The Iberian Peninsula, op cit, p. 438.
[1105] P.K. Hitti: History, op cit, p. 607.
[1106] G. Sarton: Introduction, op cit, vol 2; p. 191.
[1107] Cambridge Medieval History; VI; p. 131. in W. Durant: The Age; op cit; p. 704.
[1108] Ibid.
[1109] C.H. Haskins: Studies, op cit, p. 244.
[1110] R. Briffault: The Making, op cit, p. 212.

Muslim in his own ways, according to Sarton.[1111] Frederick had also grown up with Arabic, which was the languages of his court; and he himself mastered it so well in its classical form that he was at times able to correct his own official translators.[1112] The king also wore robes embroidered with Arabic; resembling `a powerful emir or sultan,' with a royal body-guard of Muslims, and a palace teeming with Muslim and Greek servants and functionaries.[1113]Such was the Islamic cultural influence, he raised suspicion that his culture and learning had tainted his Christianity; he, himself, being `viewed with astonishment, admiration, and envy combined with fear and suspicion.'[1114]

On the particular role played by Frederick in disseminating Islamic learning a whole book can be written, but only an outline is required here. Frederick founded the University of Naples in 1224; the first university of Europe which was founded at a definite time, and by a definite charter;[1115]a major breakthrough in the history of learning. In its library he placed a large collection of Islamic manuscripts.[1116]He made the university an academy for the introduction of Islamic science to Western Christendom, and there various translations were made from Arabic into Latin and into Hebrew, before copies of such translations were sent to Paris and Bologna.[1117]Frederick also established universities in Messina and Padua, and renovated the old medical school of Salerno in accordance with the development of Islamic medicine.[1118] From Andalusia (Spain) came also the doctrines of Ibn Rushd, which were well known and often discussed at his court, theories which were also greatly feared and hated.[1119] Scott, however, notes that the genius of Frederick II was five centuries in advance of his time.[1120] His contemporaries were incapable of understanding his motives or of appreciating his efforts for `the regeneration of humanity,' which no individual of that age accomplished so much for civilisation as he did by diffusing the learning of the Muslims throughout Europe, imparting `a new impulse to the cause of education in distant countries not subject to his sway; an impulse which, while it was often impeded, was never

---

[1111] G. Sarton: Introduction, op cit, vol 2; P. 575.
[1112] M.R. Menocal: The Arabic Role; op cit; p.61.
[1113] Ibid.
[1114] Ibid. p.63.
[1115] G. Sarton: Introduction, op cit, vol 2; p. 575.
[1116] Ibid.
[1117] De Lacy O'Leary: Arabic Thought; op cit; p. 281.
[1118] R. Briffault: The Making, op cit, p. 213.
[1119] C.H. Haskins: Studies; op cit; P. 260.
[1120] S.P. Scott: History; op cit; vol 3; pp. 56-7.

wholly suppressed.'[1121] In agreement, Burckhardt held that it was under Frederick `The first modern man upon a throne,' rather than in the days of Petrarch, that the real beginning of the Italian Renaissance is to be sought.[1122] And according to Briffault `if the name of any European sovereign deserves to be specially associated with the redemption of Christendom from barbarism and ignorance, it is not that of Charlemagne, the travesty of whom in the character of a civiliser is a fulsome patriotic and ecclesiastical fiction, but that of the enlightened and enthusiastic ruler (Frederick) who adopted `Saracenic' civilisation and did more than any sovereign to stimulate its diffusion.'[1123]

Sponsorship of Muslim scholars or scholars imbued with Islamic learning was common in the medieval period. Best known case is Roger II sponsoring of al-Idrisi, who wrote a greatly influential geographical work. This work, called *Nuz'hat al-Mushtaq* or Roger's Book, included all available knowledge of the time transcribed upon a large silver map and in a volume of descriptive text in Arabic, a project which was completed in 1154.[1124]Aspects of impact of this work will be considered in the following part. Frederick II was the patron of both Michael Scot the famed translator of al-Bitruji and the mathematician Fibonacci, who studied in North Africa and wrote *Liber Abacci*, the highly influential work of Western mathematics.

In Spain monarchical sponsorship was of Al-Riquti, a Hispano-Muslim philosopher, mathematician, physician, who was born in the Valle de Ricote, in the province of Murcia. This province had been taken from the Muslims in 1243 but continued for a time to be ruled by Muslim princes under Castilian tutelage. Alfonso the Wise the then governor of Murcia built for Al-Riquti a madrasa, wherein students of different nations were taught, each in their own language (Latin, Castilian, Arabic, Hebrew).[1125] Al-Riquti was much honoured, not just by Alfonso, but also by the second Nasrid sultan of Granada, Muhammad II al-Faqih (1273-1302), who gave him residence in the country near Granada, where Al-Riquti taught medicine, mathematics, music, etc, and where he also attended learned meetings at his patron's court.[1126]

[1121] Ibid.

[1122] J. Burckhardt, Die Cultur der Renaissance in Italien (ed. Geige, Leipzig, 1899), i.4. in C.H Haskins: Studies, op cit, p. 299.

[1123] R. Briffault: The Making, op cit, p. 212.

[1124] D.M. Dunlop: Arab Civilisation, op cit, p. 171.

[1125] His biography is included in the Ihata of Ibn al-Khatib (second half of the 14th), Ms. of the academy of history of Madrid (vol.2, f.153 verso). H. Suter: Mathematiker und Astronomen der Araber (156, 1900). in G. Sarton: Introduction; Vol II; op cit;.p.865

[1126] in G. Sarton: Introduction; op cit; Vol II; p.865

In Norman England, scholars with Islamic learning held some of the highest positions of influence. The role of Petrus Alphonsi in the court of Henry I has already been seen. After Henry II acceded to the kingdom in 1154, scholars continued to be attached to his court,[1127] and these included Roger of Hereford and Daniel of Morley, both justices of King Henry;[1128] and both very much versed in Islamic science; Daniel of Morley one of the most passionate admirers and promoters of Islamic learning as witnessed in his dedication of his *Philosophia* to John of Oxford, Bishop of Norwich.[1129]

Court blood ties acted as another main force in the diffusion of Islamic learning over the diverse lands of Europe.[1130] The expansion of Norman political power in the late 11th century and its consolidation in the 12th and 13th centuries over France, England and Sicily, played an important role in the dissemination of learned Arabic texts in translation.[1131] The blood ties, as well as the political and cultural interactions among courts scattered from Sicily to England, to Spain, with France in between, meant that there was a considerable amount of free exchange of intellectual and artistic activity as the section under Sicily in the following chapter will amply show. Here can be raised the instance of a second daughter of Eleanor and Henry II, who had married into the royal family of Castile, and as the wife of Alfonso VIII of Castile and an eminent figure in Toledo, this other Eleanor welcomed visitors from throughout Europe who came to Toledo (the seat of Islamic learning fallen into Christian hands in the late 11th) `to drink from its fountains of knowledge-and to take much of that knowledge back to England, France, and Germany.'[1132] Eleanor herself, as her progeny would also do, played a key role in the cultural and intellectual revival of those courts of Europe to be at the origin and home of the French literary renaissance of the 12th century.[1133] A key role was also played by both learning and attitudes, transmitted both directly and through example

[1127] For Henry's support of literature and learning see Haskins, 'Henry II as a Patron of Literature', in *Essays in Medieval History Presented to Thomas Frederick Tout,* ed. A. G. Little and F. M. Powicke, Manchester, 1925, Pp.71-7.

[1128] C.H. Haskins ('Henry II as a Patron of Literature', P.73) refers to Pipe Roll 31 Henry II P.146; in C. Burnett: The Introduction of Arabic Learning; op cit; p.58.

[1129] In C. Burnett: *The Introduction; op cit;* pp.61-2.

[1130] M.R. Menocal: The Arabic Role; op cit; pp.49-50.

[1131] C.H. Haskins: England and Sicily in the 12th century; *The English Historical Review*: Vol XXVI (1911) pp 433-447 and 641-665.

[1132] M.R. Menocal: The Arabic Role; op cit; pp.49-50.

[1133] Ibid.

and translation, of the courts where `the secular learning and cultural admixtures often voiced in Arabic were formative and key features.'[1134]

Translations of Islamic scientific works will be considered in great length further down, and so here one or two examples suffice to highlight the royal and princely contribution to this exercise. It is worth citing one court not dealt with, that of Dinis in Portugal (1279-1325), where translations from Arabic into Spanish and Portuguese were much in vogue; the king `doing for his country what Alfonso el-Sabio had done for his own little earlier.'[1135] At the same time as Dinis, Jacme II (king of Aragon from 1291 to 1327) employed Judah ben Astruc Bonsenyor to translate from Arabic into Catalan *The Surgery* of Abulcasis (Al-Zahrawi).[1136] In Sicily, the same operation went on under Roger's successor, William I, the chief translators, Aristippus and Eugene of Palermo, being officers of the royal administration.[1137] Michael Scot made the famed translation of al-Bitruji also in the Sicilian court, a court where there were no language barriers, and which attracted all sort of intellectual interest.[1138]Frederick made certain that every single book in Arabic was to be translated into Latin, Michael Scot being even sent to Cordoba to obtain works by Ibn Sina, which were, then, distributed to schools.[1139]

5. Crusades and Crusaders

The period elapsing from the 11th century to the 13th is when the West began its scientific and civilisation revival, and it is precisely the period when the West achieved its military control over much of the Islamic realm, whether in the East or in the West. Military successes which put at the disposal of the West the scientific and cultural riches of Islam.

A pre-crusade Christian success, the taking of Barbastro in Spain, in1064, is one of the best documented examples of forced `transfers' of

---

1134 Ibid.
1135 G. Sarton: Introduction; Volume III; op cit; p.61.
1136 Jose Cardoner in D.C. Lindberg: The Transmission, op cit, p. 70.
1137 C.H. Haskins: The Renaissance; op cit; p.60.
1138 M.R. Menocal: The Arabic Role; op cit; p.61.
1139 R. Briffault: The Making, op cit, p. 213.

Muslim cultural `booty' by southern Frenchmen led by Guillaume de Montreuil.[1140] Such spoils of war included a substantial number of craftsmen who possessed a degree of technical skill unknown north of the Alps and the Pyrenees.[1141] This and the Norman conquest of Muslim Sicily (1060-1091) were decisive factors in the rise of the new architecture, which coincides with such events.[1142] France's subsequent involvement through its knights in the re-conquista of Spain also served to enrich its thought, art and literature.[1143] The French took with them many of the trappings of the world they fought, and in some measure `recreated it'.[1144] The same process went on in Sicily, where it is precisely in the fields the Muslims excelled at (architecture, textile manufacturing, system of administration...) which were to be found disseminated within the Norman realm as far as France and England.

The crusades in the East (1095-1291) were a disastrous episode in Islamic history, causing mayhem and mass slaughter on an unprecedented scale, but for the Christian West, the outcome was otherwise. Finding themselves in contact with a civilisation, which was far superior to theirs, `the more intelligent' amongst the crusaders, in the expression of Mieli, sought to acquire aspects of such a civilisation.[1145] Eastern learning became current in the West chiefly through these crusades, which brought not just the warriors, but also the merchants of the Occident, in war or in `the chaffering and huckstering of the Bazar, against Oriental opponents as keen and as canny as themselves.'[1146]

Before looking at the impact in terms of learning and culture, it is worth mentioning, briefly, other ways the crusades impacted on the progress of the West. These included the freeing of Europe of vagrants, erratic, aggressive knights, prostitutes and criminals in considerable numbers, and relieved pressure on the land from excessive numbers.[1147] The booty from the land of Islam enriched many, especially the trading

---

[1140] M.R. Menocal: The Arabic Role; op cit; p.27.
[1141] J. Harvey: The Development of Architecture, in *The Flowering of the Middle Ages*; ed J. Evans; Thames and Hudson; pp. 85-105; p. 86.
[1142] L. Cochrane: Adelard of Bath; op cit; p. 64.
[1143] M. Defourneaux: *Les Francais en Espagne; op cit;*p.3.
[1144] M.R. Menocal: The Arabic Role; op cit; p.27.
[1145] A. Mieli: La Science Arabe; op cit; pp. 223-4.
[1146] H.L. Savage: Fourteenth Century Jerusalem; op cit p.199.
[1147] See:
-Sir S Runciman: *A History of the Crusades*, 2 vols, Cambridge University Press, 1962.
-J.J. Saunders: *Aspects of the Crusades*; University of Canterbury publishing; Canterbury; 1962.

cities, Venice, Amalfi, Genoa, etc, which benefited from the monopoly they had in displacing the Muslim competitors, and carrying trade for themselves.[1148] In the Holy Land itself, and all around, Christian landowners thrived on the lands they had taken from the Muslims and in enslaving the local people.[1149] Another gain of great substance was, of course, the weakening of the Islamic foe, in fact inflicting upon it one of the deadliest blows following the sixth crusades in particular, when in alliance with Mongols and Armenians, the Crusaders terminated the Caliphate (1258), and inflicted upon the Muslims a toll of destruction they never recovered from.[1150]

To appreciate the scope of the Islamic impact, it is worth remembering, how in the days of the crusades, the standard of living common among European princes would have seemed `poor and rustic to the nobles of the East, and apart from sending the occasional ambassador, these Eastern lords seem to have ignored the names, and sometimes even the very existence of these peoples,' notes Oldenbourg.[1151] Not so much the case in the West, where, far from disregarding the existence of the East, people cherished `fabulous and highly coloured visions of the lands from which came silks, spices, carpets, and gold, visions made up of a mixture of wonder and envy.'[1152]The men of Provence and Italy, Conder explains, were not insensible to art and beauty; but many of the Latin came from gloomier lands-from dark castles and small fortresses frowning over squalid wooden villages.[1153] They were astonished at the wealth and luxury of Asia and their hearts rejoiced thinking of the spoils that lay before them in the East, where Baghdad and Damascus were

---

1148 See for instance: V.P. Goss: *The Meeting of Two Worlds*; Medieval Institute Publications, Michigan, 1986 (appropriate articles).

1149 On this see most particularly:
B. Z. Kedar: The Subjected Muslims of the Frankish Levant, in *Muslims under Latin Rule, 1100-1300,* ed J.M. Powell, Princeton University Press, 1990.pp 135-174.
J.Prawer: *The Crusaders' Kingdom;* New York; Praeger; 1972.
H.E. Mayer: Latins, Muslims and Greeks in the Latin Kingdom of Jerusalem, *History* 63 (1978).

1150See, for instance:
- P. Pelliot: *Mongols and Popes; 13th and 14th centuries;* Paris; 1922.
-Baron G. D'Ohsson: *Histoire des Mongols,* in four volumes; Les Freres Van Cleef; la Haye and Amsterdam; 1834.
-Yves Courbage, Paul Fargues: *Chretiens et Juifs dans l'Islam Arabe et Turc*, Payot, Paris, 1997

1151Z. Oldenbourg: The Crusades; op cit; p. 7.

1152 Ibid.

1153C.R. Conder: *The Latin Kingdom of Jerusalem;* The Committee of the Palestine Exploration Fund; London; 1897. p. 30.

said to rival Byzantium.[1154] And once they reached their Muslim destinations, what they found could hardly fail to both impress them and cause them to borrow en masse; it was a new and alien world with advanced economic and cultural standards, which confronted them.[1155] Thus, William of Tyre's History goes: `The plain of Antioch are full of many rich fields for the raising of wheat and abounding in springs and rivulets,'[1156] and on the neighbourhood of Damascus `there are great number of trees bearing fruits of all kinds and growing up to the very walls of the city and where everybody has a garden of his own.'[1157]It is the size and structure of the Muslim cities, which must have been most impressive to the crusaders. At the beginning of the 11th century, Tripoli had 80,000 inhabitants and its fortifications enclosed an area of about 12,000 ha, and not only did it possess a series of palaces, its five and six storey buildings were also an impressive sight.[1158]It was a similar picture in the other cities; the bustling crowds and the busy atmosphere of the bazaars where numerous craftsmen and merchants sold a wide range of wares excited the astonishment and admiration of the conquerors.[1159] In such cities, there were centralised water supply systems, being either in the form of cisterns with pipes leading to the houses of the wealthy citizens at least, or, in individual cases, consisting of an integrated mains supply system for the entire city.[1160] Street lighting had been common in city centres since the 10th century, vegetable oil being used as fuel in Syria, for example, for this purpose.[1161]Public baths, with strict male and female segregation and sometimes of considerable artistic merit, were just as familiar a part of the urban scene as the great hospitals, libraries and schools.[1162]

One of the major impacts of the crusades was in the acquisition of construction skills and techniques. Defence fortifications spread in Europe precisely the very time when the crusaders returned to their

---

1154 Ibid.

1155 M. Erbstosser: *The Crusades;* David and Charles; New ton Abbot; First published in Leipzig; 1978; p. 130-1.

1156 Historia; IV; 10; Paulin Pari's edit.; vol I; pp. 134-5 in J. K. Wright: *The Geographical Lore of the Time of the Crusades*; Dover Publications; New York; 1925. p. 239.

1157 Historia; XVII, 3; Paulin Pari's edit.; vol ii; p. 141 in J. K. Wright: The Geographical Lore; p. 239.

1158 M. Erbstosser: *The Crusades;* op cit; p. 130-1.

1159 Ibid.

1160 Ibid.

1161 Ibid.

1162 Ibid.

homes in the Christian West. Hence Philip of Alsace, Count of Flanders, completed the castle of Ghent on his return from an expedition to Palestine (1176-8), and modelled it on the fortress of Toron (between Tyre and Acre).[1163] When Richard Coeur de Lion built the Chateau Gaillard after the Third Crusade, he took his inspiration from the Krak des Chevaliers.[1164] King Edward I, who had seen the castle at Acre, ordered the construction of similar castles at Harlech, Conwy and Caernarfon to subject the conquered Welsh.[1165] It is also admitted that the Crusaders gleaned ideas such as the use of machicolation (fr. machicoulis) from the fortresses of Syria and Egypt.[1166] Another feature of military architecture borrowed from Egypt and Syria was the `right angled' or `crooked' entrance to a fortress through a gateway in the walls, by means of which an enemy who had attained the gateway was prevented from seeing or shooting through it into the inner courtyard. These crooked entrances were first used in the `Round City' of Baghdad (8th century,) at Salah Eddin's citadel at Cairo (begun 1176) and culminated in a fine example at the citadel of Aleppo.[1167]
Techniques of constructions and building of a civilian nature were also brought by the Crusaders, such as techniques used by Seljuk masons in Anatolia, (the Seljuk being the main crusader foe in the first crusades).[1168] Cochrane says that Adelard of Bath, for instance, could have seen the bridge damaged by the earthquake, to which he refers in his *Quaestiones* being repaired, and he observed the techniques used by the Seljuk Turks, techniques which soon spread in the West.[1169] During the Crusades, just as in Spain, Muslim masons were also carried in large numbers to Europe by their new masters on their return there.[1170]

Many technological skills also appeared soon after the return of the first crusaders to Europe. Water wheels, most particularly the types hitherto unknown in Europe, were widely used in Syria, and can still be found on the Orontos River today.[1171] After coming across them, the

---

[1163] G. Wiet et al: History; op cit; p.361.
[1164] Ibid.
[1165] E. Wright: General editor: *The Medieval and Renaissance World*; Hamlyn; London; 1979; pp. 102-3.
[1166] M. S. Briggs: Architecture, in *The Legacy of Islam*, op cit; pp 155-79; pp. 167-9.
[1167] Ibid.
[1168] J.H. Harvey: `The Origins of Gothic Architecture,' *Antiquaries Journal* 48 (1968), pp. 91-4.
[1169] L. Cochrane, Adelard of Bath, op cit, p. 36.
[1170] J.H. Harvey: The Origins pp. 91-4; op cit.
[1171] D.R. Hill: Engineering, in Encyclopaedia (Rashed ed); op cit, pp 751-95, at p. 775.

Crusaders introduced them to Germany;[1172] from whence they spread to other parts. Muslim Spain (other than the crusades) could also have been another source of impact in this particular area (the ruling Ummayad of Spain were of Syrian origin.) The East (Syria) was also one of the sources from whence the Christians learnt the usage of windmills.[1173] The crusaders and pilgrims had observed windmills in use in the Orient, and, in this case, it was not long before the first examples appeared in Europe.[1174]Carra de Vaux notes that in Europe, the oldest text in relation to windmills is a French act of 1105 granting a religious community the right to establish one of these apparatuses, called *molendinam ad ventum* (moulin a vent in French: windmill in English).[1175]This coincides exactly with the return of the first French crusaders, who formed the bulk of the first crusade (began 1095). More techniques will be cited extensively in the last part, but worth adding here, how the crusaders, impressed by the enamelled glass of the Muslims, brought from the East the technical secrets that led to the improved stained glass of the developed Gothic cathedrals.[1176]

Obviously the two most important factors induced by the crusades: death from combat and epidemics, stimulated considerably the medical knowledge and practices of the Christians as they came across the superior Islamic medicine. The reputation of Islamic medicine carried by and handed on to the European countries when the Crusaders returned played a major part in its popularity and reception.[1177] The Crusades stimulated surgical efforts in particular, war being `the mother of surgery,' Sarton tells.[1178] Much of such learning can be found in Adam of Cremona, for instance, who composed for Frederick II a treatise on hygiene of an army, or of a large body of pilgrims.[1179]
The Knights Hospitaliers played a decisive part in the adoption of a `typically Oriental institution: the hospital.'[1180]Hospitals had spread greatly in the land of Islam by the time of the arrival of the first

---

[1172] G. Sarton: Introduction, op cit, vol 2; p. 27.
[1173] A. Mieli: La Science Arabe; op cit; p.118.
[1174] M. Erbstosser: *The Crusades;* op cit; p. 186.
[1175] Cited in Magasin Pittoresque, t. XX, 1852, p. 50. In Carra de Vaux: Les Penseurs op cit, p. 190.
[1176] P. Hitti: History of the Arabs; p. 346; in W. Durant: The Age of faith, op cit; p.611.
[1177] A.O. Whipple: The role of the Nestorians; op cit; p.30.
[1178] G. Sarton: Introduction; op cit; Vol II; p.519.
[1179] Ibid.
[1180] Floreal Sanagustin: Medecine et Societe au temps des croisades: de l'empirisme a la rationalite: In *De Toulouse a Tripoli*; Colloque held between 6 and 8 December, 1995, AMAM; University of Toulouse; 1997; pp 133-142. p.140.

crusaders. Possibly the earliest hospital in Islam was a mobile dispensary following the Islamic armies, dating from the time of the Prophet; a tradition which remained throughout the centuries of Islamic glory.[1181] The first known hospital in Islam was built in Damascus in 706 by the Ummayad Caliph: al-Walid Ibn Abd al-Malik[1182]Others followed at al-Fustat[1183]and elsewhere, until the prestigious al-Nuri hospital was built in 1156 by Nur Eddin Zangi.[1184]These edifices could not have failed to impress the incoming crusaders. The order of the Hospitaliers was founded in the Holy land on the initiative of Gerard, first Grand Master of the Hospital, and his successor Raymond du Puy, a foundation which favoured the passage from the model of hospice to hospital.[1185] At first, the Hospitaliers' task consisted only in the protection of roads and help to the poor pilgrims, but later they built the hospital of Saint Jean of Jerusalem.[1186] The hospitals were called Hotels de Dieu (Houses of God), where various religious orders, not just the Hospitaliers, delivered nursing duties.[1187] The Order of St John of Jerusalem, followed later by the Teutonic order saw the construction and maintenance of hospitals as one of their main duties.[1188]The Order's statutes reveal that as early as 1182, care for the patients meant that the brothers must keep four physicians watching the taking of all prescriptions, and observing food diets, and securing the comfort for all. The high degree reached by Islamic medicine has now probably marked the evolution of the hospital institution.[1189]

Not many Western scientists travelled to the East, but one of them, Adelard, seems to have made some scholarly acquisitions there.[1190] The city of Tripoli was dwelt by `a highly literate Muslim sect, the Banu Ammar,' whose safe conduct promised by the besieging Crusading army was not honoured; the city ending up being attacked and looted, its population enslaved, its college library burnt and its private libraries seized. In the process, some manuscripts fell to the invading forces,

---

[1181] A. Djebbar: Une Histoire; op cit; p. 319.
[1182] E. Abouleish: Contribution of Islam to Medicine, op cit; p 22.
[1183]F.S. Haddad in I.B. Syyed: Medicine and Medical Education in Islamic History, in Islamic Perspectives; op cit; pp 45-56, p. 48.
[1184]S.K. Hamarneh: *Health Sciences in early Islam*, 2 vols, edited by M.A. Anees, Noor Health Foundation and Zahra Publications, 1983. vol 1; p. 100.
[1185] Floreal Sanagustin: Medecine et Societe op cit; p. 140.
[1186] Ibid.
[1187] A.O. Whipple: The Role of the Nestorians; op cit; p.30.
[1188] G. Sarton: Introduction, op cit, vol 2; p. 245.
[1189]Floreal Sanagustin: Medecine et Societe op cit; p. 140.
[1190] L. Cochrane: Adelard of Bath, op cit, at pp 33-40.

possibly the sort of material Adelard was interested in.[1191] Damascus was also one place, where Adelard might have seen the methods of Muslim astronomers as it was fairly close to the Crusaders' territories. And from there Adelard might have acquired much of his astronomical learning that was to serve him well. Adelard also speaks of the old man of Tarsus who explained methods of dissection for the purpose of studying anatomy.[1192]

Not much translation was done in the East, unless, of course, the matter was explored further to prove the contrary. Haskins' chapter on Translators in Syria during the Crusades deals primarily with Stephen of Antioch, who is definitely known to have worked in the East.[1193] Stephen of Antioch was born in Pisa, and was educated at Salerno (he could have been the pupil of Constantine who lived in the city). He was both physician and translator, who resided in Antioch about 1127. The reason why Stephen travelled to Antioch and studied Arabic was `in order to mount to the fountain head of learning.'[1194] The reason was also practical: the Pisan had their quarter in Antioch since 1108, and there was already some Pisan medical translation there. In Antioch, Stephen translated in 1127 the medical writings of Ali Ben Abbas: *Kitab al-Maliki* (the same author and work translated by Constantine in the preceding century). Stephen, according to his preface, when coming across Ali's book in Arabic, found there was no complete Latin version of it, and what had been translated (under the title *Pantegni* by Constantine) suffered from omissions and transpositions, prompting him to prepare an entirely new version. His own translation of the work is entitled `*Practica pantegni et Stephanonis*'[1195]

In the East, Erbstosser observes, `manufacture and trade on an unprecedented scale for European concepts of the time were the material foundation of this world.'[1196]Consequently, the crusades vigorously stimulated trade, transportation, and the use of money in the West.[1197] A review of Oriental trade, Conder notes, not only shows us the prosperity which grew out of conquest of Syria, but also serves to explain the rapid

---

[1191] Ibid.

[1192]*Quaestiones Naturales des Adelardus von Bath,*' ed. Muller, p. 21, in L. Cochrane: Adelard of Bath, op cit, p. 34.

[1193] C.H Haskins: Studies, op cit, pp. 131-4 in part.

[1194] Ibid. p.134.

[1195] Ibid. pp. 131-4 in part.

[1196] M. Erbstosser: *The Crusades;* op cit; p. 130-1.

[1197] C.H. Haskins: The Renaissance; op cit; p.15.

growth of art and commerce in Europe, which followed that conquest.[1198] In such a Western revival, the Italian cities played the leading part, and it is precisely they which had a central place in the economic life of the crusades. The Italians established trade settlements in all captured seaports and cities: Genoa in Antioch, Laodicea, Caesarea, Acre, Jafa, Jerusalem, Beirut; Pisa in Jafa, Laodicea, Tyre, Jerusalem, Acre; Venice in Sidon, Tyre, Tripoli, Jerusalem.[1199] These settlements were usually complexes of buildings in particularly favourable locations where the merchants lived according to the law of their native land and carried on their commercial activities; the Genoese quarter in Antioch, for instance, consisted of at least thirty houses, a church and a set of buildings used as warehouses and stores.[1200] Pisa, Venice, and Genoa also organised transport of crusaders to the East and back, and with the soldiers much else that constituted intellectual awakening travelled, too, and, obviously, found room in Italy first.[1201] The chapter on trade and crafts, subsequently, will highlight this point abundantly. Briefly, here, the range of merchandise which the Northern Italian merchants obtained via Acre and Tyre and sent to Europe was exceptionally wide; from the wares produced in the Crusader states, it included silks and velvets, glassware, pottery, and agricultural produce in particular.[1202] Medicinal products included ginger, aloe, camphor, bitter wort and incense; there were spices such as pepper, cinnamon, muscat and cloves; silk, damask and muslin; textile dyes such as indigo and Brazil wood. Other articles include Damascus steel, perfume, jewellery and porcelain.[1203]In Syria, cotton, for instance, was made into cloth and buckram-a material noticed in the Assizes, just as camelots or camel hair stuffs were also highly prized in the 13th century;[1204] tyretaine or tartan took its name from Tyre, whilst the carpets used by Franks and natives alike came from Asia Minore, Baghdad and Persia.[1205]

Returning crusaders found the shipping belonging to Pisa, Genoa and Venice most convenient for coming back to Europe, and as a rule, whatever intellectual importation, whether in the form of thought or its written transcript, found its way back from the East to Europe, it was

---

[1198] C.R. Conder: *The Latin Kingdom*. pp. 334-5.
[1199] M. Erbstosser: *The Crusades;* op cit; p. 131-2.
[1200] Ibid.
[1201] J. Owen: *The Skeptics of the Italian Renaissance;* Swan Sonnenschein &Co; London; 1908; p. 25.
[1202] M. Erbstosser: *The Crusades*; op cit; p. 132.
[1203] Ibid.
[1204] C.R. Conder: *The Latin Kingdom of Jerusalem;* op cit; pp. 334-5.
[1205] Ibid.

first examined and perhaps partly appropriated in Italy before it was passed on to less favoured parts of Europe.[1206] There was an enormous stimulus this traffic imparted to the commercial activity of the great maritime ports of Italy, and its addition-neither small nor unimportant-to the civilizing influences of that commerce.[1207]Besides the multitude of objects were also ideas, trading expertise, skills and crafts of diverse sorts.[1208] This included rationalised calculating methods for book keeping and the introduction of a simplified system of payment in the shape of cheques and bills of exchange.[1209] Woodwork and metal work, as well as the manufacturing of glasses required varied knowledge, which was unknown during the Crusade times, and that was soon borrowed and spread into Europe.[1210] The art of glass painting by the appropriate fusion process, the making of ground crystal dishes and other techniques to be found in Western Christendom date only from after the 12th century.[1211]The glass-works of Tyre served as models to those of Venice; from Syria in 1277 were passed on the secrets of Syrian glass-making to Venice.[1212]

Life comforts and higher standards of living also came in large measure from the East during the crusades. It is possible, even before the crusades, that exposure to `Oriental' objects along the Spanish-French frontier for example, Seidel notes, made the Crusaders very receptive when they were confronted suddenly, and in new surroundings, with a wealth of `exotic' material splendour.'[1213]Thus, following the first crusader successes in taking Jerusalem, Antioch, Tripoli, etc, all the glorious art and colour of the East now was at the disposal of these crusaders.[1214] They rapidly adjusted to the customs and comforts of life in the Orient.[1215]The palaces of the crusaders in the cities were based on Oriental architecture, supplemented by Byzantine influence.[1216] They

---

1206 J. Owen: *The Skeptics; op cit;* p.25.
1207 Ibid.
1208 C. Singer: East and West in retrospect C.J. Singer et al: *History of Technology*; 5 vols; vol 2; Oxford at the Clarendon; 1956; pp 753-777; p. 764.
1209 M. Erbstosser: *The Crusades;* op cit; p. 202-3.
1210 G. Le Bon: La Civilisation des Arabes; op cit; p.259.
1211 M. Erbstosser: *The Crusades;* op cit; p. 186.
1212 A. Y. Al-Hassan; D.R. Hill: *Islamic Technology:* Cambridge University Press, 1986: p. 33
1213 L. Seidel: Images of the Crusades in Western art: Models as Metaphors; Ed: V.P. Goss: *The Meeting of two Worlds*; Medieval Institute Publications, Michigan, 1986. pp 377-391.p.378.
1214 C.R. Conder: *The Latin Kingdom*. Op cit; p. 182.
1215 M. Erbstosser: *The Crusades;* p. 135.
1216 Ibid. p. 149.

drank from chaced goblets of silver and gold crusted with gems, and enjoyed the baths of the castle, and the noonday siesta.[1217] Certain customs and habits became established as part of the every day life of the knights; bathrooms came into use, also in the towns, toilets appeared on the scene. [1218]Crusaders went out to hawk and hunt, or to wander in gardens and orchards; and merchants came to them with rich stuffs and jewels, and works of exquisite Oriental art; and jongleurs and troubadours, musicians, and readers of romances paid their lodging with performances at evening, in the great dining hall of the castle.[1219] The crusader tables were spread with fine white linen, and the food included game and fish, the fallow deer of Tabor, the gazelle of the plains, bears' feet from Hermon, Greek partridges, and quails, woodcock and snipe, and desert grouse, as well as mutton and beef.[1220] The fruits of Syria, oranges and lemons, damsons and pears, apricots and quinces, apples and nuts, dates and bananas, grapes and melons, were followed by spices and preserves; and flowers of orange or violet, crystallised in sugar; the sauces, learned from the Arabs, with vinegar and lemon juice, seasoned the dishes.[1221]The Franks also drank sherbets cooled with snow, and there were flowers enough in the plains and valleys, and fragrant gardens often lay within the city walls.[1222]

One manner of sophisticated living the crusaders found in the East, and they brought back home were the hot-steam baths (hammams), which by the middle of the 13th century, became available in most large cities, but the practice, soon degenerated into a kind of `sexual dissipation'.[1223]Along with the public baths, they also brought private latrines.[1224] Probably through contact with the Muslim East, the Europeans returned to the old Roman custom of shaving beards.[1225] One of the things that must have made the church authorities angry was the well documented fact that so many crusaders, both in Europe itself and in Palestine, had indeed, been culturally converted.[1226]We know that very early on, Oldenbourg observes, Crusaders coming to the East were shocked by the effeminate' behaviour of those of their countrymen who

---

1217 C.R. Conder: *The Latin Kingdom.* p. 182.
1218 M. Erbstosser: *The Crusades;* op cit; p. 201.
1219 C.R. Conder: *The Latin Kingdom;* p. 182.
1220 *Ibid.* *p*p. 182-3.
1221 Ibid.
1222 Ibid.
1223 G. Sarton: Introduction, op cit, vol 2; p. 96.
1224W. Durant: The Age; op cit; p.611.
1225 C. Day: History of Commerce; p. 88; in W. Durant: The Age; op cit; p.611.
1226 M.R. Menocal: The Arabic Role; op cit; p.47.

had become citizens of Syria: effeminate because they had got into the habit of taking frequent baths, using scents and perfumes, wearing shirts of fine cloth, sleeping in sheets, eating from vessels of metal or precious woods, and having meals consisting of various exotic dishes, flavoured with different spices.[1227]

The Crusades impacted considerably on the wider world of literature, culture and arts of Western Christianity. Thousand of Arabic words now came into the European languages, whilst Oriental romance flowed into Europe, and found new dress in the nascent vernaculars.[1228] Italy was situated between East and West at the time of the First Crusade, open to the coming and going of pilgrims, merchants, artisans, German and Norman conquerors, and then Crusaders from the Latin North and West, with ties to Byzantium and to the Islamic and new Crusaders states in the East. All that and commercial exchanges produced `some curious hybrids in the art of Italy,' crossing the indigenous Italian with the foreign.[1229]It is also in western and southern France near Spain from which the leaders of the First Crusades were drawn, where the most intense artistic imprint of Islam can be observed.[1230] In 1830 an essay was published on the *Influence of the Crusades upon the Arts and Literature of Europe* by the Revd Frederick Oakley, which gave great descriptions of such impact, in which the crusades had influenced European society and culture, a work bearing echoes of an earlier one, an essay submitted by A. Hermann Ludwig Heeren.[1231]

The Crusades, Scott insists, had also enlarged the minds of `the fierce warriors of the West.' Their respect had been inspired by `the equal valor and superior intelligence of their Mohammedan adversaries; and a Saracen was no longer, as formerly considered a demon incarnate, destitute of honor, insatiable of blood, incapable of compassion, ignorant alike of the courtesies of war and the suggestions of humanity.'[1232]

Referring to the positive long term impact of the crusades in a history published by the Society for Promoting Christian Knowledge: (SPCK) in 1865 George Perry, Prebendary of Lincoln, held:

[1227] Z. Oldenbourg: The Crusades; op cit; pp. 475-6.

[1228] W. Durant: The Age, op cit; p.611.

[1229] D.Mc Kinnon Ebitz: Fatimid Style and Byzantine Model in a Venetian Ivory Carving workshop: V.P. Goss: The Meeting; op cit; pp.309-29. p.309.

[1230] L. Seidel: Images; op cit; p.378.

[1231] E. Siberry: *The New Crusaders*; Ashgate: Aldershot; 2000; p.16.

[1232] S.P. Scott: History; op cit; vol 3; p.6.

`Thus in the natural world the violent storm which scatters havoc and ruin all around often produces valuable effects by moderating the temperature and deluging the earth with fertilising showers. Just so the errors, the short sightedness and the violence of men are overruled by the Almighty to assist in His grand designs of the advancement and development of the human race.'[1233]

And as Le Bon concludes:

`When we consider the development of commercial relations and the importance of artistic progress and industrial, engendered by the contact of the Crusaders with the oriental people, we can affirm that it was the latter who had brought the Occident out of Barbary, and prepared that movement of spirits that the scientific and literary influence, spread by the European universities, which was soon going to develop, and from which the Revival was going one day to spring out.' [1234]

[1233] In E. Siberry: *The New Crusaders*; op cit; p. 20.
[1234] G. Le Bon: La Civilisation des Arabes, op cit; p.260-1.

2. PLACES OF CONTACT, PLACES OF IMPACT

The Western Crusaders' conquest of Islamic Syria and Palestine, Geanakoplos says, transmitted to the Latin West influences in food, textiles and military science; whilst knowledge of scientific advances in medicine, optics and pharmacology came from the caliphates of Islam (East and West) and from Muslim Sicily.[1235]

Haskins expands a little more of such regional contributions. Ali ben Abbas' `*Regalis Dispositio*', whose translation was begun by Constantine in Salerno, was subsequently improved and completed by Stephen of Pisa at Antioch. Adelard of Bath can be followed in Syria. In North Africa, the city of Bejaia (today's Algeria) was the source of the new arithmetic of Fibonacci (Leonard of Pisa.) Some material, like Achmet's `Dream Book,' came via the Byzantine Empire. In Sicily in the middle of the 12th century, Idrisi wrote his `great compendium of Arabic geography', and there in the next century Frederick II promoted Islamic learning; Michael Scot's translated al-Bitruji, and more translations were made after Frederick. There is, besides, a considerable amount of Islamic material of unknown origin, some of which modified and enlarged before it reached its current Latin form.[1236]

It is also to Toledo, north of Spain, Burckhardt says, where swarmed Scholars from all `the lands of the Holy Roman Empire' to participate in the salvaging of Islamic `unprecedented treasures of learning.'[1237] The failure by the Muslims to recapture Toledo, he adds, was `to affect the intellectual life of the entire Roman Christian world, for the acquisition of Toledo had brought with it an undisturbed centre of Islamic culture, complete with its scholars, artists, and libraries under Christian rule.[1238]

Thus are summed up some of the diverse geographical sources, which through the 12th and 13th centuries brought into contact the Christian West and the Muslim land, and from where, simultaneously, diverse aspects of Islamic science and learning were taken by eager Westerners. This is only one of the two sides of the picture, though.

The other side is first summed up by Briffault who notes how: `the first parts of Europe to emerge from barbarism were those most directly under the influence of Moorish culture: the Spanish Marches of Catalonia, Provence, and Sicily.'[1239] Lorraine, too, was amongst the first

---

[1235] D.J. Geanakoplos: Medieval Western; op cit; p.498.
[1236] C.H. Haskins: Studies; op cit; p. 4.
[1237] T. Burckhardt: *Moorish Culture in Spain*, G. Allen & Unwin, London. 1972; p. 162.
[1238] Ibid. p 161.
[1239] R. Briffault: *The Making of Humanity*, op cit; p. 207.

parts of Europe to emerge from barbarism in the 10th century following its early contacts with Islam, its role particularly stressed by Haskins, Thompson, and Welborn.[1240] It was from Lorraine that Islamic learning spread throughout the Christian West; most particularly mathematics and astronomy; knowledge and use of the astrolabe, the abacus and much else, `radiating' from Lorraine to Germany, France and to England.[1241]Equally, it is from Salerno, the first faculty of higher learning in Western Christendom that sprang into existence other faculties and universities of Europe. `Coincidentally,' Salerno acquired this status of mother of Western universities soon after the arrival and the translations of Islamic medical works made by Constantine the African; by his death (c.1087), Salerno was standing at `the head of medical knowledge in the Christian West.'[1242] And it was Sicily, formerly Muslim, which was to play a great part in the civilising of northern Italy first, and the rest of the Christian West as time proceeded.[1243] The same happened with regard to the South of France standing as one of the most civilised parts of early Western Christendom as a result of its geographical and human contacts with Muslim Spain. A region, upon which, Scott tells, `semi-Barbarous Europe looked with wonder upon a land so blessed by nature and adorned by art; where the remains of classic antiquity were taught in the same schools with the botany of Syria and the chemistry of Spain; where a philosophic spirit of inquiry had awakened the noblest aspirations of the human intellect, and where knightly courtesy had replaced the rudeness of the sword.'[1244] And, it was Catalonia, the most neighbourly place of the Christian world with Islam, which was the centre of focus and attraction for all those from the barbarian north of the Pyrenees who sought to acquire learning at the earliest stages (10th century). From the Abbey of Ripoll (in Catalonia) the earliest Latin treatises of the astrolabe were taken north of the Pyrenees towards the end of the 10th- and early 11th century.[1245]

This brief outline has summed up the two matters which the overwhelming majority of historians have failed to acknowledge and explain properly, that:

1240 C.H. Haskins: Studies; op cit; M.C. Welborn: Lotharingia; op cit; J.W. Thompson: The Introduction of Arabic Science; op cit.

1241 L. Cochrane: Adelard of Bath, op cit, p. 6.

1242 W. Durant: The Age of Faith; op cit; P. 457.

1243 See: A. Amari: *La Storia dei Musulmani di Sicilia,* 3 vols, (1933-9) Revised 2nd edition by C.A. Nallino, Rome.
C. Haskins: The Twelfth Century Renaissance; op cit; etc.

1244 S.P. Scott: History; op cit; vol 3; pp 11-2.

1245 D.R. Hill: *Islamic Science and Engineering*, Edinburgh University Press; 1993; p. 221.

1) All geographical sources from where Western Christendom took its learning and science were Islamic.
2) All places in the Christian West, where learning emerged and thrived first, had the most, or closest contact(s) with Islam.
Scholarly necessity requires further substantiation of this. And so in the following, it is looked at each region's scientific awakening following its contacts with Islam, and then it acting as diffuser of such learning.

1. Lorraine

Western European astronomers before the end of the 10th century, Welborn explains, were very much handicapped by their lack of proper instruments for making observations. Up to that time they were principally reliant upon dated Greek instruments, and dated Greek methods. In reckoning the dates of Easter and the other movable feasts, and the lengths of years, months and days, they depended upon Easter cycles or tables which were founded upon those made at an earlier time by the Alexandrians. They were also aware for quite some time before the 10th century that their calculations were not correct, but were unable to improve upon them because:
`they had not received from the Arabs better astronomical theories and instruments.'[1246]
(A line extraordinarily reminiscent of our present day, but the other way round, whereby nothing of worth happens in the whole material, scientific, and learned structure of the whole Islamic world until the science of the West comes to the rescue.)

By the 11th century, things changed in the Christian West. The first elements of Islamic science were well and truly running, in one region in particular, Lotharingia, modern day Lorraine, in north East France. There, towards the end of the 10th century, became evident the first signs of Islamic science, mathematics and astronomy, most particularly;[1247] including knowledge of the astrolabe.[1248]And from there such knowledge spread to the rest of Western Christendom. Crucial developments considered herein.

[1246] M.C. Welborn: Lotharingia; op cit; p.188
[1247] L. Cochrane, Adelard of Bath, op cit, p. 6.
[1248] M.C. Welborn: Lotharingia; op cit; J.W. Thompson: The Introduction of Arabic Science; L.Cochrane: Adelard; op cit. C. Burnett: The Introduction; op cit;

Contacts between Lorraine and the Islamic world were as early as the 9th century. As Thompson charts, in 864 Charles the Bald sent two ambassadors to the Caliph of Cordova, ambassadors who returned to Compiegne in the following year. Relation of the Carolingians with Spain survived into the 10th century; the archives of Barcelona containing forty five Carolingian charters between the years 930 and 961, and those of Vich thirteen more.[1249] Then came the famed John of Gorze's trip to Spain as a result of exchanges between Abd Errahman III, caliph of Cordoba and the German emperor Otto the Great. The various political incidents related to such a trip, and other diplomatic entanglements of it are very well publicised in a variety of sources.[1250] John was an abbot in Gorze (a place near Metz, Lorraine) during the years 970-4. Before going to Spain, he had made a trip with a friend to non Muslim Italy and brought manuscripts including Aristotle's *Categories*, and porphyry's *Isagogia*. In 953, John of Gorze was sent by Emperor Otto I to treat with the Caliph, Abd Errahman III, whilst negotiations on behalf of the Caliph were conducted by Bishop Recemund and Hasdei Ibn Shaprut, the latter a Jewish physician, court official, and scholar.[1251] Hasdei (Hasdeu) understood Latin, and of course, was acquainted with Arabic, and was, most importantly, interested in astronomical subjects, especially in the luni-solar calendar; and when he asked Dunas Ben Tamin to send him a calendar, the latter sent him in reply a treatise on the phases of the Moon.[1252] Vernet also suggests that the young Al-Majriti (d. in 1007) who later revised Al-Khwarizmi astronomical tables was a member of Hasdei's research group, which would tie even closer Hasdei to the astronomical circles of Cordoba.[1253] In such contact, John stayed in Cordoba nearly three years; and as a man of intelligence and culture, he was very deeply interested in mathematics and astronomy. John in all probability brought back manuscripts of Islamic scientific nature, as he did from lower Italy.[1254] This is all the more certain as Cochrane notes, the original point of contract between Islamic science and the Christian West was the result

---

[1249] Lauer: Le Regne de Louis d'Outremer; 305-11. in J.W. Thompson: The Introduction of Arabic Science; op cit; pp 186-7.

[1250] I.e: N.Daniel: The Arabs; op cit; W. Durant: The Age of Faith; op cit; etc.

[1251] S.C. McCluskey: *Astronomies and Cultures in Early Medieval Europe;* Cambridge University Press; 1998; p. 169.

[1252] S.Stern: A Treatise on the Armillary Sphere by Dunas ben Tamin; pp. 373-7; in *Homenaje a Millas Vallicrosa*; vol 2; 1956 in S. C. McCluskey: Astronomies; op cit; p. 169.

[1253] J.Vernet: Al-Majriti; Dictionary of Scientific Biography; op cit; vol 9; p. 39

[1254] J.W. Thompson: The Introduction of Arabic Science; op cit; pp 190.

of Carolingian interest in manuscripts to be found in Cordova.[1255] John was helped in his enterprise by acquiring knowledge of the Arabic language from the Spanish Jews who understood Latin.[1256]Knowledge, or manuscripts, which he might have also acquired from Bishop Recemund, the Caliph envoy, who travelled to the Ottonian court, and stayed for much of the Winter of 955-6 at the monastery of Gorze, where, of course, John resided.[1257]

On the precise manner by which Islamic learning reached Lorraine, some difficulty remains in determining which of the learning came straight from Cordoba, and which came at different stages via Ripoll in Catalonia. What scientific treatises could have been carried from one region to another in this exchange cannot be determined, according to Lindberg.[1258] Still, given the similar interests and astronomical approaches at Gorze and Cordoba, McCluskey observes, the travels of John of Gorze and Recemund of Elvira probably provided one early channel for the transmission of elements of Islamic astronomy to the Latin West, and although, there are no records of what they learned from each other, such exchanges highlight shared interests in practical astronomy.[1259] The true scope of John's contribution remains to be studied, as he has remained a neglected figure in the intellectual movement of the 10th century.[1260] What cannot be doubted, though, according to Haskins, Thompson and Welborn,[1261] and as Lindberg notes, it is `inconceivable' that knowledge of Islamic learning in Lorraine was not `enhanced,' especially as it became an important place of mathematical and astronomical activity based on Islamic sources.[1262] Islamic learning can, indeed, be traced in many parts of Lorraine and in its diversity. An astrolabe was built in Lieges in 1025, and several books on the subject, clearly depended on the works of Muslims who had developed the instrument, were available by the midpoint of the century; which Menocal holds, were instrumental in the revolution of navigation that followed.[1263] Fairly similar observations are also made by Watt,[1264]

[1255] L.Cochrane: Adelard; op cit; p. 6.
[1256] J.W. Thompson: The Introduction of Arabic Science; op cit; pp 189-90.
[1257] Vita Johannis Gorziensis; 121; 127-130; in S. C. McCluskey: *Astronomies*; op cit; p. 169.
[1258] D.C. Lindberg: The Transmission, op cit, pp 59-60.
[1259] S. C. McCluskey: *Astronomies*; op cit; p. 170.
[1260] J.W. Thompson: The Introduction of Arabic Science; op cit; p. 188.
[1261] M C. Welborn, `Lotharingia; op cit; C.H Haskins, Studies, op cit, pp. 334-35; J.W. Thompson: Introduction of Arabic science; op cit; p. 191.
[1262] D.C. Lindberg: The Transmission, op cit, p.60.
[1263] M.R. Menocal: The Arabic Role; op cit; p.30.

but most of all by Welborn. She observes the variety of Islamic influences found in the second part of the so-called *Geometria Gerberti*, where there are several chapters containing descriptions of a quadrant astrolabe, a type developed by the Muslims for surveying.[1265] The appendix in Welborn's article further highlights the Islamic impact, showing clearly how literature on the construction of the astrolabe in Lorraine was in its wording near totally similar to that used by Masha'allah on the same subject.[1266]Masha'allah (d.815), briefly here, was one of the earliest astronomers known in Islam, who wrote on the astrolabe, and on meteorology. His work *De Mercibus* is the oldest scientific work in Arabic.[1267]His works were subsequently repeatedly translated into Latin and other languages.[1268]

The more determining aspect of Islamic impact on Lorraine is it becoming in the 11th century the centre not just of Islamic science, but the centre of science and learning in the Christian West. There was great development of Lotharingian writings on instruments, astronomy, and also mathematical operations.[1269] Soon in its (Lorraine) schools rose eminent mathematicians such as Heriger of Lobbes, Adebold of Utrecht, Reginald of Cologne, and Ralph and Franco of Liege.[1270] Mathematical sciences were particularly emphasised in Lotharingian schools.[1271] Manuscript sources also reveal how the Lotharingian geometers and astronomers first used the astrolabe in the Christian West.[1272] And it is they who spread its uses first (e.g Walcher of Malvern).[1273]

Lorraine's most important role is, indeed, in turning from a recipient into a diffuser, the European centre from which Islamic scientific knowledge, in all its forms, whether mathematical or astronomical, and the use of the astrolabe, travelled to Germany, France and England.[1274] Lotharingian mathematicians and astronomers were able to exert great

---

1264 W.M. Watt: The Influence; op cit; p. 59.

1265 M.C. Welborn: Lotharingia; op cit; p. 192.

1266 Ibid. pp 192-6.

1267 Baron Carra de Vaux: Astronomy and Mathematics, in The Legacy of Islam; 1st ed (Sir Thomas Arnold and A. Guillaume) op cit; p 380.

1268 Such as by Hugo Sanccelliensis (Hugo of Santalla, Sanctallensis, Sandaliensis etc (fl. 1119-1151).

1269 M.C. Welborn: Lotharingia; op cit; pp 192-6.

1270 J.W. Thompson: The Introduction of Arabic Science; op cit; p. 191.

1271 L. Cochrane: Adelard of Bath; op cit; p. 6.

1272 M.C. Welborn: Lotharingia; op cit;. p.188.

1273 See: C. Burnett: The Introduction; L. Cochrane: Adelard of Bath.

1274 L.Cochrane: Adelard of Bath; op cit; p. 6.

influence not only southward to Reichenau (i.eHermann Contractus/the Cripple) but also in France, and especially, owing to the preference of Knut the Great for Lotharingian churchmen in England.[1275] England, from the time of Knut on through many generations, indeed, was the popular destination of Lotharingian scholars, who were appointed as bishops and masters of the schools.[1276] Before the death of Knut, Duduc (from Lotharingia) had already become bishop of Wells; Hermann, another Lotharingian had become bishop of Ramsey; and Leofric, who had been educated in Lotharingia was bishop of Exeter (1046-1072). Under Edward the Confessor there was another group of these clerics. All these churchmen were interested in learning and many brought books with them from their own country.[1277] Earl Harold did more to encourage Lotharingian learning in England. He had travelled extensively and had discovered that the schools of Lotharingia and the nearby German cities were not only much better than those of England, but also than those of France and Northern Italy at that time.[1278] He appointed Walter as bishop of Hereford (1060-1079) and Gisa as bishop of Wells (c.1060). However, his most important appointment was that of Athelard of Liege as the head of the college of canons, which he established at Waltham.[1279] During the times of William the Conqueror and William Rufus, Lotharingians were still brought to England; and the abacus was known to the curia Regis under both rulers, introduced by Lotharingian abacists who were promptly appointed to ecclesiastical positions to relieve `the sweating calculators.'[1280]Including amongst these Lotharingians was Robert of Lorrraine, a distinguished mathematician who was finally made bishop of Hereford (1079), and who may have arrived in England even before the Norman Conquest (1066);[1281]and Thomas Bayeux who had also been to Germany and Spain to study the sciences.[1282] Other figures include Walcher of Malvern, Walcher of Durham, Thomas of York, and Samson of Worcester.[1283]

[1275] J.W. Thompson: The Introduction of Arabic Science; op cit; p. 191.

[1276] For more details on these Lotharingians, see : E. Freeman: *Norman Conquest*; 8 Vols; Oxford 1867; and T.D. Hardy: *Descriptive Catalogue*, 3 vols. London 1871; Rolls Series, Vol 26.

[1277] M.C. Welborn: Lotharingia as a center of Arabic; op cit; Pp 196-7.

[1278] Ibid. p.197.

[1279] Ibid.

[1280] W. of Malmesbury: De Gestis Regum Anglorum; ed W. Stubbs; London; 1887; lib.II.194. in D. Metlitzki: The Matter of Araby; op cit; p. 17.

[1281] C. Burnett: The Introduction of Arabic Learning; op cit; p.15.

[1282] M.C. Welborn: Lotharingia; op cit; pp 197-8.

[1283] J.W. Thompson: The Introduction of Arabic Science; op cit; p. 191.

Just named amongst the Lotharingians is Walcher of Malvern (d.1135), possibly the greatest figure of learning from Lorraine to reach England about 1091.[1284] He became prior of the Benedictine monastery of Great Malvern, a few miles from Worcester.[1285] He had become interested in astronomical observations after experiencing the darkness of an eclipse in Italy and then discovering on his return to Malvern that the selfsame eclipse had been observed in his own monastery at a different time of the day.[1286] He commenced his observations in 1090 using Roman numerals and fractions but later changed to degrees, minutes and seconds, employing an astrolabe. He learned his new methods from Henry I's physician Petrus Alphonsi, himself one of the main figures to introduce Islamic learning in the Christian West.[1287] Walcher of Malvern's experiment in the use of the astrolabe is the earliest recorded in the West, and it is, Metlitzki points out, `strictly in line' with the whole Muslim tradition of the astronomical sciences.[1288]Walcher also contributed two manuscripts, the first on lunar tables, which records his use of the astrolabe in 1092, and the second, a conversion with Petrus about solar and lunar eclipses, based on the tables of al-Khwarizmi.[1289] Walcher's newly found method, the `eclipse method', of calculating astronomical time was at the very heart of the new learning acquired from the Muslims and first brought to England before its general adoption in the West.[1290] It continued to be the most popular way of finding latitudes and longitudes until the 16th century.[1291]Thanks to Malvern, and the other Arabist, Adelard, who himself had Lotharingian family antecedents, England became an important centre of learning. That 12th century learning, it must be emphasised, based on Islamic sources, including instructions on the construction and the use of the astrolabe, the numerals system on the abacus counters, and works on arithmetic, music, geometry, and the computus. [1292]

[1284] M.C. Welborn: Lotharingia; op cit; p. 198.
[1285] C. Burnett: The Introduction of Arabic learning into British schools (referred to here as Arabic learning at British schools to avoid confusion with the other work with the same title referred to already) in *The Introduction of Arabic philosophy into Europe*; C.E. Butterworth and B.A Kessel ed; Brill; Leiden; 1994; pp. 40-57; at p. 44.
[1286] L. Cochrane: Adelard; op cit; p. 7.
[1287] Ibid.
[1288] D. Metlitzki: The Matter of Araby; op cit; pp. 17.
[1289] C. Burnett: Arabic learning; op cit; pp 44-5.
[1290] D. Metlitzki: The Matter; op cit; pp. 18.
[1291] Ibid.
[1292] C. Burnett: The Introduction; p. 38.

The English town of Hereford highlights so well, how a place first receives Islamic learning (here from Lorraine), which it cultivates, before it becomes itself a diffuser of such learning. Hereford, a cathedral town, had as bishop the renowned Lotharingian mathematician Robert, finally made bishop of Hereford (1079).[1293] Robert's Lotharingian origins are proved by several documents, most likely coming from the city of Liege (in today's Belgium).[1294]Not long after, in the 12th, in keeping with the Lotharingian tradition, Hereford became a major centre of Islamic mathematical and astronomical learning; mathematics, most particularly.[1295] The catalogue of the cathedral library shows it owned amongst others a mathematical treatise with roughly drawn diagrams and ten lines of verse on the subject of Arabic numerals.[1296] Equally important was another Roger's (of Hereford) adaptation in 1178 of the (Islamic) astronomical tables that existed for Toledo and Marseilles to the meridian of Hereford,[1297] using the Christian calendar, though, `because the years of the Arabs and their months are difficult to our people who are not accustomed to them.'[1298] Roger of Hereford indicates that he himself, by observing an eclipse in 1178, ascertained the position of Hereford, Marseilles and Toledo in relation to Arin, the world centre of the Muslims.[1299]The Madrid manuscript which preserves Robert's (of Chester) revision of the Khorasmian tables also contains various tables for the meridian of Hereford, which are obviously the work of Roger (of Hereford.)[1300] Roger of Hereford, Burnett points out, was also a teacher of astronomical and astrological subjects.[1301]

Following Roger, in the last years of the 12th century, Simon de Freine tried to entice Gerald of Wales to Hereford, which he describes as a haven for philosophers.[1302] Gerald of Wales, in turn, mentions the presence at this time (1198) of a young Robert Grosseteste in Hereford;[1303] a learned man who was to play a fundamental role in

---

1293 Ibid. p.15.

1294 Julia Barrow in C. Burnett: The Introduction; op cit; p.15.

1295 B. Lawn: *The Salernitan Questions*, op cit; p. 36.

1296 A.T. Bannister: A Descriptive Catalogue of the Manuscripts in the Hereford Cathedral Library, Hereford, 1927, pp. 10; 118; in D. Metlitzki: The Matter of Araby; op cit; p.38-9.

1297 C.H. Haskins: Studies, op cit, p. 98.

1298 D. Metlitzki: The Matter of Araby. Op cit; p.38.

1299 J.K. Wright: *The Geographical Lore of the Time of the Crusades*; Dover Publications; New York; 1925.; p. 85.

1300 C.H. Haskins: Studies; op cit; p. 120.

1301 C. Burnett: The Introduction; op cit; p.15.

1302 C. Burnett: Arabic Learning (Butterworth and Kessel edt); op cit; p. 48.

1303 Ibid.

Western learning as to be outlined in the last chapter. Hereford also counts amongst its learned men Alfred of Sareshel, who was not just the first to introduce Ibn Sina to English schools,[1304] but also, as to be shown in the next section, was one of Western Christendom's main translators from Arabic in the 12th century. Metlitzki raises further associations with Islamic learning telling of the links of Alfred the Englishman with Roger of Hereford, and raising further queries on the wider role of Hereford and Herefordshire in the transmission of Muslim learning, and the intellectual milieu of Alexander Neckam and poets like the anonymous author of *The Owl and the Nightingale*?[1305]

A thriving place of Lotharingian learning, England soon became a diffuser of Islamic based science abroad, back to France, most particularly. As noted by Metlitzki, during the period when elements of `this composite Arabian culture began to penetrate the Latin West,' France was the seat of Latin civilisation, and its schools occupied the leading position in the cultural life of the Latin world; but also that Englishmen were at the heart of this `gallic' territory.[1306] From the time of Alcuin of York, `the first French minister of education,' the activity of English teachers and students at the French schools was ever increasing, and in the diffusion of Islamic learning throughout the West, English scholars were the pioneers.[1307] Adelard, already seen, studied and taught at Tours and Laon.[1308] Thus, England, after receiving from Lorraine Islamic learning, diffused it in other places, including France.

Islamic science is the main element that also linked Lorraine with the leading scholarly figures and places in France. It is commonly assumed that it was from John of Gorze, that Gerbert of Aurillac obtained the astrolabe manuscripts.[1309] Gerbert's influence was in turn known to have been of importance in Lorraine, where he had correspondents interested in mathematical ideas.[1310] 11th century Lorraine had established itself as the chief centre for the study of astronomy and the abacus, the first knowledge of which, according to William of Malmesbury, Gerbert also

---

1304 Ibid. p. 50.
1305 A.T. Bannister: Manuscripts in the Hereford Cathedral; op cit; p. 19; in D. Metlitzki: The Matter of Araby; op cit; p. 40.
1306 D. Metlitzki: The Matter of Araby; op cit; p. 3.
1307 Ibid.
1308 See L.Cochrane: Adelard of bath; op cit.
1309 Ibid. p. 6.
1310 Ibid.

brought from the Muslims.[1311] Millas Vallicrosa also holds that Gerbert taught his students at Rheims, not that far from Lorraine, major aspects of Islamic science, mathematics in particular, and it is his students who introduced such science to the learned circles of Lorraine.[1312]

This Gerbertian-Lotharingian connection spread to other parts of France, which, following the noted pattern, soon thrived after the reception of such learning. Amongst such places is Chartres, a school founded by Fulbert, a student of Gerbert.[1313] Chartres is geographically close to Rheims where Gerbert taught; not that distant from Lorraine either, and Gerbert himself had sojourned in Chartres.[1314]

How Lorraine further impacted on Chartres is beyond the present knowledge of this author to answer satisfactorily, but one can only agree with Thompson who explains that the schools of Lorraine in the last half of the 10th century were `the seed plot in which the seeds of Arabic science first germinated in Latin Europe, from which the knowledge radiated to other parts of Germany; France and England.'[1315]And Chartres did, indeed, thrive soon after Lotharingian science flourished in France. And there is evidence of Islamic science at Chartres, learning which is of the sort found in Lorraine. Dreyer mentions that many tracts on the astrolabe based on Islamic learning were written in the 11th and 12th centuries in Chartres, at that time the principal seat of learning in France.[1316]A manuscript of the town's cathedral preserved a 1135 treatise on stars with Islamic content, and another manuscript, of the same 12th century, contained Adelard's version of the Khwarismian tables.[1317] Adelard did, indeed, belong to the broader circle of the School of Chartres.[1318]He was acquainted with the Chartres scholars at least by reputation, and his *Quaestiones* shows he held many ideas in common with Chartres most prominent scholar: William of Conches.[1319]

Chartres, however, shows traces of Islamic learning, but from other places. It was much acquainted with the early translations of medical

---

[1311] W. of Malmesbury: De Gestis Regum Anglorum; ed W. Stubbs; London; 1887; lib.II.194. in D.. Metlitzki: The Matter of Araby; op cit; p. 16.
[1312] J.M. Millas Vallicrosa: `Translations; op cit p. 143.
[1313] L. Cochrane: *Adelard of Bath; op cit;*.p.6.
[1314] J.Puig: Arabic philosophy in Christian Spain; in *The Introduction of Arabic Philosophy into Europe (*Butterworth/ Kessel ed) op cit; pp. 7-30; at p. 21.
[1315] J.W. Thompson: The Introduction; op cit; p.191.
[1316] J.L. E. Dreyer: Mediaeval Astronomy; in Toward Modern Science, op cit; Vol 1, pp 235-56; p.242.
[1317] C.H. Haskins: Studies; op cit; p. 90.
[1318] J.K. Wright: The Geographical Lore; op cit; p. 92.
[1319] Ibid.

writings from Arabic, for instance.[1320] One of Chartres most prominent learned men, William of Conches, had a vast Islamic learning, which he acquired primarily from the translations of Constantine the African in Salerno.[1321] William, besides, also carried much re-systematizing of the works of Hunain ibn Ishaq, another figure of Islamic science also translated and in vogue in Salerno.[1322]
This leads to the place where such medical learning first originated from: Salerno.

2. Salerno

Exactly like Lorraine, Salerno, in the south of Italy, acted first as a recipient of Muslim science before it turned into a purveyor of such science. Like Lorraine, too, it only came to flourish once it received the input of Islamic learning, despite having been a place where Classical learning had been available for centuries before.

According to Friend, there is an early Islamic impact in the region, which explains the presence of Islamic medical lore there; Islamic teachers having settled at Salerno early in the 8th century.[1323] The value of such learning ought to have been quite limited, though, for Muslim medicine would only develop substantially in the subsequent centuries. More Islamic science arrived around the 10th century; the work of Jewish physicians of southern Italy and Sicily.[1324] One such Jew born near Otranto, Sabbetia b. Abraham b.Yoel (also known as Donnulus or Donnolo) (913-70) learnt Islamic medicine in Palermo (which was under Islamic control) after he was taken prisoner in 925, and after some time returned to Otranto, where he wrote in Hebrew some medical treatises, of which the best known is *Sefer ha yaqar* (the precious book) that listed 120 drugs, mainly botanic.[1325] Donnolo practiced his medicine in Italy,[1326] but most importantly is regarded as one of the

1320 C.H. Haskins: Studies; op cit; p. 92.
1321 G. Sarton: Introduction; op cit; Vol 2; p. 197.
1322 Ibid.
1323 J. Freind: *History of Physick*; two parts; London; 1750. pt.ii, p.218.
1324 W. Durant: The Age of Faith; op cit; p. 403.
1325 G. Wiet et al: History; op cit; p.205.
1326 W. Durant: The Age of Faith; op cit; p. 403.

earliest people who acquainted Salerno with elements of Islamic medicine.[1327] Again, this impact might have been relatively limited.

Substantial Islamic learning came with the arrival of Constantine the African (d. ca. 1087).[1328] Constantine, Durant informs, had studied medicine in the Muslim schools of Africa and Baghdad, before travelling in 1060 to Monte Casino (where he became a monk) and to nearby Salerno, bringing with him an `exciting' cargo of Islamic medical lore.[1329] This rich cargo of books came initially from his native Tunisia, and legend has it, that he fell into the sea, and lost part of his treasure, but what he salvaged, he translated into Latin, once he converted to Christianity.[1330] Alfano, archbishop of Salerno, who himself had medical knowledge, encouraged Constantine to make translations from Arabic of several popular medical texts.[1331] One such translation was an adaptation for a Latin audience of the `*Kitab Kamil as-sin'a at-tibbiya* (the complete or `perfect' book on medical art') of `Ali ibn Abbas al-Madjusi (written before 977/978).[1332] This work Constantine called the Pantegni. It consisted of ten books of theory of medicine and an equal number on practical medicine; the most comprehensive book on medicine of its time.[1333] Constantine translated several other works by doctors from Al-Qayrawan, the Tunisian former Aghlabid capital, which under this dynasty (9h century) witnessed the birth of a remarkable flourish of science, and medicine above all.[1334] These Qayrawenese works translated by Constantine were on diets, the stomach, melancholy, forgetfulness and sexual intercourse, such as *Al-Makala fi'l malikhuliya* (*De melancholia*) of Ishak Ibn Imran (d.before 907); *Kitab al-Bawl* (*de urines*) and *Kitab al-humayyat* (*De febrilus*), and *Kitab al-Aghdiya* (*De dietis*) all of Ishak al-Israili (d. 995); *Kitab I'timad al-Adwiya al-Mufrada* (*De Gradibus)* of Ibn al-Djazzar (d.

[1327] A. Mieli: La Science Arabe; op cit; p. 219.

[1328] See: M. Mc Vaugh, `Constantine the African,' *Dictionary of Scientific Biography*, 3: pp. 393-5.

[1329] W. Durant: The Age of Faith; op cit; P. 457

[1330] A. Mieli: La Science Arabe; op cit; p. 219.

[1331] D. Matthew: *The Norman Kingdom of Sicily*: Cambridge University Press; 1992. p.116.

[1332] See also: Constantine the African and `Ali ibn al-Magusti: *The Pantegni* and related texts, eds C. Burnett and D. Jacquard, Leiden, 1994.

[1333] C. Burnett: The Introduction, op cit, P. 23.
C. Burnett and D. Jacquard: Constantine the African and `Ali ibn al-Magusti; op cit.

[1334] M.Talbi: Al-Kayrawan; in *Encyclopaedia of Islam*, vol IV, new series; pp. 824-32; p. 829 fwd.
H. Saladin: *Tunis et Kairouan;* Librairie Renouard; Paris; 1908. pp.100 fwd.

1004).[1335] Constantine also translated by the same author (Ibn al-Djazzar): *Zad al-musafir* (or the Guide for the traveller going to distant countries), which is the most accessible introduction to pathology. Translated into Latin as the *Viaticum,* it exerted a considerable impact in Western Christendom.[1336] Other texts on the stomach, forgetfulness, sexual intercourse… also translated by Constantine could also be attributed to Ibn al-Djazzar.[1337] Amongst his other translations are works by Hunayn Ibn Ishaq (including the *Isagoge* and a treatise on ophthalmology). This collection of translated works is known as the *corpus Constantinum;*[1338] a very large corpus, that has been collected by Gerhard Baader.[1339]

Constantine did not provide literal translations, avoided difficult points, cut out sentences and even whole passages, and in most cases, his work was more adaptation than translation.[1340] This, of course, can be explained by the fact that his work is one of the earliest if not the earliest translation of a complex work by an Arabic taught person into Latin, with no advanced knowledge of the latter language. Besides, unlike Toledo a century later, there was neither an organised `academy' for translations, nor a group of intermediaries to clear difficulties. Moreover, there was no scientific tradition in the Christian West at the time, and no Latin equivalents for many of the words, diseases, technical expressions etc, which Constantine had in the Arabic versions, which goes some way to explain the imperfections of his translations. Besides, with regard to Constantine's failing to refer to Muslim authorship of some works, Micheau explains, the translator, aware and fearing his translations of Muslim works might not be favourably received in the Christian West, decided to keep the sources hidden.[1341]

These reservations aside, Constantine's translations of Islamic medical lore, however, resurrected science in Italy, and made the school of

---

1335 F. Micheau: La Transmission; op cit; p. 404.

1336 Ibid.

1337 Ibid.

1338 L.G. Ballester: Introduction: in *Practical Medicine from Salerno to the Black Death.* Edt L.G. Ballester et al; Cambridge University Press; 1994; pp. 1-29; p.13.

1339 G. Baader: Die Schule von Salerno; *Medizinhistoriches journal*; 13; 1978; pp. 14-145.

1340 M.T. D'Alverny: Translation and Translators, in *Renaissance and Renewal in the Twelfth Century*, edt: R.L. Benson et al, University of Toronto Press, 1982, pp 421-62, at p. 425.

1341 F. Micheau: La Transmission; op cit; p. 403.

Salerno the head of medical knowledge in the Christian West.[1342] His translations, led to the rise of a generation of prominent medical teachers in northern Europe.[1343] His translations were soon to become the common property of the Salerno School, and the centre of its medical teaching;[1344] eventually enabling it to build both a great reputation, and to become the first place of advanced learning in Europe.[1345] And it was subsequent to Constantine's translations, and with Dominicus Gundissalinus (further details on him later) the promoter of translations in Toledo, that medicine was given its due rank in his *Of the division of philosophy,* and became a recognised science in Western Christendom.[1346] More importantly, Constantine was one of the first, if not the first, to realise the need for the translation of Muslim science, centuries ahead of others;[1347] thus, turning as noted by Sarton, into the first initiator of the Latino Islamic revival.[1348] Campbell equally acknowledges that he was one of the most important figures in the history `of mental development of Europe in the Middle Ages.'[1349] A pioneering role, which even then earned him the title of `*orientis et occidentis doctor*':[1350]

Obviously, as with every other scientific change of the time, mainstream modern history attributes the rise of Salerno as the first centre of Western higher learning to the usual recovery of Classical/Western learning, owing little if anything to Islamic influence. Such Classical/Western influences, that had any positive impact for centuries, yet, again, soon after the Islamic factor entered the equation, in this case via Constantine's translations, suddenly coming to effect.[1351] A position held by Ballester,[1352] who, like most of those with the same views, also resorts to Latinising names such as that of Hunayn Ibn Ishaq, only referred to as Johannitius, and his work *Isagoge*, at no time

---

[1342] W. Durant: The Age of Faith; op cit; P. 457
[1343] M. Meyerhof: Science and medicine in the Legacy of Islam; 1st edt, op cit, p. 351.
[1344] P.O. Kristeller: `The School of Salerno: Its development and its contribution to the History of learning,' *Bulletin of the History of Medicine* 17 (1945): 151-7, at p. 155.
[1345] C.H. Haskins: The Renaissance; op cit; p. 22; G.Le Bon: La Civilisation; op cit.p.391:
[1346] F. Micheau: La Transmission; op cit; p. 414.
[1347] P.O. Kristeller: `The School of Salerno: p. 155.
[1348] G. Sarton: Introduction; op cit; Vol II; p.67.
[1349] D. Campbell: Arabian medicine; op cit; p. 123.
[1350] Ibid.
[1351] See, for instance, B. Lawn: The Salernitan; op cit. and Piero Morpurgo: Le traduzioni di Michele Scoto in *La diffusione delle scienze islamiche nel medio-evo europeo*; Rome; 1987; pp. 167-91.
[1352] L.G. Ballester: Introduction: in *Practical Medicine; op cit;* pp 23 fwd.

given its Arabic form (*massa'il fi'l tib*) (medical questions). Ballester also turns every Salernitan change into neo Galen, or neo Aristotle development, and making the sort of statements such as:
`The well known organisation of medical knowledge made by the Arab author of the *pantegni,* straddling both theory and practice, is simply a transferral to medicine of Aristotle's doctrine.'[1353]
Which is wholly untenable, in equating a complex organisation of medical knowledge with an abstract, speculative thought. It is also false, for there is nothing in Aristotle which has any organisation of knowledge of the sort made by Al-Madjusi, the author of the *pantegni,* as can easily be checked by comparing both authors.
Going further than Ballester is Breckenbridge:
`Before he (Constantine) died in 1087 he had translated a large number of medical works from Arabic to Latin. Almost single handedly he laid the foundation for European medicine by restoring access to the classical scientific tradition which, lost to the West, had survived in Arabic texts.'[1354]
This is false, for what Constantine translated was not Greek in any sense, but came mostly from al-Qayrawan, from Muslim authors, and again, as can be verified, medical learning that included overwhelmingly matters not addressed or touched upon by the Greeks.
Breckenbridge is also making an absurd comment, for on one hand he says Constantine revived classical learning that was lost, and yet, in the previous page, he says: quote:
`The earliest identifiable medical writer at Salerno seems to have been one Gariopontus, author of a work on fevers and, more significantly, of a popular book called the *passionarius*, a compilation of passages from the writings of Galen and other ancient medical authorities.'[1355]

Rather than Classical influence, the Salerno experience confirms once more the patterns of Islamic impact observed with regard to other changes, in other places. First, it shows that the medical revival in the Christian West took place, first, in Salerno, precisely the place where Islamic medical learning first arrived. Secondly, there is the matter of timing, again, such revival taking place precisely soon after the arrival of Constantine, and not before. The third pattern, the medical learning that thrived in Salerno is precisely the same in substance to the Islamic medical learning that was introduced by Constantine.

[1353] Ibid. p. 11.
[1354] J. D. Breckenridge: The two Sicilies; in *Islam and the Medieval West*; S. Ferber Editor; State University of New York; 1975; pp. 39-59; at p. 49.
[1355] Ibid; p. 48.

If one looks at the third pattern (the transferred substance of learning) in more detail, it is easy to observe that it was Constantine's translations, focusing most particularly on works, where the place of theory and practice is fundamental, which `put in place the foundations of a true science' in the Christian West.[1356] This is particularly traced in both the *pantegni* (by Ali Ibn al-Madjusi), and the *isagoge* (by Hunayn Ibn Ishaq).[1357] Constantine's translations impacted on the development of Salernitan anatomy most particularly; the earliest Salernitan anatomy ascribed to Copho dating from the end of the 11th century, or more probably from the beginning of the 12th.. Called *Anatomia porci*, it bore very strong Islamic influence;[1358]which is also traced to the next work. The second Salernitan Demonstration was very similar to the *Anatomia porci* and dates from the first half of the 12th century. Its purpose and arrangement are the same as the first, but is more elaborate and more than four times longer, besides making corrections to the earlier text. The author is unknown, although evidence would suggest Maurus (second half of the 12th century) as the second anatomy has many points of contact with the *Anatomia mauri.*[1359] Some of the content of this second demonstration are taken almost bodily from Constantine's *Pantegni*, and the dissection proper is preceded by an introduction wherein the organs are classified according to their functions also largely taken from the *Pantegni.*[1360]The anatomical texts by Bartholomeus, Maurus, and Urso, all proceeding from the school in the 12th century show the influence of the Islamic tradition in their language and fuller treatment, and in the tendency to organize anatomical information along scholastic lines.[1361] The overwhelming Islamic impact is due primarily to the basic fact, that these authors had inherited virtually no anatomical literature from the classical past,[1362] and that the situation was changed only by Constantine's translation of the Pantegni with its anatomical chapters.[1363]Just as is the case with the work of the

---

1356 F. Micheau: La Transmission; op cit; p. 414.

1357 Ibid.

1358 G. Sarton: Introduction, op cit; Vol II: p.238.

1359 Ibid.

1360 First edition by C.L. Nagel: *Commentatio de anatomia salernitana per compendium salernitanum* (Breslau 1852). reprinted by Salvatore de Renzi in his Collectio salernitana (1853). Revised edition by K. H. Benedict: *Die Demonstratio anatomica corporis animalis* (Diss., Leipzig 1920). Tr by G.W. Corner: Anatomical texts of the earlier Middle Ages (54-66, Washington 1927). In G. Sarton: Introduction, Vol II, p.238.

1361 M. McVaugh: History of Medicine, in Dictionary of Middle Ages; op cit; Vol 8; pp 247-54; at p. 248.

1362 Ibid.

1363 Ibid.

greatest Salernitan surgeon Roger of Salerno (fl about 1170), whose *Practica chirurgiae* is the earliest surgical treatise of the Christian West; the first also to incorporate the Salernitan experience, and to win universal recognition.[1364] It became the surgical textbook of the school of Salerno, and various commentaries were devoted to it. Among other things it describes a remarkable technique in herniotomy and the use of mercury salts to fight chronic dermatoses and parasites (skin diseases had been traditionally abandoned to the surgeon.).[1365]

One of the main translations of Constantine includes a treatise on ophthalmology by Hunayn Ibn Ishaq: *Tarkib al'Ayn (de oculis),* which could have had its impact on the development of the subject in the same school. However, other influences might have been at work, and they are Islamic, too; but from the East. This owes principally to the eastern Islamic pioneering advance in the field. Nearly every medical compendium covers some aspect of eye diseases, although the best are by monographs solely devoted to the subject;[1366]being innovative in many ways.[1367] Al-Mosuli's *Kitab-ul Muntakhab fi Ilaj-ul Ayn* (Book of Choices in the Treatment of Eye Diseases), for instance, discusses forty eight diseases, and clinical cases and adaptations of surgical instruments.[1368] In discussing the treatment of a cataract, Al-Mosuli introduces an instrument of his own design, a hollow needle to remove cataract by suction, inserted through the limbus (where the cornea joins the conjunctiva).[1369] How did this eastern learning travel to Salerno? Three eye doctors lived apparently at about the same time (12th century) in Salerno, little is known about any of them, except that they all were

---

1364 G. Sarton: Introduction; op cit; vol ii; p. 435.

1365 Text: Editio princeps in the last edition of the Collectio chirurgica veneta (Venice 1546). S. De Renzi: Rogerii medici celeberrimi chirurgica (Collectio salernitana, vol 2, 426-496, 1853). K. Sudhoff: Die Chiurgie des Roger Frugardi von Salern (*Beitrage zur Geschichte der Chirurgie im Mittelalter*, vol.2, 148-236, 1918). This new edition is followed by various medieval commentaries; it is preceded by the edition, p. 103-147, of another surgical text of Salerno which perhaps antedated a little Roger's practica, the so called Bamberg surgery. Previous editions of the *Collectio chirurgica veneta* (1498, 1519) contain another text entitled *Rogerii practica*, which may be somewhat anterior to the work just considered; it is ascribed to an unknown Roger de Barone (or varone). Choulant mentions the following editions of the *Collectio chirurgica veneta*: 1490 (?), 1497, 1498, 1499, 1513, 1519, 1546 (*Handbuch der Bucherkunde*, 416-417, 1841). In G. Sarton: Introduction; op cit; pp. 434-5.

1366 E. Savage Smith: Medicine, in the Encyclopaedia (Rashed ed), op cit, pp 903-62. at p. 948.

1367 G.M. Wickens: The Middle East, op cit, p 116.

1368 E.S. Smith: Medicine; op cit; p 949.

1369 A. Mieli: La Science Arabe; op cit; p.125.

influenced by Islamic models.[1370] How did this Islamic eastern influence transfer to Salerno then? Without elaborating too long, it was most probably due to returning Norman crusaders (Salerno was in Norman hands in the 12th century, and the Normans played a primary role in the first crusades). Bohemund, the son of Robert Guiscard who took Sicily from the Muslims, took the crusaders' oath as early as June 1096, and his followers included members of the most prominent Norman families of south Italy.[1371] Returning crusaders from the East most probably brought the science, and possibly learned men with them. The local Salernitan and Eastern influence can be found with the most illustrious of all Salernitan eye surgeon of the time: Benevenutus Grapheus/ Benvenuto Grasso (fl. 12th century), born or lived, according to some sources for a time in Jerusalem; travelled considerably in Italy and in Languedoc, and lived in Salerno and in Montpellier.[1372] He was the most famous non-Muslim oculist of medieval times. His *Practica oculorum* (or *Ars nova, Ars probatissima de egritudinibus oculorum*)[1373] is the most popular Latin textbook on the eye diseases, its popularity proved by the number of manuscripts, most of them in Latin, but some of them in Provencal, French, English, and possibly Hebrew.[1374] His *practica* in content is wholly derived from Islamic writings.[1375]

Despite these non-Constantinian inputs, and despite the impact of other translations to follow in the 12th century, in Toledo in particular, Constantine's initial role remains uniquely decisive, as Mieli acknowledges, his influence of a continental dimension.[1376] His translations became `a ferment,' which applied the study of Muslim medicine; and which stimulated the rise of medical schools throughout Europe.[1377] Salerno eventually turning into the `mother of European Universities,' according to Campbell.[1378] Bologna, one of its daughters, was one of the first centres of higher learning in the Christian West, where, at the beginning of the 12th century the best Salernitan tradition

---

[1370] G. Sarton: Introduction; op cit; Vol II; p.243.
[1371] D.C. Douglas: *The Norman Achievement 1050-1100;* Eyre and Spottiswoode; London; 1969; p.163.
[1372] G. Sarton: Introduction; Vol II; p.243
[1373] Editio Princeps (Ferrara, undated, 1474). Later editions: Trevisio 1492; Venice 1497, 1500, 1549. See Ch.Laborde: *Bienvenu de Jerusalem et son oeuvre. Le manuscript de Metz;* these 76 p., Montpellier 1901.
[1374] G. Sarton: Introduction; op cit; Vol II; p.243.
[1375] A. Mieli: La Science; op cit; p. 223. G. Sarton: Introduction; Vol II; p.243
[1376] A. Mieli: La Science Arabe; .op cit; p. 223.
[1377] Ibid. p. 220.
[1378] D. Campbell: Arabian Medicine; op cit; p. 125.

was taken by Roland of Parma.[1379] Under the combined influence of Salerno and Bologna a new surgical school was created by Hugh Borgognomi (a veteran crusader) and his son Theodoric; their effort continued throughout the century (the father died before 1259 but the son lived until 1298.)[1380] The greatest South Italian physician, Bruno da Longoburgo, a Calabrian, was educated in Salerno, but his science also bearing other complementary Islamic influences, Bruno's main authority being Al-Zahrawi.[1381]Bruno's life and fame were obtained in the North, in Padua, where he completed, c. 1252, his *Chirurgia magna,* a work, which marked a new stage in the transmission of Islamic medicine to the West.[1382] Bruno's *Chirurgia* was translated into Hebrew before the end of the century, and had great impact on both Jewish and Christian medicine.[1383]

The influence of Constantine and Salerno stretched to the South of France, Chartres, Paris, and also to England.[1384] One English doctor, Herbert, is known to have given Durham cathedral Library in the third quarter of the 12th century works translated by Constantine: *Liber febrium* and *Liber Urinarum* by Ishaq al-Israeli; *Kitab al-Malaki* by Al-Madjusi; and Ishaq Ibn Imran's work on melancholy.[1385] Sources generally agree in tracing the Salernitan impact in northern Europe in the 12th century beyond the Alps to Chartres, Paris, and also Tours.[1386]Sarton also traces this influence to the last quarter of the 12th, mainly through emigration from Salerno, which was caused by unsettled conditions in south Italy (under the rule of William the Bad 1154-1166, which caused huge Islamic exodus out of the island) and the attraction of foreign centres, above all Paris whose university had already become a powerful magnet.[1387] Giles of Corbeil (d. c. 1222) also carried Salernitan medicine to Montpellier and later to Paris, where he became the chief physician to Philip Augustus (king from 1180 to 1223). He explained the teachings of Salerno in a number of Latin poems; two of these, *De urinis* and *De pulsibus*, were used as textbooks for more than

---

[1379] G. Sarton: Introduction; Vol II, op cit; p. 782.
[1380] Ibid.
[1381] Ibid.
[1382] Ibid.
[1383] Ibid.
[1384] C. Burnett: Arabic Learning; op cit; p. 46.
[1385] C. Burnett: Arabic Learning; op cit; p. 46.
[1386] M.T. D'Alverny: Translations and Translators; J. Jolivet: The Arabic Inheritance; H. Schipperges: Die Schulen von Chartres; all in L.G. Ballester: Introduction; op cit; p. 27.
[1387] G. Sarton: Introduction; op cit; ii; p.307.

three centuries.[1388] Salernitan knowledge was introduced into Scandinavia by the Danish physician Henrik Harpestraeng (1244), who explains it in various treatises dealing with medicine, astrology, and related subjects.[1389]The English became acquainted with such Salernitan medicine through Alfred of Sareshel, Robert Grosseteste, Gilbert the Englishman, and Richard of Wendover. The most important Latin treatises of the first half of the 13th were due to these Englishmen: the *De motu cordis* to Alfred, the *Micrologus* to Richard, and the *Lilium* to Gilbert.[1390] Haskins also notes, that `No list can be attempted of Norman and English students at Salerno,'[1391] lesser known, or unknown names, whose role was still crucial in the diffusion of such learning.

The Salernitan corpus can also be traced to various libraries, as in the library catalogue of 1160 at Hildesheim,[1392]which shows that the medical works (at least up to this time) were exclusively the translations of Constantine.[1393] The earliest manuscript in England of one of Constantine's Arabic translations can be found at Bury St Edmunds.[1394] This manuscript is now Wellcome 801A, a manuscript of the medical collection known later as the *Articella*, which included Constantine's translation of the `Questions on medicine' by Hunain b. Ishaq (*the isagoge* of Johannitius).[1395] The manuscript is written in the Beneventan script of Southern Italy in the early to mid 12th century. Bury St Edmunds also possessed at least two manuscripts of Constantine's *Pantegni*, one of which survives in the library of Trinity College, Cambridge.[1396]

The `splendid efforts,' according to Sarton, which placed the Christian medical world for the first time on the same level with the Muslim and Jewish, were brutally interrupted by the vicissitudes of war, as Salerno `the nursery of European medicine,' was destroyed in 1193 by emperor Henry VI.[1397] But the learning had already travelled, and taken roots North. Bologna, Padua, Chartres, Paris, Montpellier, and England, all

---

1388 Ibid. p.309.
1389 Ibid. p. 521.
1390 Ibid. p.70.
1391 C.H. Haskins: England and Sicily; op cit; p. 435.
1392 M.Steinschneider: *Virchow's archiv; B*erlin, 1866, xxvii, pp 351-410. The author discusses the Arabic sources of Constantine.
1393 K.Sudhoff: *Arch f.Gesch.d. med.* Leipzig, 1916, ix, p. 348.
1394 C. Burnett: The Introduction; op cit; p.25.
1395 Ibid.
1396 Ibid.
1397 G. Sarton: Introduction; op cit; ii; p.307.

were to play a decisive role in the thriving medical knowledge of Western Christendom subsequently as will be seen in the following part.

3. Spain

In the words of Briffault: `It was under the influence of the Arabs and the Moorish revival of culture, and not in the 15th Century that a real renaissance took place. Spain, not Italy, was the cradle of the re-birth of Europe.'[1398]

An opinion adhered to by others, including Lane Poole, who in a flowery account sums up the Peninsula's wider impact:

`For nearly eight centuries, under the Mohammedan rulers, Spain set to all Europe a shining example of a civilised and enlightened state. Her fertile provinces, rendered doubly prolific by the industry and engineering skill of her conquerors, bore fruit a hundredfold. Cities innumerable sprang up in the rich valleys of the Guadelquivir and the Guadiana, whose names, and names only, still commemorate the vanished glories of their past. Art, literature, and science prospered, as they then prospered nowhere else in Europe. Students flocked from France and Germany and England to drink from the fountain of learning which flowed only in the cities of the Moors. The surgeons and doctors of Andalusia were in the van of science: women were encouraged to devote themselves to serious study, and the lady doctor was not unknown among the people of Cordova. Mathematics, astronomy and botany, history and jurisprudence were to be mastered in Spain, and Spain alone.... Whatsoever makes a kingdom great and prosperous, whatsoever tends to refinement and civilisation was found in Muslim Spain.'[1399]

The attraction and impact of Muslim Spain has also been alluded to in other studies,[1400]which hardly means, though, that the Islamic role is

---

[1398] R. Briffault: The Making of Humanity, op cit; pp 188-9.

[1399] S. Lane-Poole: *The Moors in Spain*; Fisher Unwin; London; 1888.Preface; pp.vii-viii.

[1400]For good accounts on the role of Muslim Spain in science and civilisation, see, for instance:

-Jose M. Millas Vallicrosa: *Estudios sobre historia de la ciencia espanola*, Barcelona, 1949.

gracefully accepted, including in Spain itself. Thus, Sanchez Albornoz,[1401]literally led a war of attrition against Castro because of the latter's support for the Islamic foundations of Spanish culture.[1402] Sánchez-Albornoz held that Castro had exaggerated both the extent and nature of the contact between Muslims and Christians, that it was conflictive and therefore not conducive to creative cultural interchange, and that most of the components of "Spanish" culture are `either idiosyncratic or consist of Roman, Gothic, or elements of other than Semitic provenance.'[1403]Going further than Albornoz, Francisco Javier Simonet sought to prove that every achievement of note made by the Andalusian Muslims had been the result not of Eastern cultural importations, but of purely local sources, and the fact that the Andalusians had been ethnically Spaniards and, therefore, as he implied, racially superior to mere Orientals.[1404] Spanish television, in a program entitled "la noche de los tiempos," also held: "Saracens, Moors, unknown and enigmatic beings who in a few weeks violated the stupendous Celtic-Iberian-Phoenician-Carthaginian- Roman-Visigothic Spain only to lose it little by little, for they were uncultured, indolent, maladroit, unbelievers ..."[1405] Ignacio Olague went further, stating in his famed *Les arabes n'ont jamais envahi l'Espagne* that the Muslims never even set foot in the Peninsula.[1406] Others such as Perez,[1407] echoed by

---

-Jose M. Millas Vallicrosa: *Nuevos estudios sobre historia de la ciencia espanola,* Barcelona, 1960.

-J. Ribera: *Disertaciones Y Opusculos,* 2 vols. Madrid 1928.

J. Vernet: *Ce que la culture doit aux Arabes d'Espagne*, translation by Gabriel Martinez Gros, 1985, Paris.

-A. Castro: *The Structure of Spanish History*, English translation with revisions and modifications by Edmund A.King. Princeton: Princeton University Press, 1954.

[1401] S. C. Albornoz: *L'Espagne Musulmane*, French translation of earlier Spanish version, Paris, 1985.

[1402] A. Castro: *The Structure of Spanish History*, op cit.

[1403]In T. Glick: Islamic and Christian Spain; op cit; p. 8.

[1404] F.J. Simonet as in text by J.T. Monroe: The Hispano Arabic World; in *Americo Castro, and the Meaning of Spanish Civilisation*. ed By Jose Rubia Barcia:; University of California Press, Berkeley, 1976; pp. 69-90; at p. 71.

[1405] Note 25; p. 132; in Americo Castro, op cit; See Antonio de los Reyes, "lucha de razas, " in *La Verdad* (Alicante), March 1972.

[1406]I. Olague: *Les Arabes n'ont jamais envahi l'Espagne*; Paris; Flammarion; 1969. Monroe tells of Olague right wing leanings, and how he, Olague, rewrites history using only those sources that suit his thesis. in J.T. Monroe: The Hispano Arabic World; op cit; p. 71.

[1407] J. Perez: Chretiens; Juifs et Musulmans en espagne; Le mythe de la tolerance religieuse (VIII-XV e siecle); in *Histoire*, No 137; October 1990.

Conrad,[1408] even denounced as myth the widely established view of Muslim tolerance of others. Summing up Muslim Spain, Fletcher informs us, that only a maximum of 300,000 Muslims were expelled in 1609-1610 from Spain,[1409] and that not much harm done to them, contrary to what earlier historians say.[1410]He adds that such an expulsion only mirrors earlier deeds by the Almoravid Muslims who forcibly deported Christian populations.[1411]Fletcher also attacks Anthony Burgess of the Independent, who on 21 August 1991, wrote in praise of the beauty, tolerance and learning of Muslim Spain. In response, Fletcher asks:

`Learning? Outside the tiny circles of the princely courts, not a great deal of it could be seen. Good order? Among the feuding Berber tribesmen?...' [1412]

Fletcher attributes the positive image of Muslim Spain to:

`The nostalgia of Maghribi writers, reinforced by the romantic vision of the nineteenth century. This could be flavoured by a dash of Protestant prejudice from the Anglo Saxon world: it can be detected in Lane Poole's reference to the Inquisition. A powerful mixture! But that is not yet the end of the recipe. In the second half of the twentieth century a new agent of education makes its appearance: the guilt of the liberal conscience, which sees the evils of colonialism-assumed rather than demonstrated-foreshadowed in the Christian conquest of al-Andalus and the persecution of the Moriscos (but not, oddly, in the Moorish conquest and colonisation). Stir the mix well together and issue it free to credulous academics and media persons throughout the Western world. Then pour it generously over the truth...'[1413]

`Moorish Spain,' he concludes `was not a tolerant and enlightened society even in its most cultivated epoch.'[1414]

Monroe had long before raised questions about this growing anti Islamic bias, telling how for centuries, any mention of the Muslims and their role in the formation of Spanish culture, has drawn furious hostile

---

[1408] P. Conrad: *Histoire de la Reconquista*; Que Sais je? Presses Universitaire de France; Paris; 1998.

[1409] R. Fletcher: *Moorish Spain;* op cit; p.168.

[1410] H.C. Lea: *A History of the Inquisition in Spain*, in four volumes, The MacMillan Company, New York, 1907, volume three, in particular.
H.C. Lea: *The Moriscos of Spain*; Burt Franklin; New York; 1968 reprint.
S.P. Scott: History of the Moorish; op cit.

[1411] R. Fletcher: *Moorish Spain;* p.172.

[1412] Ibid.

[1413] *Ibid.* p.172-3.

[1414] *Ibid.* p.173.

response.[1415]The subject, Monroe adds, shows no sign at present of losing its capacity for arousing nationalistic passions.[1416]Just as Menocal fairly recently experienced, noting in her long preface:
`No specific of any of the theories called `Arabist' can be successful so long as the most general views we have of the medieval period are as hostile to the notions of such influence and interaction as they currently are.'[1417]

And yet, again, looked at from a diversity of angles, and setting aside the translation contribution of Toledo, which will be lengthily considered in the next chapter, the Muslim Spanish influence was absolutely fundamental in the rise of learning and civilisation in Western Christendom. Most powerful, indeed, for as Campbell points out, it was thanks to 10th century, Cordova, Granada, Toledo, and Seville, that the sciences were preserved from extinction in Europe.[1418] Muslim Spain not only preserved but also transmitted such learning to the Barbarian West. The strong Christian community, both independent, and also those living under the Muslims (Mozarabs), carried north all forms and manners of civilisation seen, or learnt amongst Muslims. The Christian population of Cordova, itself, had as early as the 9th century adopted the Muslim way of living, and found delight in Arabic fiction, poetry and the study of Muslim philosophical and theological doctrines.[1419] Alvarus (a mid 9th Spanish Christian opponent to Islam and supporter of the Cordovan Christian `martyrs') was distressed by this, and his distress, Menocal holds, had he witnessed, a hundred years later, `the cultural prestige and success of the descendants of the Arab invaders and those who had adopted their language and culture, would have been even more warranted and more acute.[1420] Christian pilgrims to Spain, too, have never fallen in number; the pilgrims routes of the Romanesque period forming the norm for many actual or potential patrons and taste-makers in Romanesque Europe.[1421]It has also been seen above how the learning which spread into Lorraine arrived from Spain. And Spain was to play a crucial role in every single manifestation of science and civilisation that was to affect Western

---

[1415] J.T. Monroe: The Hispano-Arabic World: op cit; p. 69.
[1416] Ibid.
[1417] M.R. Menocal: The Role; op cit; p. xiii.
[1418] D. Campbell: *Arabian Medicine, op cit;* p.42.
[1419] P.F. Kennedy: The Muslim sources of Dante? in *The Arab Influence in Medieval Europe*, ed D.A. Agius and R. Hitchcock, Ithaca Press, 1994, pp. 63-82, at pp 71-2.
[1420] M.R. Menocal: The Arabic Role; op cit; p.28.
[1421] O. Grabar: Islamic architecture and the West: Influences and parallels; in *Islam and the medieval West*; S. Ferber ed; op cit; pp 60-6; at p. 62.

Christendom throughout the medieval centuries as the following will show to some extent, and as the final part of this work will amply reveal.

Muslim Spain's fundamental role in the enlightenment of Western Europe is due to large measure to its geographical proximity to the Christian West. One illustration of this geographical factor is highlighted by Burnett, who notes that the most northerly outpost of Arabic rule was the kingdom of the Banu Hud, who did not capitulate to the Christians until 1140.[1422] One of the Banu Hud, Abu Amir yusuf al-Mu'taman-was a well known mathematician, and his works show that he had access to a remarkably large collection of mathematical works.[1423] The translator Hugo of Santalla tells us that Michael, Bishop of Tarazona from 1119 to 1151, sought an astronomical text in the library of Ruta, the capital of the Banu Hud from 1110 until 1140, and he may well have been benefiting from the resources of Abu Amir's collection.[1424]

It was, however, Christian Catalonia, the most neighbourly Christian land to Islamic Spain, which played, most certainly, the earliest leading role in the Western awakening. `The size and opulence of 10th century Cordoba' far outstripped any city in the Latin West; and the contrast between scientific cultures of al-Andalus and Latin Christendom was just as extreme, and so it is hardly surprising that Islamic science should overflow into its nearest Christian neighbour, Catalonia, Burnett says.[1425] Catalonia did not just receive, it acted as a relay, conveying Islamic learning to other parts of Christianity. The territory of Barcelona, which received Muslim learning, Puig notes, was intellectually linked to France, whose well developed cultural milieu welcomed any novelty;[1426]Barcelona's intellectual activity exceeding its small geographical dimensions.[1427] An intellectual role highlighted by the fact that one of the first written indications of the astrolabe in the Latin West comes precisely from the Spanish Marsh, the Christian enclave on the borders of Islamic Spain as late in the tenth century an unknown writer, possibly Archdeacon Lupitus of Barcelona (fl. Ca 975-

---

[1422] C. Burnett: Hermann of Carinthia; in *A History of Twelfth Century Western Philosophy;* Edited by P. Dronke; Cambridge University Press; 1988; pp. 386-404; p. 388.

[1423] See P. Hogendijk: Discovery of the 11th century geometrical compilation: the *Kitab al-istikmal of Yusuf al-Mu'taman ibn Hud; Historia Mathematica;* Xiii; 1986; pp. 43-52.

[1424] C. Haskins; 1927; p. 73; in C. Burnett: Hermann of Carinthia; op cit; p. 388.

[1425] C. Burnett, The Introduction of Arabic learning, op cit, p. 3.

[1426] J. Puig: The Transmission; op cit; p.8.

[1427] Ibid.

995), wrote a preface to a lost treatise on the astrolabe.[1428]The preface praises the nobility and usefulness of astronomical study, noting the physical dominance and moderating influence of the aetherial fire over the terrestrial elements, the influence of the Moon on the tides.[1429] Just as in the Islamic tradition, the author rejects the astrologers' attempts to forecast a person's fate from the state of the stars at the time of conception or birth as a frivolous superstition, since a person's fate is wholly committed to divine disposition.[1430] The author then notes that the text that follows, drawn from Islamic sources, discusses both the uses of the astrolabe and the method of its construction.[1431] The earliest Latin astrolabe, in the 10th century, was related with Catalonia, probably constructed by a Muslim, but inscribed by a Catalan scholar.[1432] This astrolabe, Cochrane notes, which can be found at the Institut du Monde Arabe collection in Paris, is a `Carolingian' astrolabe thought to have been produced in Europe at the end of the 10th Century. And the symbols used on its circumference for the measurement of degrees reflect a possible transitional phase in the introduction of Arabic numerals into Europe.[1433]

The primary role of diffusion of Islamic learning via Catalonia was played by its monasteries, Ripoll, above all. The monastery of Ripoll had a relatively good library that included translations of Muslim works on the sciences.[1434] It is in Ripoll, where, in all likelihood, was located `the first corpus of Latin texts on the practical side of the science of the stars,' a corpus consisting of texts on the astrolabe and astronomy, that was put together from Islamic and Latin sources.[1435] And it was, indeed, the Ripoll monastery, which `partook of the riches of Andalusian writings' on scientific subjects.[1436] Ripoll was accessible to the learned, who were in those days all Church people. One of its best known visitors was Gerbert who spent three years there, where he also built and kept very powerful contacts with other ecclesiastics at the monastery.[1437] Gerbert, after returning north to teach at Rheims, maintained contacts

---

[1428] Lupitus of Barcelona?: Fragmentum de astrolabio; in S. C. McCluskey: *Astronomies; op cit*; p. 175.
[1429] S. C. McCluskey: *Astronomies;* p. 175.
[1430] Ibid.
[1431] Lupitus of Barcelona?: Fragmentum de astrolabio; in S. C. McCluskey: *Astronomies; op cit;* p. 175.
[1432] C. Burnett: The Introduction; op cit; p. 3.
[1433] L. Cochrane: Adelard; op cit; p. 6.
[1434] W.M. Watt: The Influence, op cit, p. 59.
[1435] C. Burnett: The Introduction; op cit; p. 3.
[1436] M. R. Menocal: *The Arabic Role; op cit;* p.28.
[1437] J.C. Garcin: Etats; op cit; p. 401.

with the Catalan scholars and requested works to be sent to him.[1438] He asked Miro Bonfill, cousin of Count Borell and Abbot of Gerone, to send him a copy of the *De Multiplicatione et divisione*, whose title points to a Muslim treatise on arithmetic;[1439]and in 984, also requesting from Lupitus of Barcelona his translation of Astrologia, a treatise on the astrolabe.[1440]

Quite crucial is the fact that the learning that was delivered from the abbey of Ripoll was dressed in the Christian garb, and not taken straight from the foe, maybe cleansed; and of course, delivered by good Christian hands to their own centres, such as monasteries and cathedrals. The importance of this Christian handled Islamic learning can be easily appreciated, if one briefly returns to the hostility seen few paragraphs back experienced today by Arabists in Spain (such as Castro), or as noted by Monroe, Menocal and others. One would imagine the experience in the Middle Ages, when war between Islam and Christianity was relentless, and when the fear of, and hostility to Islam (as seen in part one of this work) were acute. Thus Islamic learning could be accepted only with Christian blessing, and hence the primary role of Ripoll and Catalonia, which, certainly, were the pioneers through which Islamic learning was gradually legitimised and allowed in. Whilst Catalonia legitimised, Cordova, however, enlightened.

Cordova was the magnet that attracted and stunned the visitors; the foreign emissaries, and those seeking the new and refined, were dazzled by the splendour of the city,[1441] which was described by a German nun as `the Jewel of the world.'[1442]It was in the 10th century, `the most civilised city in Europe, the wonder and admiration of the world, a Vienna among Balkan states.'[1443] The city is said to have had 200,000 houses, 600 mosques,[1444] 70 public libraries during the time of Caliph Hakam II, and 900 public baths.[1445] Over the quiet guadalquivir Arab

---

1438 G. Wiet et al: History; op cit; p.206

1439 F. Micheau: la Transmission;; op cit; p. 401.

1440 Gerbert: *Epistola* 24 in Gerbert, *Opera mathematica*; pp. 101-102; translated as Letter 32 in Gerbert *Letters*; pp. 69-70; note 28 in S. C. McCluskey: Astronomies; op cit; p. 175. and F. Micheau: La Transmission; op cit; p. 401.

1441 T. Burckhardt: *Moorish Culture in Spain*, op cit; pp. 9-22.

1442 Hrotsvitha in *Scriptores rerum Germanicarum; Hrotsvithae opera*, ed. Paulus de Winterfeld (Berlin, 1902), p. 52, l.12 in P. K. Hitti, *History of the Arabs*, 6th ed, London, 1970, p. 527.

1443 J.B. Trend: Spain and Portugal, in The Legacy of Islam, (1st ed) op cit; pp 1-39, at p. 9.

1444 F.B. Artz: The Mind, op cit, p.149.

1445 J.B. Trend: Spain and Portugal, op cit, p. 9.

engineers threw a great stone bridge of seventeen arches, each fifty spans in width. One of the earliest undertakings of Abd Errahman I (ruled 756-788) was an aqueduct that brought to Cordova an abundance of fresh water for homes, gardens, fountains, and baths. The city was famous for its pleasure gardens and promenades.[1446] A sophistication unknown in Western Europe for centuries.[1447] The desire to emulate could never be stronger; jealousy and fear, Menocal pointing out, acting as veritable spurs for the desire to imitate, viewing such other culture as `chic and challenging, and to want some of the same and similar things.'[1448] Beyond the desire to emulate were practical needs, whenever the rulers of Leon, Navarre or Barcelona needed a surgeon, an architect, or a dress maker, for instance, Hitti notes, they applied to Cordova.[1449] Wealthy Christians visited Cordova to benefit from the medical skills of its distinguished physicians who worked in a number of local hospitals; Queen Tota of Navarre, for instance, brought her son Sancho the fat for a cure of his obesity.[1450]

One of the major elements sought from Cordova by northern Christians was, of course, scientific learning. It was Cordoba, Cochrane states, which was the original point of contact between Islamic science and the Christian West due to Carolingian interest in manuscripts to be found in that city.[1451] People having taste for learning and for elegant amenities, found their way into Spain from all adjoining countries.[1452] Cordova's eight hundred public schools were frequented by Muslims, Christians and Jews; and there the Spanish Muslim received knowledge at the same time and under the same conditions as the literary pilgrims from Asia Minor and Egypt, from Germany, France, and Britain.[1453]The Spanish universities were filled with ecclesiastics from many parts of Europe Draper notes.[1454] Peter the Venerable, the friend and protector of Abelard, who had spent much time in Cordova, mentions that on his first arrival in Spain, he found several learned men even from England, studying astronomy.[1455] In the great Muslim university of Cordova, Scott observes, both Jews and Christians attained to acknowledged

---

1446 W. Durant: The Age of faith, op cit; chap 13;p.302.
1447 M.R. Menocal: The Arabic Role; op cit; p.28.
1448 Ibid. p. 53.
1449 P.K. Hitti: History, op cit, p 527.
1450 P. Mansfield: *The Arab World;* New York; Cowell; 1976; P.45
1451 L. Cochrane, Adelard of bath, op cit, p. 6.
1452 J.W. Draper: A History; op cit; vol 2; p. 36.
1453 S.P. Scott: *History; op cit;* Vol iii, at pp 467-8.
1454 J.W. Draper: A History; op cit; vol 2; p. 12.
1455 Ibid.

distinction as professors.[1456] And although the effect of all such learning cannot be quantified, or that history has kept little evidence of its concrete effect, its effect was nonetheless extremely powerful. Sweetman observes, how: `Our tendency is to reduce such influence (of Islamic culture on Europe), or to hold it proved by, the actual possession of books and translations, but it should be borne in mind that there would have first to be built up the conviction of the desirability of the translation of certain books before the work was actually attempted. This could only be done by oral instruction which doubtless was supplied by wandering scholars of France and Spain.'[1457]

Even as the Muslims were losing their control over Spain, the Islamic impact remained crucial as Spanish Muslims constituted throughout the centuries a great reservoir of skills for northern Christendom. The siege and capture of Barbastro in the north-east of Spain in I064 illustrating this very well, when an army of Normans and Frenchmen, with the blessing of the Pope and under the command of William VIII, Duke of Aquitaine, took many Muslim prisoners, sending several thousand into France, 1500 to Rome, and 7000 to Constantinople.[1458] Singers, musicians and other artists are stated to have been among these number, and presumably also the Muslim corps of engineers which had defended Barbastro.[1459] Following the 13th century Muslim loss of most of Spain, Muslim skills in trades and crafts were made use more intensely, Muslim craftsmen working for Spanish sovereigns, like those who before the 14th built the Alcazar of Seville.[1460]The Andalusian techniques continued until the end of the 16th century and were associated with the rising influences of Gothic art or Revival, and one of the most beautiful human achievements, says Perroy.[1461] Muslim skills were needed and found to run many industries, paper, textiles, pottery, sugar, etc, and also needed in farming, irrigation above all.[1462] All these Islamic contributions will be explored in the third part.

[1456] S.P. Scott: History; vol 3; op cit; pp 467-8.
[1457] J.W. Sweetman: *Islam and Christian Theology*; Lutterworth Press; London; 1955; Vol I; Part II. P. 73.
[1458] J. Harvey: The Mason's Skills; in *The Flowering of the Middle Ages*; ed by J.Evans; pp. 67-106; at p. 86.
[1459] Ibid.
[1460] E Perroy: *Le Moyen Age*, Presses Universitaires de France, 1956. p.524.
[1461] Ibid.
[1462] T. Glick: Islamic and Christian Spain; op cit.

4. Sicily

In his entry on Sicily in the Encyclopaedia of Islam, and referring to the Normans taking of Sicily from the Muslims, Traini quoted the dictum which went: `Arabia defeated by arms, subjugated its conquerors with its genius.'[1463] From its Norman conquerors down to its last Hohenstaufen rulers, Briffault observes, Sicily remained a centre of Muslim culture and became the focus of `awakening civilisation.'[1464] Sicily says Amari, `owes its civilisation to the Arabs, and the whole of Italy owes to Sicily its initiation to the masterpieces of Arabic civilisation.'[1465] Thus, in Italy, the revival of culture was first manifest, not in the traditionally held North, but in the South due to the links with Islamic learning in most parts.[1466]

First, of course, to be looked at is the Islamic impact on the Island before looking at how it awakened the north.

Sicily was under Islamic rule from 902 to 1091. Muslim divisions and infighting opened the way to Norman conquest of the island in the later decades of the 11th century.[1467] Once, as Miranda explains, Sicily was freed from the devastation of war, its people devoted themselves `to the cultivation of their literature, poetry, legislation and the scientific knowledge they had received from the East.'[1468] The end of Muslim Sicily leading, as Hitti puts it, to `the efflorescence of an interesting Christian-Islamic culture.'[1469]The reason for this was the Norman acceptance of Muslim culture, Roger I and his successors being `wise enough' to realise the superiority of the Muslims, says Le Bon.[1470] The Norman rulers adopted the Muslim institutions, covered the Muslims with their protection, and in the end secured the country an era of prosperity, pursues Le Bon.[1471] The same point also made by Miranda,

---

[1463] R. Traini: Sikillya; *Encyclopaedia of Islam*; New Series; Vol IX: Leiden; Pp. 582-9 at p. 588.

[1464] R. Briffault: The Making, op cit, p. 212.

[1465] M. Souissi: La presence Arabo-islamique dans la culture Sicilienne; in *Cahiers de Tunisie*; Vol 29: (1981):pp 211-19; P. 211.

[1466] C. H. Haskins: The Renaissance; op cit; p. 21.

[1467]J. D. Breckenridge: The two Sicilies; op cit; p. 45.

[1468] A. H. Miranda: The Iberian Peninsula and Sicily, in *The Cambridge History of Islam*, vol 2, ed: P. M. Holt. A.K.S. Lambton, and B. Lewis, Cambridge University Press, 1970, pp 406-439, p. 437.

[1469] P. K. Hitti: History, op cit, p. 606.

[1470] G. Le Bon: La Civilisation; op cit; p.231.

[1471] Ibid.

telling how Roger I, acknowledging the Muslim superiority to the Greeks and Latin in numbers and `talents,' treated them with a kindness `then hardly heard of; and recognising his impartiality and moderation, the Muslims `obeyed him blindly.'[1472] His son, Roger II followed in the same line, and was so enthralled with Islamic culture that there were rumours that he was a crypto-Muslim. The Islamic impact on every aspect of life, including learning and science was felt, and in all parts of the Norman kingdom.[1473] The Muslims stood high in the confidence and favour of the Norman princes; Muslim cavalry enrolled by thousands in the Norman armies, whilst Muslim councillors stood in the shadow of the throne.[1474] Muslims also collected taxes and administered the public revenues, conducted diplomacy, whilst the prevailing language of court and city alike was Arabic.[1475]

The role of Islamic culture on the Island peaked under Frederick II. Frederick became king of Sicily in 1198 (of age in 1208), the head of the Holy Empire in 1220, and king of Jerusalem in 1229.[1476] In his `brilliant court,' Briffault writes, `under the stalactite roofs of Moorish halls, and amid oriental gardens adorned with murmuring fountains... the professors of Arabian sciences forgathered as honoured guests, and discussed mathematical problems and questions of natural history... that wonder court, the seat of learning, refinement and beauty, so utterly contrasting with the gloomy, rush littered halls of other European potentates, which swarmed with monks and vermin, ignorance and superstition, was an object of astonishment and malicious rage.'[1477] At his court the doctrines of the maligned Ibn Rushd were well known and often discussed.[1478] Widely respected, admired, and envied in certain circles, he was anathema to the Church and was excommunicated on many occasions, just as was William of Aquitaine.[1479] His contemporaries `shook their heads over the current stories of Frederick's scepticism and unbelief.'[1480]At the Council of Lyon, Pope Innocent III (pope 1198-1216) made it clear that his association with heretics (the Muslims) had caused Frederick's own heresy.[1481] Unhappiness with the

---

[1472] A.H. Miranda: The Iberian Peninsula, op cit, p. 437.
[1473] D. Metzliki: The Matter of Araby; op cit.
[1474] S.P. Scott: History; op cit; vol 3; p. 27.
[1475] Ibid.
[1476] G. Sarton: Introduction, op cit, p. 575.
[1477] R. Briffault: The Making, op cit, at pp. 212-3.
[1478] C.H. Haskins: Studies; op cit; P. 260.
[1479] M.R. Menocal: The Arabic Role; op cit; p.63.
[1480] C.H. Haskins: Studies, op cit, p. 260.
[1481] M.R. Menocal: The Arabic Role; op cit; p.63.

emperor's show of favours to the Muslims, stirring dissent amongst his closest friends, `and thrusting daggers and poison into their hands.'[1482]

Despite all opposition, Frederick remained an unabashed patron of Islamic culture, his court one of the apogees of European culture.[1483] Frederick's court was the intellectual capital of a world `already in upheaval' due to the effect of the translations from Spain that were spreading throughout the north, and Frederick became the patron of the new knowledge.[1484] He was an assiduous cultivator of knowledge from any and all sources, a collector of manuscripts from all parts of the learned world.[1485]He fostered learning in a diversity of sciences such as medicine, sciences which were viewed in some European quarters with hostility and fear.[1486] Frederick also kept intellectual exchanges with Muslim rulers of the East, and we hear of geometrical and astronomical problems such as the squaring of a circle's segment, solved for the emperor at Mosul.[1487] In the time of al Malik al-Kamil, sultan of Egypt (1218-38), the emperor sent seven difficult problems to test Muslim scholars, receiving in exchange from Al-Ashraf, sultan of Damascus, a magnificent `planetarium,' which bore figures of the sun and moon marking the hours on their appointed rounds.[1488] During his crusade in 1228, in Jerusalem, in the company of Sultan Malik al-Kamil, he discoursed of the latest advances in `his beloved mathematical sciences.'[1489] While in the East, Frederick asked for and got a most learned astronomer and mathematician al-Hanifi.[1490]

It was under Frederick that lived Sicily's main translator from Arabic: Michael Scot. Michael Scot was born in Scotland sometime in the last quarter of the 12th century, and died in 1235. From 1224 to 1227 the papal registers show that he had the active favours of Pope Honorius III and his successor, Gregory IX.[1491] Michael Scot learned Arabic and composed treatises on astronomy, astrology and physiognomy under the influence of Muslim learning.[1492] In 1217, he completed his translation

---

1482 R. Briffault: The Making; op cit; p. 213.
1483 M.R. Menocal: The Arabic Role; op cit; p.63.
1484 *Ibid.* p.61.
1485 Ibid.
1486 Ibid. p.64.
1487 C.H. Haskins: Studies; op cit; 265.
1488 Ibid.
1489 R. Briffault: The Making; op cit; p. 214.
1490 C.H. Haskins: Studies; op cit; p. 253.
1491 Ibid; p. 274.
1492 J.K. Wright: *The Geographical Lore; op cit;* pp. 99-100.

of al-Bitruji (alpetragius) `On the sphere) after spending some time in Spain.[1493] From his Sicilian period, Scot's works include the *Abbreviatio Avicenne de animalibus (Ibn Sina's treatise on the animals)*, which he dedicated to Frederick.[1494] Scot was also the author of two treatises on chemistry. His collaboration with Jewish and Muslim experimenters was obvious.[1495] Michael Scot's translations of al-Bitruji brought a fundamental questioning on the part of Western Christendom of Greek astronomy, most particularly Ptolemaic views of the planets.[1496]

Another court translator of astronomy was Plato of Tivoli, who translated a number of Muslim astronomical works, including al-Battani. Plato also did his translations in Spain. Both he (Plato) and Fibonacci were ordered by Frederick to gather Jewish and Muslim scholars to undertake translations of every available Muslim book.[1497]The emperor also sent Michael Scot to Cordoba to obtain more works to distribute to existing schools.[1498]

Sicily, a recipient of Islamic culture, became the purveyor par excellence of Islamic learning and science; its role much enhanced by its straddling two distinct cultures, and two distinct eras. `Lying between the Middle Ages and the Renaissance,' Haskins notes, `it (Sicily) was central in the history as in the geography of the Mediterranean lands.'[1499] The island became the leading intellectual centre of Europe, and `the foremost clearing house for cultural exchanges of all kinds.'[1500] Rising to occupy a position of `peculiar importance in the history of medieval culture,' adds Haskins.[1501]It was `A crucible for East-West artistic relations, according to Sweetman.[1502] Northern scholars visited Sicily in large numbers, and `wished to carry back some specimen of that eastern learning whose fame was fast spreading in the lands beyond the Alps.'[1503]

[1493] C.H. Haskins: Studies; op cit; p. 273.
[1494] Ibid. p. 279.
[1495] G. Sarton: Introduction, op cit, p. 579.
[1496] See: C. Burnett: Michael Scot and the transmission of scientific culture from Toledo to Bologna via the court of Frederick II Hohenstaufen, in Science at the Court of Frederick II; *Micrologus: Nature, Sciences and Medieval societies*, Brepols, 1994; pp. 101-26.
[1497] R. Briffault: The Making, op cit, p. 213.
[1498] Ibid.
[1499] C.H. Haskins: Studies, op cit, p. 243.
[1500] G. Sarton: Introduction, op cit, p. 496.
[1501] C.H Haskins: Studies, op cit, p. 156.
[1502] J. Sweetman: *The Oriental Obsession*: Cambridge University Press, 1987.p.5
[1503] C. H. Haskins: Studies, op cit, pp 156-157.

From Sicily originated key scientific accomplishments derived from Islamic sources. Beginning with mathematics and Fibonacci (fl early 13th century). Fibonacci learnt mathematics in Bejaia, in North Africa; later travelling about the Mediterranean Sea, on a journey that took him to Syria, Egypt and Sicily, studying the arithmetical means used by the merchants of many countries. He completed his *Liber Abaci* in 1202, which he would dedicate to his patron, Frederick.[1504] Frederick was the rightful patron, for both he and Fibonacci spoke the same language, handled the same notions, and shared the same values.[1505]Both had been impregnated since childhood by a Mediterranean culture with a dominant Islamic culture, one in Palermo and the other in Bejaia, and both had Muslim teachers, one spoke the language, and the other understood elements of it.[1506] Whilst Frederick's patronage was crucial, Fibonacci's contribution was equally so, the mathematical renaissance in the West may be dated to him.[1507] His *Liber Abaci's* second edition finally established the `Andalusian number system as the basis of modern mathematics.'[1508]

The island also pioneered in medical studies and practice, beginning with the innovative regulation by Roger II, in promulgating in 1140 that anyone practicing medicine must obtain authorization.[1509]This is precisely similar to Caliph al-Muktadir's order centuries back, the caliph appointing an officer to enforce the rule upon physicians and pharmacists.[1510]These measures ultimately led to the specialization of the study of medicine and the granting of degrees by the medical faculties of universities, which were major breakthroughs in the Christian West, soon adopted by other rulers of Christendom.[1511] The same regulations also applied to the making and sale of drugs, again following an earlier Islamic tradition dating from 761.[1512] Pharmacists were strictly supervised and had to pass an examination, just as happened in Europe centuries later.[1513]One of the earliest European

---

1504 M.R. Menocal: The Arabic Role; op cit; p.62.
1505 R. Rashed: Fibonacci et les mathematiques Arabes, pp 145-160; in Science at the Court of Frederick II. Op cit; pp. 146-7.
1506 Ibid.
1507 G. Sarton: Introduction; Vol II; op cit; p.611.
1508 M.R. Menocal: The Arabic Role; op cit; p.62.
1509 D. Campbell: Arabian Medicine; op cit; p. 119.
1510 Ibid.
1511 Ibid.
1512 F. Reichmann: *The Sources of Western Literacy;* Greenwood Press; London; 1980. p.209.
1513 Ibid.

pharmaceutical ordinances was enacted by King Roger II of Sicily in 1140, and the statutes of Frederick II, in 1231, greatly influenced the legislation in many Italian cities.[1514]

Geographical knowledge took a leading place following Roger II's sponsoring of the Muslim scholar Al-Idrisi (b. 1099-1100- d. 1166). The latter's main work, Roger's Book, was completed in 1154, and became the most comprehensive medieval treatise of geographical knowledge.[1515] This work includes a description of the earth as a globe, of the hemispheres, climates, seas and gulfs, and a lengthy account of the regions of the earth surface, and maps.[1516]Al-Idrisi's description of each of his divisions is of exceptional merit when compared with the Christians', mainly due to the vast amount of detail he assembled and his scientific method.[1517]Based on such knowledge, De la Ronciere says, the use of coast charts was destined to become general in Sicily; `a rational method of navigation to be substituted for the routine of pilotage, and thus the way was prepared for the progressive conquest of the world.'[1518] It is from the Sicilians that the Genoese learned the arts of navigation in the early 13th century and transmitted them subsequently to the Spaniards, Portuguese, French, and English; and a new science of the seas was developed upon the foundations originally laid by Sicilian Muslims and Normans.[1519]

There is a strong Islamic artistic legacy that thrived first in Sicily before it radiated North. One such legacy is in the art and use of ceramics as outlined here by Schnyder.[1520] The crossed arch frieze in the South of Italy and Sicily decorates stone buildings in the form of arcades which cross each other, such as at the Church of St. Michael in Caserta Vecchia completed in 1153.[1521] The same models are found in Cordoba[1522]and on the towers of Zaragoza and Teruel,[1523]similar to

---

[1514] Ibid. p.210.
[1515] D.M. Dunlop: Arab Civilisation, op cit, p. 171.
[1516] G.H. T. Kimble: *Geography in the Middle Ages;* Methuen &Co Ltd; London; 1938; p. 57.
[1517] Ibid.
[1518] De La Ronciere: Marine Francaise; vol 1; 1909; p. 136 in J.K. Wright: *The Geographical Lore; op cit;* p. 81.
[1519] De La Ronciere: Marine Francaise; vol 1; 1909; p. 136-7.
[1520] R. Schnyder: Islamic Ceramics: A source of Inspiration for Medieval European Art; in *Islam and the Medieval West (Ferber ed)*; op cit; pp. 27-38; pp. 29-30.
[1521] Heinrich Decker, *Italia Romanica,* Wien-Munchen (1966), pl. 123f.
[1522] M. Gomez-Moreno Martinez, "El arte arabe espanol hasta los Almohades," Ars *Hispaniae III,* Madrid (1951), p. 107f.

Caserta Vecchia, on the Giralda in Seville built between 1176-1196.[1524] In typical manner it also appears now in England[1525] and Normandy,[1526] where it had, undoubtedly, been brought by the Normans from Sicily.[1527] The expansion of he use of this decorative theme, Schnyder insists, is convincing evidence that the new contacts with the Islamic world during the 12th century had begun to exercise a profound influence far into Europe.[1528]

Islamic artistic influence can also be found in other areas, including in the ceremonial cloak originally made for the Norman King Roger II in Palermo in 1133, and subsequently worn as the coronation robe of the Holy Roman Emperors until 1806.[1529] This is a large semi-circular garment with a twice-repeated, monumental scene of a lion destroying a camel, its origin, the creation of Muslim craftsmen in the service of their new Christian ruler indicated by a large Arabic inscription.[1530]

Movements of people between the Norman kingdom of Sicily and other northern Norman courts (France and England) were very dense, and worked through trade, family ties, pilgrims, inter-marriage etc, and had their wide impact.[1531] Links in the 12th century between King Roger II of Sicily and France included the Abbey of Cluny, where lived a grandson of William the conqueror, as Boase records, who was to give an Islamic carpet to an English Church.[1532] There was, most particularly, a constant to and fro between Norman England and Norman Sicily. Under William the Good four prelates of English origin are known.[1533]Royal policy encouraged the presence of Englishmen at the Sicilian court and there was continuous interchange in administrators,

---

1523 Leopoldo Torres Balbas, "Arte Almohade, Arte Nazari, Arte Mude,jar," *Ars Hispaniae* IV, Madrid (1949), p. 282; Luis Llubia Munne', *La ceramica de Teruel,* Teruel (1962), lam. IX, X.

1524 Torres Balbas: Arte, op. cit., pp. 23-29.

1525 E.g.. Graville Sainte-Honorie. Lucien Musset, *Normandie Romane,* Paris (1974), pi. 92f.

1526 An early example of this is the treasury of the Cathedral of Canterbury built from 1151-1167. Robert Th. Stoll, Jean Roubier, *Britannia Romanica,* Wien-Munchen (1966, plate 8.

1527 R. Schnyder: Islamic Ceramics; op cit; pp. 29-30.

1528 Ibid.

1529 R. Ettinghausen: Muslim decorative arts and painting, their nature and impact on the medieval West; in *Islam and the Medieval West (* S. Ferber ed) op cit; pp. 5-26. at p.16.

1530 Ibid.

1531 C.H. Haskins: England and Sicily in the 12th century; *The English Historical Review*: Vol XXVI (1911) pp 433-447 and 641-665; at p. 435.

1532 In J. Sweetman: *The Oriental Obsession; op cit;*.p.5

1533 C.H. Haskins: England and Sicily; op cit; p. 437.

clerks and scholars among whom Peter of Blois as the common teacher of both William II and Henry II holds a special place.[1534] The chroniclers of Mont St Michel and Bec were well informed concerning events in the south, as were English historians of the close of the century.[1535]These contacts between Sicily and England were very important `as to affect matters of trade and culture,' notes Haskins.[1536] An Englishman, Robert of Salesby, stood as the head of King Roger's chancery. Although no great scholar himself, his lavish hospitality to visiting Englishmen, delighted John of Salisbury when he was his guest in the summer of 1150, and must have surely helped those who had literary and scientific interests like John of Salisbury himself.[1537]The continuous intercourse between Norman England and Norman Sicily was the means by which many elements of Muslim culture came directly to distant Britain.[1538]The influences that were transmitted from `the tripartite culture of Sicily' flourished in England and were encouraged by royal patronage as is clear from the many learned and scientific works dedicated to Henry II, including Adelard of Bath's treatise on the astrolabe.[1539] `Your king is a good scholar, but ours is better,' writes Peter of Blois to Walter Ophamil, archbishop of Palermo, another ecclesiastic from England. `I am well acquainted with the abilities and the performance of both. With the English king there is daily study, constant conversation with the best scholars and eager discussion of all questions.'[1540]It was not surprising, therefore, that the English court under Henry II and Eleanor of Acquitaine reflected a new cosmopolitan culture.[1541] Such was the importance of the Sicilian impact on England during those times, Sir Frank Stenton, who, although appreciating the Anglo Saxon achievement, conceded that `every aspect of English life was changed by the Norman conquest.'[1542]

It is Sicily, which pioneered in the system of administration, which it also inherited from its Muslim forebears, before it exported it to England. Wiet et al note how the first states to emerge strongly

---

1534 D. Metlitzki: The Matter of Araby; op cit; p.8.
1535 C.H. Haskins: England and Sicily; op cit; p.436.
1536 Ibid; p.434.
1537 D. Metlitzki: The Matter of Araby; op cit; p.8.
1538 R. Briffault: The Making; op cit; p. 212.
1539 D. Metlitzki: The Matter of Araby; op cit; p.8.
1540 *Petri Blesensis Opera Omnia*; ed. I. A. Giles; Oxford; 1847; I; pp 194-5; in D. Metlitzki: The Matter of Araby; op cit; p.9.
1541 D. Metlitzki: The Matter of Araby; op cit; p.9.
1542 Anglo-Saxon England, p. 677. in D. C. Douglas: *The Norman Achievement*; Eyre and Spottiswoode; London; 1969; p. 170.

consolidated were the kingdoms of Sicily and England, comparatively small, but both under Norman rule.[1543] In Sicily, all business relating to land tenure or property in land, was part of a department of the Treasury taken over bodily from the Muslims and known as *Diwan tarikh al-Mamur*, or in Latin as the Duane de Secretis.[1544] The Normans took over the Muslim Diwan, the *Dohana de secretis* appearing during the rule of Roger I with greater frequency.[1545] The Normans neither refrained from using Arabic extensively in their administrative system.[1546]The chief fiscal officials, or *magistri dohanae*, drew up the lists of villains on the royal demesne; they kept the land books and the record of customs dues; and they prepared the registers of fiefs and naval and military services.[1547] The masters of the Dohana also travelled through the country to hear fiscal appeals and audit the accounts of the local officials.[1548]There is also mention, in later Norman deeds relating to land, of the authority of certain Arabic registers known as *deftarii*.[1549]

The Anglo-Norman institution, the Exchequer and its Pipe Rolls, may have its beginning, in fact, in the Sicilian *duana* (Arabic *diwan*,) which was largely staffed by Muslim officials, which kept voluminous registers, and seems plainly to go back to Islamic antecedents.[1550] This Sicilian impact on England goes back to the links between the Norman kingdoms of Sicily and England. Both William the Good (1166-1189) (of Sicily) and Henry II (of England) kept themselves informed about contemporary conditions in each other's kingdom; and a `restless experimenter' like Henry II was not the man to despise a useful bit of administrative mechanism because of its foreign origin.[1551] In respect to the administrative system of King Roger's time, Henry `had an ever ready source of information' in the Sicilian official he had called to his side, `his almoner and confidential advisor,' Master Thomas Brown.[1552] Before leaving Sicily for England, Thomas Brown is traced as Qaid Brun in a branch of the government, the Diwan, where, with the

---

[1543] G. Wiet et al: History ; op cit; p.267.

[1544] C. Waern: *Medieval Sicily*; Duckworth and Co; London; 1910; p. 32.

[1545] E.M. Jamison et al: *Italy and Medieval Modern History*; Oxford at the Clarendon Press; 1917; P. 108.

[1546] H. Bresc: Mudejars des Pays de la Couronne d'Aragon et Sarrasins de la Sicilie Normande: le Probleme de l'acculturation; In *Politique et Societe en Sicile; XII-Xv em Siecle*; Variorum; Aldershot; 1990; pp. 51-60. p.58.

[1547] E.M. Jamison et al: *Italy and Medieval Modern History*; op cit; p. 108.

[1548] Ibid.

[1549] C. Waern: *Medieval Sicily*; Duckworth and Co; London; 1910; p. 32.

[1550] C.H. Haskins: *The Normans in European History*; New York; 1966; p. 229; in D. Metlitzki: The Matter of Araby; p.8.

[1551] C.H. Haskins: England and Sicily; op cit; p.434.

[1552] Ibid. p. 438.

secretary Othman, he attaches his *alama* to a transcript from the record of the bureau.[1553] His title of master probably indicates that he was one of the high officials of this department.[1554] He was a certain member of the Sicilian king's court, found in 1149 engaged in the diwan or financial department of the administration.[1555] His name is mentioned in both Arabic and Greek in official Sicilian documents.[1556]Thomas had to leave Sicily on the death of Roger II in 1154, and the accession of William the Bad (1154-1166), and was invited by the English king to enter his services.[1557] As an official of both King Roger II and Henry II, Thomas Brown was a major link between the fiscal systems of the two kingdoms when he transferred his services after the death of Roger II of Sicily to the court of Henry II in England.[1558] From 1158, there are signs of his being in the English King Henry II's employment. From 1160 to 1180 (year of his death), he was in receipt of 5d.a day from the farm of Hereford, the regular stipend of a clerk; and in some years he had in addition 5s. a day from Essex and Hertfordshire, the same amount as the vice chancellor.[1559] Thomas Brown sat at the exchequer table, and kept a watch on all proceedings in the upper and lower exchequers, keeping an eye on the writing of the roll.[1560]Thomas Brown had a clerk who wrote a roll himself. This third roll is kept by him as a check on the rolls of the treasurer and chancellor, and this roll, doubtlessly was intended for the private information of the king, which Thomas carries about him wherever he goes.'[1561] This roll is said by the Dialogue to contain `the rights of the kingdom and the secrets of the king' (*regni iura regisque secreta*).[1562]

Obviously, Islamic influences via Norman Sicily have been particularly disputed or suppressed, and chief amongst such

---

[1553] Caspar, No 218, printed from the Arabic original by S. Cusa: *I Diplomi Greci ed Arabi di Sicilia*; I; Palermo 1868; i. 28.

[1554] Garufi: archivio storico italiano, fifth series, xxvii. 235; 237; 239; 252, interprets the Title Kaid as meaning one who was over the local collectors of tribute.

[1555] R.L. Poole: *The Exchequer in the 12th Century*; Oxford at the Clarendon Press; p. 118.

[1556] S.Cusa: *I Diplomi Greci ed Arabi di Sicilia*; I; Palermo 1868; pp. 30; 313.

[1557]This information is found in the Dialogue, I.6 p.190; which concerns the Exchequer, written by Richard, Bishop of London (1189-1198), who sets out to explain the system in which he had been trained, and which enlightens on the history of the Exchequer at its beginnings. See R.L. Poole: *The Exchequer*; op cit; pp.2-6. And also p. 118.

[1558] R. Briffault: The Making, op cit, p. 212.

[1559] R.L. Poole: The Exchequer; op cit; p. 119.

[1560] Ibid. p. 120.

[1561] C.H. Haskins: England and Sicily; op cit.

[1562] Dialogue; i.6 p.191; in L. Poole; op cit; pp. 2-6; pp. 118-9.

suppressions was the Islamic role in the development of the English Exchequer, and the particular role of Thomas Brown (Qaid Brun) in this.[1563] Thus, we are told, that Thomas Brown is English in Origin, and went to exert in Sicily before returning to his native country (England).[1564] Which is logically and historically untenable. First, if this was the case, Thomas Brown would have had to be born in the late 11th century to exert first in England in the exchequer, go to Sicily for a long number of years under Roger II (exert there in the 1140s), come back and serve in England until his death in 1180, at the age of a hundred or near a hundred (having served the English crown in his eighties, and even nineties) which will be a unique case in history. Second, whilst the name of Thomas Brown (as Qaid Brun) is recorded in Sicilian documents in Arabic and in Greek, there is no trace of him in English documents before he supposedly went to Sicily (1130s-1140s). If those who deny the Muslim influence were right, and if the exchequer existed before the arrival of Thomas brown from Sicily (in 1154) his name would have been recorded in Norman English documents of the 1120s-1130s. The fact that he (Thomas Brown) bore the Arab title of Qaid (leader), that his name is mentioned in Arabic in Sicilian documents, that he knows Arabic, that his secretary was Othman, proves he was vastly knowledgeable of Arabic accounting/administration. Also, as Bresc pertinently reminds, the shortage of well read personnel explains why, still, as late as 1240, functions of the Duana Secretis in Sicily are still filled with Muslim scribes.[1565] The issue raised is: how could, in Sicily, any non Muslim run a Muslim run system of administration derived from Islamic antecedents?

Looking at the issue from a purely historical perspective, the arrival of Qaid Brun in England is no mere accidental happening, but is related to the experience of Muslims in Sicily. Qaid Brun had to leave Sicily on the accession of William I (the Bad) (ruled 1154-1166). The question to ask is why should he leave the island if he was not Muslim? Christians remained, whilst many Muslims left Sicily at more or less the same time. The Muslims had to leave Sicily in large numbers during the

---

[1563] Such as by F.M Powicke (on whom more further on), who paying tribute to Haskins, insists that Haskins did not believe in the Islamic impact on the beginning of the exchequer, whilst, on reading the article by Haskins on the subject, as referred to above, one finds that contrary to what Powicke holds, this is exactly what Haskins did. Tribute to C.H. Haskins; by F.M. Powicke: *The English Historical Review* vol 52; (1937); pp 649-56: at pp 651-2.

[1564] I.e R.L. Poole: The Exchequer; op cit. p. 118.

[1565] H. Bresc: Mudejars des Pays de la Couronne d'Aragon et Sarrasins de la Sicilie Normande: le Probleme de l'acculturation; In *Politique et Societe; op cit;* pp. 51-60. p.58.

particular rule of William I, just when Qaid Brown did, because precisely then, following power struggle in the palace, Muslims within the court were slain in large numbers. In 1161, courtiers were massacred, many caught in the streets on their way to find refuge at the houses of friends.[1566]The mob also killed many Muslims in their warehouses, or, more pertinently here, in their fiscal offices (diwans.)[1567] The court atmosphere was very heavy, and very difficult to bear for Muslim functionaries, courtiers and women.[1568] It became even dangerous for Christians to have Muslims friends.[1569] More than twenty years later, in the 1180s, Ibn Jubayr's during his travel to Sicily from Spain talks of Muslim high officials who had lost all, men such as Qaid Abu Kassim ibn Hammud, surnamed Ibn al-Hagar, `one of the nobles of this island, who had been imprisoned in his house, and had all his palaces confiscated and also the possessions inherited from his ancestors.'[1570]Ibn Hammud expressed to Ibn Jubayr his dearest wish to sell everything left and to leave with his family the island.[1571] At Messina the civil servant `Abd al-Massih told Ibn Jubayr: `You can boldly display your faith in Islam... But we must conceal our faith and, fearful of our lives, must adhere to the worship of God and the discharge of our religious duties in secret.'[1572] Thomas Brown, thus, is no unique case of Muslims deserting Sicily following the change of fortunes of Muslims on the island, and he is no unique case of Sicilian Muslims exerting positive impacts in their new places of adoption, as told by Sarton in relation to medical learning.[1573] What Thomas Brown did was to escape for his life, and here, the English merit, England, the land where he could find refuge.

5. The South of France

It is from the south of France, Menocal explains, that streamed the new literature and arts, architecture and good living, and chivalry in prose

---

[1566] N. Daniel: The Arabs; op cit; p. 149.
[1567] Ibid.
[1568] Ibid. pp. 150-1.
[1569] Ibid.
[1570] Ibn Jubayr: *Travels*. in C. Waern: Medieval Sicily; op cit; pp. 74-5.
[1571] Ibid.
[1572] Ibn Jubayr: *The Travels of Ibn Jubayr*; Tr; R.J.C. Broadhurst; London; 1952. p. 342.
[1573] G. Sarton: Introduction; op cit; ii; p.307.

and deeds.[1574]It is the langue d'Oc which allowed France to import `the goodness of Arabic civilisation,' adds Fabre d'Olivet. [1575]

Many factors concourse to make the south of France one of the main places that received and in turn disseminated Islamic culture and science.

First, trading links between the south of France and Islamic parts were early, and carried much Islamic cultural influence over the Pyrenees. The Jews, from the 9th century, constituted a dense network of exchanges between their communities on either side of the frontier. Agobard of Lyons (d. 840) protested against these coming and going of Spanish Jews between Spain and the Frank kingdom.[1576]Hebrew trade affected France, Portugal and Italy; whilst Provence and Languedoc were long subject to Hebrew influence.[1577] Marseille was also, in 1138, in a position to obtain a direct treaty with the king of Morocco. The commune had at that time privileges and possessions in the Orient.[1578] The traveller Benjamin of Tudela noticed in 1173, that there were in Montpellier many foreign traders, particularly merchants from the Maghrib, Syria, Lombardy, Rome, Genoa, Pisa, Egypt, Gaule, Spain, and England.[1579]The ports of this region, above all Barcelona, Montpellier, Narbonne and Marseilles, were in relation with Muslim trading states of the Balearic Islands and Spain, and also Africa and the Levant, and these relations were far from being solely commercial. [1580] It is through these regions, just as through Sicily and Toledo, Dawson explains, that Western Christendom first established contact with Islamic thought.[1581] Marseilles and Montpellier, were according to Duhem, `gates open to Oriental sciences.'[1582]

The geographical proximity of Spain and the south of France, obviously, played a primary role, Burnett highlighting how the littoral of Provence and Languedoc had close cultural links with northern Spain.[1583]Contacts between the men of Provence and those whose sphere of influence was

---

[1574] M R. Menocal: The Arabic Role; op cit.
[1575] A.Surre-Garcia: L'Image du sarrasin dans les mentalites de la litterature Occitanes: in *De Toulouse a Tripoli*, AMAM, Toulouse, 1997. pp 181-89; p.186.
[1576] J.W. Thompson: The Introduction; op cit; p.192.
[1577] S.P. Scott: History; op cit; Vol II, p.154.
[1578] M.L. de Mas Latrie: Traites de paix et de Commerce, op cit; p.117.
[1579] Benjamin of Tudela: Itinerar. Terrae Santae." *Bibl. de l'Ecole des Chartes*, 2nd series, Vol III, p. 203.
[1580] C. Dawson: Medieval essays; op cit; p. 221.
[1581] Ibid.
[1582] Ibid.
[1583] C. Burnett: Hermann of Carinthia; op cit; p. 387.

still mainly limited to south of the Pyrenees were, thus, frequent and varied.[1584] There is evidence of a Muslim community in Montpellier in the mid 12th century,[1585] and Muslims still formed one fifth of the population of Aragon after the Christian conquest of 1087.[1586] Literature, philosophical and military adventures, the luxury, the taste, and also the chivalrous gallantry and elegant courtesies of `Moorish society' found their way from Cordova and elsewhere to Provence and Languedoc.[1587] Some of the earliest Latin translations of Islamic sciences were made in fact at Marseilles, Toulouse, Beziers, and Narbonne, just as in Barcelona and Tarragona.[1588]

Military campaigns were another main source of impact; the French of the south acting as a very large reservoir of nobles who, first fought in Spain, and also went on the first crusade. William VI of Aquitaine, was involved on the side of Aragon to fight the Muslim counter-offensive at Barbastro, and Raymond St Gilles of Toulouse fought the Almoravids in Spain in 1087.[1589] What the Franks took from Barbastro back to Western Christendom in terms of skilled personnel has already been seen.

One of the leading military chiefs of the first crusade was no other than Raymond IV of Saint Gilles, count of Toulouse, and future count of Tripoli.[1590] What the Franks, who to great measure came from the south of France, brought from their crusading trips in the East has also been considered in part. The Franks in the East, also, as some chroniclers tell, sometimes crossed the barrier of hate and learnt Arabic, and nourished themselves with Muslim culture and learning, often, even, choosing the way of life of their adversaries.[1591] Thus, this knight, who, having frequented the Muslim milieus could no longer eat like a Frank, and recruited Egyptian female cooks to prepare his meals.[1592] Another example cited by Ibn Shadad, of a grand Lord, who having learnt Arabic

---

1584 M.R. Menocal: The Arabic, op cit; p. 30.

1585 J. Jomier: Notes sur les steles funeraires arabes de Montpellier; in Islam et Chretiens du Midi (xiie-xive siecle), *Cahiers de Fanjeaux* XVIII (1983); pp. 60-3; one of the tombstones commemorates the death of a Muslim fakih in 1138-9.

1586 C. Burnett: Hermann of Carinthia; op cit; p. 387.

1587 J.W. Draper: A History; op cit; vol 2; pp. 34-5.

1588 C. Dawson: Medieval essays; op cit; p. 221.

1589 N.Clement: Al-Andalus et les Croisades; in De Toulouse; op cit; pp 67-81. at p. 67.

1590 Presentation, in De Toulouse a Tripoli; op cit.

1591 A.M. Nanai: L'Image du Croise dans les sources Musulmanes, in De Toulouse; pp 11-39; at p. 36.

1592 Ibn Munqid in A.M. Nanai: L'Image du croise; p. 36-7.

studied the culture deeply, and finally decided to live amongst the Muslims for many years.[1593]

The subsequent conquests of Ferdinand and Jaime, the occupation of Cordova, Seville, Majorca, and Valencia, also sent to Languedoc tens of thousands of Muslim refugees.[1594]And, of course, as Menocal explains, `In the tradition of all those throughout history who have been forced from their homeland, they took with them many of the trappings of the world from which they came, and in some small measure they recreated that world.'[1595] In Narbone, Beziers and Montpellier, Jewish and other Andalusians, thus, passing on some of the learning that already distinguished Al-Andalus as an advanced culture.[1596]

Not all Muslim influence was willingly received, though; the Occitans, themselves, who had contributed to the Crusades, soon became themselves the victims of the bloody crusade against them. These Occitans, Surre Garcia says, were equated with the `Saracens,' and all their stereotypes: `unfaithful, vindictive, pervert, hypocrite.' [1597] Michelet explains that in the crusade against the country of Oc: `the eaters of garlic, oil, and figs remind the crusaders of the impure Moorish and Jewish blood, and the Languedoc seemed to them another Judea.'[1598] The French southerners were also suspected of betrayal and siding with the Muslims,[1599] claims such as `Eudes making a pact with Munuza; the Provencal duke Mauronte composing with a Muslim chief against the Franks, of Raimon III or Richard Lion-heart making treaty with Saladin; of Eleanor of Aquitaine, accused of infidelity during her stay in Tripoli, leaving the king of France for Henry II of Plantagenet, and even having intimate relations with Saladin. `The Menestrel of Rheims will damn the Muslim Saladin responsible for the divorce of Eleanor.'[1600]

Worse than betrayal was heresy. Already in 1134, Peter de Brueys had been burned in Languedoc for denying infant baptism, the worship of the cross, and transubstantiation, and so was his disciple, Henry the Deacon.[1601] The `Heresy' nonetheless spread throughout the 12th century especially carried in the songs of the Troubadours, denouncing the

---

[1593] Ibn Shadad in A. M. Nanai: L'Image du croise; pp. 36-7.
[1594] S.P. Scott: History; op cit; vol 3; p. 76.
[1595] M R Menocal: The Arabic Role; op cit; p.27
[1596] M. Defourneaux: *Les Francais en Espagne; op cit;*p.3.
[1597] A.Surre-Garcia: L'Image du sarrasin; op cit; p.184.
[1598] Ibid.
[1599] Ibid. p. 185.
[1600] Ibid.
[1601] J.W. Draper: A History; op cit; vol 2; pp.60.

priestly class most particularly.[1602] Scott also notes how in the heyday of its prosperity, the court of Toulouse just as that of Palermo, was `in all but name and costume, Mohammedan.'[1603]The count of Toulouse was also charged of protecting heretics and Jews, and intermeddling with the rights of clergy.[1604]

Accumulated charges were followed by a bloody crusade against the Albiginsians (After the inhabitants of Albi, south of France) in the early years of the 13th to eradicate the heretical spread.[1605] At Beziers, the crusaders scaled the walls, captured the town, and slew 20,000 men, women, and children in indiscriminate massacre; even those who had sought asylum in the church.[1606] Arnaud, the papal legate, was asked should Catholics be spared, he answered, `Kill them all, for God knows His own'.[1607]

Despite such hostility, Islamic culture impacted on the southern Provence, and from there spread in all directions, exerting crucial changes north of the continent.[1608] In such a diffusion the Jews played the major role; a role that has been considered already, only requiring brief notes here. The south of France was the Jewish stronghold par excellence, the Jewish colony at Montpellier in particular, a very large one, especially among the medical men in the 10th and 11th centuries.[1609]And just like Hebrew `colonists' of Narbonne and Marseilles, they were educated in Spain, and all spoke Arabic with fluency.[1610] It is these Jews, who familiarised the population of Languedoc and Provence with `the art, the science, and the literature of the Arabs,' according to Scott, and through whose agency, `an acquaintance with the Arabic language and literature became in Southern France and in Sicily indispensable to the education of a scholar.'[1611]

[1602] Ibid. pp.60-1.
[1603] S.P. Scott: History; vol 3; op cit; p. 101.
[1604] J.W. Draper: A History; op cit; p. 61.
[1605] Ibid. pp. 61-2
[1606] Ibid.
[1607] G.C. Coulton: *Life in the Middle Ages*; Cambridge University Press; 1930; 4 vols. I; p. 68.
[1608] C. H. Haskins: Studies, op cit, p. 96.
[1609] T. Pushmann: *History of Medical Education;* tr and ed E.Hare; London; 1891. p. 212.
[1610] S.P. Scott: History; op cit; vol 3; p. 87.
[1611] Ibid.

The South of France, most probably after Toledo, was the main centre of translation of Islamic science, and the links between translators and local scholars were established in earnest.[1612] It was in the Jewish schools of Beziers, Lunel and Montpellier, most primarily, where were made the translations of some of the most important Islamic sciences.[1613] Scholars like Abraham ibn Ezra at Narbonne prepared the way for the translations from Arabic into Hebrew of Al-Biruni's commentary on Al-Khwarizmi's tables.[1614]The Tibbonide family, who had settled in Southern France before the end of the 12th century,[1615]translated medical treatises from Arabic to Hebrew, and from Hebrew to Latin. Other than Samuel Ibn Tibbon, who produced translations of Islamic works in places such as Arles, Marseilles, Toledo, and Barcelona, his son, Moses of Montpellier was also a famed translator, and so was his son in law, Jacob Anatoli of Montpellier.[1616] The latter Jacob Anatoli, who married Samuel Ibn Tibbon's daughter was the first translator of Ibn Rushd's commentaries (1232), and also translated al-Farghani's astronomy.[1617] A pupil of the Rabbi master, Abbon of Narbonne, published `The Book of healing of Montpellier' derived from Ibn Sina.[1618]

As elsewhere, the Jews also served as intermediaries to the Latin; John de Planis, for instance, relied on the Jew Maynus to translate Ibn Rushd's treatise on laxatives from Hebrew into Latin, whilst John of Brescia worked with Jacob ben Mahir at Montpellier in 1263 to translate into Latin al-Zarqali's treatise on the astrolabe (*Liber tabulae qaue nominatur saphaea patris Isaac Azarchelis*). Jacob translated from Arabic into the vernacular, John wrote the Latin equivalent.[1619]

Many other learned men also resided, studied and were active in the south of France amidst the scholarly communities, and also in the vicinity of Spain. Beziers was where Herman of Carrinthia (originally from the Balkans), the translator of Abu Ma'Shar and Al-Khwarizmi, had resided and made such translations in the 1140s.[1620] Hermann could have had intimate contact with Muslim scholarship on either side of the

---

1612 M.T. d'Alverny: Translation, op cit, p. 458.

1613 H .Harant and Y. Vidal: La Medecine Arabe et Montpellier; pp. 60-85; In *Cahiers de Tunisie*; Vol 3: p.62:

1614 Narbonne (South of France) 1160.

1615 G. Sarton: Introduction; op cit; Vol II; p.731.

1616 C. Dawson: medieval essays; op cit; p. 222.

1617 G. Sarton: Introduction; op cit; Vol II; p. 493.

1618 H. Harant and Y. Vidal: La Medecine Arabe; op cit; p.63.

1619 G. Sarton: Introduction; op cit; Vol II; p.831.

1620 See for details: C. H. Haskins; Studies; op cit.

Pyrenees.[1621] So did Christian missionaries such as Raymond Lull, who was a `famous Arabist' pupil of Montpellier.[1622] Another famed Arabist was Arnold of Villanova,[1623] a professor at the University of Montpellier and physician-regular to three kings of Aragon and three popes.[1624]He was also a prolific translator of Muslim works, including Al-Kindi's *(De medicinarum compositarum gradibus*); Qusta ibn Luqa: *de Physics ligatures*; Ibn Sina's *De viribus cordi;* Abu-l-Ala Zuhr's *De Conservatione corporis et regimine sanitatis*;etc.[1625] Another doctor, educated in Montpellier, Berenger, or Berengarius, Berenger of Thumba (?), wrote medical treatises in Montpellier c.1334, and also translated al-Zahrawi's tract on diet from Catalan into Latin.[1626] Abraham ibn Ezra, a famed translator of mathematical sciences, in particular, visited the local Jewish communities in Narbonne, and spread their works for their communities of Provence and Languedoc.[1627] Jacob Anatoli was from Marseilles, but flourished in Languedoc, whilst the Spaniard, Solomon ibn Ayyub, did most of his work in Beziers.[1628] Levi ben Abraham ben Hayim, who compiled two scientific encyclopaedias, and Gershon ben Solomon, who wrote a third work of the same kind, are sometimes spoken of as Catalan, but both were connected with Roussillion, Gershon residing in the main city of Perpignan.[1629]

One particular science that thrived in the south of France was astronomy. It is there, where one of the earliest attempts to adapt the astronomy of Muslim Spain to places North of the Pyrenees was made. This is found in the planetary tables drawn up in 1140.[1630] They are preserved in a 12th century manuscript of the Bibliotheque Nationale, a set of astronomical tables of Marseilles, the work of a certain Raymond of Marseilles (fl.1140).[1631] Raymond says that students of astronomy are compelled to have recourse to `worthless writings going under the name of Ptolemy and therefore blindly followed; that the heavens were never examined, and that any phenomena not agreeing with such books were

---

[1621] C. Burnett: Hermann of Carinthia; op cit; p. 387.
[1622] J. Freind: *History of Physick,* 2 parts, London, 1750. pt. ii. p. 254.
[1623] Freind, Hist of physick, pt. ii. p. 254.
[1624] R.I. Burns: Muslims; op cit; pp 90-1.
[1625] G. Sarton: Introduction; op cit; Vol ii; p.893.
[1626] Ibid. Vol III; p.246.
[1627] Ibid. Vol II, p.731.
[1628] Ibid. p. 492-3.
[1629] Ibid. p.731.
[1630] C.H. Haskins: Studies; op cit; p.96
[1631] Bibliotheque Nationale Mss., Fonds latin, No 14704, fol 110, col. A, to fol. 135 vo. In J.K. Wright: The Geographical Lore; op cit; p. 96.

simply denied.'[1632] He, thus, decided to rely on the tables, which al-Zarqali had computed for the meridian of Toledo and adapted to Muslim years, and re-arranged them for the meridian of Marseilles and according to years `dated from the birth of our Lord.'[1633] The Marseilles tables contain a lot of material of astronomical geography, including a list of cities with their latitudes and longitudes derived from al-Khwarizmi.[1634] The *Marseilles Tables* give a rule for finding the longitude by the observation of the eclipses.[1635] Raymond also wrote a treatise on the astrolabe before 1141, relying on al-Zarqali, al-Battani, Abu Ma'shar, and Mash'Allah.[1636] Raymond declares himself the first Latin to acquire Islamic science, obviously ignoring that in this he was already preceded by scholars such as Adelard of Bath, Plato of Tivoli, Gerbert, Walcher of Malvern, etc.[1637]

The translations of Islamic astronomical works in the south were just as other sciences, too many to dwell upon here. Just to note Hermann of Carinthia's translations of Abu Ma'shar: *Kitab al-madkhal ila ilm Ahkam al-Nujum* and Al-Khwarizmi's Astronomical tables made at Beziers, and John of Brescia who translated Al-Zarqali's treatise on the astrolabe at Montpellier.

The south of France championed medical studies. The city of Montpellier, in 1137, already, had become one of the first centres in Christendom, and the first in France for the study of medicine.[1638]Its location close to Muslim Spain, of course, as Colish points out, explains Montpellier medical eminence.[1639]According to Watt, this owes to the very substantial minority of Jews and Muslims and also Arabic speaking Christians living in the city.[1640]The city, Campbell adds, was an `Arabist centre' with Italy on one flank and Cordova on the other; rich in books, having obtained all Constantine's and Gerard's (of Cremona) translations, and this at a time when the medical library of Paris was limited to `under a score.'[1641] Sarton's point that the birth and rise of Montpellier medical university can be traced back to the 12th century as

[1632] J.L. E. Dreyer: Mediaeval astronomy; op cit; p.243.
[1633] Ibid.
[1634] J.K. Wright: The Geographical Lore; op cit; p. 96.
[1635] *Ibid.* p. 85.
[1636] C.H. Haskins: Studies; op cit; p.96
[1637] Ibid.
[1638] W.M. Watt: The Influence, op cit, p 66.
[1639] M.L. Colish: *Medieval Foundations; op cit* p.270.
[1640] W.M. Watt: The Influence, op cit; p. 67.
[1641] D. Campbell: Arabian Medicine; op cit; p.160.

an offshoot from Salerno also holds good ground.[1642] Montpellier, it was, where were performed the first public human anatomical demonstrations of Christian Europe; those of the School of Salerno having been principally confined to the lower animals.[1643] In the 13th century, the corpse of a criminal was every year given to the faculty of Montpellier for this purpose; two hundred years before similar demonstrations were authorised by the university of Paris.[1644] Muslim and Jewish operators had carried into France the advanced ideas of Muslim Spain, which, `in defiance of ancient prejudice and medieval superstition, sought for the knowledge of the location and functions of the human organs in the intelligent and systematic dissection of the human body.'[1645]

Montpellier must have also derived prestige from its proximity to the comtat d'Avignon and the comtat Venaissin (Vaucluse), which were papal territories. The presence of the curia in Avignon attracted there the faithful from the whole Catholic world, Montpellier tending to become the medical centre for all these people, from the popes down. The popes, most particularly, took a deep interest in the medical faculty, which helps us know about the course of studies followed in Montpellier.[1646]

Montpellier spread its science in every direction, most particularly thanks to its learned men such as Arnauld of Villanova, already cited. Others include the leading representatives of Anglo-Norman medicine, Bernard de Gordon, Richard of Wendover, Gilbert the Englishman, and John of Gaddesden.[1647]Bernard de Gordon (a Scottish professor), for instance, taught at Montpellier from 1285 to 1297, and wrote the `*Lilium medicinoe* which he began in 1305 and is said to have completed in 1307, `a characteristic Arabist textbook on the practice of medicine.'[1648] *The Rosa medicinae* of John of Gaddesden (c.1314) includes many important clinical observations that have been very useful to contemporary physicians, `the finest symbol of the English medicine of its time.'[1649] The Rosa was appreciated in England and on the Continent, and also in Ireland, translated into Irish in the Yellow Book of Lecan in 1390.[1650] Other famed figures who spread the learning of Montpellier

---

[1642] G. Sarton: Introduction; vol 2; pp 352-3, and Volume III. p.247.
[1643] S.P. Scott: History; op cit; vol 3; p. 77.
[1644] Ibid.
[1645] Ibid.
[1646] Says Rashdall (2, 127-28, 1936) in G.Sarton: Introduction; Volume III; p.247.
[1647] D. Campbell: Arabian Medicine; op cit; p. 162.
[1648] Ibid; p. 163.
[1649] G. Sarton: Introduction; op cit; Vol III; p.247.
[1650] C. Burnett: Translations and translators; Dictionary of the Middle Ages; op cit; pp. 139-40.

include the leading exponents of Islamic surgery, Guy de Chauliac `the restorer of surgery' and Henry de Mondeville (or Hermondeville).[1651]

The south of France, finally, played a major part as a recipient, first, and then as a diffuser throughout the Christian West of Islamic architecture, art, and literature. Fikry has made a very good study of this Islamic artistic impact.[1652] Male also shows very interesting lines of communication between Islamic art and the rest of Europe through the south of France.[1653] Watson has looked at the relationship between French Romanesque and Islam, and the Islamic Spanish influences on architectural decoration,[1654]the routes, and the diffusion of such influences. Much of the architecture of southern Europe, and especially those buildings devoted to religious worship, present unmistakable evidences of their Islamic origin.[1655]The Islamic influence is equally strong on the literature of the region as well developed by Menocal;[1656] influence, which Geanakopolos denotes as `The literary efflorescence of southern France' a result of Islamic Spanish influence, not just with respect to the content of French troubadour poetry, but also to Arabic poetic devices and techniques.[1657]

Influences in the arts, architecture, and culture which will be amply developed in the final part of this work.

[1651] D. Campbell: Arabian medicine; op cit; p. 162.

[1652] A. Fikry: *l'Art roman du Puy et les Influences Islamiques;* Librairie Ernest Leroux, Paris; 1934.

[1653] E. Male: *Art et Artistes du Moyen Age*; Paris 1927.

[1654] K. Watson: French Romanesque and Islam: influences from al-Andalus on architectural decoration' *Art and Archaeology Research Papers* 2 (1972), pp. 1-27.

[1655] S.P. Scott: History; op cit; vol 3; p. 11.

[1656] M.R. Menocal: The Role of Arabic; op cit.

[1657] D. J. Geanakoplos: Medieval Western Civilisation; op cit; p.498.

3. TRANSLATIONS FROM ARABIC

As a consequence of the Islamic conquest (early 8th century), Spain, Haskins reckons, became for the greater portion of the Middle Ages a part of the Muslim East, `heir to its learning and its science;' `the principal means of their introduction into Western Europe.'[1658]
It is from Spain, precisely form the town of Toledo, decades after it fell in Christian hands (1085), that was delivered the bulk of Muslim scientific knowledge to Western Christendom in the form of translations. Scholars of Western Christendom seeking this Oriental lore turned chiefly to Spain, Spain, which throughout the 12th and 13th centuries, remained the land of mystery, of the unknown yet knowable, for inquiring minds beyond the Pyrenees. `The great adventure of the European scholar lay in the peninsula,' says Haskins.[1659] Metlitzki explains that the failure to defeat the Muslims in the East by force of arms, especially as the Crusades were now faltering, apparent to all even before the recapture of Jerusalem by the Muslims in 1187, meant for the Christian West that Spain was the source for the new vigour.[1660] At the dawn of the influx of Western translators to Spain, it was already clear what they had come for. In 1150, one of the leading figures of Christendom, Peter the Venerable, held: `The Saracens are very clever men, whose libraries are full of books dealing with the liberal arts and the study of nature, and that the Christians have gone in quest of these.'[1661] An influx of translators from Italy, Germany, England and elsewhere, descended on Spain `to seize on the wondrous secrets of the world of thought.'[1662]One after another they sought the key to knowledge in the mathematics and astronomy, the astrology and medicine and philosophy which were there stored up.[1663] They joined with native born Spaniards, whether Christians, Jews, or Muslims, to engage in the grand enterprise of converting the technical science and philosophy of the Arabic language into a language (Latin) that had been `largely innocent of such matters.'[1664]And not long after, their translations `descended on the barren scientific soil of Europe,' having

[1658] C.H. Haskins: Studies; op cit; p.4.
[1659] Ibid.
[1660] D. Metlitzki: The Matter; op cit; p.6.
[1661] Peter the Venerable: Liber contra sectam sive haeresim Saracenorum; in J. Kritzeck: *Peter the venerable and Islam*; Princeton; 1964; p. 238.
[1662] G. Wiet et al: History; op cit; p.465.
[1663] C.H. Haskins: Studies; op cit; p.4.
[1664] E. Grant: Physical Science; op cit; p. 16.

the effect `of fertilizing rain,' says Meyerhof.[1665] Translations, which for Grant, were to constitute `one of the true turning points in the history of Western science and intellectual history in general.'[1666]Translations in Spain, coinciding with the remarkable outburst of learning in the Christian West, the rise of the first great institutions of learning, Bologna, Montpellier, Padua, Oxford, Paris, etc, and the commonly known 12th century Renaissance.

It is the labour of such translators, and the impact of their translations, which are looked at in this chapter. First, it, it is necessary to look at the foundations, or background to such translation effort.

1. Background for Translations

The eagerness in the appropriation of Islamic learning at Toledo, that was to take place in the 12th century, was no fortuitous act on the part of the Western Christians. Latin Christians knew what such translations were to mean even before they undertook them. The southward advance of the conquering Christian armies, Hill insists, was accompanied by a desire to assimilate the superior culture of the Muslims.[1667] As Micheau observes, the translations from Arabic into Latin did not proceed despite the military hostilities between the two parties, but were the result of the same lust as for the wealth of the Muslim Orient.[1668]The translators/scholars were well aware that Islamic civilisation was much superior to theirs, Adelard of Bath, for instance, as Daniel points out, felt he was bringing something new and important to Europe, and was impatient, even contemptuous, of the purely indigenous developments of the north, literary, humanistic, and theological.[1669] The same feelings shared by Gerard of Cremona, who pitied the poverty of the Christian West, and even when falling ill in 1187, did not stop his translations, worried at what might happen once he was gone to the so `precious Arabic books;'[1670] translating until the very last moments of his life to

---

[1665] M. Meyerhof: Science and Medicine, in The Legacy of Islam, 1st ed; op cit; pp 311-55, at p. 351.
[1666] E. Grant: Physical science; op cit; p.15.
[1667] D.R. Hill: Islamic Science, op cit, p. 221.
[1668] F. Micheau: La Transmission; op cit; p. 400.
[1669] In. N. Daniel: The Arabs; op cit, p.268.
[1670] M.I. Shaikh: extract from `Penzance Manuscript; *'The International Conference of Islamic Physician's Contribution to the History of Medicine* (International Institute of

complete the staggering amount of 82 works.[1671] These medieval copyists (involved in the translation of Islamic works) were, indeed, conscious of the service they were rendering to civilisation.[1672] They were, Dawson notes, `by no means unconscious of the greatness of the issues at stake or of the revolutionary character of their work.'[1673] Petrus (Alphonsi) felt, that he has laboured hard-`magno labore.... et summo studio' to translate the work from the Muslims for the benefit of the Latin;[1674] expressing `a sense of mission,' even, in spreading Islamic science among the Latin.[1675] A fervour also caught in the words of Raymond of Marseilles, he, too, fully aware the Muslims will enrich Europe.[1676] Writing in 1140, he held: `If God, as we hope, approves, we strive to compose in honour of Christ Jesus, and for the common advantage of the Latin world."[1677]
As Grant concludes:
`Latin scholars in the 12th century were painfully aware that with respect to science and natural philosophy, their civilisation was manifestly inferior to that of Islam. They faced an obvious choice: learn from their superiors or remain for ever inferior. They chose to learn and launched a massive effort to translate as many Arabic texts into Latin as was feasible. Had they assumed that all cultures were equal, or that theirs was superior, they would have had no reason to seek out Arabic learning, and the glorious scientific history that followed might not have occurred.'[1678]

Western Christians had already had first hand knowledge of the learning and civilisation of Islam long before, indeed. Travellers and others, visiting Cordova, Sicily and other places were stunned by what they saw. Students in ever increasing numbers learnt Arabic and were setting aside their Latin background as the Christian apologist Alvarus lamented.[1679] Early scholars such as Gerbert and John of Gorze have

---

Islamic Medicine.) June 26-30, 1998; The International Convention Centre Birmingham, U.K.

[1671] R. Lemay: Gerard of Cremona; Dictionary of Scientific Biography; op cit; Vol 15; Supplement I; pp. 173-92.

[1672] G. Wiet et al: History; op cit; p.465.

[1673] C. Dawson: Medieval Essays; op cit; p. 141.

[1674] D. Metlitzki: The Matter op cit; pp.24-5.

[1675] Ibid.

[1676] N .Daniel: The Arabs; op cit; pp 269-70.

[1677] Ibid.

[1678] E. Grant: *The Foundations of Modern Science in the Middle Ages*; Cambridge University Press, 1996:p. 206.

[1679] Alvaro, Indiculus luminosus, chap. 35, in MPL, CXXI, 554-56; trans. Dozy, *Spanish Islam*, Trans. F. G. S. Styokes, London, 1913. p. 268.

brought north the first written aspects of such learning, which impressed many, and which made its early acquirers, the Lotharingians, the most sought after people.[1680]When the astrolabe was first introduced in the West from Islamic Spain via Catalonia in the early 11th century, it had a profound effect due to its capacities to allow calculations related to the planets hitherto impossible.[1681] The 11th century translations by Constantine the African had, it could be said, single handedly, revolutionised learning in general, and medical science in particular; the school of Salerno soon to stand `at the head of medical knowledge in the Christian West.'[1682] And the works of the early pioneers: Gerbert, John of Gorze, Hermann of Reichnau etc… had had the time to incubate and earn many disciples, who all within the Church, within the cathedral schools, or with power, could shift opinions and policy, too. All in all, by the 12th century, thus, the value of Islamic learning was better appreciated, even if considerable hostility to Islam prevailed, Western Christianity willing to absorb Islamic learning, but, it must be said, out of good, trusted, Latin hands (no surprise in religious figures taking in charge the translation effort as will be seen further on.)

Scholarly passion for Islamic learning, the need to catch up with the foe, and the realisation of the high value of such learning were served by a remarkable concurrent development: the collapse of Islamic power, which opened the road to Islamic scholarly riches. This power disintegrated just when the West was ready to benefit most from this influx of learning. Sicily fell to the Normans in the late 11th, the crusades began in 1096, and opened vast territories to the Christians, and, of course, of greater interest here, Toledo fell in 1085. The beginning of the disintegration of Muslim rule in Spain, Metlitzki says, had now brought the Latin and Islamic worlds into direct contact.[1683] In fact, it had opened the Muslim land and its scientific riches to the Christians, and now Christian Europe came into possession of great centres of Islamic learning.[1684]The translations of scientific and philosophical works from Arabic, Haskins emphasises, depended, indeed, upon the Christian re-conquest of Northern Spain (Toledo in

[1680] Mary C. Welborn, `Lotharingia; op cit; C.H Haskins, Studies, op cit, pp. 334-35; J.W. Thompson: Introduction; op cit; p. 191.
[1681]O. Pedersen: `Astronomy' in Science in the Middle Ages; D. C. Lindberg ed; op cit; pp 303-37 at p. 309.
[1682] D. Campbell: Arabian Medicine; op cit; p. 123. W. Durant: The Age of Faith; op cit; P. 457.
[1683] D. Metlitzki: The Matter of Araby; op cit; p.30.
[1684] E. Grant: Physical Science; op cit; p.16.

1085 and Saragossa in 1118,) to open the learning of the Muslims to the Christian scholars from the North who turned eagerly to the Peninsula.[1685] Daniel, too, accepts that the explosion of scientific translation was the product, in practice, of military success.[1686] Following the steps of the Christian armies of Alfonso, d'Alverny notes, scholars from all countries rushed down to Spain to unearth `the treasures locked in the `armaria' (those libraries attached to the mosques and courts) of the infidels, whose prestige only grew as their political power faded.'[1687]

Books in Arabic were now readily at hand and intellectually starved Europeans were eager to make their contents available in Latin, the universal language of learning in Western Europe. In this `wealth of Arabic books' delved masters of the two tongues (Arabic and Latin), helped by Mozarabs and resident Jews. [1688] The penetration into these `treasure chests' of learning in northern Spain brought about the excited discovery that it was, indeed, the Muslims who were the true representatives of classical knowledge, and `the giants on whose shoulders Latin science and philosophy had to be placed.' [1689]

Amongst those who had flocked to Toledo were Robert of Chester, Gerard of Cremona, Plato of Tivoli, Daniel of Morley, and many others who now laboured incessantly to acquire Islamic learning and `the signature of Toledo on many of the most famous versions of such learning.'[1690]Toledo, perhaps modest in stature today, but then refuge for men of learning, the likes of Daniel of Morley, who fled in horror from England and Paris, and hastened to hear `wiser philosophers of the universe' at Toledo where `the teaching of the Arabs.... was greatly famous in those days.'[1691]Toledo, it was, which gave rise to a regular school for the translation of science which drew from all lands those who `thirsted for knowledge.'[1692]

[1685] C.H. Haskins: The Renaissance; op cit; p.14

[1686] N. Daniel: The Arabs; op cit; p. 263.

[1687] M.T. D'Alverny: Deux Traduction Latines du Coran au Moyen Age in *Archives d'histoire doctrinale et litteraire du Moyen Age*; 16; Paris; Librairie Vrin; 1948; in La Connaissance de l'Islam dans l'Occident Medieval; edt by C. Burnett. Variorum; 1994; pp 69-131. at p.70.

[1688] V. Rose: `Ptolemaus und die Schule von Toledo' in *Hermes*, viii. 327; (1874); in C.H. Haskins: Studies, op cit, p. 12.

[1689] D. Metlitzki: The Matter; op cit; p.6.

[1690] V. Rose: Ptolemaus und die Schule von Toledo; op cit, p. 12.

[1691] See: Daniel of Morley's praise to the Bishop of Oxford, in C. Burnett: Introduction; op cit; pp 61-2.

[1692] V. Rose: `Ptolemaus; in C.H. Haskins: Studies, op cit, p. 12.

The translations were placed under ecclesiastical patronage, especially of Raymond de Sauvetat, archbishop of Toledo (1126-1151), and his contemporary Michael, bishop of Tarazona, both of them, coincidently, Frenchmen.[1693] Long after the passing of the first patron, Raymond, his successor, John (1151-66), had the translating activity brought within the precincts of the Cathedral.[1694] To him was dedicated the prologue and several parts of Ibn Sina's philosophical encyclopaedia, the *Shifa*, turned into Latin by the archdeacon, Dominicus Gundissalinus.[1695] This translating activity must have continued after the death of Archbishop John in 1166, for Gundissalinus is still signing documents in 1181.[1696] And of course, Gerard was also making translations from the same place long after the death of John, in 1187.[1697] Archdeacon Mauritius could have been in charge, then. He was well acquainted with Arabic, and played a major role in supporting Mark of (Toledo) in translating Islamic texts;[1698] and he could have had similar role as promoter of translations in the early 13th century as Gundissalinus had had in the 12th.[1699] Another translator, Robert of Chester was himself archdeacon of Pamplona's cathedral in 1143.[1700]The wider spread of these ecclesiastic endeavours raises the possibility that Michael Scot could have been introduced to the works of Gundissalinus and his collaborators in Italy or France, and above all in his native Great Britain which had a close relationship with Spain and where several early manuscripts of the translations survive.[1701]

Other than Toledo, translations were undertaken in Barcelona, Tarazon, Segovia, Leon, Pamplona, and even beyond, in the south of France at Toulouse, Beziers, Narbonne and Marseille. It is in Barcelona, that Arnau of Villanova translated a version of Ibn Sina *Makal fi ahkam al-adwiya al-kalbiya* (*de viribus cordis*). His nephew, Amengaud of Blaise, translated in Montpellier in 1284 *Udjuzza fi'l tibb* (*miracles of medical sciences*) by Ibn Sina and the commentary by Ibn Rushd. Johannes de Planis (Jean des Plans of Montreal (?) was active in the diocese of Albi, near Toulouse, and was involved in the translation of

[1693] J.Puig: Arabic Philosophy; op cit; p. 11.
[1694] C. Burnett: Michael Scot; op cit; p.103.
[1695] Ibid.
[1696] C. Burnett: Michael Scot; p.103.
[1697] R. Lemay: Gerard of Cremona: Dictionary of Scientific Biography; op cit.
[1698] See M.T. D'Alverny: Deux Traduction Latines du Coran au Moyen Age; op cit.
[1699] C. Burnett: Michael Scot; op cit; p.106.
[1700] J.Puig: Arabic philosophy in Christian Spain; op cit; at p. 11.
[1701] C. Burnett: Michael Scot; op cit; p.106.

Ibn Rushd's *canones de medicinis laxativis* from Hebrew into Latin, just as were Qalonymos ben Qalonymos and Samuel ben Judah of Marseille.[1702] In Padua, Italy, Bonacossa translated the *Kulliyat (The Book of generalities* (on medicine*)* of Ibn Rushd from Arabic in 1255, whilst Paravicus (John of Capua) translated the *Taisir (the accessible book in the matters of healing and diets)* of Ibn Zuhr from the Hebrew with the help of a Jew, Jacob, in Venice c. 1281.[1703] Most early editions of Islamic works were to be undertaken in Italy (see below Translations at a glance).

As Campbell points out, the knowledge of Arabic among the Westerners was insufficient for the effective translation of Arabic works on medicine and the other sciences, until at least the latter part of the 12th century.[1704] Thus, the need to partner those who knew the language was essential, hence the great role played by both Jews and Mozarabs. Apparently, Haskins explains, such interpreting frequently took the form of translating from Arabic into the current Spanish idiom, which the Christian translator then turned into Latin.[1705] The greatest pair of translators was certainly that of John of Seville (a converted Jew who acted as dragoman, besides doing his own translation work) and Domingo Gundisalvo (Archdeacon of Segovia,) who is the author of many translations and adaptations that include works the `*Fons Vitae* of Ibn Gabirol (Avicebron), the classification of the sciences of al-Farabi, and the philosophy of Al-Ghazali. His lack of knowledge of Arabic made him very much dependent on John, who gave him the Spanish word which the Archdeacon then turned into Latin.[1706]Everywhere, under Christian authority supervision, Latin scholars were able to work with intermediaries, Muslims, Mozarabs, and Jews.[1707]
Subsequently, at the court of Alfonso X of Castile (el-Sabio) (1252-84), Jews and Mozarabs played the role of translators into Castilian, and the king's clerks transcribed everything into Latin as is obvious with the remarkably influential (see following chapter) *Kitab al-Bari* (*Libro complido en los iudizios de la estellas*) (treatise on the stars) of Ali Ibn al-Ridjal of Qayrawan (d.1040).[1708] This work was put into Castilian by

---

[1702] G. Sarton: Introduction; op cit; Vol III; p.461.
[1703] F. Micheau: La Transmission; op cit; pp. 411-2.
[1704] D. Campbell: Arabian medicine; op cit; p. 136 .
[1705] C.H. Haskins: Studies; op cit; P. 17.
[1706] Ibid. p. 13.
[1707] M.T. D'Alverny: Deux Traduction Latines; op cit; D. Metlitzki: The Matter; op cit; p.6.
[1708] F. Micheau: la Transmission; op cit; p. 411.

Muslims and Jews, then Alavaro of Ovideo, first, then, Aegidius of Tebaldis and Petrus of Reggio, a second time, made it into Latin.[1709]

A large amount of translations into Latin was done not directly from Arabic, but into Hebrew, first, and then later into Latin.[1710] One cites at random Solomon ben Pater ha Kohen's translation of an astronomical treatise by Ibn al-Haytham from Arabic into Hebrew,[1711] and also of Al-Farghani's astronomy by Jacob Anatoli, and Ali ibn Ridwan's commentary on the *Tegni*, by Samuel ibn Tibbon.[1712] Qalonymos translated treatises by Al-Kindi, Thabit ibn Qurra, Ibn al-Samh (treatise on cylinders and cones), Jabir ibn Aflah, and `Abu Sa'dan (treatise on the triangle,) whilst Samuel Ben Judah translated Ibn Rushd's commentary on the Almagest, and astronomical treatises by Ibn Mu'adh and Al-Zarqali; and from Jacob ben Mahir, he obtained the translation of the *Islah al-majisti* (Refutation of the Almagest) and revised it again in Aix in 1335.[1713] The Jewish link was all the more important as they had good knowledge of both Arabic and Latin. Singer explains that in Castile, for instance, Jews were the natural intermediaries between Christianity and Islam because Arabic was spoken and written by all educated Spanish Jews.[1714] The skill of translating often passed from one generation to another, as, for instance, in the Tibbonid and Kalonymus families.[1715]The Jews were also interested in Muslim science and customarily wrote Arabic scientific works in Hebrew letters.[1716] This odd practice, Singer points out, was even continued by Christian scholars, and long gave rise to misunderstandings as the distinctiveness between Arabic and Hebrew.[1717] Quite importantly, some translations into and from Hebrew, such as that Ishaq al-Israeli's treatise on the elements and an ethical treatise of al-Ghazali both by Ibn Hasdai were extremely useful, because, here, as in many other cases, these works are lost in the Arabic original.[1718]

[1709] Ibid.
[1710] C.H. Haskins: Studies; op cit; P. 17.
[1711] G. Sarton: Introduction; op cit; Vol III; p.130.
[1712] For a brief outline on translations into and out of Hebrew, see B.Z. Richler: Translations and Translators; Dictionary of Middle Ages; op cit; vol 12; pp. 133-6.
[1713] G. Sarton: Introduction; Vol III; p.128.
[1714] C. Singer: T*he Earliest Chemical Industry;* The Folio Society; London; 1958; p. 63.
[1715] C. Burnett: Translations and Translators; Dictionary of the Middle Ages; op cit, vol 12; pp. 136-42; at p. 137.
[1716] C. Singer: T*he Earliest*; op cit; p. 63.
[1717] Ibid.
[1718] G. Sarton: Introduction; op cit; Vol II, p.495.

Although the translations of Muslim sciences went on for centuries, and in diverse places, it was principally those performed at Toledo, which went from about 1135 until the time of Alfonso X (1252-84), which laid the foundations for European learning.[1719]The number of copies of these translations that have been recovered remaining an indication of the scale of the impact;[1720]one of the turning points in the history of the West and intellectual history, according to Grant.[1721]Translations, it must, however, be pointed out, that were not alone in triggering the rise of science and learning in the West. No society, whether Muslim, or Latin, can come out of slumber by translations of sciences alone. Translations can have great effects as with Salerno, but Salerno would have never developed the way it did without other contributing elements, such as the availability of an emerging class of scholars, who diffused Salerno's science, the setting up of other institutions of learning which benefited from Salerno's science, the introduction of the hospital, which came in the 12th-13th century, the need for surgery (because of crusade warfare, mainly) etc. In the awakening of Western Christendom, thus, other factors such as the crusades, travel, trade, regional impact, etc, had their crucial impact on sciences and civilisation, trades, crafts, technology and farming. And one essential element in the success of the translations was the translators themselves, and what they invested in the endeavour.

2. Translators and their Labours

Focus must be, first, put on Gerard of Cremona, the greatest translator of the age. Gerard of Cremona, also known as Gherardo Cremonese, born in Cremona, Lombardy, Italy around 1114; died in 1187 in the Spanish town of Toledo; by far the most prolific of all translators of original scientific works in history.[1722] Gerard went to Toledo to either find Ptolemy's Almagest, according to Grant,[1723]or at the command of Barbarossa in order to translate the Canon of Ibn Sina, according to

---

1719 C.H. Haskins: Studies: op cit, p. 12.

1720 G. Wiet et al: History; op cit; p.465.

1721 E. Grant: Physical science; op cit; p.15.

1722 By far, the best outline on the life and works of Gerard of Cremona is the entry by R. Lemay in the Dictionary of Scientific Biography; op cit; vol 15; supplement.

1723 E. Grant: Physical Science; op cit; p.17.

Campbell.[1724] Still, once there, he was impressed by the intellectual riches of Toledo, and had to learn Arabic for the purpose of his translations.[1725] In front of the `multitude' of Arabic books in every field, he `pitied the poverty of the Latin.'[1726] Sarton points out, how Constantine (the African), it was, who opened the sluice gates to admit the first large stream of Islamic learning, but during the second half of the 12th century, a new stream, even larger than the first was liberated through the work of a greater man, Gerard of Cremona, who opened the second sluice gates; his activity truly gigantic.[1727] He translated around eighty works from Arabic into Latin. The list includes twelve works on astronomy, seventeen on mathematics (including al-Khwarizmi's algebra,) Thabit ibn Qurra's work *On the Kariston* (The Arabic name for a balance of unequal arms, or Roman Balance), al-Kindi's optical work, chemistry works by Al-Razi, and Ibn Sina's medical encyclopaedia: the *Canon* etc.[1728]

Most certainly Gerard could not have done all the translation without assistance, and was, without doubt, the head of a school of translation, which included Jewish intermediaries. He certainly had the assistance of a Mozarab named Galippus (Ibn Ghalib). Both he and Gallipus also lectured on astronomy.

On the whole, Gerard's translations resemble that of John of Seville: closeness to the Arabic original, preservation as far as possible of the construction of the Arabic sentences, and scrupulous rendering of nearly every word contained in the Arabic.[1729] Where Gerard's versions were tested, Haskins states, they were proved `closely literal and reasonably accurate.'[1730]

Falling ill in 1187, Gerard did not stop his work, worried at what might happen once he was gone to the so `precious Arabic books.'[1731] And so, he resumed the task despite his failing health. Hence, to Haskins, he became `master of the content of Latin learning.'[1732] Sarton also sees, that while the 12th century Latin writers had imperfect knowledge of Islamic science such as medicine, after Gerard's time the essential was available in Latin.[1733]

[1724] D. Campbell: Arabian Medicine; op cit; p. 144.
[1725] E. Grant: Physical science; op cit; p.17.
[1726] C.H. Haskins: Studies, op cit, p. 14.
[1727] G. Sarton: Introduction; op cit; Vol II; p. 310.
[1728] R. Lemay: G of Cremona; op cit.
[1729] Ibid.
[1730] C.H Haskins: Studies, op cit, p. 15.
[1731] M.I. Shaikh: Extract from `Penzance Manuscript,' op cit.
[1732] C.H. Haskins: Studies, op cit, p. 14.
[1733] G. Sarton: Introduction; Vol II; p. 309.

Other translators include John of Seville, who was also quite prolific, translating amongst others astronomical treatises by al-Kindi, al-Battani, Thabit ibn Qurra, al-Qabisi, al-Farghani and Abu Ma'shar; *al-Shifa* (the healing) of Ibn Sinna and *Maqasid al-Falasifa* (the ways of philosophers) by Al-Ghazali; a treatise of al Khwarizmi on arithmetic, and a popular version of the medical portion of the *Secretum secretum* (by al-Razi).[1734] John worked in Toledo under the patronage of Raymond I, archbishop of Toledo, and more importantly, as dragoman for Domingo Gundissalinus, Archdeacon of Segovia, who himself became head of the translation school.

Hugo Sanctallensis is a Spaniard translator, also known under various names including Hugh of Santalla. He was active in the first half of the 12th century between 1119-1151, working under the patronage of Michael, bishop of Tarazona (in the state of Aragon). His work was probably accomplished there or in the neighbourhood, as he mentions a local library at Roda or Rueda. Hugo wrote a commentary on the astronomy of al-Farghani. His translation of Abu Ma'ashar on meteorological predictions is found in many manuscripts. Hugo is also the author of the earliest Latin version of the chemical treatise `The Emerald Table' (*Lawh Zabarjad.*) In the introduction to al-Biruni's commentary on the Khwarismian tables, Hugh refers to the discovery of a text in the most secret parts of a library, a success earned by the bishop's `insatiable longing for philosophising.'[1735]

Plato of Tivoli was of Italian origin, but spent most of his working career in Barcelona. He was mathematician, astronomer, astrologer and translator, active between the years 1132-46. Plato did not have necessarily good knowledge of Arabic but was assisted in his task by Abraham bar Hiyya (Savasorda). Rabbi Abraham bar Hiyya of Barcelona, also called Savasorda, in addition to writing original works in Hebrew, collaborated with Plato of Tivoli to produce a large number of scientific works in the 1130s.[1736] Amongst these are astronomical and mathematical works *De horarum electionibus* by Al-lmrami, Al-Battani's *De motu stellarum,* and a version of Bar Hiyya's own geometrical treatise *Liber embadorum.*[1737]

One must here take issue with the entry on Plato of Tivoli in the Dictionary of Scientific Biography by Minio Paluello, who writes that Plato of Tivoli was:

1734 C.H. Haskins: Studies; op cit; p. 13.

1735 N. Daniel: The Arabs; op cit; p.268.

1736 B.Z. Richler: Translations and Translators; op cit; p. 133.

1737 Ibid.

`one of the first scientist-scholars to be active in the Iberian Peninsula to provide the Latin West with some of the works of Greek authors as transmitted or elaborated in Arabic and Hebrew.'[1738]

With such an introduction, one obviously expects to see a list of Greek names; the first Western translator focusing interest on Greek works rather than Islamic. Yet, candidly, Palluello gives the list of Plato's translations, and out of the seven works, only two are Greek, and the others are mainly works on astronomy by Al-Battani, Al-Imrani, and Abu Ali al-Khayat.[1739]

Glick reminds that in the medieval milieu, translation was by no means a mechanical or uncreative function, but was one of the numbers of things a scientist did, one of the most important and creative of scientific functions, particularly when early in the process of diffusion and synthesis.[1740] First to come to mind is Arnold of Villanova, for instance, who translated a variety of Islamic works which include Al-Kindi's, Ibn Sina's, Qusta Ibn Luqa's, Abu Salts' and Abu'l Al Zur's medical works,[1741]whilst amongst his other professions was professorship at the University of Montpellier, physician-regular to three kings of Aragon and three popes,[1742] including Court physician to Pedro III of Aragon from at least 1281, intimate adviser to Jaime II of Aragon and Frederick II of Sicily.[1743] Hermann of Carinthia was called *scholasticus* and Gerard of Cremona, *dictus magister;* both were teachers who taught the underlying subject matter that interested them; several scholars having studied under Hermann and Gerard.[1744] Armengaud son of Blaise (d.1313), who counts amongst his translations al-Zarqali's treatise on the astrolabe, was also a physician in France, in Montpellier, and also exerted as physician to Jayme II (King of Aragon from 1291 to 1327) and to Clement V (pope from 1305 to 1314).[1745]

1738 L.Minio-Paluello: Plato of Tivoli; Dictionary of Scientific Biography; op cit; Vol xi; pp.31-3. at p. 31.

1739 Ibid. p. 32.

1740 T.F. Glick: *Islamic and Christian Spain in the Early Middle Ages*. Princeton University Press, 1979; p. 256.

1741 G. Sarton: Introduction; op cit; Vol ii; p.893.

1742 R.I. Burns: Muslims in the Thirteenth Century Realms of Aragon: Interaction and Reaction, in *Muslims under Latin Rule, (J.*M. Powell, Ed) op cit; pp.90-1.

1743 J. Carreras Artau: *Relaciones de Arnau de Vilanova con los reyes de la casa de Aragon;* Barcelona, 1955, pp 43-50.

1744 C. Burnett: Translations and Translators; op cit. p. 137.

1745 G. Sarton: Introduction; op cit; Vol II; p.831.

All such early figures of Western science had one common link: Islamic learning, and this Islamic link connected them in their endeavours and lives, too. Adelard of Bath, for instance, had family antecedents from Loraine, the first seat of Islamic learning in the Christian West. Adelard's translation of the astronomical tables of Al-Khwarizmi and Abu Ma'ashar had an impact as great as his eagerness for Islamic science (the *studia Arabum)*.[1746] Adelard had a considerable impact on his followers: Robert of Ketton, Daniel of Morley, Roger of Hereford, Alfred of Sarechel, and Michael Scot, all continuing his aim of *`Arabum studia scrutari*"[1747] (enquiry into the learning of the Muslims). Most of these Englishmen went to Spain in search of astronomical and mathematical treatises and took an active part in the systematic work of translation at Toledo and other seats of learning in the valley of the Ebro and the region of the Pyrenees.[1748] Robert of Chester, most possibly one of the pupils of Adelard,[1749]adapted Adelard's translation of the tables of al-Khwarizmi,[1750]and devised a set of astronomical tables for the meridian of London in 1149-50 (based on the tables of al-Zarkali and al-Battani.)

Hermann of Carinthia; also known as the Dalmatian, the Slav etc was acquainted with Adelard's translation, and lived in both Spain and the French southern region of Languedoc. Just like Adelard, Hermann was anxious to produce a synthesis of Muslim ideas, and so drew up a list of scientific books.[1751] His translations include the eight books of the *Maius introductorium* of Abu Ma'ashar (Albumasar),[1752]and al-Khwarizmi's astronomical tables. Both works were undertaken, appropriately in the Languedoc region, in the town of Beziers in the 1140s.[1753] Hermann and his associate Robert of Ketton were strongly attached to their own culture, Daniel notes,[1754] but both devoted their working lives to the translation of Islamic science into Latin. Ketton speaks of the inadequate knowledge of the Latin in the field of astronomy, and Hermann refers nostalgically to `their joint efforts to extract the innermost treasures of the Arabs".[1755] Not only were Robert of Ketton and Herman well versed in Arabic, but they had access to the

[1746] C. Burnett: The Introduction of Arabic Learning; op cit; p.22
[1747] D. Metlitzki: The Matter of Araby; op cit; p.30.
[1748] Ibid.
[1749] C. Burnett: The Introduction; op cit;p.56.
[1750] Ibid.
[1751] G. Sarton: Introduction, op cit, vol 2; p. 173.
[1752] N. Daniel: The Arabs; op cit; p. 270.
[1753] C. Burnett: The Introduction; op cit; p.57. C. Haskins; Studies; op cit.
[1754] N. Daniel: The Arabs; op cit; p. 271.
[1755] Ibid.

intimate `chests'-armaria-of the Muslims from which they had gathered an abundance of material.[1756] We know from Robert himself that he was deeply engrossed in astronomical and geometrical study when he was interrupted by Peter.[1757] Peter the Venerable, the abbot of Clunny, when he sought the men to translate the Quran (for the object of its refutation) could not have made better choice for his purpose, says Metlitzki.[1758]
Abraham Ibn Ezra was also in Toledo before 1140, on the river Ebro, where he met Hermann of Carinthia and Robert of Ketton on the banks of the same Ebro. It is more than likely they had both known Ibn Ezra, and collaborated together.[1759] Ibn Ezra moved from North Spain to Pisa in the early 1140s.[1760]
Pisa at that time was a flourishing commercial centre with its quarters in cities throughout the Mediterranean as at Antioch.[1761] Stephen (of Antioch), a Pisan, in 1127 made a new version of the earlier Constantine's pioneering text, the *Liber Regalis* `the great medical epitome' of al-Madjusi.[1762] Stephen objected to Constantine's version, which was unfaithful to the original text, and was presented as if it were the original. Stephen, like others, did not just preach the importance of transferring knowledge from Arabic into Latin, but also exemplified the newly felt need for accurate translation, and a sense of obligation to the source.[1763]
This remarkable chain of links amongst early figures of Western learning built around Islamic learning, if it is to prove one thing, is that their works and the rise of modern science in the Christian West have no other foundation other than Islamic learning.

The translators, although cosmopolitan in origin, were also structured along the same line,[1764]and their work had a shared aim. They formed cohesive groups with clearly identifiable lines of inter communication.[1765] With the exception of Hugh of Santalla, a Spanish priest who worked alone in Tarazona, they knew one another,

---

[1756] D. Metlitzki: The matter.p.31.
[1757] Ibid.
[1758] Ibid.
[1759] See C.H. Haskins: Studies; op cit; chapters 3 and four; C. Burnett: The Introduction; op cit.
[1760] C. Burnett: The Introduction; op cit p.56.
[1761] Ibid.
[1762] N. Daniel: The Arabs; op cit; p.264.
[1763] Ibid.
[1764] T.F. Glick: *Islamic and Christian Spain; op cit;* p. 256.
[1765] R. Lemay: Dans l'Espagne du XII siecle: LesTtraductions de l'Arabe au Latın, *Annales,* 18 (1963), 647-9.

exchanged views, shared the same methodology of translation and synthesis, and responded to the demands of specific, and substantially (and more importantly,) the same, reading public.[1766]The public for which translations were made, Burnett explains, was as various as the subjects of the translations and the languages into which they were made.[1767] Translations of philosophical and scientific works were most frequently meant for a university readership or for the use of specialists in particular fields, whilst the translation of works from Latin into various vernaculars suggests that literacy was spreading beyond the precincts of the schoolroom and the church.[1768] For instance, Burnett observes, Adelard of Bath's treatise on falconry into Old French and Provencal in the 13th century, suggests that the nobility was reading these works, and Voigts describes how one medical work was "Englished" for a barber-surgeon.[1769]But the main audience for translations, Burnett pursues, was the schoolroom.[1770]

Hence it becomes obvious that the translation effort and the 12th century intellectual surge were not the result of local changes or spontaneous developments but a concerted effort aimed at the recovery of Islamic learning for the aim of promoting science in the Christian West.

3. Translators' Aims, and Today's Re-Interpretations

The very origins of the translators, Benoit and Micheau note, go to show that if the chief sites of the meeting between Islamic science and the West were on the borders of Christendom, the effort of translation and adaptation had mobilized intellectuals from all over Western Europe in a large scale, and sometimes systematic endeavour.[1771]It aimed at the appropriation of Islamic learning in its wealth and variety. One Latin translator, Hermann of Carinthia reminding another, Robert of Ketton, of `the trappings and decorations which long vigils, and most earned

---

[1766] Ibid.
[1767] C. Burnett: Translations and Translators; op cit; p. 140.
[1768] Ibid.
[1769] Ibid. pp. 140-1.
[1770] Ibid. p. 141.
[1771] P Benoit and F. Micheau: The Arab Intermediary in *A History of Scientific Thought*, edited by M. Serres; Blackwell, 1995; pp 191-221; p. 216.

labour, had acquired for them from the depths of the treasures of the Arabs.'[1772]

All translators contrast the poverty of Latin Christendom with the superiority of Islamic learning. Whilst dedicating his work to the first bishop of Tarazona (after its conquest from the Muslims) by Alphonso VII, Hugh of Santalla makes it clear that he was executing a conscious policy of `literary re-conquista,' taking over `the useful learning of the conquered Moors.'[1773]And this policy was the bishop's.[1774]Hermann of Carinthia refers nostalgically to `their (his and Robert of Ketton's) joint efforts to extract the innermost treasures of the Arabs".[1775] Seeing the abundance of books in Arabic in every science, and deploring the poverty of Western Christendom, of which he was aware, Gerard of Cremona learnt Arabic for the purpose, surveyed all that was written in the language, and did not stop translating till the end of his life, `legating to Western Christendom, as `one would for a dear inheritor' the books which seemed to him the best in every discipline, in the clearest manner, and the easiest to comprehend.'[1776] As the obituary notice by Gerard's pupils also says:
`In this way he (Gerard) passed on the Arabic literature in the manner of the wise man who, wandering through a green field, links up a crown of flowers, made not just from any, but from the prettiest.'[1777]
Gerard of Sabbionetta also a great European translator associated with Toledo, and like his namesake of Cremona, worked strenuously in order to pass on the Islamic heritage to Latin Europe.[1778] Stephen of Antioch even learned Arabic in order to advance from "the naked beginnings of philosophy,"[1779]and proposed, that `if the favour of God should permit,' to go on from his study of the things of the body to `things far higher, extending to the excellence of the soul, more famous things which the Arabic language contains, the hidden secrets of philosophy.'[1780]
Plato of Tivoli prefaces his translation of Al-Battani's treatise on astronomy by boasting the richness of Muslim scholarship, whilst the Latins have not got one single author, instead of scientific works, only having `follies, dreams, and old wives' fables. This is the reason that has

---

[1772] H.of Carinthia: *De essentiis;* ed and trans C. Burnett; Leiden; 1982; p. 70.
[1773] N. Daniel: The Arabs; op cit; p.268.
[1774] Ibid.
[1775] Ibid. p. 271.
[1776] F. Micheau: La Transmission; op cit; p. 407.
[1777] R. Fletcher: *Moorish Spain;* Phoenix; London; 1992; p.151.
[1778] C. Singer: Science; in Medieval Contributions to Modern Civilisation, op cit; p. 127.
[1779] N. Daniel: The Arabs; op cit; p.264.
[1780] Ibid.

moved me, Plato of Tivoli, to enrich our tongue with that which it lacked the most by drawing on the treasures of an unknown language.'[1781] The phrase *Latinorum penuria* ("the poverty of the Latins"), Burnett insists, is repeated like a litany and is echoed by translators from Latin into the vernacular.[1782]

These personal accounts on the part of the pioneers of Western learning tells us of both the poverty of the Christian West, the richness of Islamic culture, and these pioneers' passionate urge to transfer West the riches of Islam. These contemporary accounts by these early scholars contradict completely the main argument found in modern Western history (seen in part one) that the rise of science and learning in medieval times owed to internal conditions or changes within Western Christendom, for such translators' aim was precisely aimed at the recuperation of scientific riches from **external,** Muslim, sources.

This brings us to the next issue, as historians, even those favourable to Islamic civilisation and its impact, and the best amongst them (such as Burnett much referred to here), as lengthily seen in the first chapter, telling us that the Latin recovered science written in Arabic, but it was `Greco-Islamic learning' in Arabic. Yet, as excellently outlined by Burnett, himself, such a recovery from Arabic was by no means an easy matter. Arabic, because not an Indo-European language, Burnett explains, is less amenable than Greek to a word-for- word translation into Latin. Hugo of Santalla gives a good picture of the difficulties facing Arabic-Latin translators, `Often the translator gasps under the strain of the difficulties.'[1783] He sees some strange word that `resists being translated correctly because of either the variety of diacritical marks on the letters, or the lack of marks—often, too, because of the incompatible differences of languages in all of which the significance of the roots is different;' then he simply guesses what the word means.[1784] John of Seville in the preface to his translation of Pseudo-Aristotle's *Regimen sanitatis* apologises for not completely following the letter, but, in certain cases, following the sense instead, whilst Hermann of Carinthia complains about the prolixity of the Arabic language and abbreviates his original texts considerably.[1785] Many methods were used to resolve such problems, such as by Gerard of Cremona who

[1781] In P. Duhem: le Systeme du Monde; op cit; iii; pp. 199-200.
[1782] C. Burnett: Translations and Translators; op cit; 138.
[1783] Ibid. p.140.
[1784] Ibid.
[1785] Ibid.

`Latinised' the text whilst the intermediary was "interpreting it." The interpreter translated the Arabic text into a vernacular Romance language, which was then `Latinized;' or the intermediary pronounced (proferente) the Arabic words one at a time as they were spoken by the people (vulgariter), while the Christian archdeacon, Dominicus Gundissalinus, who presumably spoke Arabic but did not read the language, wrote down the Latin equivalent to each of these words as he heard them.[1786] None of these methods, of course, Burnett concludes, would be as good as a direct translation from the Greek text if that were available, as was noted by the anonymous 12th century translator of Ptolemy's Optics.[1787]
Which brings us to the essential point: Why get from Arabic what can be obtained from Greek if this Greek learning was available.

If the Muslims can make translations from Greek into Arabic, Western Christians cannot fail to do the same, which is many times easier for them, and which is tens of times easier than translating from Arabic. Yet, apart from one or two Sicilian translators, and from Burgundia of Pisa, who translated directly from Greek, all translators did translate from Arabic, directly or via Mozarabic or Jewish assistance.[1788] This would make anyone conclude that such translators had no choice other than translate from Arabic, despite all difficulties, because such learning was not available in Greek. They were, somehow, forced to go the hard way and translate from Arabic, for nothing was available in Greek. This is the conclusion we come across in nearly every single work on the history of science, as already seen in part one. But this conclusion is flawed, and fallacious, as can be seen now.

Greek learning was not unavailable to Western Christendom. Western Christendom and its scholars had access to Greek learning as much as they wished and throughout the centuries, such access at no time interrupted throughout the whole medieval period, centuries before translations from Arabic were made. There are hundreds of sources, which speak, independently, of the Byzantine richness of culture in that period, and the considerable contact between East and West.[1789]Western historians, themselves, in their near entirety, tell us that the Renaissance of the 16th century was the result of the Turks taking of Constantinople

---

1786 Ibid.
1787 Ibid.
1788 C. Dawson: Medieval Essays; op cit; p. 140.
1789 See, for instance, D. J. Geanakoplos: Medieval Western Civilisation, op cit; W. Durant: The Age of Faith; op cit; Chapter XVIII, most particularly.

in 1453, which brought West all the treasures of learning of the Greeks.[1790] It is after the Turks took Constantinople in 1453, Mieli holds, that the fleeing scholars contributed to the new discoveries of the West of the treasures of Greek literature and science.[1791]

Centuries before such event (1453), even, as Burnett, himself, reminds us, the Christian West had direct contacts with the living Byzantine Greek traditions in science, philosophy, and theology through Ravenna in the 6th century, through the Ottonian court in the 9th century, through Sicily and southern Italy from the 11th to the 14th century, and through the Pisan and Venetian quarters in Constantinople itself in the 12th century.[1792] And of course, during the crusades, between 1095-1291, when the Byzantine empire called for Latin help, and the Western presence rose considerably in Byzantium.[1793] Eustathius, archbishop of Thessalonica, says that in 1180 there were no fewer than 60,000 Latins in Constantinople.[1794] After the establishment of the Latin Empire in 1204 we are told of the presence of Provencaux, Spaniards, citizens of Ancona, and also Danes and English.[1795] A Brief by Pope Innocent III of 1208 mentions the presence of Lombards, Danes and English.[1796] This considerable intercourse between Western Christians and Greek culture completely contradicts the generally found assertion that the Western Christians had no access to Greek learning except via the Muslims and Arabic. And to tell us, as most Western historians do, that translations of Greek works had to be made from Arabic because the Latins had no access to them in Greek, is false.

The question to ask, then, is: Why did those Western Christians not take from the source (Byzantium) what was easily available to them, instead of choosing the complicated Islamic route, and its impossible language? Why, one asks, did the translators chose Spain instead of Constantinople, Ravenna, Venice, southern Italy, etc, all under Byzantine influence. Why did not they chose Sicily, where Greek culture was very strong, Greek an official language, and the island in

---

[1790] One of the latest offerings of this explanation comes from a television program Gods in the Sky; Channel Four; seen by this author on S4C on the night of Thursday to Friday (4-5 Sept 03); 1.50 am.

[1791] A. Mieli: La Science Arabe; op cit; p. 217.

[1792] C. Burnett: Translations and Translators; op cit.p.136.

[1793] See, for instance:

Sir Steven Runciman: *A History of the Crusades*, Cambridge University Press, 1962.

J.J. Saunders: *Aspects of the Crusades*; Canterbury; 1962.

C. Cahen: *Orient et Occident au Temps des Croisades*, Aubier Montaigne, 1983.

[1794] W.Heyd: *Histoire du Commerce*. Op cit; vol 1; p. 221.

[1795] Ibid. p. 295.

[1796] Note 313, p. 478 in J.K. Wright: *The Geographical Lore; op cit.*

Christian (Norman) hands? Even Michael Scot, the Sicilian court translator, chose Spain, the country where Greek and Greek culture are the least to be found in the whole of Western Christendom. Thus, the point that these early Western scholars went to look for Greek science in Spain, in the country with the least Greek influence in the whole of the Christian world, makes no sense at all; unless such scholars were of the most cretin sort, which they were not, for they were at the foundation of the revival of learning in the Christian West.
The answer is simple, and is very obvious: These scholars were after Islamic learning, the one they all praised, not the Greek learning our modern historians keep forcing on them as one would force feed a goose prior to Christmas.

And, as the following outline, kept as simple as possible, shows, although translation of some Greek works from Arabic took place, the overwhelming majority of works in Arabic, which the early pioneers of Western science translated, were of Muslim scholars.

4. Translations at a Glance

This list owes mostly to the compilation done by Nakosteen in his appendix,[1797]and, above all, from Sarton's voluminous study.[1798]

First, a few anonymous works:
-The *Sirr al-Asrar* (Secret of secrets) was translated in Latin, partly by Theodore of Antioch, completely by Philip of Tripoli.
-An Islamic algebra was translated by William of Lunis.
-A treatise on falconry, by Theodore of Antioch.
-The book of the apple (Hebrew version) of Ibn Hasdai.
-*De practica geometrie*. By Gerard of Cremona.
- *Algorismus in integris et minutiis* by Gerard of Cremona.
-Treatise on chemistry by Robert of Chester.
-Treatise on fevers (compilation dated 1362,) and divided in eight sections.

[1797] M. Nakosteen: History, op cit, Appendix V; Translators; pp. 277-294.
[1798] G. Sarton: Introduction, op cit.

By Judah ben Solomon Nathan.

- Moses ibn Tibbon (1240-1283) translated:
- *Kitab al-sama al-tabi'i* (medical treatise).
- *Kitab al-sama wal'alam (Book of the sky and the universe)..*
- *Kitab al-kawn wal-fasad (Book of the universe).*
- *Kitab al-nafs (Book of the soul).*
- *Maqala fi ta'dir al-sihha (Treatise on well being).*
- *Al-sumum wal-mutaharriz mi al-adwiya al-qitalah (Book on poisons and remedies).*

-Two books on the universal plate by Alfonso X the El Sabio, also known as Alfonso X the Wise.

a) <u>Selected list of translators of Arabic works into Latin:</u>

1) Adelard of Bath translated: astronomical tables of Al- Khwarizmi, as revised by Maslama (Ms. Bodleian, Chartres, Madrid)
-Treatises by Abu Ma'ashar; and Thabit Ibn Qurra.

2) Alfred of Sareshel (also known as Walafred, Alvred, Alphiatus, Sarewel, Sarchel, Serechel) end of the 12th and the beginning of the 13th translated:
-Ibn Sina: *Shifa* as *Liber de Congelatis* (1200) (The chemistry part)

3) Armengadus, son of Blaise:
-Ibn Sina: *Al-arjuzat fi'l tibb* (1280-1284) (Medical treatise).

4) Bonacossa also known as Tobiyah:
-Ibn Rushd: *Kulliyat* (Colliget: complete works)-a medical encyclopaedia.

5) Constantinus Africanus translations include:
-Ishak Ibn Imran (d.before 907): *Al-Makala fi'l malikhuliya* (*De melancholia*);
-Ishak al-Israili (d. 995): *Kitab al-Bawl* (*de urines*)
Kitab al-humayyat (*De febrilus*), and *Kitab al-Aghdiya* (*De dietis*);
-Ibn al-Djazzar (d. 1004): *Kitab I'timad al-Adwiya al-Mufrada* (*De Gradibus)*

Zad al-musafir (or the Guide for the traveller going to distant countries).
Hunayn Ibn Ishaq: *Isagoge.*
And a treatise on ophthalmology.

6) Domigo Gundisalvo or Gonzales (Dominicus Gonissalinus) Archdeacon of Segovia translated in collaboration with John of Seville:
-*De divisione philisophiae* which is essentially derived from the *Kitab ihsa al-ulum* (the division of sciences) of Al-Farabi (lived first half of the tenth century).

7) Faraj ben Salim (Moses Farachi or Faragut etc) translated in 1279:
Al Razi: *Kitab al-Hawi (The compendium).*
Ibn Jazla: *Taqwim al-Abdan (medical treatise).*

8) Gerard of Cremona: also known as Gerardus Cremonensis) translated with his school of translators in the second half of the 12th century between seventy and eighty two works, including:
-Ibn Sina: *Qanun.*
-Banu Musa: *Liber trium fratrum.*[1799]
-Al-Khwarizmi: *De jebra et elmucabala.*
-Al-Nairizi: commentary on Euclid's elements.[1800]
-Abu Kamil: *Liber qui secundum Arabes vocatur algebra et almucabala.*
-Arib ibn Sa'ad: *Libri anohe (anwa*') (A Christian calendar containing astronomical and agricultural information).
-Al-Zarqali: *Canones Arzachelis.*
-Abu'l Qasim Al-Zahrawi: *Liber Azaragui de cirurgia* (treatise on surgery).[1801]
-Al-Farabi: *De scientiis.*
-Al-Kindi' works on physics and mechanics: *De aspectibus*; followed by *De umbris et de diversitate aspecturm.*[1802]
-Ibn al-Haytham's work on physics: *De crepusculis et nubium ascensionibus.*[1803]
-Al-Kindi: *De gradibus medicinarum* (on medicine).[1804]
-Four medical works by Al-Razi.

[1799] Edited by Max Curtze (Halle 1885).
[1800] Books I to X. Edited by M. Curtze.
[1801] First printed together with Chauliac's Latin surgery (Venice 1498).
[1802] Edt: A. Bjornbo and Seb. Vogl (Leipzig, 1912)
[1803] Printed in Lisbon in 1542, and in Basle in 1572.
[1804] Printed with the Latin translation of Ibn Butlan's *Tacuinum* (Strasbourg 1531).

-Ibn al-Wafid: *De medicinis et cibis simplicibus.*[1805]
-Al-Razi's chemical treatise: *De aluminibus et salibus*.

9) Giovani da Brescia:
-Al-Zarqali: Treatise on the astrolabe.

10) Herman the Dalmatian translated in 1140:
-Abu Ma'shar: *Kitab al-madkhal ila ilm Ahkam al-Nujum* (Introduction to the science of the Stars) (lived first half of the 9th century).
-Al-Khwarizmi: Astronomical tables.

11) Hugo Sanccelliensis (Sanctallensis, sandaliensis etc..) translated between 1119 and 1151:
-Al-Farghani: Commentary on the astronomy.
-Masha'Allah (fl second half of the 8th century) astronomy.
-The earliest Latin version of the alchemical text called The Emerald Table (*tabula smaragdina, Lawh Zabarjad*).

12) John of Seville translated:
-Al-Kindi: *The Flores astrologiae* (treatise on astrology.)
-Ahmad ibn Yusuf ibn Daya: Commentary on Ptolemy's Centiloquium at about 1130-1136.
-Al-Qabisi: *Al-madkhal ila sina'at ahkam al-nujum (Introduction to the knowledge of the stars).*
-Al-Battani: Treatise on astronomy and other works.
-Thabit ibn Qura: *De imaginibus astronomicis*.
-Maslama ibn Ahmed al Majriti: *De astrolabio*.
-Un-authored (but likely to be Al-Razi): *Sir al-Asrar (Secret of secrets).*
-Qusta ibn Luqa: *Al-Fasl bain al-ruh wal nafs (The distinction between body and soul).*
-Al-Farabi: *Ihsa al-Ulum (The division of sciences).*
-Ibn Sina: *Al-Shifa (The Book of healing).*
-Abu Ma'shar: *Al-Madkhal ila `ilm ahkam al-nujum (Introduction to the science of the stars).*
-Al-Ghazali: *Maqasid al-falasifa (The aims of the philosophers).*
-Al-Farghani: *Kitab fi harakat al-Samawiya wa jawami' ilm al-nujum (Book on the sky and the stars).*

13) Joanes Saracenus Afflacius:

1805 Ibid.

-Ali ibn Abbas: Surgical part of *Kitab al-Maliki* (Constantine translated the first half of this work under the title the Pantegni).

14) Michael Scot (13th C):
-Al-Bitruji: Astronomical treatise: *On the Sphere.*
-Ibn Sina: *de animalibus* (Abbrevatiated).

15) Plato of Tivoli (Plato Tiburtinus):
-Abu-Ali al-Khaiyat: De judiciis nativitatum.[1806]
-Al-Battani: *de motu stellarum*.(astronomy) in 1145.
-Ibn al-Khasib: *De revolutionibus nativitatum.*
-ibn al-Saffar: *Liber Abulcasim de operibus astrolabiae.*

16) Rudolf of Bruges:
-Maslama ibn Ahmad al-Majriti: Treatise on the astrolabe.

17) Robert of Chester translated:
-Al-Khwarizmi: Algebra (The first translation of).
-Al-Kindi: *De judiciis* and *De proportione et proportionalitate.*
-The Quran (The first translation begun in 1141).
-A treatise on the astrolabe.
-Revision for the meridian of London of the tables of Al-Khwarizmi (translated by Adelard of Bath).

18) Salio of Padua:
-Abu Bakr: Astrological treatise.

19) Stephen of Antioch:
-Ali ibn Abbas: *Kitab al-Maliki (Book Regalis).*

20) Stephanus Arnoldi, Arlandi (or Orlandi) translated in the first quarter of the fourteenth century:
-Qusta ibn Luqa: *Kitab al'Amal bil-kurra al-fulkiya (Book on the sphere and constellations).*
-A treatise on cataract.
-A treatise on blood letting.

21) Avendoth translated:

[1806] Also translated by John of Seville. It is the latter's translation which was printed in Nuremberg in 1546 or 1549.

-Ibn Sina *Sufficientia* (Arab: *Schafa*), *De Anima VI naturalium, Metaphysics* (MS. Par. 6443), *De coelo et mundo.*
-Qusta ibn Luqa: *Differentia inter animama et spiritum*,
-Al-Farabi's *De scientiis.*
-Al-Ghazali's three books on logic, metaphysics, and physic.
-Al-Kindi's *De intellectu.*
-Thabit Ibn Qurra's *De imaginibus astronomicis.*

b) <u>Selected list of translators of Arabic works into Hebrew:</u>

1) Abraham ben Meir ibn Ezra translated:
-Masha'Allah: Two treatises on astrology (before 1148).
-Al-Biruni: Commentary on Al-Khwarizmi's tables.[1807]

2) Joseph ben Joshua II ha-Lorqi (died before 1408):
-Ibn Sina: Part of the *Qanun*.

3) Jacob ben Mahir ibn Tibbon (died before 1304):
-Astronomical tables for the longitudes of Montpellier.
-Qusta ibn Luqa: *Kitab al-amal bil Kuraat al-fulkiyya* (on celestial spheres). Translated in 1256.
-Ibn al-Haytham: *Fi hai'at al-alam* (on configuration of the world).[1808]
-Ibn al-Saffar: *Kitab al-amal al-astrulab* (on the astrolabe).
-Al-Zarqali: *Kitab al-amal bil-safihi al-zijyia* (on zijs (astronomical tables).
-Al-Ghazali: *Mizan al amal* (an ethical treatise).
-Jabir ibn Aflah: *Islah al-majisti* (refutation of the Almagest).
-Ibn Rushd: *Compendium of the Organon.*
- *Saphaea Arzachelis* (al-Zarqali's astrolabe).

4) Judah ben Solomon Nathan (Fourteenth century):
-Umaiyya ibn abi'l Salt: *Kitab al-adwiyyat al-mufrada* (on drugs).
-Al-Ghazzali: *Maqasid al-falasifa* (aims of philosophers).
-Ibn Wafid: *Kitab al-wisad* (book of pillow) (a treatise on simples.

5) Moses ibn Tibbon (1240-1283):

[1807] Narbonne (South of France) 1160.
[1808] This translation was into Latin by Abraham de Balmes at about the second half of the fifteenth. The original Arabic of Ibn al-Haytham was translated into Spanish for Alphonso X by Abraham of Toledo.

-Al-Batalyusi: *Kitab al hadaiq* (Book of gardens).
-Al-Farabi: *Kitab al-mabadi* (a philosophical and political treatise.)
-Unauthored: *Maqala fi sina'at al-mantiq (on logic).*
-Jabir ibn Aflah: *Kitab al-haia or islah al-majusti (correction of the almagest).*
-Muhammad al-Hassar: Treatise on arithmetic and algebra (translated in Montpellier).
-Al-Bitruji: *Kitab al-haia (On the Sphere).*
-Ibn Sina: *Arjuzat* (with the ibn Rushd commentary).
-Ibn Sina: *Alqanun al'saghir (The lesser canon).*
-Ibn al-Jazzar: *Zad al-Musafir (Guide to the traveller).*
-Al-Razi: *Kitab al-taksim wal-tashjir (The book of separation and planting).*
-Al-Razi: *Kitab al-aqrabadhin* (treatise on pharmaceutics).

6) Nathan ben Eliezer (translated during the years 1279-1283):
-Ibn Sina: *Qanun.*
-Un-authored: *Muntakhib fi'ilaj al'ain* (treatise on eye disease.)
-Al-Razi: A treatise on vivisection entitled in Hebrew: *Ma'amar be-Haqqazah.*
-Ibn Zuhr: *Kitab al-aghdiya* (on diets).

7) Qalanymos ben Qalanymos (born in Arles in 1286 or 1287):
-Jabir ibn Hayyan: treatise on poisons.
-Al-Kindi: treatise on nativities, and other works.
-Thabit ibn Qurra: *Kitab fi shakl al-qat'a (Mathematical treatise).*
-Al-Farabi: *Kitab fi'l akl wa'l ma'kul* (book on reason and the reasonable).
-Al-Farabi: *Kitab fima yanbaghi an yuqaddam qabla ta'alim al-falsafat* (book about prerequisites before learning of philosophies).
-Ali ibn Ridwan: *Kitab al-umudi fi usul al-tibb* (a treatise on medicine).
-Abu Sa'adan: Treatise on the triangle.

8) Samuel ben Judah of Marseilles (also known as Miles Benjudad etc.. b. in 1294):
-Ibn Rushd: Commentary on Plato's republic.[1809]
-Ibn Rushd: Commentary on Ptolemy.
-Ibn Mu'adh of Seville: Treatise on the solar system.
-Al-Zarqali: Treatise on the movement of fixed stars.

[1809] Completed at Arles in 1320, and revised in the prison of Beaucaire (France) in 1321 .

9) Samuel ben Judah ibn Tibbon (1150-1232) translated:
-Yahia ibn Batriq: Aristotle Meteorology.
-Ali ibn Ridwan: Commentary on Galen's *Tegni*.
-Ibn Rusd: `three small treatises.'

10) Samuel ibn Motot:
-Al-Batalyusi: *Kitab al-hadaiq* (the orchard).

11) Shem-Tob Ben Issac (also called Babi ha-Tortosi) translated.
-Abu al-Qasim al-Zahrawi: *Kitab al-Tasrif.*
-Al-Razi: *Kitab al-Mansuri*.
-Ibn Rushd: Middle commentary on Aristotle's *De anima*.

12) Todros Todrosi also known as Todros ben Meshullam ben David Todrasi (14th century):
-Al-Farabi: *Kitab al-uyun al-masail* (including some 60 theses concerning Aristotlianism.)
-Ibn Sina: *Kitab al-najat* (A Summary of Aristotelian philosophy.)
-Ibn Rushd: Three dissertations (the first two dealing with ibn Sina's theory of the three modes of being.)

13) Jospeh ibn Waqar (end of 13th century):
New Hebrew translation of the surgery of Abu-l-Qasim (Al-Zahrawi).

c) <u>Selected List of translators into Spanish, and some dates of translation:</u>

1) Abraham of Toledo (also known as Don Abraham Alfaquin) (13th Century):
-Ibn al-Haytham: Treatise on the configuration of the universe.
-Al-Zarqali: Treatise on the construction and the use of his astrolabe.

2) Alfonso X El Sabio, also known as Alfonso X the Wise:
-Ibn abi-I-Rijal: *Kitab al-bari fi ahkam al-nujum*,) (Book on the properties of the stars) translated by Judah ben Moses in 1256.
-Al-Battani: *Canones* (translated by Isaac ibn Sid).
-A series of astronomical works edited together on Alfonso's order in 1276-77 under the title *Libros del saber de astronomia*. This includes

eleven parts, the first being some sort of introduction to the stars, the other ten dealing with instruments.
-Abd al-Rahman al-Sufi: Four books derived from his *Kitab al-kewakib al-tabit al-musawar (Book on the planets)* (tr. in 1256 by Judah ben Moses and Quillen Arremon Daspa.)
-Qusta ibn Luqa: Revised translation of the *Kitab al-amal bilkura al-falakiya* (on the celestial globe.)
-Two books on animals: essentially derived from al-Zarqali but elaborated by the translator, Isaac ibn Sid.
-Two books on the plates of the seven planets (*aequatoria*). One was written by ibn al-Samh, the other by al-Zarqali at Seville.
-Scores of other works on quadrants, astrolabe and clocks, all elaborated by Isaac ibn Sid.

3) Isaac ibn Sid (Isaac ha-Hazzan) also called Rabbi Zag or Cag and Aben Cayut (worked in Toledo from c. 1263 to 1277):
-Author of not less than nine translations and adaptations included in the *Libros del saber* (just referred to).
-Al-Battani: *Canon (on astronomy).*
-Two books on the spherical astrolabe.
-Two books of the universal plate.
-Un-authored work on astronomy.

4) Judah ben Moses ha-Kohen (Mosca el menor?) translated from Arabic into Spanish (mid 13th):
-Qusta ibn Luqa: Treatise on the sphere.
-Ibn abi-I-Rijal: *Kitab al Bari* (on astronomy and the stars).

5) Samuel ha-Levi Abulafia:
-Anonymous: *fabrica y usos del relogio della condela* (construction and use of the candle clock).

6) Stephen of Saragossa (Stephanus caesaraugustanus...) translated in 1233:
-*Kitab i'timad fi-l-adwiya al-mufrada* (treatise on simple drugs) by Ibn al-Jazar.

7) Abraham of Tortosa translated:
-*De Simplicibus* of Serapion Junior,
-The *Liber Servitoris* of Al-Zahrawi.

8) Alfonso of Toledo:

-*De separatione primi principii* which was ascribed to Ibn Rushd.

9) Stephanus Arnoldi (of Barcelona):
-*Dietarium* by Qusta ibn Luqa.

10) Franciscus de Macerata translated:
-*Metaphysica* of Ibn Sina.

Few Others:
-Simon Januensis (c.1290), together with the Jew Abraham Tortuosiensis, translated the *Synonyma*, the *Simplicibus* of Serapion Junior (Ibn Sarabi).

-Witelo the Pole translated the Optics of Ibn al-Haytham.

-Zucchero Bencivenni of Florence (fl. 1310-13) Translated works by al-Farghani and al-Razi from French into Italian.

-John of Brescia translated Saphaea Arzachelis (al-Zarqali's astrolabe).

5. The Impact of Translations

Campbell notes that translations of Islamic science were to exert a dominating influence over the minds of the thinkers of the West from the 12th until the 15th century.[1810] Durant, for his part, puts it:
`In the twelfth century Europe discovered the wealth of Spain in books; scholars descended upon Toledo, Cordova, and Seville, and a flood of new learning poured over the Pyrenees to revolutionize the intellectual life of the adolescent North.'[1811]
Micheau insists that thanks to the translations from Arabic into Latin, Western Christendom discovers a learning hitherto unknown. `This new *translatio studii* is inseparable from Islamic culture as well as from Western culture. It meant for the former unexpected extension of its

[1810] D. Campbell: Arabian medicine; op cit p.xii.
[1811] W. Durant: The Age of faith, op cit; p. 909.

scope beyond its frontiers. For the latter it meant the intellectual renaissance of the 12th century, and the beginning of the universities in the 13th century.'[1812]

Grant goes even further, entitling Chapter II of his book:
`The beginning of the beginning, and the Age of translation, 1000 A.D to 1200 A.D.'[1813] Which, obviously, captures in the best possible way the impact of such translations.

Of course, translations were only part of the equation. Other factors, already considered, such as travel, trade, the crusades, court exchanges etc, also had their impact. The impact of translations, themselves, can be, sometimes, difficult to dissociate from these and other factors, for they all worked together. However, in the following outline, will be attempted to show the specific impact of translations. Of course, not everything will be said, because no work can tell everything. More on such impact will also be seen in the next chapters, particularly under the Islamic impact on sciences.

Beginning with trigonometry and astronomy (the two being very much related,)[1814] the interest in the subject meant that in the first half of the 12th century no less than four scholars: Hermann of Carinthia, Robert of Chester, Plato of Tivoli and Adelard of Bath were engaged in the task. Al-Khwarizmi's astronomical tables (revised by Maslama of Madrid in the 10th century) were translated by both Adelard of Bath in 1126 and by Hermann. From such translations were made adaptations of Islamic tables to Latin locations, such as Robert of Chester's adapted version of al-Battani and al-Zarqali's tables for the coordinates of London in 1149; and his revision of al-Khwarizmi's tables for the same position.[1815] Al-Zarqali's tables for the meridian of Toledo were also adapted by Raymond of Marseilles, Walcher of Malvern, Roger of Hereford, and others. The meridian of Toledo was in fact long the standard of computation for the West,[1816] in 1178, Roger of Hereford adapting the astronomical tables that existed for Toledo and Marseilles (themselves based on Toledo) to the meridian of the city of Hereford.[1817]

[1812] F. Micheau: La Transmission; op cit; p. 399.
[1813] E. Grant: Physical science; op cit; p.13
[1814] As Sarton explains, trigonometry was the natural introduction to astronomy. It was in fact part of it until much later stages.
[1815] See: C. Burnett: The Introduction; C.H. Haskins: Studies; L.Cochrane: Adelard etc.
[1816] C.H. Haskins: Studies; op cit; P. 18.
[1817] D. Metlitzki: The Matter of Araby; op cit; p.38.

The most popular Muslim astronomer amongst Western Christian scholars was Abu Ma'ashar. To Allain of Lille, who had probably read the *Introduction to Astronomy* in the translation of Herman of Dalmatia, Abu Ma'ashar was the undisputed master of stellar science.[1818] But he was not alone to impact on Western Christian astronomy. The 12th century treatise of Jabir ibn Aflah: *Islah al-Majisti* (correction of the Almagest) (translated into Latin by Gerard of Cremona about 1187) helped refute Ptolemy. More refutations of Greek astronomy is to be found in the works of al-Battani and Al-Zarqali, and most of all in Michael Scot's translation of Al-Bitruji (*On the Sphere*) constituting literally the point of departure of modern astronomy on a definite non-Ptolemaic line.[1819]

Translations of treatises on the astrolabe by Robert of Chester, and the so called *Saphaea Arzachelis (*the name given to al-Zarqali's astrolabe) had a considerable impact not just in stimulating a whole subsequent Latin literature about the instrument, but also in its uses. More translations of al-Zarqali were done in other centuries; i,e by Jacob ben Mahir and John of Brescia.

In mathematics, Algebra, taken as an instance here, was transmitted to the West via the translations of Adelard of Bath, John of Seville and Plato of Tivoli. Robert of Chester in his translation of al-Khwarizmi's algebra says in gratitude: `Praise be to God, beside whom there is no other. Here ends the book of restoration and opposition of number which Robert of Chester in the city of Segovia translated into Latin from Arabic.'[1820] This particular translation of the Algebra of al-Khwarizmi in 1145 marks `a fundamental landmark in the history of that subject, as it may be considered the beginning of European algebra,' according to Sarton;[1821] breaking completely new ground for Latin Europe, says Metlitzki.[1822] This Book of Algebra and *Al-mucabola* (of `making whole' and `balancing') introduced the name and function of a new branch of mathematics-algebra, from Arabic *jabara*, to restore.[1823] The name of the author, al-Khwarizmi, was itself becoming a new concept from the opening sentence (`Dixit algoritmi') of another of his works,

---

1818 A de Lille: Anticlaudianus; ed R.Bossuat; Paris; 1955; lib IV; p. 108; I. 63 in D. Metzliki: The Matter; op cit; p. 60.

1819 C. Burnett: Michael Scot; op cit.

1820 `Prohemium' Reprinted in L.C.Karpinski: *Robert of Chester's Latin Translation of Al-Khwarizmi*; New York; 1915; p. 125.

1821 G. Sarton: Introduction; op cit; vol ii; p. 126.

1822 D. Metlitzki: The Matter of Araby; op cit; p.35.

1823 L.C. Karpinski: Robert of Chester; op cit.

the *Arithmetic;* the concept is algorism.[1824] The practical importance of Algebra to the West is noted by Metlitzki: `This, then, is the method by which all proposed problems concerning commercial transactions or weights and measures and all related problems are to be solved.'[1825]

Optics, until the time of al-Kindi (10th century), remained the realm of the Greek, but a `science' based on erroneous definitions and theories.[1826] Al Kindi's criticism of Euclid opened the way for a better and more correct understanding of vision.[1827] It was, however, the translation by Gerard of Cremona of Ibn al-Haytham's *Kitab al-Manazir* (*the Opticea thesaurus* of Alhazen in Latin), which came, not just as a decisive refutation of Greek theories of vision, but also laid the foundations for the whole science of optics. Ibn Al-Haytham's most important achievements in spherical mirrors, the refraction of light, which is examined experimentally, and other optical subjects[1828] were to form the foundations of all subsequent development of the science (as will be expanded further on in the chapter on sciences). It was a starting point for Witelo, Kepler and many in the 16th century.[1829]

Early translations in chemistry included Robert of Chester's *Liber de Compositione Alchemise*, and Hugh of Santalla's Emerald Table (*Lawh Zabarjad*). Alfred of Sareshel, for his part, translated the chemical part of Ibn Sina's *Kitab al-Shifa* (the Book of Healing) toward the end of the 12th century. It is, however, Gerard of Cremona who took the leading role in translating both Jabir (ibn Hayyan) and Al-Razi's study of salts and alums. The diverse interpretations of Jabir's work and his impact have been studied by Holmyard, Ruska, Kraus and others.[1830] Kraus went to great lengths to demonstrate how modern chemistry owes in great measure to the translations and editions of Jabir's work.[1831] Al-

---

1824 D. Metlitzki: The Matter of Araby; op cit; p.35.

1825 Ibid.

1826 See: D.C. Lindberg: *Theories of Vision from al-Kindi to Kepler*, Chicago, 1976.
-D.C. Lindberg: *Studies in the History of Medieval Optics*, London, Variorum Reprints, 1983.

1827 D.C. Lindberg: Al-Kindi's Critique of Euclid's Theory of Vision, *ISIS;* 62, 1971, 469-89.

1828 Ed Baarman: *Abhandlung uber das licht von Ibn al-Haitham*, Arabic text with German trslt. Older Latin trslt ed. Risner, *Alhazeni Opticae Thesaurus*, Basel, 1572.

1829 O. Pedersen: Early Physics; op cit; p. 349.

1830 See for a good outline of such studies:
D.M. Dunlop: *Arab Civilisation 800-A.D to 1500 A.D*, Longman Librairie du Liban, 1971, at pp. 209-12.

1831 P. Kraus: Jabir ibn Hayyan, Essai sur l'Histoire des idees scientifiques dans l'Islam, *Textes Choisis*, Paris & Cairo, 1935.

Razi's contribution legated a variety of chemical products upon which subsequent industrial crafts and trades developed,[1832] besides his pioneering of laboratory experimentation.[1833] It is also worth adding that one amongst many direct impacts on the Muslim followers, such as Vincent of Beauvais, was largely derived from the *aluminibus et salibus* of Al-Razi (translated by Gerard of Cremona.)[1834]

The translation by Alfred of Sareshel entitled *Avicennae Mineralia* was an important source of geological knowledge; on the formation of mountains, most particularly.[1835]The striking modern description of the geological processes resulting in the formation of mountains by the forces of erosion and the accumulation of soil and earth goes:
`Mountains may arise from two causes, either from uplifting of the ground such as takes place in earthquakes or from the effects of running water and wind in hollowing out valleys in soft rocks and leaving the hard rocks prominent, which has been the effective process in the case of most hills, Such changes must have taken long periods of time, and possibly the mountains are now diminishing in size. What proves that water has been the main agent in bringing about these transformations of the surface is the occurrence in many rocks of the impression of aquatic and other animals. The yellow earth that clothes the surface of the mountains is not of the same origin as the framework of the ground underneath it but arises from the decay of organic remains, mingled with earthly materials transported by the water. Perhaps these materials were originally in the sea which once overspread the land.'[1836]

Plenty of time and effort can be devoted to the impact of translated Islamic medical texts. Excellent works are available by erudite old Western authors to enlighten on this matter.[1837] Much has also already been seen with regard to Constantine's translations, and their impact through the faculty of Salerno; and more will be seen in the final chapter. Briefly, here, Gerard of Cremona supplemented Constantine

---

P. Kraus: Jabir Ibn Hayyan, Contribution a l'Histoire des idees scientifiques dans l'Islam, Vols i-ii, *Memoires presentes a l'Institut d'Egypte*, vols 44-45, Cairo, 1942-43.

[1832] R.P. Multhauf: *The Origins of Chemistry*; Gordon and Breach Science Publishers; London, 1993. I, and L. Al-Faruqi: *The Cultural Atlas of Islam;* op cit; p. 328.

[1833] E.J. Holmyard: *Makers of Chemistry*; Oxford at the Clarendon Press, 1931.

[1834] G. Sarton: Introduction; op cit; Vol II; p.768.

[1835] Ibid. Vol II; p.515.

[1836] Geikie: Founders of Geology; 1905; p. 43. in J.K. Wright: Geographical Lore; op cit; p.213.

[1837] N.L. Leclerc: *Histoire de la Medecine Arabe*; op cit; D.Campbell: *Arabian Medicine; op cit*; E.G. Browne: *Arabian Medicine*; Cambridge University Press; 1962.

translations with what Sarton sees as two fundamental texts to the Latin world: *The Kitab al-Mansuri* (Al-Razi) and the *Qanun* (Ibn Sina).[1838] The works of Ibn Sina and Al-Razi (translated by Gerard) formed the very core of Western medieval medical studies.[1839] Al-Razi's *Al-Hawi* (the Continens, in Latin), propagated in numerous manuscripts in the following centuries, repeatedly printed, exerted a considerable influence on Western Christian medicine.[1840] Ibn Sina's medical encyclopaedia, The *Qanun* (the Canon) had such an impact that for centuries, it was printed in Latin in more than thirty editions.[1841]Ibn Zuhr (Avenzoar) better known work is *Al-Taisir* translated into Latin from Hebrew by John of Capua and then by Paravicious. *Al-Taisir* was meant to be some sort of counterpart to Ibn Rushd's *Kulliyat*, which dealt with the generalities of medicine, whilst *Al-Taisir* dealt with more specific matters such as pathology and therapeutics, including many clinical descriptions, which influenced greatly the development of Western medicine.[1842] Ibn Rushd' *Kulliyat* (Colliget: complete works)-a medical encyclopaedia- was translated into Latin by Bonacossa. Both The *Taisir* and The *Kulliyat* were according to Sarton `the most valuable of their kind in medieval times.'[1843] Further great landmarks were the Latin translation of the *Kitab al-Maliki* by Stephen of Antioch, c. 1127, and that of the *Kitab al-hawi* by Faraj ibn Salim in 1279.[1844] Surgery received a very considerable boost from the translation by Gerard of Cremona of *Kitab al-Tasrif* of Abu al-Qasim al Zahrawi, which Shem tob ben Isaac, a century later, translated into Hebrew.[1845] Guy de Chauliac (1300-68) was considerably influenced by al-Zahrawi, just like the Italian surgeon, Saliceto (1201-77); such an influence, which Campbell notes, led to the propagation of Islamic surgery throughout the rest of Europe.[1846] In general, under Muslim influence, anatomy experienced a revival in Europe; better text books on surgery were produced; gynaecology and obsterics, hitherto the monopoly of midwives became subjects of scientific interest, whilst ophthalmology passed from the hands of wandering cataract couchers into those of learned physicians.[1847] Ammar ibn Ali's works on eye diseases were

[1838] G. Sarton: Introduction; Vol II; p.67.
[1839] E .Grant: Physical Science; op cit; p.17.
[1840] M. Meyerhof: Science and Medicine; op cit; pp.324-5.
[1841] F. Gabrieli: Transmission of Learning, op cit, p. 862.
[1842] see D. Campbell: Arabian Medicine; op cit.
[1843] G. Sarton: Introduction, op cit, vol 2; p. 69.
[1844] Ibid. p.67.
[1845] D. Campbell: Arabian Medicine; op cit.
[1846] Ibid. p.43.
[1847] M. Meyerhof: Science and Medicine, op cit, p. 351.

translated into Hebrew by Nathan he'Me'ati, and the same subject taken up by others subsequently to great effects. And many more translations having the same overall impact; Whipple pointing how these translations of Islamic medical works imposed Muslim modes of thought on Western European medicine from the 12th to the 17th centuries.[1848]

In pharmacy and botany, the Islamic impact in general, and of translation in particular, has received the attention of Sezgin,[1849] Meyerhof,[1850] Ullmann[1851] and Silberberg, the latter having early in this century salvaged the essential work by Abu Hanifa al-Dinawari (d.895).[1852] Ibn al-Baytar occupies a high position, and his work on the *Collection of Simple Drugs* was translated profusely and of course much used in the centuries to follow. Other works bearing great influence include the anonymous *Kitab i'timad fi-l-adwiya al-Mufrada* (treatise on simple drugs) translated by Stephen of Saragossa in 1233; another is Ibn al-Wafid's treatise on drugs translated by Gerard of Cremona; and on the same subject Masawaih al-Maridini as translated into Hebrew by Jacob of Capua. Following these translations, many of the Muslim complicated recipes transferred to European dispensaries, and several names passed from East to West (*rob* for a conserve of fruit-juice with honey, *julep* for a medicinal aromatic drink; sirup (Arabic *sharab etc*).[1853]

Other than directly reviving sciences, these translations had further impacts, many of which will be dealt with in great detail in the following chapters, some briefly looked at here. As Read points out, the early translations were voyages in uncharted seas: there literally existed no Latin equivalents for many of the technical expressions of the Islamic manuscripts, and so many words passed unaltered into English and other European languages.[1854]Translations as re-translations carried

---

1848 A.O. Whipple: The role of the Nestorians; op cit; p.36.
1849 F. Sezgin: *Geschichte des Arabishen Schrifttums*, Leiden, 1970---
1850 Some of the works by Meyerhof are available in English. Most are in German.
1851 M. Ullmann: *Medizin in Islam*, Leiden/Cologne, 1970.
" " : *Die Natur und Geheimwissenschaften im Islam*, Leiden, coll. handbuch der Orientalistik, I. VI, 2, 1972.
1852 B. Silberberg: `Das Pflanzenbuch des Abu Hanifa Ahmed ibn da'ud al-Dinawari. *Ein Beitrag zur Geschichte der Botanik bei den Arabern*,' dissertation, Breslau, published in part in *Zeitschrift fur Assyriologie* 24 (1910): 225-65; 25 (1911): 38-88.
1853 M. Meyerhof: Science and Medicine, op cit, p 339.
1854 J. Read: *The Moors in Spain and Portugal*: Faber and Faber, London, 1974.P. 178

over the Arabic article.[1855]As Campbell explains, the Latin equivalent was placed over the Arabic, and where the translator was at a loss for the correct Latin interpretation, the Arabic was transcribed bodily, with the result that such terms as alcohol, alchemy, and zero have been passed on to us.[1856] Technical terms offered most difficulty.[1857]They were literally transposed from Arabic into Latin, hence giving us in the 12th century a scientific and technical lexicon based on Arabic.[1858] For instance, in one of the manuscripts of the tables of al-Khwarizmi can be found the greatest number of un-translated Arabic terms, including even phrases in Arabic, which have been left untouched such as:

`All changes are related to the moon in its waxing and waning,' and `all the planets were in their exaltations except Mercury when Adam was created.'[1859]

Read rightly notes, that `even a bare word list gives some idea of the impoverished state of knowledge and the material limitations of medieval Europe and of the tremendous scope of information now made available.'[1860]

Which puts the focus on two crucial points:

-The role of Muslims in the foundation and establishment of a technical vocabulary and terminology, which complements the transfer of learning.

-The poverty of Western Christendom before the inflow of Islamic knowledge, which, again, refutes the idea that Western Christianity had the required internal conditions/learning for a scientific upsurge from within.

Just as the first institutions of learning in Western Christendom (Chartres, Salerno, cathedral schools in Lorraine, etc) rose following the reception of early Islamic learning, Western Christian institutions of higher learning, without one single exception (Oxford, Cambridge, Italian universities, Paris etc,) all rose following the translations of the 12th century. The evolution of the university curriculum during the 13th and 14th centuries reveals the sure penetration of many translations, primarily those by Gerard of Cremona, which` nourished the awakened interest in natural science until the end of the Middle Ages,' tells

---

1855 C.H. Haskins: Studies, op cit, p. 18.

1856 D. Campbell: Arabian medicine; op cit; p.xii.

1857 Ibid. p. 141.

1858 F. Micheau: La Transmission; op cit; p. 408.

1859 In C. Burnett: Arabic Learning; op cit; p. 45.

1860 J. Read: *The Moors*. P.178

Lemay.[1861]The sum total of his translations would have alone drastically altered the course of Western science, notes Grant.[1862]In the universities that had medical schools, medicine was taught from Latin translations of Islamic texts by Hunayn ibn Ishaq, Al-Razi, Ibn Sina, and also Galen.[1863] At Montpellier, manuscripts of Islamic authors were abundant and many `Compendia' containing Islamic learning were issued under the control of the universities, particularly those of Bologna and Padua.[1864] The mere list of medical works published from the discovery of printing to the close of the 15th century is sufficient proof that medical teaching was exclusively Islamic throughout Europe.[1865] The Latin translation of Ibn Sina was printed at Milan in 1473, at Padua in 1476, and at Strasbourg somewhat earlier. The translation of Mesue (Ibn Massawih al-Maradini) had appeared in Venice in 1471, and was reprinted almost simultaneously in five or six other cities.[1866]The works of Ibn Sina, for instance, remained for over six hundred years the universal codice of Medicine; serving as the foundation of medical studies in all French and Italian universities.[1867] Ibn Sina's works, in fact, were re-printed until the 18th century, and commentaries were made upon them in the University of Montpellier as late as the 19th century.[1868]

The mass of `new' science, overwhelming in scope and magnitude, had first to be absorbed, a process that occupied virtually all of the 13th century.[1869] Which explains the rise at the same time of some of the greatest names of Western scholarship: Aquinas, (d 1272), Albertus Magnus (1206-1280), Alfonso X (d. 1288), Robert Grosseteste (1168-1253); Roger Bacon (1220-1294), Arnold of Villanova, Raymond Lull (ca. 1232-1315), among others.[1870]

[1861] R. Lemay: G of Cremona; op cit; at p. 189.
[1862] E. Grant: Physical Science; op cit; p.17.
[1863] A.O. Whipple: The Role of the Nestorians; op cit; P. 36
[1864] D. Campbell: Arabian Medicine; op cit; p.201
[1865] P. Lacroix: Science and Literature; op cit; p.168.
[1866] Ibid.
[1867] G. Le Bon, La Civilisation des Arabes; op cit; p.388.
[1868] Ibid.
[1869] E. Grant: Physical Science; op cit; p. 18.
[1870] A.Chejne: The Role of al Andalus; op cit; p. 119.
See The Encyclopaedia of the History (Rashed ed) ; op cit; for various articles on the impact of Muslim science on the Latin West; most particularly:
-H. Hugonnard-Roche: The Influence of Arabic Astronomy in the Medieval West; pp 284-305.
-D.C. Lindberg: The Western Reception of Arabic Optics, pp 716-29.
-R. Halleux: The Reception of Arabic Alchemy in the West; pp 886-902.

Schools for Arabic also developed in the wake of the translations. Spaniards, such as Raymondo (d. 1151), founded a school of translation in Toledo. Bacon's advocacy for learning Arabic was taken up by Ramon Lull, the latter, in 1276 founding a school of Oriental Studies at Toledo, and pushing for similar programs in Salamanca, Rome, Bologna, Paris and Oxford.[1871] Lull also successfully argued for the implementation of language learning in the universities at the Council of Vienna in 1312, where, for the first time officially, the Church ordained that lectureship in Arabic, Hebrew, Greek and Chaldee (i.e., Aramaic) be given[1872]

The new learning from translations, together with another crucial advance, the manufacturing of paper, also coming through Islam (the invention of paper is Chinese), led to the development of printing of scientific works, which in the early stages were to be of religious text, of course, but also of scientific texts. Rodinson notes that from the beginning, everything was published, from Ibn Sina's medical and philosophical works to books of grammar, geography, and mathematics.[1873]Abu Ma'Ashar's work on the stars, for instance, was printed in Venice in 1489, 1495, and 1506.[1874]The majority of the works by Al-Razi were printed many times, principally in Venice in 1509, and in Paris in 1528 and 1548. His treatise on small verole, for instance, was reprinted in 1745. Courses in medical schools and universities of Europe have relied for centuries on his and Ibn Sina's works, and so the need for their re-print until the 18th century.[1875] Brought together, scientific translations, paper, and printing became the fundamental elements in the rise of modern science.

-D. Jacquart: The Influence of Arabic Medicine in the Medieval West; pp 963-84.

1871 A. Chejne: The Role of al Andalus; op cit p. 119

1872 C. Burnett: The Introduction; op cit; p.79.

1873 M. Rodinson: *Europe and the Mystique of Islam*; trans: R. Veinus; I.B. Tauris and Co Ltd; London; 1988. p.41

1874 J.K. Wright: The Geographical Lore; op cit; p.503.

1875 G. Le Bon, La Civilisation des Arabes; op cit; p.387.

Final Remarks:

Any future study of Islamic impact through translations will have to return to the earlier works that have dealt with the matter, but were not widely used here (i.e Suter, Wiedemann, Steinchneider, Diercks, Prutz, Vernet, Millas Vallicrosa, Ribera, Castro....) and deliver a larger, and better executed work on the translation of Islamic science than this one. D'Alverny also notes that the history of 12th Century translation is incomplete, and the diffusion and impact of such translation require further investigation to be adequately appreciated.[1876]

Translations of Muslim works went on in the subsequent centuries. Many such translations were widely used in the universities, most particularly those of northern Italy and France;[1877] their impact on learning and major scientific breakthroughs in such places remains to be known. Even in recent times, much was still being translated.[1878] A full list of all Muslim translated works throughout the centuries will not be just useful in itself, it will also give an idea on the use and impact of such science in any given place and time

Also, in agreement with Levey, very few of the hundreds of thousands of Muslim scientific manuscripts have been studied whether for their content `or their influence upon further works,' which calls for greater attention to be paid to the matter.[1879]

And finally, it is best to finish this chapter, by quoting Grant:
`Without the valiant labours of this small army of translators in the 12th and 13th centuries, not only would medieval science have failed to

[1876] M. T. d'Alverny: Translations, op cit, p. 457
[1877] M. Meyerhof: Science and Medicine, op cit, p. 351.
[1878] Here follow instances of recent translations of Muslim works:
-Al-Jazari: *The Book of Knowledge of Ingenious Mechanical Devices*, English translation with notes by D. R. Hill, Dordrecht/Boston, 1974.
-Ibn Nadim: *al-Fihrist*: English translation by Bayard Dodge, *The Fihrist of al-Nadim.* A tenth Century Survey of Muslim Culture, 2 vols, New York/London, coll. Columbia Records of Civilisation, Sources and Studies, 1970.
-Al-Khazini, `Abd al-Rhaman (1941) *Kitab Mizan al-Hikma*, Hyderabad; partial English translation by N. Khanikoff (1859) `Analysis and extracts of *Kitab mizan al-Hikma* (Book of Balance of Wisdom), *Journal of the American Oriental Society* 6:1-128; also Russian translation: by M.M. Rozhanskaya and I.S. Levinova (1983) `Al-Kazini. Kniga vesov midrosti,' Nauchnoye nasledstvo, Moscow, vol 6. pp 15-140.
[1879] M. Levey: Early Arabic, op cit, preface vii.

materialise, but the scientific revolution of the 17th century could hardly have occurred.'[1880]

And concluding with Dawson:

`The derivative character of the movement and its lack of originality ought not to detract from the achievement of these Western scholars who faced so many difficulties and overcame so many obstacles in the disinterested pursuit of scientific knowledge. For, however strange their scientific ideas may seem to us, there can be no doubt that the ideal which inspired their activity was a genuinely scientific one and that they are the humble and half-forgotten founders of the long and glorious line of Western scientists.'[1881]

[1880] E. Grant: Physical Science; op cit; p. 18.
[1881] C. Dawson: Medieval Essays; op cit; p. 141.

Part Three

AREAS OF IMPACT

Islamic science and civilisation impacted on the Christian West, and modern science and civilisation on a wide diversity of areas. This includes learning, which is examined in the first chapter; sciences, looked at in the second; trade, farming and industry, seen in the third; and architecture, arts and culture, as to be seen in the fourth.

Again, it must be remembered, not everything will be addressed in detail, for the work will lose its cohesiveness if some areas are too detailed in comparison to others. It is also impossible for this author to have such a great competence to analyse everything adequately in great detail. What is shown, hopefully, will indicate the thoroughness of the Islamic impact. It will also show that changes occurred in Western Christendom all at once following contact with Islam. They also all bear the Islamic distinct link and substance that would not have been easily seen had any one matter been examined in isolation.

1. ON LEARNING AND MODERN SCIENCE

Prior to the examination of the Islamic impact on some specific sciences such as astronomy, mathematics, optics, etc, it is first necessary to look at how the Islamic influence revolutionised learning. How Islamic science was taken up by a second generation of influential Western scholars, knowledge which they Latinised and legitimised for their milieus, and which allowed the first Western institutions of higher learning to emerge. Islam also provided modern science with observation, measurement, the search for accuracy, scientific methodology, etc, all seized upon by Western Christendom.

1. Early Men of Learning of the Christian West

The first wave of Western Christian scholars has already been dealt with at great length. This included the likes of Adelard of Bath, Gerbert, Petrus Alphonsi, Walcher of Malvern, Daniel of Morley, Constantine the African etc... all scholars, and for most, translators, too. Their crucial role in the awakening of Western Christendom has been considered, the English, amongst them, as a group, for instance, as Haskins notes, put England at the centre in the diffusion of Islamic sciences throughout Western Europe in the 12th century, mainly thanks to Adelard,[1882] whose works, and pioneering trust for Islamic learning, mark a significant stage in the history of ideas.[1883] The labours of these early men led to a wide variety of scientific advances in the 13th century.[1884] Advances furthered by scholars on whom emphasis is placed in the following.

The list includes the likes of Roger Bacon (1220-1294), Robert Grosseteste (1175-1253), Albertus Magnus (1206-1280), Thomas Aquinas (d.1274), Arnold of Villanova (d.1311) etc. They were the first to adapt Islamic learning on Western ground, Latinise such learning, not just in form (as those before them did), but also in the manner it is diffused, besides, of course, building upon it. All these second wave scholars appeared to the fore in the 13th century, in the wake of the

---

[1882] C.H. Haskins: Studies, op cit, Chapter II: Adelard of Bath.
[1883] L. Cochrane: Adelard of Bath; op cit; P.1.
[1884] B. Stock: Science, Technology, and Economic Progress; op cit; p.39

translations just discussed, and all of them, were connected in one way or another with institutions or regions where Islamic learning was dominant: Southern Italy, Spain, Montpellier, etc. All knew Arabic; and evidently, all their works bear, some up to the totality, Islamic influences. These characteristics are looked at here through the lives and works of Aquinas, Bacon and Grosseteste.

Before these three are dealt with, it is appropriate to skip briefly through some other names and their works, as diversely as possible, to highlight the Islamic influence on them.

Beginning with optics and John Peckham (fl. Second half of 13th) (theologian, mathematician, and physicist), a Franciscan, who spent his life in Paris, Oxford, Rome and as Archbishop of Canterbury from 1279 to his death. His optics is largely derived from Ibn al-Haytham, where he also refers to the camera obscura, just as to be found in the works of Bacon and Witelo.[1885]

The Polish philosopher and physicist Witelo (Vitelo) (1230-1275) was a Dominican born in Silesia, whose optics is largely derived from the work of Ibn al-Haytham. The value of his work is much impaired if one realises how much of it was of such provenance, Sarton observes, but his followers did not realise this and admired him far beyond it should have been the case.[1886]Witelo's work did lack explicit acknowledgement of the source, though.[1887] In his lengthy introduction to *Optica Thesaurus,* Lindberg highlights Witelo's close reliance on Ibn al-Haytham.[1888] The best demonstration for such resemblance, Lindberg points out, being `simply to follow the cross-references between Al-Hazen (Ibn al-Haytham) and Witelo in the Pisner edition of their works: one quickly learns that for the most part Witelo treats the same topics in the same fashion, and sometimes in even the same words. Occasionally Witelo omits a topic, and sometimes he seeks to clarify Alhazen's points by further elaboration on a tightening of the argument, but seldom does he depart from his principal source.'[1889]

Witelo's optical treatise *Perspective*, Birkenmajer says, is well ordered and full of good facts, and its scientific worth is not compromised by the

[1885] G. Sarton: Introduction; op cit; Vol II,p.1028.

[1886] Ibid.p.760

[1887] S. Devons: Optics Through the Eyes of the Medieval Churchmen: in Science and Technology in Medieval Society; P.O Long: ed: *Annals of the New York Academy of Sciences*, vol 441, New York, 1985. pp 205-224. p. 215.

[1888] D.C. Lindberg: *Optica Thesaurus: Alhazen and Witelo*; editor: H. Woolf. Johnson Reprint Corporation, New York, London, 1972. Introduction pp v-xxxiv At p. xiii:

[1889] Ibid.

fact that the author derived the largest part of his knowledge from the *Aspectibus* of Ibn al-Haytham.[1890] Even when he sought to explain the problem of optical illusion in his *Denatura demonum*, Witelo also relied on Ibn al-Haytham.[1891] Ibn al-Haytham deeply impacted on Witelo on other matters, which include the study of Ibn al-Haytham's optical treatises at Padua, in Italy, in seeking to explain optical phenomena met in the grottos of Covolo, and also, in his *Scientia motuum coelestium*, where he, Witelo, deals with the proportion of distance between the earth and the sphere of fixed stars.[1892] Witelo's work on visual illusions, which he derived from Ibn al-Haytham had an impact on Nicolas Oresme via his commentary on the *Meteore.*[1893]

Theodoric of Freiberg, just like Witelo, leaned, and considerably, on Ibn al-Haytham (referred to as `*auctor perspectiva*') and to a lesser extent on Ibn Rushd (`*Commentator*'), Ibn Sina and Al-Farabi.[1894] His theory of colour was somewhat more novel, following Ibn al-Haytham, and in contrast to Bacon, he treated colour as real as light itself.[1895]

Leopold of Austria was an astronomer and meteorologist, who flourished probably in the middle of the second half of the 13th century. He composed an astronomical compilation, appropriately entitled *Compilatio de astronum scientia,* divided into ten treatises. The author was acquainted with the tables of al-Zarqali, and a very large part of his work was derived from the *Kitab al-madkhal* (The Introduction) of Abu Ma'ashar.[1896] A French translation of Leopold's Compilatio (*li compilacions Leupo le fil le duc d'Austeriche de le science des estoiles*) came to be owned by Mary of Luxembourg, queen of France (d. 1324).[1897]

The astronomical work by John of Holywood (d. 1250) who was long a teacher at Paris, was universally popular, existing in numerous manuscripts, and was translated into most European vernaculars.[1898] It

---

[1890] A. Birkenmajer: Coup d'oeil sur l'histoire des sciences exactes en Pologne; in Studia Copernicana; 4; 1972; pp. 3-4. in J.B. Korolec: La Premiere reception de la philosophie Islamique a l'Universite de Cracovie; in The Introduction of Arabic philosophy; op cit; pp. 112-30 at p. 114.

[1891] J.B. Korolec: La Premiere reception; at p. 114.

[1892] A. Brikenmajer: Les Astronomes et les astrologues silesiens au moyen age; Studia Copernicana; 4; p. 441; in J.B. Korolec: La Premiere; op cit; p. 114.

[1893] A. Brikenmajer: Coup d'Oeil; op cit; p. 170; in J.B. Korolec: La premiere; p. 114.

[1894] S. Devons: Optics; op cit; p. 217.

[1895] Ibid. p. 218.

[1896] G. Sarton: Introduction; op cit; Vol II, p.996.

[1897] Ibid.

[1898] C. Singer: *A Short History of Scientific Ideas; op cit;* p. 173.

contains, however, no new or original elements and is put together from translations of Muslim works.[1899] The *Tractatus de Sphaera, or Sphaera Mundi,* completed in 1233 by Sacrobosco (John of Holywood) is, indeed, nearly a word by word reproduction of al-Farghani and al-Battani.[1900]

Vincent of Beauvais's *Speculum naturale's* astronomy is a reproduction of al-Bitruji's theory (on the sphere) as distorted by Albert (Magnus).[1901] Chaucer's (1340-1400) treatise on the astrolabe written in 1390, appears to be a re-statement of an Islamic work of the 8th-9th Century.[1902] Chaucer's use of the `contemporary sciences' in presenting the physical and spiritual condition of man, medieval and universal, reflects the observations, ideas, and methodology of great `Arabian' masters who occur throughout the body of his works, as he names them: Alkabucious, Alocen, Arsechiel, Averrois, Avycen, Haly, Razis.[1903] Chaucer equally refers to Constantyn (the African) and Piers Alfonce (Petrus Alfonsi), the pioneer of Islamic studies on English soil.[1904]

John of Genoa, another astronomer (fl 1332-37), compiled tables for the computation of eclipses in 1332 derived partly from al-Battani;[1905] whilst Ristoro d'Arezzo (fl c.1282) completed in Arezzo (Tuscany) an encyclopaedic treatise on the composition of the world, in Italian: *Della composizione del mondo colle sue cagioni,* which deals with astronomy, meteorology, and geology, largely derived from Latin translations of Islamic works of the 9th century by al-Farghani, Sahl ibn Bishr, Abu Ma'ashar; and he may also have used Ibn Sina' *Qanun*, and Ibn Rushd's commentary on Aristotelian meteorology.[1906]

The geological ideas of the great encyclopaedists, Vincent of Beauvais and Albert the Great, were essentially derived from Muslim sources, including The *Kitab al-Shifa* of Ibn Sina, the so called *Avicennae Mineralia* translated by Alfred of Sareshel. When they explain the movements of the sea, erosion, the generation of mountains, they are simply repeating the words of Ibn Sina or of the unknown author of the

---

[1899] Ibid.
[1900] A. Mieli: La Science Arabe; op cit; p.241.
[1901] G. Sarton: Introduction, Vol II, p.930.
[1902] C.H. Cotter: *A History of Nautical Astronomy:* Hollis and Carter; London; 1968.P. 61.
[1903] D. Metlitzki: The Matter of Araby; op cit; p. 74.
[1904] Ibid.
[1905] G. Sarton: Introduction; op cit; Volume III; p.641.
[1906] Ibid. Vol II, p.928.

De elementis.[1907] Vincent of Beauvais's geological part of *Speculum naturale* is derived from Ibn Sina through Albert the Great.[1908]
Al-Biruni's *Tahdid nihayat al-amakin (The identification of the end of places)*, written in 1025, speaks of the alternations of dry land and sea, and in another text he remarks that the Indus valley should be considered an ancient sea basin filled with alluvium.[1909] Similar views appeared in Albert the Great (Albertus Magnus) and Ristoro d'Arezzo (13th century); the latter even referred to fossil fishes, and so did Joinville in his life of St. Louis.[1910]

Lanfrank, who was both practioner in Paris, and also a teacher is the author of the *Chirurgia magna,* where he insists on the study of good clinical cases, and where he sets down the foundations of French surgery. Lanfrank relies, and vastly, on Islamic sources, which include Hunain Ibn Ishaq, Al-Razi, Ishaq al-Israeli, Ali Ibn Abbas, Abu-l-Qasim, Ibn Sina, Constantine, Ibn Sarabi, Ibn Rushd, etc.[1911]
Equally, Arnold of Villanova's sources of influence were mainly Muslim Spain, Valencia, most particularly, and Montpellier.[1912]His translations and other aspects of his scholarly life have already been covered, just to add here observations made by Daniel, that Arnold copied so much Al-Razi, that he (Daniel) sees in him a sort of lesser and European Al-Razi.[1913] Arnold covers so large a field, Daniel observes, that he must be thought a re-editor as much as an author;[1914] plagiarism, Daniel notes, is meaningless in the mediaeval context, `but almost the whole of the medical culture of Europe with all its acquisitions from the Arabs seems to pass through his pen.'[1915]
John of St Amand (d. early 14th) was a Belgian physician (working in Paris,) and canon (of Tournai, Belgium.) His fame is based upon two works: a commentary on the antidotary of Nicholas of Salerno *Expositio sive additio super antidotarium Nicolai*, and a medical compendium

[1907] Ibid. p.48.
[1908] Ibid. p.930.
[1909] Ibid. Vol III. p.213.
[1910] Ibid.
[1911] The Chirurgia magna was first printed in Latin in Venice 1490, but the French translation by Guillaume Ivoire has appeared before (260 leaves, Lyon c. 1479). English translation, Lanfrank's Science of surgery, edited from the Bodleian Ashmole MS. 1396 (c.1380) and the British Museum additional MS. 12056 (c. 1420), by Robert von Fleischacker (early English text Society, 102, Part 1, Text, 355 p., London, 1894). In G. Sarton: Introduction; op cit; Vol II. p..1080.
[1912] L. Garcia Ballester: *La Minoria musulmana y morisca*, vol I; op cit.
[1913] N. Daniel: The Arabs; op cit; p. 293.
[1914] Ibid.
[1915] Ibid.

called *Revocativum memoriae*.[1916] The first work deals, exactly in the Salernitan tradition as introduced by Constantine, with digestion, evacuation (spontaneous, or artificial by means of purgation, bloodletting, leeches, etc.), up-building, bloodletting, uroscopy, diet etc. For both works, his main sources include Al-Razi, Hunain Ibn Ishaq, Ishaq al-Israeli, Ali Ibn Abbas, Ibn Sina, and, obviously, Constantine the African.[1917]

The *Regimen du corps* was written by Aldobrandin of Siena in 1256 for Beatrice of Savoy on the occasion of a journey which she undertook to visit her four daughters, the Queen of France, the Queen of England, the Queen of Germany, and the countess of Anjou (later Queen of Sicily).[1918] Such is the stature of Aldobrandin, that Countess Beatrice recommended him as a doctor to the French king Saint Louis himself.[1919] The *Regimen du corps* is divided into four main parts dealing respectively with general and special hygiene of various organs (hair, eyes, ears, teeth and gums, face, stomach, liver, heart); dietetics and physiognomy.[1920]This work is a near total reproduction of Muslim medical learning; its first two parts wholly based on Ibn Sina, and also on Ali Abbas and Hunayn Ibn Ishaq.[1921] The third part follows Ishaq al-Israili, whilst the fourth and final part is a near literal translation of a part of the *Kitab al-Mansuri* of Al-Razi.[1922]

Medical books often included a study of the weights and measures used by doctors. The best example of this class is the *De Ponderibus e mensuris* of Dino del Garbo (d.1327), which is more elaborate than other studies appearing in medical treatises, and is valuable for comparative purposes, for it includes Greek, Hebrew, and Arabic terms as well as Latin ones; but Dino's main authority was the *Qanun* of Ibn Sina.[1923]

And finally, here, mention must be made of John of Gaddesden (C.1280-1361), a fellow of Merton College, Oxford, who compiled the famous treatise *Rosa Anglica*, which is mainly based on the works of both `Arabists' Bernard de Gordon and Henry de Mondeville.[1924]

[1916] G. Sarton: Introduction; op cit; Vol II. p.1089.
[1917] Ibid.
[1918] Ibid. pp 1083-4.
[1919] A. Mieli: La Science Arabe; op cit; p. 230.
[1920] Ibid. pp 1083-4.
[1921] A. Mieli: La Science Arabe; op cit; p. 230.
[1922] Ibid.
[1923] G. Sarton: Introduction;. Volume III; op cit. p.712.
[1924] D. Campbell: Arabian Medicine, op cit; p.164.

Very brief mention must be made of Albert the Great (1206-1280), who re-occurs quite often in this work, to note that his philosophical ideas are mainly derived from Al-Farabi, Ibn Sina, Al-Ghazali; Ibn Baja; and Ibn Rushd.[1925] Hammond has shown that al-Farabi's influence on Albertus Magnus (as on his pupil Aquinas) is clearly visible in ontology, cosmology, psychology and theology.[1926] In his comments on Aristotle, he chiefly uses Ibn Sina;[1927] In anatomy and medicine, Albert must have used the *Anatomia vivorum,* or the translation of Ibn Sina's *Qanun* by Gerard of Cremona.[1928] In meteorology and climatology, his views are mainly a clear summary of those transmitted by the Muslims. In geology and mineralogy, it was Ibn Sina's *De Congelatione et conglutionatione lapidum;* Ibn Sina's influence also present in Albert's Zoology.[1929]

The first of the three 13th century main figures who is dealt with here is Robert Grosthead or (Greathead) Robert of Lincoln, better known as Robert Grosseteste (1175-1253). He was born of humble parentage at Stradbrook, Suffolk, and was educated in Oxford and Paris(?). He was first chancellor of the University of Oxford; first lecturer to the Oxford Franciscans, 1224; Bishop of Lincoln from 1235 to his death in 1253. His scientific works are indebted to the texts brought to England in the earlier stages of Islamic influence, records speaking of him as a master at Hereford, where Burnett reminds us, Muslim mathematics and sciences flourished.[1930] Grosseteste is also one of the earliest English authors to be acquainted with the writings of the Salernitan school.[1931] It was, indeed, he who introduced that Salernitan medicine, with all its Islamic garb in England,[1932]which later on a number of his students disseminated in turn. Just as his other sciences were also of Islamic origin to great measure. Grosseteste astronomical ideas were partly derived from Al-Bitruji after the latter was translated by Michael Scot.[1933] His basing natural philosophy upon mathematics and experiment was extremely far reaching, although in this respect he was

---

[1925] R. Hammond: *The Philosophy of al-Farabi and its Influence on Medieval Thought*; New York; The Hobson Book Press; 1947.
[1926] Ibid.
[1927] De Lacy O'Leary: Arabic Thought; op cit; p.285.
[1928] D. Campbell: Arabian Medicine; op cit; p.143; G. Sarton: Introduction; vol 2; pp 935-40.
[1929] G. Sarton: Introduction; Vol II; pp. 935-40.
[1930] C. Burnett: Arabic Learning; op cit; p. 56.
[1931] G Sarton: Introduction; Vol II, p.584.
[1932] Ibid. p. 520
[1933] Ibid. p.584.

by no means the inventor of the experimental method, Muslims having preceded him by centuries (as seen in part one). A thorough study will indeed show from which source Grosseteste derived his ideas on experimentation, but it could well be Ibn al-Haytham. This was very much obvious in other areas as Grosseteste knew of the properties of convex lenses from a Latin version of Ibn al-Haytham.[1934] And Grosseteste developed from them a theory of the formation of the rainbow.[1935]In this way he was clearly the forerunner of his most famous pupil, Roger Bacon, and he may have influenced the whole of Western Christendom, partly through his own writings, and partly through these new tendencies emphasised by Bacon and others.[1936]

Roger Bacon (1220-1294) who lectured in both Paris and Oxford used Muslim philosophers in order to make polemic points against Islam, but seems genuinely to have liked what he quoted.[1937] He argued that `our apprehension of the future life is like that of a deaf man's of music,' and supported this from Ibn Sina.[1938]Bacon was fond of this passage: `A man shall not be freed of this world and of its deceptions until, wholly taken up with that other heavenly world... the love of the things there draws him altogether away from thinking of anything lower.'[1939] In his medical work *Epistola de accidentibus senectutis* Bacon also drew heavily from Islamic sources, that include the writings of Ibn Sina, Al-Razi, and Isaac Judaeus.[1940] In mathematics his inspiration was al-Farabi, in astronomy it was Ibn al-Haytham and al-Kharaqi, and the former also influenced him with respect to optics, as also did al-Kindi.[1941] In turn, Bacon influenced John Pecham and William st Cloud. He was in fact the first Latin to make exposition of Ibn al-Haytham's account of the eye, with its lens, as an optical system; following Ibn al-Haytham closely in accounting for the structure and function affecting vision.[1942] Using the works Ibn al-Haytham (and al-Kindi's) on lenses, he gave a geometrical description of the rainbow's position in the sky understanding it to be composed of a multiple of droplets.[1943] Bacon's commentary on the

---

1934 C. Singer: *Short History of Scientific Ideas; op cit*.p. 180.
1935 Ibid.
1936 G Sarton: Introduction; Vol II, p.583.
1937 N. Daniel: *The Cultural Barrier*, op cit; p. 175.
1938 Ibid.
1939 Ibid.
1940 D. Campbell: Arabian Medicine; op cit; p.158.
1941 See G. Sarton: Introduction, Vol II, pp.952-60.
1942 A.C Crombie: Science, Optics; op cit; p.202.
1943 M. Authier: Refraction and Cartesian `Forgetfulness' in *A History of Scientific Thought*; M. Serres; editor; Blackwell, 1995; p. pp 315-43; p.328.

Secretum secretorum (a book of miscellaneous precepts for the guidance of human affairs, which was many times translated from Arabic during the Middle Ages, altered, augmented and edited by Bacon) shows good material on astronomy, on the size and sphericity of the earth, and on the relative extent of land and Sea.[1944]

Bacon did step out of the Church boundaries in his too close borrowings from Islamic sources. After Stephen Tempier's condemnation of Ibn Rushd's theories in 1277, the Franciscan censorship struck harder, and in the following year Bacon was condemned for teaching `suspected novelties'. According to a Franciscan chronicle (*Chronica viginti quattuor generalium,* to 1374) he was imprisoned from 1278 to 1292.[1945]In his third letter to Pope Clement, Bacon held: `It is on account of the ignorance of those with whom I have had to deal that I have not been able to accomplish more.'[1946]

Still, his legacy was considerable. He was an important link in the chain of scientific development, an authority at Oxford for centuries, an influence traceable through Pierre d'Ailly and the *Imago Mundi* to Columbus and through Paul of Middleburg (1445-1534), and the reform of the Gregorian calendar to Copernicus.[1947] It was also he, Bacon, who first insisted that Latin science of the Middle Ages came for the best part from other civilisations, and that it was useful to have a direct knowledge of original texts upon which was based that science.[1948] He never wearied of declaring that `knowledge of Arabic and Arabian science was for his contemporaries the only way to true knowledge.'[1949] Forster, it is, who, said, Bacon `drank deeply of the Arabian learning at the fountain head' and provided `the undoubted origin of the rue astronomy as afterwards unfolded in the Copernican system'.[1950]

Born to a noble family near Naples, Thomas (Aquinas) (c.1225-1274) was educated as a boy at the famous abbey of Monte Cassino. Later he studied at the newly established University of Naples (both institutions bed-sits of Islamic learning). Naples University, it must be remembered

---

[1944] Oxford Ed., fasc.V in J.K. Wright: The Geographical Lore; op cit; note 97 for chapter IV; p.410.

[1945] G. Sarton: Introduction, op cit; Vol II, p.956.

[1946] J. Draper: A History; op cit; Vol II:p.155.

[1947] D. Campbell: Arabian Medicine; op cit; p.158.

[1948] J. Richard: l'Enseignement des langues Orientales en Occident au Moyen Age: *Revue d'Etudes Islamiques* Vol 44; 1976; pp 149-164;p.150

[1949] R. Briffault: The Making; op cit; p. 201.

[1950] C. Forster: *Mohametanism Unveiled*; London; James Duncan and John Cochran; 1829 in C. Bennett: *Victorian Images of Islam*; Grey Seal; London; 1992. p.23.

was founded by Frederick II, and this goes far, according to O'Leary `to account for his more accurate appreciation of Islamic teaching.'[1951] After becoming a Dominican friar, Aquinas set out for Paris to study theology.[1952] In the wide area that lies on the margins of theology and philosophy, he relied heavily on Muslim sources, mostly Ibn Sina, al-Ghazali and Ibn Rushd.[1953]Aquinas appreciated Ibn Rushd most particularly, as `the supreme master in logic, but heretical in his metaphysics and psychology.'[1954] Indeed, all kinds of subversive elements conglomerated around the views of Ibn Rushd as distorted by their `bigoted' adversaries.[1955] Supporters of Ibn Rushd were accused of questioning the fundamental doctrines of the Church, especially of doubting the dogmas of creation and of the immortality of the soul, of being materialists, etc.. They also had the bad reputation of being scientifically minded and prone to dialectics.[1956] The enlargement of horizons by the Crusades, the increasing acquaintance with Islamic life and thought in East and West-all these, Durant holds, `could have produced an Aquinas even if Aristotle had remained unknown; indeed the industry of Aquinas was due not to love of Aristole but to fear of Averroes (Ibn Rushd).'[1957]Thus, while St Thomas was fighting for Christian rationalism and using many of the weapons forged by Ibn Sina, Al-Ghazzali, and Ibn Rushd, he was also fighting the subversive Ibn Rushd.[1958] The aim of St Thomas, in this seeking to reproduce the arguments, formulas, and methods of Ibn Sina and his predecessors, was in seeking to reconcile reason and religion.[1959] He was particularly prone to adopt the thoughts of Al-Farabi, Ibn Sina, Al-Ghazali, Ibn Baja, and, of course, Ibn Rushd, just as his teacher, Albertus Magnus was.[1960]The particular impact of Al-Farabi (c.870-950) on Aquinas (just as on his teacher) is obvious in matters of cosmology, psychology and theology.[1961]In the discussion of topics that were of great importance to his natural theology like the principle of causality and the `cosmological

---

[1951] De Lacy O'Leary: Arabic Thought; op cit; p. 287.
[1952] D.J. Geanakoplos: Medieval Western Civilisation; op cit; p.331.
[1953] N. Daniel: The Cultural Barrier; op cit; p. 175
[1954] De Lacy O'Leary: Arabic Thought; op cit; pp. 286-7.
[1955] G. Sarton: Introduction; op cit; Vol III.p.83.
[1956] Ibid. p.84.
[1957] W Durant: The Age of Faith, op cit; p. 954.
[1958] Thus the triumph of Thomism was represented as a triumph over heresy and over Averroism. Remember the Pisa altarpiece by Francisco Traini; in G. Sarton: Introduction; Vol III. p.84.
[1959] R. Briffault: The Making; op cit; p. 219.
[1960] R. Hammond: The Philosophy of al-Farabi; op cit; p. 21.
[1961] Ibid.

proofs' of God, Aquinas merely repeats al-Farabi's proofs.[1962] Gilson also finds Ibn Sina's influence on Aquinas in this particular area.[1963]

Aquinas, Durant points out, was always seeking his ways through, for the introduction of Islamic thoughts, but it must be reminded, this was the time of the Crusades after all, and by his time, they were already nearly two century old of incessant warfare.[1964]Where St Thomas accomplishes his great achievement is in his adopting the medium line as far as the situation in the Christian West was concerned. He fought both Muslim rationalism and Christian irrationalism, following a line between the `Averroists' of the left and the Scotists and Augustinians of the right, a conciliatory attitude, which made his prestige;[1965] and which became the route for subsequent followers, opening the road to query whilst remaining within Church guidelines.

2. Institutions of Higher Learning

Haskins observes that, throughout the earlier Middle Ages, the chief centres of culture had been the monasteries. `Set like islands in a sea of ignorance and barbarism, they had saved learning from extinction in Western Europe.''[1966] Not all such monasteries were centres of light and learning, though, he points out; learning, which in most instances, primarily consisted of the *Opus Dei*, daily chanting of the office in the choir, then study and meditation on the Bible or the fathers.[1967] Libraries were equally meagre in content (as already contrasted with the Muslim world in the first part). Learning only concerned a minority of ecclesiastics, and until late in the high Middle Ages, it `had few friends and many detractors,' notes Daniel.[1968]Within the Church, some complained that those who spent their lives learning were wasting time, living in ivory towers, and concentrating on the wrong issues.[1969] New

---

[1962] Ibid.
[1963] E. Gilson: *History of Christian Philosophy in the Middle Ages*; New York; 1955; p.187.
[1964] W Durant: The Age of Faith, op cit; p. 954.
[1965] G. Sarton: Introduction; op cit; Vol III. p.84.
[1966] C.H. Haskins: The Renaissance; op cit; pp.33-8.
[1967] Ibid. p.34
[1968] N. Daniel: *The Cultural Barrier, op cit;* p. 170.
[1969] R.N. Swanson: The Twelfth Century; op cit; p.37.

religious orders in the period often began by shunning academic life, Bernard of Clairvaux (1090-1153), despite his own extensive learning, derided the new approaches of the secular schools, which he said `blocked divine illumination and distracted from the truth,' whilst Francis of Assisi held that knowledge beyond Christ's gospel message was superfluous.[1970] The Church, Daniel reminds, was almost the sole patron of scholarship and learning in medieval Europe,[1971] and cathedral schools had a narrow objective consisting in the preparation of clerics and priests.[1972] The level of scientific learning consisted of basic arithmetical computations, the propositions of Euclid (without the proofs), and astronomy based mainly on the folklore of Germanic tribes, rudimentary geometry and chemistry consisting of basic metallurgy and the dyeing of cloth.[1973] Nevertheless, Hill rightly points out, it was from the cathedral schools that the universities were to be established, and it was mainly from the cathedral schools and early universities that Islamic knowledge was to enter the Latin West.[1974]

It was, indeed, the cathedral schools, and some pioneering figures of the Church, John of Gorze and Gerbert, most particularly, who triggered the beginnings of Middle Ages learning in the West. It was the schools of Lorraine, and subsequently the transfer of Lotharingians to the Cathedral schools of England, above all, which promoted the first elements of mathematical and astronomical knowledge; a learning that was, however, Islamic in essence and content.[1975] Because of that, understandably, the progress was slow, yet advances were made with Walcher of Malvern, Petrus Alphonsi, and Adelard of Bath.[1976] 12th century translations, of primarily Islamic science, armed cathedral schools: Laon, Chartres, Rheims, and Paris, with greater prominence; the number of students attracted to them increasing greatly.[1977]

[1970] Ibid.
[1971] N. Daniel: *The Cultural Barrier, op cit;* p. 170.
[1972] D. R. Hill: Islamic Science; op cit; p.220
[1973] Ibid.
[1974] Ibid.
[1975] See M.C. Welborn: Lotharingia; op cit; J. W. Thompson: The Introduction of Arabic Science; op cit.
[1976] See: L. Cochrane: Adelard; op cit; C. Burnett: The Introduction; op cit; M.C. Welborn: Lotharingia; op cit; and, previous chapter.
[1977] M. Clagett: The Growth of Learning in the West; in *Chapters in Western Civilization*; Edited by the Contemporary Civilisation Staff of Columbia College; Columbia University Press; Vol 1; third ed; 1961; pp. 64-90; at p. 79.

Universities, too, as Haskins expands upon, emerged in the 12th century, primarily. The Greeks and the Romans, Haskins, says, strange as it may seem, had no universities in the sense in which the word has been used for the past seven or eight centuries.[1978] Clagett points out that it was in the last quarter of the 12th century that the universities of Bologna and Paris took form.[1979]The roots of others, such as Oxford, Cambridge, Angers, and Padua, can be found in the latter part of the 12th or early 13th.[1980] Sarton, too, notes, that by the end of the 12th century, five universities were at different stages of development: two in Italy: Salerno and Bologna, two in France: Paris and Montpellier, and one in England: Oxford. Among the new universities of the first half of the 13th, the most important were Padua, a daughter of Bologna, born in 1222; Naples deliberately established by Frederick II in 1224; the law schools of Orleans and Angers; Cambridge, issued from Oxford in 1209.[1981] Rome, Pisa, Avignon, Prague, Vienna, and Cracow were all founded in the 14th century;[1982] Rome by Pope Boniface VIII in 1303; Avignon (1303); Perugia (1308). Grenoble was established in 1339 by Benedict XII for all faculties except theology; Pisa receiving the privileges of a studium generale only in 1343 from Clement VI; and the same Clement VI establishing Prague in 1347 and Florence in 1349; Perpignan receiving a new charter and a new lease on life from Pope Clement VII in 1379.[1983] In Spain, Campbell notes, thanks primarily to the Islamic influence, there were sixteen of them before the end of the 15th century.[1984]

How, and why did such universities rise at this juncture is what is seen in the following.

The Rise of Western Universities, and the Islamic Role:

The Islamic role can be traced in two principal ways:

-Islamic learning, firstly, triggered both birth and functioning of such universities, whose outbursts coincide precisely (as on the Salerno model) with translations from Arabic.

[1978] C.H. Haskins: The Rise; op cit; p. 3

[1979] M. Clagett: The Growth*; op cit; p. 79.*

[1980] *Ibid.*

[1981] G. Sarton: Introduction; Vol III. pp.471-2.

[1982] M. Clagett: The Growth*; op cit; p. 79.*

[1983] G. Sarton: Introduction; op cit; Vol III. pp.471-2.

[1984] D. Campbell: Arabian Medicine; op cit; p.152.

-Secondly, Islam supplied Western universities with formal and institutional models and organisation.

a. The Impact of Translations from Arabic:

The role of the 12th century translations in such upsurge is clear to Wiet et al, who ascertain that never in history `has so great an accumulation of learning been uncovered at such chronological distance in so short time. It was around their tremendous revelation that there grew up, in the twelfth and thirteenth centuries, a system of education in Europe.'[1985] Education entered a state of upheaval, Menocal observes; so many of the revolutionary additions and transformations of old modes of thought and expressions, shared with thinkers `whose Arabic writings, once translated, had permeated Europe.'[1986] The same for Singer, who sees in the Scholasticism of medieval times in the main a direct outcome of `the Arabic revival' in Europe.[1987]

The great influx of new knowledge into Western Europe between 1100 and 1200, which came partly through Italy and Sicily, but chiefly through Spain,[1988] transformed learning in its essence. The addition of the new logic, the new mathematics, and the new astronomy to the older Latin trivium and quadrivium are but several of the many features of the world of learning that now tied the two intellectual worlds together.[1989] All scientific learning in Western Christian universities was dominated by translated Islamic learning. Medicine provides an excellent instance of this. In the universities that had medical schools, medicine was taught from Latin translations of Islamic texts by Hunayn ibn Ishaq, Al-Razi, Ibn Sina, and also of Galen.[1990] At Montpellier, manuscripts of Islamic authors were comparatively abundant and many `Compendia' containing `Arabist doctrines' were issued under the control of the universities, particularly those of Bologna and Padua.[1991] The expounders of mediaeval medicine drew on the Islamic material (in their Latin translations) thereby completely `Arabizing' the

---

[1985] G. Wiet et al: History; op cit;p.467.
[1986] M. R. Menocal: The Arabic Role; op cit; p. 55.
[1987] C. Singer: A Review of the Medical Literature of the Dark Ages, with a new text of about 1110,' *Proceedings of the R.S.M.* 1917, vol x., pt .ii. pp 107-60 at p. 109.
[1988] C.H. Haskins: The Rise; op cit; p. 8.
[1989] M. R. Menocal: The Arabic Role; op cit; p. 55.
[1990] Allen O. Whipple: The role; op cit; P. 36.
[1991] D. Campbell: Arabian Medicine; op cit; p.201.

system of medicine in Europe.[1992] One major text of learning, Al-Razi's book *al-Kitab al-mansuri fi'l Tibb*, translated into Latin as *Liber al-Mansorem* was studied by medical students, and medical men knew it by heart.[1993] The commentators, especially at first, gave of the text only the beginnings of sentences after the pattern of Bible exegesis. These commentaries were written by members of the faculty of Pavia, and were used in the afternoon lectures on practical medicine as *ad.lecturam Almonsoris*.[1994]The Canon of Ibn Sina was the leading medical authority, and after its translation into Latin by Gerard of Cremona, it served for many centuries as the chief representative of the Islamic school of medicine in Western Europe, holding its place in the universities of Montpellier and Louvain down to A.D. 1650.[1995] As late as 1520 in Vienna, and 1588 in Frankfurt on the Oder, the medical curriculum was still largely based on Ibn Sina's *Canon*, and on the ninth book *Ad Almonsorem* of al-Razi.[1996]And so was the case at the University of Tubingen (in 1481) where the `Arabists' were dominant.[1997]The majority of the works by Al-Razi were translated into Latin, and printed many times, principally in Venice in 1509, and in Paris in 1528 and 1548; his treatise on small verole, for instance, reprinted in 1745. In the latter portion of the 15th and in the early part of the 16th century the `Arabists' in Latin Europe were undoubtedly the most influential of the learned members of society, and there was considerable demand for Latin versions of the works of the `Arabians' in general, and Ibn Sina, Ibn Rushd, and Ibn Sarabi in particular.[1998] Even in the 17th century in France and Germany scholars kept to Arabic erudition, whilst Islamic pharmacology survived until the beginning of the 19th.[1999]

Muslim scientific works fed, and above all, circulated between places of higher learning in the Christian West. The university of Naples, most particularly, had a large collection of Arabic manuscripts,[2000]as the popularity of Frederick with the Muslim princes of the East gave him

---

[1992] Ibid. p.155.
[1993] H.D. Isaac: Arabic Medical Literature; in *Religion, Learning (*M.J. L. Young et al ed) pp 342-364; at p. 354.
[1994] Ibid.
[1995] De Lacy O'Leary: Arabic Thought; op cit; p. 174.
[1996] Edward J. Jurji: The Course of Arabic Scientific thought: in *The Arab heritage*, N.A. Faris edt: Princeton University Press, 1944. pp 221-250. p. 249
[1997] D. Campbell: Arabian Medicine; op cit; p.201.
[1998] Ibid.
[1999] E. J. Jurji: The course of Arabic. p. 249.
[2000] G. Sarton: Introduction; op cit; ii; p. 575.

exceptional facilities for the acquirement of literary treasures.[2001] Frederick made Naples University an academy for the purpose of introducing Islamic science to the Western world, a centre of translations from Arabic into Latin; having copies of such translations sent to Paris and Bologna.[2002] Burnett also points to translator scholars such as Petrus of Alfonsi, Robert of Ketton and Ibn Ezra, who as examples of scholar-translators, travelled between Spain and England and may have brought not just translations from Arabic, but also manuscripts themselves.[2003]Burnett also points to at least one English doctor, called Herbert, whose library included Constantine's translations of the Tunisian doctors, and also of later translations (12th century) by John of Seville, and works by Qusta Ibn Luqa, proving how quickly works travelled from Spain to England.[2004]

Courtesy of Burnett's erudition, it is possible to look at Oxford University, as an excellent case of how Islamic science held a decisive place in an institution of Western higher learning. Gerard Langbaine (1609-1658) who was the keeper of the archives of the university during the commonwealth had charge of the university's Arabic type.[2005]He compiled material from the Bodleian and other libraries in Oxford to illustrate the history of the study of Arabic in England, from the beginnings up to his own time, material which is contained in a notebook marked with the astrological sign for Leo.[2006]He starts with Adelard's transcribing the opening of his Natural Questions, underlining Adelard's mention of *Saraceni and Studia Arabum*, then refers to three translations from Arabic made by him; then Plato of Tivoli's translation of al-Battani's astronomical tables, then quotes portions of the dossier that Roger Bacon sent to Pope Clement IV that are relevant to the learning of Arabic, and he goes on to transcribe the introduction of Daniel of Morley's *Philosophia*, in which Daniel describes his visit to Toledo.[2007] There is a powerful link between Islamic works and Oxford University, via Alfred of Sareshel's translations, which helped shape the teaching of later masters, such as Adam of Buckfield, Roger Bacon, and Henry of Renham, and also the `Avicennist,' John Blund.[2008] John

---

[2001] S.P. Scott: History; op cit; vol 3; p.44.
[2002] De Lacy O'Leary: Arabic thought; op cit; p. 281.
[2003] C. Burnett: Arabic Learning; op cit; p. 46.
[2004] Ibid.
[2005] C. Burnett: The Introduction; op cit; P. 80
[2006] Now no. 12 in the Langbaine collection of the Bodleian library; in C. Burnett: The Introduction; op cit; P. 82.
[2007] C Burnett: The Introduction; op cit; P. 82.
[2008] C. Burnett: Arabic Learning; op cit; p. 51.

Blund was teaching at the faculty of arts from around 1200 to 1209, before having to leave as the university was closed down because of riots; John Blund migrating to the marshy fens to lay down the foundations of Cambridge.[2009]Although he seemingly praises Aristotle, and the fact that the `Arabs' had recently handed his (Aristotle) science back to the Latin, Burnett notes, Blund in his surviving work, *De anima*, relies mainly on Al-Kindi, Ibn Sina, Al-Farabi, Al-Ghazali and Qusta Ibn Luqa.[2010]In 1200, at the time Blund, and possibly Alfred of Sareshel were teaching at Oxford, Grosseteste was also teaching the arts there, before he was appointed the first chancellor, his personality and scholarship eventually making Oxford a rival to Paris.[2011]

Even a late arrival on the scene of higher learning, the university of Cracow, exhibits the same dependence on Islamic science as competently charted by Isaievych and Korolec.[2012] At the university was founded towards 1405 a chair in astronomy, at that time, as underlined by Brikenmajer, no other university in Central Europe had similar chair devoted solely to astronomical studies.[2013] During their studies, whether graduates or masters at the university, all had to be knowledgeable of the works of Muslim scholars.[2014] This includes works by Al-Qabisi: *al-madkhal ila Sina'at Ahkam al-Nujum)* (Introduction to the science of the stars), which was translated into Latin by Johannes Hispalensis; Abu Ma'shar's *De revolutionibus* and *Liber florum, e substantia orbis* of Ibn Rushd; *De fatis astrorum* of Ali ibn Rijal; *the Liber 157 verborum* of Al-Razi etc.[2015] The lectures also included Al-Kindi, Masha'Alllah, Thabit ibn Qurra, Al-Battani, Al-Zarqali, Al-Farabi; Al-Farghani; and Jabir ibn Aflah.[2016]It is towards 1450 that studies of astronomy at Cracow blossomed mainly thanks to the contribution of Martin Krol, who in his collection owned the works of Muslim astronomers, such as the commentaries on Ptolemy's *Almagest*

[2009] M.R. Hackett: The Original Statues of Cambridge University; Cambridge; 1970; p. 46. in C. Burnett: Arabic Learning; op cit; p. 51.
[2010] C. Burnett: Arabic Learning; op cit; p. 52.
[2011] Ibid. p. 56.
[2012]I. Isaievych: George Drohobych's astronomical treatises and their Arabic sources; in The Introduction of Arabic philosophy; op cit; pp. 59-64;
J. Korolec: la Premiere Reception; op cit;
[2013] A. Brikenmajer: l'Universite de Cracovie, center international d'enseignment astronomique a la fin du moyen age. In *Studia Copernicana,* 4; 1972; pp. 483-95.
[2014] J. Korolec: la Premiere Reception; op cit; p. 116.
[2015] Ibid.
[2016] Ibid. pp. 116-21; and also p. 129.

by Ali ibn Ridwan (ms. 587; ff. 1-151v),[2017] the same author's comments on Ptolemy's *Centiloquium* (ms BJ 1859), [2018] the *De Pluviis* of al-Kindi (mss BJ 1865 and 2495), [2019]*The Liber introductorius* of Al-Qubaysi (MS BJ 1918), [2020]etc. Korolec goes on to make an extremely good list of the Islamic manuscripts that served the teaching at Cracow.[2021]Thus, there is little mystery or surprise in the fact that Cracow rose as the dominant institution with regard to astronomical studies and to produce a Copernicus. Further decisive influences through Drohobych who lectured whilst Copernicus was a student at Cracow are also examined by Isaievych (briefly cited already), and will be addressed in the next chapter (under Sciences).

b. Institutional/Organisational Impact:

Translations were essential, but were not alone to lead to both beginning and operations, or functioning of institutions of higher learning in the West. A variety of other factors, also derived from Islam, contributed to such developments. These influences have been studied by Ribera[2022]and his followers, but refuted by Rashdall and his.[2023]

Before looking at the Islamic influences, it is first necessary to look at, and refute, Rashdall and his followers' argument, which insists that Western universities were first on the scene, and as such owe nothing to any Islamic influence.

Rashdall and his followers' main point is that Western universities were the first true universities because they were set up by royal prerogative.[2024]This is historically false. Contrary to what Rashdall and his followers[2025] hold, no Western university, with the exception of Naples (set up by Frederick II in 1224) was established by prerogative,

---

[2017] F.J. Carmody: *Arabic Astronomical and Astrological Science in Latin Translations, A Critical Approach;* Berkeley; 1956; pp. 19 and 155.
[2018] J. Zathey: Bibliotheka Jagiellonska w latach 1364-1492; In Historia Bibliotski Jagiellonskiej; Vol 1; Cracow; 1966; p. 108.
[2019] Ibid. p. 109.
[2020] Ibid. p. 109.
[2021] J. Korolec: La Premiere; op cit; p. 117 fwd.
[2022] J. Ribera: *Disertaciones y opusculos;* 2 vols. Madrid 1928.
[2023] H. Rashdall: The Universities of Europe in the Middle Ages, New edition by F.M Powicke and A.B. Emden, 3 Vols. Oxford University Press, 1936; pp 536-39
[2024] Ibid.
[2025] For instance: A.B. Cobban: *The Medieval Universities, their Organization and their Development*; Methuen; London; 1975.

or as a distinct institution. Haskins, indeed, notes, that at least five universities go back to the 12th century: Salerno, Bologna, Paris, Montpellier and Oxford. `Nevertheless,' he points out, `these have not entirely emerged from the general group of schools: the name university is scarcely known in this sense; its distinctive organisation is scarcely recognised; universities do not yet associate exclusively with other universities, nor has the Papacy laid its guilding hand upon them.'[2026]There are, for instance, no statutes for the Parisian medical faculty before 1270.[2027] Similarly, Sarton notes, the eighth hundredth anniversary of the university of Bologna having been celebrated with considerable pomp in 1888, led many people to conclude that it must have been founded in 1088. But this is purely arbitrary Sarton adds, as it is impossible to say when the university was founded, for there never was a charter of foundation for it.[2028] It was only by the middle of the 12th century that its school of law was famous, and the university was only completely organised towards the end of that century (12th).[2029] Likewise, Clagett explains that the use of the term "university" (Latin, universitas) is somewhat misleading.[2030]During the 13th century it designated "an association or guild of either masters or students or both," but it was not limited to educational groups or learning associations, but was used for other associations or guilds. Thus a university did nor mean, as it does today, a group of faculties or schools.[2031] Something more in line with our use of the word today, Clagett pursues, was the Latin term `studium generale,' but even this expression is also misleading, since `generale' does not refer so much to different faculties as to the fact that the studium was open to all comers. The studium referred to the institution, its place and courses, but not to the organization of its personnel.[2032] And, again, back to Haskins, who insists, that despite indications of considerable bodies of masters and students and of vigorous intellectual life, there is very little evidence of formal university organisation.[2033] It is, equally found vain by Sarton to try and fix the exact dates of the foundation of these universities, for the simple reason that, indeed, they were not deliberately founded.[2034]

[2026] C.H. Haskins: The Renaissance; op cit; p.65.
[2027] M McVaugh: Medical Knowledge at the time of Frederick II, in Micrologus; Sciences at the Court of Frederick II; op cit; pp 3-17; p.3.
[2028] G. Sarton: Introduction; op cit; Vol II. p.351.
[2029] Ibid.
[2030] M. Clagett: The Growth; op cit; pp.79-80.
[2031] Ibid.
[2032] Ibid.
[2033] C.H. Haskins: The Renaissance; op cit; p.381.
[2034] G. Sarton: Introduction, op cit; Vol II, p.285.

Various acts of incorporation were given to them later, sometimes much later, when they had grown to a respectable size and shown by their own being what a university was. And the fact that not merely one university grew in that manner-somewhat unconsciously, like a living thing-but many, in different countries, proves, Sarton concludes, `that these creations answered a definite need of the time.'[2035] And that need, he explains, was due to the vast influx of knowledge in the 12th century, so large learning, `that systematic methods of education became necessary. In the meantime the growth of cities had made the application of such methods at once more tempting and more easy. Thus our universities appeared in the second half of the 12th century, and not before, because there had not been sufficient scope nor opportunity for them until that time, and they appeared then because the need was suddenly urgent.'[2036]

From the preceding two conclusions can be derived:

First, contrary to what Rashdall and his followers hold, all Western institutions of higher learning operated for decades, at least, before they were officially set up.

Second, it was the influx of Islamic learning that was at the foundation of the origin, and very existence of such institutions.

And whilst both these two points have been amply proved, Rashdall and his followers cannot provide a single piece of evidence to show one single document establishing such institutions officially at the very start of their existence. They can neither provide one single piece of evidence showing these universities providing any advanced teaching prior to the translations from Islam, or lecturing anything advanced other than what was translated from Arabic, except in theological sciences.

To reinforce the points just made, the first university to be founded at a definite time, by a definite charter in Western Christendom was the University of Naples, founded in 1224 by Frederick II.[2037] Its other distinction: it was the first university in the Western world that relied primarily on Islamic learning and Islamic model of teaching. Lest the learning of the scholars whom he had assembled should die with their deaths, Durant holds,[2038]Frederick founded it in 1224, a rare example of a medieval university established without ecclesiastical sanction.[2039] Frederick's deep knowledge of the Muslim world, allowed him, according to Mieli, to know and appreciate the Muslim precedents,

---

[2035] Ibid.

[2036] Ibid.

[2037] G. Sarton: Introduction, vol 2; p. 575.

[2038] W. Durant: The Age of Faith; op cit; p. 720.

[2039] Ibid.

which explains his founding of Naples University.[2040] More importantly, Frederick called to its faculty scholars in all arts and sciences, and paid them high salaries; and he assigned subsidies to enable poor but qualified students to attend.[2041] Frederick also established universities in Messina and Padua, and renovated the old medical school of Salerno `in accordance with the advances of Arab medicine.'[2042]

Naples was, thus, unique, and Rashdall and his followers, hence, are telling a major fallacy when they attribute what is proper and unique to Naples to other Western Christian universities, when neither Rashdall nor his followers can show an earlier single piece of evidence of official founding at a precise date for any such universities. And Naples was unique because it was the most directly inspired institution from Islamic models, founded by an Islamic inspired ruler, its teaching based on Islamic science, and its principal function being to disseminate Islamic learning.

To demonstrate further both the Islamic pioneering role in higher learning, and the Islamic impact on the Christian West, it is important to address the issue from two distinct angles:

-First to show that institutions of higher learning were established in Islam centuries before their counterparts in the Christian West.

-Second, to show in detail some models of borrowing in the organisation of the first Western universities from their Islamic counterparts.

On the first point (the pioneering aspect), in Islam, there was some organisation of higher education as early as the beginning of the 9th century, Watt notes, and by the end of the 11th century, university-type institutions had been established in most of the chief cities.[2043] Earliest of all, is Bayt al-Hikma (the house of Wisdom), founded in the 9th century by Caliph Al-Mamun, and which has in all manners and forms the making of the earliest modern institution of advanced learning, including scientific equipment, a translation bureau, and an observatory. Instruction included rhetoric, logic, metaphysics and theology, algebra, geometry, trigonometry, physics, biology, medicine, and surgery.[2044] The institution was set up by the Caliph, himself, officially, and was funded by the central authority. In such an academy worked or collaborated the most eminent court scholars of the time: The Banu

---

[2040] A. Mieli: La Science Arabe; op cit; p. 228.

[2041] W. Durant: The Age of Faith; op cit; p. 720.

[2042] R. Briffault: The Making, op cit, p. 213.

[2043] W. Montgomery Watt: The Influence; op cit; p. 12.

[2044] F.B. Artz: *The Mind, op cit;* p. 151.

Musa Brothers (mathematicians, and astronomers,) Al-Khwarizmi; al-Battani, and so on and so forth.[2045] In the same institution were recorded some of the earliest Islamic achievements. In astronomy, for instance, there was determined the position of the solar apogee,[2046]the inclination of the ecliptic,[2047]was calculated the earth circumference,[2048]and were made observations of solar and lunar eclipses and planetary positions.

Then, of course, are the university mosques; Watt pointed out (in 1972) that teaching has been going on continuously for a thousand of years in the university-mosque of Al-Azhar in Cairo.[2049] And also at Al-Qarawiyyin (Fes), which dates from the middle of the 10th century;[2050]and at Al-Qayrawan even earlier, as some of the medical texts mentioned above (that were translated by Constantine the African) date from the 9th century.[2051]The curriculum in such places, Nakosteen points out, reminds us in its extensive and intensive nature of curricular programs of modern advanced systems of education, particularly on higher levels of education.[2052] It was not unusual to find instruction in algebra, trigonometry, geometry, chemistry, physics, astronomy, medicine, pharmacy, history, geography etc.[2053] Some of the professors of polite literature, Draper notes, gave lectures on Arabic classical works; others taught rhetoric or composition, or mathematics, or astronomy.[2054] Specific instances show that astronomy and engineering were studied at Al-Azhar,[2055] medicine also at Al-Azhar and the mosque of Ibn Tulun in Egypt (9th century).[2056] At the Qarrawiyyin, were dispensed courses on grammar, rhetoric, logic, elements of mathematics

---

[2045] See: R. Briffault: The Making; op cit; pp. 187 fwd.

[2046] W. Hartner: The Role of Observations in Ancient and Medieval Astronomy; in *The Journal of History of Astronomy*; Vol 8; 1977; pp 1-11; at p. 8.

[2047] J.L.E. Dreyer: A History; op cit; p.246.

[2048] M. A. Kettani: Science and Technology in Islam: The underlying value system, in *The Touch of Midas; Science, Values, and Environment in Islam and the West*; Z. Sardar ed: Manchester University Press, 1984, pp 66-90. p. 75.

[2049] W. Montgomery Watt: The Influence; op cit; p. 12.

[2050] R Landau, The Karaouine at Fes *The Muslim World* 48 (April 1958): pp. 104-12. M. Alwaye: `Al-Azhar...in thousand years.' *Majallatu'l Azhar*: (Al-Azhar Magazine, English Section 48 (July 1976): pp. 1-6.

[2051] See Entries on Al-Qayrawan, E*ncyclopaedia of Islam*; Brill; Leyden; first or second editions.

[2052] M. Nakosteen: *History of Islamic; op cit;*p.52.

[2053] Ibid.

[2054] J.W. Draper: A History; op cit; Vol II; p.36.

[2055] M. Alwaye: `Al-Azhar; op cit.

[2056] J. Pedersen:. `Some aspects of the history of the madrassa' *Islamic Culture* 3 (October 1929) pp 525-37, p. 527.

and astronomy,[2057] and possibly history, geography and elements of chemistry.[2058] At Al-Qayrawan and Zaytuna in Tunisia, alongside the Quran and jurisprudence were taught grammar, mathematics, astronomy and medicine.[2059] And these were no subjects of later centuries, quite the opposite. At Al-Qayrawan, in particular, classes in medicine were delivered by Ziad Ben Khalfun, Ishak Ben Imran and Ishak Ben Sulayman (all scholars of the 9th century),[2060] whose works were subsequently translated by Constantine The African in the 11th century at Salerno.

And whilst in the Christian West, the name, university, Haskins notes, eludes search before the 13th century, when it appears incidentally in 1208-09 in the letters of a former student (Pope Innocent III), where, as often in the history of institutions, the name follows after the thing itself,[2061] this is not the case in Islam. The word `Jamia' (university in Arabic) appeared extremely early, and was linked with the first mosque universities of Islam such as Al-Qarrawiyyin in Fes, Al-Azhar in Cairo, Al-Qayrawan mosque, etc.[2062] Jamia derives precisely from Jamaa (mosque), the two institutions, thus, having intricate links in curriculum and in name.[2063]

And the same mosque/university linkage observed with respect to student organisation. The number of students at al-Azhar always included hundreds of foreign students, many from far distant lands; students who did not have homes in Cairo were assigned to a residential

---

2057 R. Le Tourneau: *Fes in the Age of the Merinids*, tr from French by B.A. Clement, University of Oklahoma Press, 1961, p. 122.

2058 Ibid.

2059 H. Djait et al: *Histoire de la Tunisie* (le Moyen Age); Societe Tunisienne de Difusion, Tunis; p. 378.

2060 Al-Bakri, Massalik, 24; Ibn Abi Usaybi'a, *Uyun al-anba,* ed. and tr A. Nourredine and H. Jahier, Algiers 1958, 2.9, in M. Talbi: Al-Qayrawan; in *Encyclopaedia of Islam,* Vol IV, pp 829-30.

2061 C.H. Haskins: The Renaissance; op cit; p.381.

2062 See for instance:

B Dodge: *Muslim Education in Medieval Times*, The Middle East Institute, Washington, D.C. 1962.

Rom Landau, The Karaouine at Fes, op cit.

A.H. Tazi: *La Mosque Al-Quaraouiyyine*, 3 vols, edt Dar al-Kitab Allubnani, Lebanon, 1973.

-R. Le Tourneau: *Fes avant le protectorat* (Societe Maroccaine de Librairie et d'Edition, Casablanca, 1947, pp. 453-471).

M. Alwaye: `Al-Azhar...in thousand years; op cit.

2063 J. Waardenburg: Some institutional Aspects of Muslim Higher Education and their relation to Islam. *Nvmen*: International Review for the History of Religion 12 (April 1965) pp.96-138.

unit, which was endowed to care for them.[2064] Generally, the unit gave the resident students free bread, which supplemented food given to them by their families, whilst better off students could afford to live in lodgings near the mosque. Every large unit also included a library, kitchen and lavatory, and some space for furniture.[2065]At the Qarrawiyyin (Fes), students were given monetary allowances periodically.[2066]There, students lived in residential quadrangles, which contained two and three story buildings of varying sizes, accommodating between sixty and a hundred and fifty students, all also receiving a minimal assistance for food and accommodation.[2067]

With regard to the second point, the Islamic impact in relation to organisation, is visible in all form, structure and also methods of teaching and examination, which are seen in turn.

Ribera insists that in their structure and organisation, Western universities were based on the Nizamiyah madrasa (college) founded by the Seljuk minister in 1065 in Baghdad.[2068] The students often lived in boarding houses (khan) under supervision of their teacher and employed an inkwell as a symbol.[2069]A chapel and a library, as well as residential arrangements for students and teachers were a distinct feature of the madrasas, the precursors of the residential colleges of British universities.[2070] The Studia of medieval Europe, according to Hossein, were just imitations of madrasas both in their name and free growth, and that `the great Muslim madrassah was also the archetype of the Studium General which, with the later requisite of the royal or papal authorization, came to be known as university in Europe.'[2071] In going back to the origins, Makdisi points out, as it first appeared in Paris, Oxford and elsewhere, the college was a previous product of Islam; and that, in Merton College in Oxford, `we have a watershed in the history

---

[2064] B. Dodge: Muslim Education, op cit, pp 26-7.
[2065] Ibid. pp 26-7, in particular.
[2066] J. Waardenburg: `Some institutional..' op cit, p: 109.
[2067] B. Dodge, Muslim Education, op cit, p 27.
[2068] J. Ribera: Origen del Colegio Nidami de Baghdad en Disetaciones y opusculos, vol I; see A. Mieli: La Science Arabe etc; op cit; p.145.
[2069] F. Reichmann: *The Sources of Western Literacy;* Greenwood Press; London; 1980. p.207.
[2070] S.M Hossain: A Plea for a Modern Islamic University: Resolution of the Dichotomy. in *Aims and Objectives of Islamic education*: S.M. al-Naquib al-Attas edt; Hodder and Stoughton; 1977. pp 91-103. P. 101.
[2071] Ibid. pp 101-2.

of the college.'[2072] Merton stands as a dividing point between the college of Islam on the one hand, and that of the United States on the other.[2073]

Both Islamic pioneering role and impact are also found in the manner of teaching. At the madrasas, centuries before Abelard, the dialectical method (jadal) was employed in disputations (munazara).[2074] The different opinions were enumerated (khilaf), a consensus (ijma) was sought in order to harmonise reason with faith. In teaching, the dictation method was used, as teaching was synonymous with dictation (imla).[2075] Classes were directed by a mudarris, who can be compared to a professor, with `naib' (substitute professor,) and also a muid who acts as a `drill master,' the latter repeating the teachings of the professor like a `repetiteur' of Western universities. From these institutions many of the practices observed in Western colleges were derived, says Draper.[2076] They held commencements, at which poems were read and orations delivered in presence of the public.[2077] Whilst going through the Azhar mosque during professorial lectures, Le Bon notes, `it seemed a magic stick had taken me back to our old 13th century universities. The same confusion in the theology and literary studies, same methods, same organisation of students gathered in corporations, and benefiting of the same immunities and franchises.'[2078] Thus, Gerard of Cremona, the first university lecturer, most probably in the first Western university, Toledo,[2079] was being heckled, but was not troubled, for we find him conducting his collegium like a Muslim faqih (learned religious person), anticipating counterarguments and sharpening his points in a lively encounter with his students.[2080] In Paris, students sat on the floor, covered with straw, whilst a professor lectured from a platform.[2081]

A major step in the advance of higher learning was the introduction of a system of examination and diplomas, and here, again, was the primary role of the Islamic system and its impact. It was under Roger II of Sicily, who was deeply influenced by Islamic antecedents and culture, that was pioneered the foundation and establishment of medical

---

2072 George Makdisi: On the origin and development of the College in Islam and the West, in *Islam and the Medieval West*; (Semaan ed): pp 26-49; at. p.28.
2073 Ibid.
2074 F. Reichmann: *The Sources*. op cit; p.207.
2075 F. Reichmann: *The Sources*. op cit; p.207.
2076 J.W. Draper: A History; op cit; Vol II; op cit; p.36.
2077 Ibid.
2078 G. Le Bon, La Civilisation des Arabes; op cit; p.336
2079 D. Metlitzki: The Matter of Araby; op cit; p.37.
2080 Ibid.
2081 W.K. Ferguson: *A Survey of European Civilisation*, London, George Allen and Unwin. p.277

faculties and the granting of medical degrees. In 1140, he enacted that everyone who desired to practice medicine must, under pain of imprisonment and confiscation of goods, present himself before a magistrate and obtain authorization.[2082]Roger introduced examination by experienced physicians of all candidates for the profession of medicine and surgery, restricting those whose learning was deficient to `the clandestine ministrations of the shrine and the confessional.'[2083] Other rulers of Western Christendom followed his example, and these measures ultimately led to the specialization of the study of medicine and the granting of degrees by the medical faculties of universities.[2084] The inception of the idea of the regularization of medical practice by Roger of Sicily was probably related to his `Arabist' leanings, for the Arabs had a system of licensing in vogue in the centuries previously.[2085] It is necessary to remember that it was in 931, that Caliph al-Muqtadir ordered that physicians had to have licence before setting up practice.[2086] The beginnings of the system of medical examinations, thus, are to be sought among the `Arabs.'[2087]Obtaining a certificate was also the practice in even the earliest mosque study, and as a rule, once a student had been able to collect certificates from a number of teachers, he was in position to seek employment in a mosque, college, law court, government office or village school.[2088]

Also amongst others, Islam pioneered and influenced the West and the course of university scholarship in the doctoral thesis and its defence, and in the peer review of scholarly work based on the concensus of peers.[2089] A characteristic of the teaching in Islamic schools of Spain was that `dialectic tournaments' were customary among the students and also among the teachers; this practice was introduced with renewed vigour among the High scholastics of Medieval Europe, through the Western Caliphate.[2090] The practice of these disputations was thus not entirely a new idea to the Latin West, and it is to this custom that we owe the modern practice of demanding Theses and

---

[2082] D. Campbell: Arabian Medicine; op cit; p.119.
[2083] S.P. Scott: History; op cit; vol 3; p. 26.
[2084] D. Campbell: Arabian mMdicine; p.119.
[2085] Ibid.
[2086] Abu al-Faraj Bar Hebraeus: *Tarikh mukhtasar ad-Dual*; ed. Antun as-Salihani; Beirut, 1890; pp 281-2; in S.K Hamarneh: *Health and Sciences in Early Islam*, edited by M.A. Anees, Noor Health Foundation and Zahra Publicaations; 1983, edt Vol 1, at p. 98.
[2087] T. Pushmann: *History of Medical Education from the most remote to the most recent times*, trans and edited by E.H. Hare (London, 1891); p. 181.
[2088] B. Dodge: Muslim Education; op cit; p. 25.
[2089] G. Makdisi: The Rise of humanism, op cit; p.350.
[2090] D. Campbell: Arabian medicine; op cit; p.58.

Dissertations from aspirants to University Honours.[2091] And it is only in 1270 that we first find formal degrees granted by Bologna.[2092]After having well studied his *trivium*, the candidate for the Baccalaureat underwent an examination, and had to enter into arguments upon grammar, rhetoric, and dialectics.[2093] The title of doctor of medicine, first used by Giles of Corbeil with reference to Salernitan graduates (when Salerno was then under the rule of Frederick) became the badge of honour of the most learned physicians, and graduation ceremonies were made as impressive as possible.[2094]
More on these matters can be found expanded upon by Makdisi.[2095]

Bringing the two main sources, or traits, of Islamic influence on the West (via learning, and models and organisation of learning) is the 12th century Toledan experience. Toledo supplied the Christian West with learning more than any other place did before in history through the translations effected there. It was also Gerard's (of Cremona) fame as a teacher and expounder of Islamic science that gave Toledo its international stature and fame, says Metlitzki.[2096] Daniel (of Morley) found him lecturing to a body of students, just like his Muslim predecessors, at the Toledo Mosque, which shows that Toledo was the first de facto university in Christian Spain, though it was not an official *studium generale*.[2097] Daniel's eyewitness account of the proceedings is a unique medieval document, Metlitzki observes; the effects of which, even on the intellectual climate of medieval England, remain to be fully investigated.[2098]And when he left Toledo, Daniel, on his return to England did not just take with him `a precious multitude of books,' but, most importantly, in order `to explain the teaching of Toledo to Bishop John of Norwich (1175-1200),'[2099]he wrote his *De philosophia*.[2100]

[2091] Ibid. p.59.
[2092] M McVaugh: Medical Knowledge at the time of Frederick II, in Micrologus; op cit; pp 3-17:p.3.
[2093] P. Lacroix: Science and Literature; op cit; p.16.
[2094] G. Sarton: Introduction, op cit; Vol II, p.96.
[2095] In G. Makdisi: The Rise of Humanism, op cit; especially the last chapters.
[2096] D. Metlitzki: The Matter of Araby; op cit; p.37.
[2097] Ibid.
[2098] Ibid.
[2099] C.H. Haskins: The Reception of Arabic science in England; *English Historical Review*; Vol xxx; London; 1915; pp. 56-69. pp. 67-8.
[2100] J.K. Wright: The Geographical Lore; op cit; p. 97.

Concluding words:

Even if all that has just preceded was set aside, the Islamic link is still easy to ascertain. The sudden appearance of institutions of higher learning in the Christian West in the 12th century cannot be owed to local, Western conditions for the simple reason that like everything else, universities began to appear simultaneously in the 12th century. There must be a similar link to all changes in the West, not a variety of diverging causes, which Western historians, in their majority, concoct left and right. It is, of course, easy, to concoct such reasons for one specific case or item, but once tens of other major transformations take place at once, there must be a common trigger. Why a common trigger in respect to this birth and rise of Western universities: because had it been local conditions behind the appearance of universities, it would have required the most powerful artificial engineering process ever witnessed in history to get such local conditions to operate at once, at the same time, in the same manner, towards the same end, and all over Western Christendom. Had Western universities owed their origin to local conditions they would have also appeared at different centuries apart from each other, and in different forms and manners hardly related to each other.

There must be a common trigger when there is evidence of the same link, whether in form, in substance, or in the place of contact, or in timing, as is briefly outlined in the following.

As seen already, all early universities that sprang into existence in Western Christendom, whether Oxford, Paris, Salerno, Montpellier, Bologna, Naples, etc, all have a direct link with Islam in one way or another, especially in relation to the learning they dispensed.

As also seen, Western institutions of higher learning did not appear in any century before (7th, 8th, 9th…), they did so exactly following the translations, especially 12th century translations from Arabic, which provided the learning, and the need for institutions of higher learning. And it was not, it must be reminded again, Classical learning, which was the source of such an upsurge for the reasons already seen in previous chapters: this classical learning has been available for centuries before, and if it was the foundation, such universities would have appeared centuries before they began to do (12th century).

Timing, again, but from another perspective (but still Islamic perspective,) also shows that just like the founding of hospitals in the West, or the appearance of baths, windmills, castle construction etc, the earliest known college in Western Christendom was founded in Paris precisely following the return in 1180 of its founder, a certain John of London (Dominus Jocius de Londoniis), returning from Jerusalem where he had gone on pilgrimage.[2101] The college eventually taking its name from the eighteen poor students who were its resident members; hence the name `College des Dix Huit, Rashdall informs us.'[2102] For an odd reason, though, he (Rashdall) fails to note, or more appropriately, to appreciate the rest of the connection. Why it did not happen before, and why it was not done by someone other than that John who had been to the Holy Land (just like the founders of hospitals and early castle builders in the West, who also built these institutions only after they returned from the East, and did so for the first time in the history of the Western world) Rashdall and his followers do not explain.

Then the geographical factor: as Erbstosser points out, the great universities of southern France and Italy were not only in the vicinity of Spain and southern Italy but were also the traditional centres of the crusades and the trade with the Orient.[2103] There is evidence, he adds, that many scholars did not keep to the `contact zone' with the Orient but went further afield. Practitioners, such as Huggo of Lucca, also known as Hugo of Bologna, took part as personal physicians to kings and princes in the crusades of the 13th century and used the opportunity to extend their knowledge.[2104] Had such a geographical link with Islam been absent, nothing would have prevented the first Western Christian universities to appear in York, Rome, or even Athens, all great centres of Western culture and civilisation, if really any other factor than the Islamic was at play.

The last words on this issue, deservedly, go to Ribera, who observes that the rise of European universities did not suggest itself to him merely on the basis that `Oriental universities' and the channels of communication opened by the Crusades had preceded in time the European universities, but also on the examination of certain phenomena which, if not accepted, would constitute an enigma.[2105] He cites the following three phenomena:

1) The swiftness with which the universities appear and propagate themselves (indeed, it seems the Western universities, in the space of a couple of decades, had everything sorted out and ready, whilst it would

---

2101 G. Makdisi: On The Origin and Development; op cit; p. 38.
G Makdisi: *The Rise of Colleges*; Edinburgh University Press, 1981.p. 224.
2102 H. Rashdall: The Universities of Europe; op cit; pp 536-9.
2103 M. Erbstosser: *The Crusades;* op cit; p. 188.
2104 Ibid.
2105 J. Ribera: *Disertaciones;* 2 vols. Madrid 1928, 1, pp. 227-359.

have normally taken centuries for similar elements to develop had they been owed to no external influence.)

2) The contrast noted at first sight between the exemption and privileges, on the one hand, and the cosmopolitanism and democracy, on the other, which prevailed in the customs and organisation of these universities, especially in the most ancient University of Bologna, betraying a fusion of opposing tendencies of two distinct civilisations.

3) The custom of granting certificates or degrees is without precedent in the Christian Middle ages, or in Rome, or in Greece, whereas Muslim masters were already doing so for three or four centuries in that form used in the beginning by university professors, to be converted later in Europe into monopolistic patents and surviving down to the present day. Ribera concludes, `in any case, even if these considerations carried no weight, I would resist resorting to the completely discredited, theory of spontaneous generation which appears to be in vogue.'[2106]

3. Modern Science and Methodology

Modern science is based, other than on knowledge, on basic principles, which include mainly:

Experimentation and observation.

Use of instruments.

Organisation/classification of learning and knowledge.

Intellectual freedom.

Little would it occur to most people to doubt that these principles date with the `Renaissance' of the modern times (16$^{th}$–17$^{th}$ century). Crombie, however, did `demonstrate' that Grosseteste pioneered one such fundamental, experimentation, much earlier in the 13th century.[2107] More focused or attentive research could have, however, revealed that it was, instead, during the Islamic scientific pre-dominance (7th-13th) that most such fundamentals, if not all of them, were set in motion, and impacted decisively on the subsequent scientific advances.

[2106] See, for instance, Gabriel Compayre: *Abelard and the Origin and Early History of Universities*, London 1893, page 26, where he says: `The universities sprang from a spontaneous movement of the human mind.' A very pretty phrase for those who can find any sense in it.' In G. Makdisi: The Rise of Colleges; p. 295.

[2107] A.C. Crombie: Robert Grosseteste; op cit.

Very early, as noted by Briffault, in astronomy, the Muslims compiled new sets of planetary tables, and obtained more accurate values for the obliquity of the ecliptic and procession of equinoxes, that were checked by two independent measurements.[2108] One stresses here `the reliance upon two independent measurements.' Hence, in contrast with their Greek predecessors, whilst Ptolemy made his astronomical calculations no other Greek scholar came to check them, whilst there are literally tens of Muslim astronomers who revised each other's tables. Al-Faruqi explain how the search for knowledge in Islam is done through istidlal (calling for evidence).[2109] Istidlal implies `observation of the data and their examination through experimentation, measurement and more observation.'[2110] In optics, for instance, Hill observes, that the principal reason that delayed progress in optics under the Greeks was their incapacity, unlike their Muslim successors, to carry experiment.[2111] The Greek (Ptolemy) did carry experiment in fact but only to support already held views; experiment succeeding the findings, rather than the other way round, preceding them.[2112] Ibn al-Haytham's conclusions, on the other hand, only reflected the evidence, and he was quite prepared to modify or even reject a hypothesis if it conflicted with experimental results.[2113] Thabit ibn Qurra in *On the Kariston* (a Balance with unequal arms) had an approach that was clearer and more sure than that of his Aristotelian predecessor, and unlike Archimedes, who `just assumed in his proof of the law of the lever,' Thabit, first proved that law.[2114] Al-Biruni travelled forty years to collect mineralogical specimen and Ibn Al-Baitar collected botanical specimen from the whole Muslim world and compared them with those of Greece and Spain.[2115]

Algebra and the new mathematics also emerged with the Muslims' resolve to obtain precision and accuracy in every calculation. Accuracy in Islam is a crucial element for the observation and application of the faith itself, whether in inheritance matters, or in the direction of prayers, or the timing of fasting and breaking the fast, etc. No surprise, thus, in the development of the astrolabe under Islam, and its uses on land and

---

[2108] R. Briffault: The Making, op. cit, p. 193.
[2109] I. and L. L. al-Faruqi: The Cultural Atlas; op cit; p. 322.
[2110] Ibid.
[2111] D.R. Hill: Islamic Science, op cit, pp 72-3.
[2112] Ibid.
[2113] Ibid.
[2114] J.E Brown: The Science of Weights, in Science in the Middle Ages, ed. D.C. Lindberg; pp. 179-205. at p. 187.
[2115] R. Briffault: The Making, op cit, pp 192-4.

sea to perform the most minutely precise calculations.[2116]To ascertain findings scientifically, prolonged and continuous observation of the planets and stars also became established in Islam, lasting over twelve years at the observatories of Baghdad, Cairo, and Damascus.[2117] And in order to reach such an aim, larger and more accurate instruments were built and put into application, and as early as the 11th century under Seljuk rule.[2118]

Having pioneered in experimentation, search for precision, and use of instruments, Islamic civilisation impacted on the subsequent Western experience accordingly. Islamic science and techniques in their practice, Garaudy notes, being the major sources of the revival in the West.[2119] It is remarkable, he observes, that the precursor of the methods of observation and experimentation in the West was Roger Bacon (1214-1294), who had studied Arabic, and who had written that the knowledge of Islamic science was for his contemporaries, the only means of access to true knowledge.[2120] Roger Bacon was a pupil of Adam Marsh (d.1259), and from his experimental works, he derived a great deal from Islamic sources, and also indirectly from the Arabist Roger Grosseteste, in particular.[2121]
Many specific examples of Islamic impact on Western experimenters in chemistry are highlighted by one of the current web-sites.[2122]In the following, is examined laboratory experiment and the pioneering role of al-Razi in it. His laboratory includes many items still in use today: Crucible; Decensory; Cucurbit or retort for distillation (qar) and the head of a still with a delivery tube (ambiq, Latin alembic); various types of furnace or stove etc.[2123]In his *Secret of secrets*, he makes the earliest known suggestions for furnishing a chemical laboratory,[2124] which

---

2116 W. Hartner: `The Principle and Use of the Astrolabe,' in W. Hartner, *Oriens-Occidens*, Hildesheim, 1968, pp. 287-318.
2117 R. Briffault: The Making, op. cit, p. 193.
2118 L.Sedillot: Memoire sur les instruments astronomique des Arabes, *Memoires de l'Academie Royale des Inscriptions et Belles Lettres de l'Institut de France* 1: 1-229; Reprinted Frankfurt, 1985.
2119 R. Garaudy: *Comment l'Homme devint Humain;* Editions J.A. 1978; p.208.
2120 Ibid.
2121 D. Campbell: Arabian medicine, op cit; p.175.
2122 http://mercury.spaceports.com/~islam/Science%20Frame/alchemy.htm
2123 D.R. Hill: Islamic Science, op cit, p. 83. C. Singer: Short History of Scientific Ideas. Op cit; p. 185.
2124 Al-Razi, Instructive or practical Introduction was edited and translated by H.E. Stapleton; R.F. Azo and H.Husain: Chemistry in Iraq and Persia, in *Memoirs of the Asiatic Society of Bengal VIII*; Calcutta; 1929. This paper includes the inventory of the

foreshadows a laboratory manual, besides dealing with substances, equipment and processes.[2125] Al-Razi divides the equipment into a) apparatus for melting metal; b) instruments for manipulating substances. In the list are included blacksmith's hearth, bellows, crucible, refractory stills, ladles, tongs, shears, pestle and mortar, moulds, curcubites, alembics, receiving flasks, aludels, beakers, glass cups, iron pans, sieves, flasks, phials, cauldrons, sand-baths, water baths, ovens, hair cloth, linen filters, stoves, a kiln, funnels and dishes.[2126] A laboratory stocked in the manner of his (Al-Razi), according to Singer: `cannot have looked very much different from that of an English laboratory of a thousand years later. It was certainly not one of those witches' kitchens usually portrayed as abodes of alchemists.'[2127]Al-Razi's lead in careful experimentation and observations also left a steadily increasing body of reliable chemical knowledge upon which built succeeding generations.[2128]And, when it is written in certain books, Le Bon says, that chemistry was created by Lavoisier, it is forgotten, that no science was ever created in all its entirety, and that without the Muslim laboratories of a thousand of years ago, Lavoisier and his accomplishments would have been impossible.[2129]

In the use of instruments, the Islamic dependence on well made apparatuses did not just mean, as Stock explains, that theory and practice were brought closer together, but also that scientists such as al-Battani, who were also expert makers of instruments, enhanced their powers of observation and calculation.[2130]Al-Zahrawi devised and made his own instruments for surgery,[2131] whilst Al-Khazini built his Balance of Wisdom to measure densities and weights.[2132] Ibn al-Haytham, too, Hill explains, took utmost care in the construction and assembly of equipment for his experiments. He made `the radical innovation' of

---

substances and equipment from the *Secret of Secrets*. In C. Singer: *The Earliest Chemical Industry*; The Folio Society; London; 1958. p. 50.

2125 D.R. Hill: Islamic Science, op cit, p. 83.

2126 In C. Singer: *The Earliest Chemical Industry*; p. 50.

2127 Ibid.

2128 E.J. Holmyard quoted in G. Anawati: `Science', in *The Cambridge History of Islam,* vol 2, ed P.M. Holt, A.K.S. Lambton, and B. Lewis, Cambridge University Press, 1970, pp 741-779, at p. 777.

2129 G Le Bon, La Civilisation; op cit; p376.

2130 B. Stock: Science, op cit, p. 21.

2131 M.S.Spink and G.L.Lewis: *Abulcasis on Surgery and Instruments*; The Wellcome Institute, London, 1973.

2132 Al-Khazini: *Kitab Mizan al-Hikma*, Hyderabad; partial English translation by N. Khanikoff (1859); op cit; also Russian translation: by M.M. Rozhanskaya and I.S. Levinova `Al-Khazini; op cit; See also R.E. Hall: Al-Khazini; op cit.

including dimensions as an integral part of his specifications, which was crucial to serious experiment, and which led to major improvements in instrument design.[2133] The list of instruments devised by the Muslims in nautical sciences, as will be considered further on, is plentiful. In surveying, Muslim scientists and craftsmen excelled at the design and utilisation of measuring instruments,[2134]and it was their efforts that resulted in the astrolabe becoming a valued instrument in land surveying.[2135] The astrolabe was also used by the Muslims to perform a considerable number of other operations, from calculating heights of mountains, to depths of wells, widths of rivers, etc.[2136] And, of course, the astrolabe could also be used for telling the time and often had an alidade and scale for that purpose on the back.[2137] In their observation of the planets, Muslim astronomers devised tables and calculations using sophisticated apparatuses and instruments for such operations.[2138] At The Maragha observatory, alongside astronomers were also instrument makers, one of them Mu'ayyad al'din al'Urdi al-Dimishqi, was the constructor of the `splendid collection of instruments' there.[2139] Sighting tubes were also employed by Muslim astronomers; al-Battani (858-929) used them in his Raqqa observatory, just as Al-Tusi did, attaching one to a sextant at his Maragha observatory in 1259 to study the sun.[2140]The Islamic collection of instruments in their observatories was not just impressive, but even exceeded in accuracy those developed in Germany in the 15th century.[2141]

Western Christianity recuperated many astronomical instruments conceived and made by Islamic artisans, and used them for centuries

---

[2133] D.R. Hill: Islamic Science, op cit, pp 73-4.

[2134] F.J. Swetz: Surveying: in *Encyclopaedia of the History of Science, Technology, and Medicine in Non Western Cultures*. Editor: H Selin; Kluwer Academic Publishers. London, 1997. pp. 922-26; at p. 926.

[2135] Ibid.

[2136] J. D. North: The Astrolabe, *Scientific American* 230, No 1, 1974, pp 96-106.
-W. Hartner: The Principle and Use of the Astrolabe, op cit.
-C. Singer: *Short History of Scientific Ideas to 1900*, op cit.

[2137] C Singer: Short History of Scientific Ideas; op cit, p. 1483.

[2138] See for instance:
L.Sedillot: Memoire sur les Instruments; op cit.
B. Hetherington: *A Chronicle of Pre-Telescopic Astronomy*; John Wiley and Sons; Chichester; 1996.
R.P. Lorch: The Astronomical Instruments of Jabir Ibn Aflah and the Torquetom; *Centaurus,* 1976; vol 20; pp 11-34.
A Sayili: *The Observatory in Islam and its Place in the General History of the Observatory*, Ankara, Publication of the Turkish Historical Society, Series, VII, N° 38.

[2139] G. Sarton: Introduction, op cit, p.13.

[2140] J.A. Smith: Telescope: Encyclopaedia (Selin ed); op cit; pp. 953-4: p. 954

[2141] R. Briffault: The Making, op. cit, p. 193.

adapting them to various usages; or by constructing similar instruments based on the same principles.[2142] Gerbert (d. 1003) was the first to introduce into the schools instruments as an assistance to the study of arithmetic, astronomy, and geometry, in arithmetic, for instance, introducing the abacus.[2143]He provides another link with the Muslim science of Spain by the introduction of the astrolabe as the principal new timekeeping device.[2144] The astrolabe, by far the earliest most sophisticated instrument, must have reached Ripoll in Catalonia as early as the 10th century, and from there travelled north of the Pyrenees, the astrolabe soon making its way into the curriculum and cathedral schools.[2145] A recently discovered manuscript fragment from the vicinity of the monastery of Reichenau includes several chapters, one of them numbered forty eighth, of an extended treatise on the astrolabe.[2146]The surviving chapters are excerpts from earlier astrolabe treatises and concern the stars of the astrolabe and how to observe the sun and those stars to determine the time of day or night; a text, which has been dated on palaeographical grounds to around the year 1000, reflecting the incorporation of the astrolabe into the study of astronomy at Reichenau.[2147]Treatises on the astrolabe commonly ascribed to Gerbert and Hermanus Contractus (of Reichenau) and containing numerous Arabic words,[2148]highlight that acquaintance with this instrument, which had passed into Western Christendom in the course of the 11th century.[2149]Walcher of Malvern, unsurprisingly from Loraine (the first place to discover Islamic astronomy north of the Pyrenees), was the first to use the astrolabe in the Latin West. In 1092, he observed the eclipse of the moon and fixed it accurately by means of the astrolabe, using it in its Muslim form as devised in Toledo, and named after al-Zarqali.[2150] In the excited accounts of his new experiment Walcher mentions three of the instrument's points by their Arabic names, Almagrip, Almeri, and

---

2142 A. Djebbar: *Une Histoire de la Science Arabe*; Le Seuil; Paris; 2001; p. 178.
2143 R. Allen: Gerbert Pope Silvester II; *The English Historical Review*:Year 1892: pp 625-68; pp 630-1.
2144 S. C. McCluskey: *Astronomies; op cit;* p. 175.
2145 Ibid. p. 176.
2146 Ibid.
2147 Borst: Astrolab und Klosterreform; pp. 44-7; 114-7 in S. C. McCluskey: *Astronomies*; p. 176.
2148 N. Bubnov: *Gerberti postea Silvestri II papae opera Mathematica*: Berlin; 1899; pp 109-47;
J.P. Migne: *Patrologia Latina*, 221 vols; Paris; 1844-1864; cxI iii, pp. 379-412.
2149 C.H. Haskins: The Reception of Arabic science in England; *The English Historical Review*:Vol XXX (1915):pp 56-69.p. 58.
2150 D. Metlitzki: The Matter; op cit; pp. 17.

Almucantaraz,[2151] which in Chaucer, explaining to Little Lewis three hundred years later, appear as `aziumtz, almury and almycanteras.'[2152] Walcher's tables in the first treatise are worked out by the clumsy methods of Roman fractions, but in the second, written in 1120, he uses degrees, minutes, and seconds, and the more exact observations, which he had learned in England from Petrus Alphonsi.[2153] Translations from Arabic played a major role for such acquisition and dissemination of instrument use, particularly the use of the astrolabe. These include treatises on the astrolabe by Maslama al-Majriti and Ibn Saffar translated by John of Seville and Plato of Tivoli; Al-Zarqali's treatise on *Safiha az-Zarqalia* translated many times by Don Abraham in Hebrew, and a Spanish version by Ferrando.[2154] A whole literature has in fact been derived from al-Zarqali's treatise on the Safiha. In addition to the translations into Hebrew, such as that of 1263 in Montpellier, King Alfonso of Castile made two translations of it into Spanish; a further Spanish edition added by Rico Y Sinobas in the third volume of Libros del Saber.[2155] A Florentine, Gueruccio, who was passing by Seville, translated the work into Italian, and in France, Master Jean de Ligneres, in the first half of the 14th century, wrote in imitation of *Al-Zarqali's saphea*, or description of the universal astrolabe.[2156] The famed Regiomontanus, in the 15th century, composed problems based on the Saphea, which were published in Nuremberg: `*problemata XXIX Saphaea Nobilis instrumenti astronomici 1534.*'[2157] Chaucer, for his part, in 1380 used Masha'Allah's theories in his European introduction of the astrolabe as a scientific instrument.[2158] Such translations and adaptations helped the Latin in using the instrument in systematically every branch demanding measurement and calculation just as the Muslims did before them.[2159]

An Englishman, Robert (the Englishman,) who flourished in France, at Montpellier (c. 1271), wrote a treatise on the quadrant before 1276. The treatises describes an astronomical instrument by means of which

---

2151 Ibid.
2152 C.H. Haskins: Studies; p. 114; note 8.
2153 C.H. Haskins: The Reception; p. 58.
2154 A. Djebbar: Une Histoire. p.178.
2155 Carra De Vaux: Les Penseurs; op cit; vol 2; pp. 229-230.
2156 Ibid.
2157 Ibid.
2158 F.J Swetz: Surveying: op cit; p. 926
2159 See:
-J. Bensaude: *L'Astronomie Nautique; op cit.*
-D. Howse: Navigation and Astronomy the first three thousand years; in *Journal of Renaissance and Modern Studies*, vol 30; pp 60-86;

angular altitudes could be measured; e.g., the altitude of the sun (hence, with the help of solar tables, its place in the ecliptic), and also the hours of the day (again with the help of tables).[2160] So popular was the treatise, it could be found in a considerable number of manuscripts and translations into Greek, Hebrew and German, plagiarized even in the *Margarita philosophica* of Gregory Reish.[2161] The quadrant described as an invention of the second half of the 12th century, was `hardly more than the adaptation of an Arabic instrument to Christian and Western needs,' Sarton points out.[2162]Mc Cluskey, too, insists, that the quadrant was an Islamic invention, described in a group of treatises on the *Qadrant vetus* which entered the corpus astronomicuym; the most commonly used text being that written, of course, by John or Robert the Englishman.[2163]

Other instruments and instrument uses include Campanus' instructions for making and using the equatorium, which he, too, knew from an unknown Islamic source.[2164] The equatorium is designed as a mechanical computer for converting the mean motions of a planet found in the tables to the planet's true position without extensive computations.[2165]

As for armillary spheres, taken from Islamic sources, they were used in Western Europe for the teaching of astronomy until well into the 18th century.[2166]

By far, the greatest impact Islam exerted on the Christian West is in relation to the appreciation, or the adoption of science itself. In the preceding chapter was seen how the necessity to catch up with Islam has opened the way to the 12th century translations. The most decisive impact of Islam, though, is summed up by Durant who says that medieval Church power derived principally from the fact that men suspected that no one could answer their questions; `it was prudent, they felt, to take on faith the replies given with such quieting authoritativeness by the Church; they would have lost confidence in her had she ever admitted her fallibility. Perhaps they distrusted knowledge as the bitter fruit of a wisely forbidden tree, a mirage that would lure

2160 G. Sarton: Introduction; op cit; Vol II, p.993
2161 At least in the edition of 1508.
2162 G. Sarton: Introduction; Vol II, op cit; p.994.
2163 S. C. Mc Cluskey: *Astronomies; op cit*; p.202.
2164 Ibid. p.203.
2165 Ibid.
2166 H.C. King: The Planetorium: *Endeavour*; vol 18 (1959); pp 35-44; p.35.

man from the Eden of simplicity and an undoubting life....'[2167] `You cannot perish,' said Philip Augustus to his sailors in a midnight storm, `for at this moment thousands of monks are rising from their beds, and will soon be praying for us.'[2168]

Muslims, although very devout, knew how to separate science and reason from superstition and folklore. Thus, Draper notes how whilst: `the Christian peasant fever stricken or overtaken by accident, tried to the nearest saint shrine and expected a miracle; the Spanish Moor relied on the prescription or lancet of his physician, or the bandage and knife of his surgeon.'[2169]

Conder insists that the influence of Eastern philosophy was fatal to the superstition of Europe.[2170] And one of the major effects of the 12th century translations, Dawson notes, is in producing a mass of new learning, which on the Western mind could have nothing, but `startling effects.'[2171] It raised the whole question of the relations between religion and science, and between reason and faith, in a very sharp and accentuated way.[2172] The material conveyed to the Latin West through the medium of the translators, Campbell observes, `caused a reawakening in the intellectual outlook'.[2173] Among the bishops, sovereigns, and even popes, there were many men of elevated views, Draper notes, who saw distinctly the position of Europe, and understood thoroughly the difficulties of the Church.[2174] It had already become obvious to them that it would be impossible to restrain `the impulse arising from the vigorous movements of the Saracens, and that it was absolutely necessary so to order things that the actual condition of faith in Europe might be accommodated to or even harmonised with these philosophical conceptions, which it was quite clear would, soon or late, pervade the whole continent.'[2175] Thus, Durant concludes, the very seeds of the Renaissance and the Enlightenment were partly the unwitting revenge of Islam. Invaded in Palestine, and driven from nearly all of Spain, the Muslims transmitted their science and philosophy to Western

---

2167 W. Durant: The Age of Faith, op cit; p. 737-8.
2168 Coulton: Five Centuries; I; p. 300 in W. Durant: The Age; p. 737-8.
2169 J.W. Draper: History, op cit, vol II, p. 40.
2170 C.R. Conder: *The Latin Kingdom of Jerusalem;* The Committee of the Palestine Exploration Fund; London; 1897. p. 427.
2171 C. Dawson: Medieval Essays; op cit; p. 142.
2172 Ibid.
2173 D. Campbell: Arabian Medicine, op cit: p.149.
2174 J.W. Draper: A History; op cit; Vol II; p.131.
2175 Ibid.

Europe, and it proved to be a force that `infected Christianity with the germs of rationalism.'[2176]

The earliest scholar, championing Muslim rationalism is Adelard of Bath. In his wide travels[2177] and in his translations from Arabic, he exemplifies another phase of the awakening intellectual life of the age, a turning to Muslim literature for new sources of information and inspiration beyond the standard and easily available collections of classical, Scriptural, and patristic authorities.[2178]The *Quaestiones* fights the claim of authority in defence of the `moderns'. Adelard attributes to his Islamic teachers a new attitude of mind:

`I with reason for my guide have learned one thing from my Arab teachers- you something different-dazzled by the outward show of authority you wear a headstall, for what else would we call authority but a headstall? just as brute animals are led by headstalls where one pleases so many of you are led into danger by the authority of writers...'[2179]

Such eagerness and faith in human reason found fitting expression in his words: `If reason be not the universal arbiter, it is given to each of us in vain.'[2180] In Adelard's mind, in contrast to the use of reason in the Arab world and professionalism, France seemed to him, not only ignorant, but amateur.[2181]It is not possible to define exactly what the `opinions of the Arabs' meant to Adelard, but it is at least clear that he felt he was bringing something new and important to Europe, and that he was impatient, even contemptuous, of the purely indigenous developments of the north, literary, humanistic, theological.[2182]In the *Quaestiones Naturales* which he composed in praise of Islamic learning, he expresses his excitement at the new scientific outlook of the `Arabs which had left the Latin schools far behind.'[2183]

On Adelard's overall contribution, Stock observes:

`what we must be grateful for is that among a number of scholars who brought scientific information to the attention of the Latin West Adelard took the initiative not only in translating Arabic works but in recording

---

2176 W. Durant: The Age of faith, op cit; p. 982.

2177 *De eodem et diverso* indicates that Adelard had already visited Salerno and Sicily; in the Quaestiones, Adelard mentions Tarsus and Antioch as places where he had been. In J.K. Wright: The Geographical Lore; op cit; p. 92.

2178 J.K. Wright: The Geographical Lore; op cit; p. 92.

2179 L. Cochrane: Adelard of Bath; op cit; p.43

2180 G. Wiet et al: History; op cit; p.465.

2181 In. N. Daniel: The Arabs; op cit; p.268.

2182 Ibid.

2183 D. Metlitzki: The Matter of Araby; op cit; p. 29.

their usefulness and developing the reasoning on which they were based.'[2184]

Another Islamic legacy is, according to Daniel, the fact that Europe in the 12th century needed scientific knowledge and method, and was desperate for new material and new methods, and found them in Arabic.[2185] Scientific methodology was largely inherited from Al-Farabi, who in his *Ihsa al-Ulum* `Catalogue of the sciences' enumerates the sciences; setting down the paradigms upon which, and around which scientific knowledge could be both organised and built. This book had two Latin translations, which are known, one was by Dominicus Gundisalvus, and the other by Gerard of Cremona.[2186]The work was widely distributed, and on Al-Farabi's methodology was built subsequent classification of sciences. Gundisalvus in his Division of the sciences completely shatters the old Western framework.[2187] He opens with the familiar three theoretical sciences; then come the Seven Arts, with medicine inserted between the Trivium and Quadrivium (in this he follows Adelard of Bath), but he includes between geometry and astronomy several sciences, which have been developed by the Muslims.[2188]

Another aspect of Islamic methodology is the work of Al-Razi who systematised his medical writing, and classified his chemical substances (in his *Secret secretum*). Following suite, in medicine, Arnauld of Villanova proceeded by the same manner of Al-Razi, so much so, that Daniel sees in him a sort of lesser European Al-Razi.[2189] And in chemistry, European scientists of the Renaissance followed the Muslims' classification of substances (primarily al-Razi's), gradually developing more complex and accurate classifications; and still using the same system as Muslims did centuries before them.[2190]

The Islamic state, at its earliest stages, institutionalised strict rules and regulations. This was in obedience of fundamental requirements of the faith, which demands precise calculation of inheritance shares, financial contributions as part of alms giving, etc. Regulations, which spread to

---

2184 Quaestiones, ch vi, on why man must use reason with which he is endowed, Gollancz p. 98; Muller, p. 11. in L. Cochrane: Adelard of Bath; op cit; p. 108

2185 N. Daniel: The Cultural Barrier, op cit; p.149.

2186 Alonso: Traducciones del Arc . Gundislavo; pp. 298-308 in J. Puig: Arabic Philosophy; op cit; p. 16.

2187 J. Jolivet: The Arabic Inheritance; op cit; p. 126.

2188 Ibid.

2189 N. Daniel: The Arabs; op cit; p. 293.

2190 E. Holmyard: *Makers of Chemistry*; Oxford; 1931; pp. 68 fwd.

all sorts of activities; dispensaries of urban hospitals, for instance, being obliged to prescribe accurate amounts of drugs of controlled composition.[2191]To insure that every type of rule and regulation was observed, state inspection was set up under the Muhtasib (the state inspector). He made sure that merchants and druggists did not use false weights and measures, that adulterated medicines were not sold, that animals did not carry more than a certain weight, that boats did not go out on the sea under certain conditions, etc.[2192]Also in the days of al-Mamun and Al-Mutassim, pharmacists were obliged to pass examinations to become licensed professionals, and they were pledged to follow the prescriptions of the physicians.[2193] So much interest was attached to accuracy that the records of early Islamic scientists that were of particular interest were signed on oath in legal form.[2194]

The same measures were adopted by the Islamic leaning Sicilian rulers: Roger and Frederick of Sicily. Frederick, for instance, passed the edict concerning the medical profession, which amongst others, obliged every physician exerting in his kingdom to obtain a licence from Salerno.[2195] He determined the length of medical studies to five years, plus one year for practice under the guidance of an experienced physician, and one more year for surgeons.[2196] He also passed regulations in the preparation of drugs as well as the relations between doctors and apothecaries.[2197] Frederick's measures, according to Sarton, witnessed the transformation of a profession organised on a purely individualistic basis, mainly controlled by the rules and ideals of its own brotherhood, into one consecrated and protected by academic and governmental regulations and privileges.[2198] Other rulers of Western Christendom followed in the same steps.[2199]

Islamic rigour in no manner restricted scientific query, though. Multhauf, for instance, points out that `while all learning, sacred and profane, long remained an ecclesiastical monopoly in Europe, alchemy,

---

[2191] B Stock: Science; op cit; p. 21.
[2192] See L.I. Conrad: Muhtassib; Dictionary of Middle Ages; op cit; Vol 8; pp. 526-8.
[2193] I.B. Syed: Medicine and medical education in Islamic history, in Islamic Perspectives in Medicine, op cit, pp 45-56, at p. 54.
[2194] R. Briffault: The Making, op. cit, p. 193.
[2195] A. Mieli: La Science Arabe; op cit; p. 228.
[2196] G. Sarton: Introduction, op cit, vol 2; p. 576.
[2197] Ibid; p.96.
[2198] Ibid.
[2199] D. Campbell: Arabian Medicine; op cit; p.119.

and science in general, was a secular pursuit in Islam.'[2200] Until the 13th century in the Latin West, and with few exceptions, learning was only available in monastic and cathedral schools. The great medieval universities that emerged in the 12th-13th centuries (and the 14th) were under the control of the Church and had mostly ecclesiastics on their teaching staff.[2201] It took gradual developments in the Christian West to advance along Islamic lines, and it is the adoption of the value system of Islam, which opened doors for advancement.[2202] It is in Islam, Makdisi observes, where was found the model of academic freedom, amongst both professors and students.[2203] One of the principal tenets of Islam, Scott says, was toleration, and the rapid and `almost miraculous development of the human mind' during the 13th century was the inevitable consequence of a policy based upon those principles whose application had promoted the wonderful progress of every nation ruled by `the enlightened' followers of Islam.[2204] A point adhered to by Owen who maintains that in the leaders of Islam, as in the Prophet himself, are examples of men who are eminent for enlightenment, liberality, and toleration; and the history of Islam, taken as a whole, must be regarded as `a powerful propaganda of free thought and liberal culture, which is all the more striking when contrasted with the barbarism by which it was surrounded.'[2205]

Finally, here, are two other crucial elements of Islamic influence upon Western learning. The First is related to the use of paper in Islam, and its eventual transfer to the West. Pedersen insists that in diffusing paper production and use, the Muslims accomplished a feat of crucial significance not only to the history of the Islamic books but to the whole world of books.[2206] Which, of course, led to the second development, printing, whose impact on modern science and civilisation does not need to be told here.

[2200] R. P. Multhauf: The Science of Matter, in Science in the Middle Ages, ed. D.C. Lindberg, op cit; pp. 369-90; at p. 376.
[2201] D.J. Geanakoplos: Medieval Western Civilisation; op cit; p.320.
[2202] S.P. Scott: History; op cit; vol 3; p. 108.
[2203] G. Makdisi: The Rise; op cit; p.350.
[2204] S.P. Scott: History; op cit; vol 3; p. 108.
[2205] J. Owen: *The Skeptics of the Italian Renaissance;* Swan Sonnenschein &Co; London; 1908. p. 64.
[2206] J. Pedersen: *The Arabic Book,* (1928) tr. G. French; Princeton, (1984); p. 59.

2. ISLAMIC IMPACT ON SCIENCES

One of the reasons why the Islamic impact has failed to be seen and understood, other than sheer pure historian malice or ignorance, has been mainly due to the fact that each area of impact has been examined separately. No author has looked at such an impact on every science or aspect of civilisation. Here is an attempt to correct this, however partially (due to lack of space and competence to deal with every issue adequately.) Once an attempt is made to address the Islamic scientific impact from a diversity of angles, and from as wide spectrum as possible, similarities and patterns become more easily visible as they repeat themselves. Thus are found again the same mechanisms of influence, the same timing, manners of transmission, regions of origin, agents of transmission etc, repeating themselves with regard to the scientific changes that took place in the medieval Christian West. All are related to Islam. And the substance of the scientific changes itself is also Islamic. This confirms the Islamic source of medieval changes, and once more, challenges the argument of spontaneous, coincidental or purely local/Classical origins for such changes as found amongst most Western historians.

In this chapter, we shall avoid dwelling, unless strictly necessary, on the translation of Islamic scientific works and their impact, and other matters that have already been seen in detail. Not all sciences will be looked at either. Focus, instead, is on aspects of impact not seen, and some of the sciences that have escaped attention before: geography and nautical sciences, and technology, principally. And to lessen the risk of dwelling on the same facts as before, subjects looked at already (mathematics, astronomy and optics) are grouped together under the same heading, and so are all the medical sciences also joined in the briefest of outlines.

1. Mathematics, Optics and Astronomy

a. Mathematics:

A succinct and adequate outline on the Islamic impact in mathematics can be found at the following sites:
http://mercury.spaceports.com/~islam/Science%20Frame/math.htm

http://www-history.mcs.st-andrews.ac.uk/history/index.html

A little more in detail, the Islamic impact can be seen first in algebra. Al-Khwarizmi it was who wrote in about 825 a treatise on Algebra entitled *Al Gebr Wa'l Mukabala* (Calculation by Symbols) Called in the original `*Kitab al Mukhtassar fi'l hisab al jabr wa'l muqabalah*' (Compendious Book of Calculation by Completion and Balancing ), it became in Latin simply `algebra'. This work became `the prototype' for all Islamic and medieval Latin works on Algebra.[2207] The title of his algebra text gave name to that art, the first work in which that word appears in the mathematical sense, `Algebra' meaning in Arabic `restoration', that is the transposing of negative terms of an equation.[2208] Of its original three parts, only two were transmitted to Europe, and those two arrived separately. It took Latin scholars some time to realise that the two parts fit together.[2209] Algebra was translated into Latin twice during the 12th century, by Gerard of Creomona, who retained the Arabic title, *De jebra et almucahala*, and by Robert of Chester, who gave a Latin rendering of it *Liber restaurationis et oppositionis numeris*.[2210] Jacob of Florence wrote *Tractatus algorismi*, dated 1307, the algebraic part of which contains six types of quadratic and linear equations as given by Al-Khwarizmi, but with numerical examples different from those of al-Khwarizmi, Abu Kamil, and Leonardo of Pisa.[2211] In his *Trattato di praticha arismetricha*, master Benedetto of Florence devotes a section to `*La reghola de Algebra Almuchabale*,' borrowing the Arab words directly: `One square (zenso) plus 21 units (dramme) equal 10 of its roots, that is to say 10 things.'[2212] Another early follower was Jean de Meurs (d. after 1350), a French writer of popular textbooks on mathematics and music, and astrologer. His *Opus quadripartitum* completed in November 1343, in its arithmetical and algebraical parts, contains nothing new, derived principally from al-Khwarizmi, and also from other followers of Islamic mathematics (Leonardo of Pisa, and John of Sacrobosco.) The dependence on al-Khwarizmi is slavish,

---

2207 M. S. Mahoney: Mathematics in Science in the Middle Ages (D.C. Lindberg): Op cit; pp 145-78; p. 157.

2208 C. Singer: *Short History of Scientific Ideas to 1900*, op cit; p. 148

2209 M. S. Mahoney: Mathematics; op cit; p. 157.

2210 F. Gabrieli: The Transmission of learning; and Literary influences in Western Europe; in *The Cambridge History of Islam;* P.M. Holt et all ed; vol 2; Cambridge University Press; 1970; pp. 851-89; at p.863.

2211 G. Sarton: Introduction. Op cit; Volume III; p.638.

2212 P Benoit: Algebra, Commerce and Calculation: in *A history of Scientific Thought* (M. Serres ed); op cit; pp 246-279; p.268.

Sarton notes, it extends in some cases to numerical illustrations.[2213] Much of al-Khwarizmi's algebra had already been incorporated in the works of Leonardo of Pisa, but Jean de Meurs was directly acquainted with Al-Khwarizmi through the translation by Robert of Chester, and he occasionally quotes al-Khwarizmi's examples not used by Leonardo of Pisa.[2214] Many more early mathematicians such as Firmin de Beauval (fl 1338-45)also show this influence.

The title of Al-Khwarizmi's algebra gave name to that art, and from a variant of the name of the author, we obtain the word "algorism," and logarithm. Al-Khwarizmi's work is undoubtedly the beginning of algebraic calculus and decimal arithmetic.[2215] There were many adaptations of Al-Khwarizmi's Arithmetic, translated by Adelard of Bath; John of Seville's *Alghoarismi de arismetrice*, Sacrobosco's *Algorismus* and finally, the *Carmen de Algorismo* by Allexandre de Villedieu, composed in verse so as to be easier to remember.[2216] John of Holywood's (Sacrobosco) book on arithmetic, or rather `algorisms,' was both extremely popular, and did more to introduce the Muslim notation (Arabic numerals) than any other.[2217] It was, Singer holds, much more popular than Leonardo's work, from the time it appeared about 1240, and was reprinted continuously down to the 17th century.[2218]

Sabra observes that the finest treatise of Islamic arithmetic was written long after Al-Khwarizmi, in the year 1427, in Samarkand. The author was less known than al-Khwarizmi: Al-Kashi (1380-1429), a distinguished astronomer and mathematician at the service of Sultan Uluh Beg.[2219] Al-Kashi's treatise, entitled `The Key to Arithmetic' was meant for the use of merchants, clerks and surveyors, as well as theoretical astronomers. One of the notable contributions of al-Kashi's treatise was its thorough investigation and novel treatment of decimal fractions, which `anticipated similar developments in Europe by about two hundred years.'[2220] How Al-Kashi impacted on subsequent Western mathematics need to be clarified so as to show the routes and manners

---

2213 G. Sarton: Introduction; op cit; Volume III; p.652-3.
2214 Ibid.
2215 C. Singer: *Short History of Scientific Ideas to 1900*, op cit; p. 148
2216 P Benoit and F. Micheau: The Arab Intermediary, in A history of Scientific Thought; op cit; pp 191-221; p. 216.
2217 C. Singer: A Short History of Scientific ideas; op cit; p. 174.
2218 Ibid. p. 175.
2219 A.I Sabra: The Scientific Enterprise, in *The World of Islam*, ed. B. Lewis, Thames and Hudson, London, 1976; pp 181-92, at p. 184.
2220 Ibid.

of transmission as many of the subjects it addressed were soon taken up by Western mathematicians.[2221]

In trigonometry, Savasorda (Rabbi bar Hiyya)'s *`Liber embadorum*' introduced Islamic trigonometry mensuration into the West, and had an influence on the geometry of Leonard of Pisa.[2222] It is the view of Levey that this work was one of the first works to introduce Muslim trigonometry into Europe.[2223] Most likely, indeed, for Savasorda worked principally with Plato of Tivoli (see preceding chapter on translations), and Plato's main translation work was of al-Battani, who pioneered in trigonometry.

Subsequently Muslim trigonometry was fully exploited by Jewish astronomers and translators working in Toledo for Alfonso X el Sabio.[2224] These translators (namely Ishaq Ben Sid) also introduced in the same court the later trigonometry found in Jabir Ibn Aflah's *Refutation of the Almagest*.[2225]

John Mauduith (fl 1310) was an English mathematician and astronomer, a fellow of Merton College (Oxford) and the real initiator of Western trigonometry, preceding both Levi ben Gerson and Wallingford.[2226] His *Parvus Tractatus,* deeply influenced by al-Zarqali, is especially important, as it was a source of Wallingford's *qadripartitump.*[2227] Richard Wallingford (c.1292-1335) is the greatest English mathematician of his time, one of the introducers of trigonometry into Christian Western Europe, who other than Mauduith was also influenced by Bradwardine. A Vatican manuscript[2228]of the *perspectiva communis* of John Peckham contains four propositions added by Bradwardine, which show that the latter was familiar with cotangent and tangent and their reciprocal relations. He was also one of the earliest Western writers on trigonometry, but these notions can be

---

2221 See:
-A.Youschkevitch: *Les Mathématiques arabes* (VIIe-XVe siècles). Paris: J. Vrin, 1976.
-R. Rashed: *The Development of Arabic mathematics: between arithmetic and algebra.* Dordrecht: Kluwer. 1994.

2222 C.H. Haskins: Studies; op cit; P. 11.

2223 M. Levey: Abraham Bar Hiyya Ha-Nasi: *Dictionary of Scientific Biography*, vol 1, p. 22.

2224 G. Sarton: The Appreciation of Ancient and Medieval Science during the Renaissance (1450-1600), University of Pennsylvania Press, 1955. p.160.

2225 F.Micheau: La Transmisison; op cit; p. 417.

2226 G. Sarton: Introduction; op cit; Volume III; p.660.

2227 Ibid.

2228 (Cod. Vatic. 3102)

found in Islamic writings of a much earlier date, e.g. those of Abu-l-Wafa.[2229]

In geometry, the influence of al-Jawhari, Ibn al-Haytham, Omar Khayyam and Nasr al-Din al-Tusi (translated into Latin and Hebrew) was quite evident on European works of late medieval and renaissance times.[2230] Smith's comparative study of Khayyam and Saccheri and their theories of parallels clearly demonstrates the influence of the former upon the latter. According to Ginsburg (Smith's collaborator in this study) his exhaustive research into the bibliography of the subject clearly shows that Khayyam was the precursor of al-Tusi, Wallis, and Saccheri in laying the foundation of non Euclidian geometry.[2231]To demonstrate the influence of Khayyam upon Saccheri's work, Smith establishes the fact that the first Saccheri's theorems are essentially the same as some of Khayyam's propositions, with not only identical proofs and purpose for which they were put to use but even with the same way of lettering some figures.[2232]

The route of such influence is via Al-Tusi. Nasir al-Din al-Tusi (1201-1274) manuscript contains an important part of Khayyam's geometrical treatise[2233] as well as al-Tusi's commentary on it. A sizeable book of Al-Tusi on the elements of Euclid and his postulates was published in Arabic in the end of the 16th century in Rome, and about the middle of the following century Al-Tusi's ideas on the Euclidean postulates became available in Latin translations;[2234]the source of influence on the work of Girolamo Saccheri, in the 18th century.[2235]

Also as noted by Hill, geometry `impinges' on various technologies and sciences; thus the Islamic impact stretched to subjects such as land surveying, civil and mechanical engineering, and construction.[2236] On this latter matter, Cochrane offers good examples of associations of geometry and construction techniques leading to the development of such techniques in the Christian West.[2237] Constructional geometry was

---

2229 G. Sarton: Introduction; op cit; Volume III; p.670.

2230 D.R. Hill: Islamic Science, op cit, p. 26.

2231 D.E. Smith: Euclid, Omar Khayyam and Saccheri in *Scripta Mathematica*, Vol 3; No 1 (1935); pp 6 and 8.

2232 Ibid. pp 8-10.

2233 O. Khayyam: Discussion of Difficulties in Euclid trans A.R.Amir-Moez, in *Scripta Mathematica,* vol 24.

2234 H. Suter; G. Sarton; A.Taton... in A. Sayili: *The Observatory in Islam*; Publications of the Turkish Historical Society, Series VII, No 38, Ankara, 1960. p.383.

2235 Ibid.

2236 D.R. Hill: Islamic Science; op cit; p. 26.

2237 L. Cochrane: Adelard; op cit.

also applied to land surveying and to hydraulic works; Hill reminding appropriately that in the Arab word `handassa' applies to both geometry and engineering.[2238]

Al-Khwarizmi's treatise on calculation with the numerals employed separate symbols for the numbers from 1 to 9 (plus a symbol for 0 as a placeholder) in a decimal place value system and to set forth written arithmetical techniques consonant with the system.[2239] The numerals in Spain were called Ghubar or dust numbers because they could be scratched in dust or sand.[2240]Thus, there is a need to understand some form of early passage between the two sources (al-Khwarizmi and Spain). Here might lay the reason for historical confusion on the origins of such numerals: the manner and substance of use of the numerals is from al-Khwarizmi, the form is from Muslim Spain/North Africa (from where much transferred to Spain). The numerals could well be an outcome of Al-Khwarizmi's calculation methods from Eastern Islam combined with forms of decimals of Western Islamic origin (which explains why the Ghubar numerals survived in the western portion of Islam, and are different from those of Eastern Islam).

There were early attempts, already seen, made by Gerbert to introduce the Islamic system in Western Europe from Spain. However, the use of zero in combination with the nine Ghubar numbers in a decimal system was not understood in the West until the translation of al Khwarizmi's instructions on how to calculate with them.[2241] Still, the process by which Arabic numerals took root in Europe was incredibly slow. The antiquated Roman numerals and abacus persisted till the early part of the 13th. The best proof of Western backwardness in this respect is the fact that the Alfonsine tables, completed c.1272, contained probably none but Roman numerals.[2242] Muslim and Jewish mathematicians engaged in the compilation of these tables were of course familiar with the Ghubar numerals, but these numerals were associated with the Arabic script, were in fact an intrinsic part of it, and were almost naturally dropped by them, together with that script, as soon as they began to write in Latin or in Spanish.[2243]

[2238] D.R. Hill: Islamic science; op cit; p. 26.
[2239] M. S. Mahoney: Mathematics. Op cit; p. 150.
[2240] L. Cochrane: Adelard of Bath; op cit; p.24.
[2241] Ibid. p.25.
[2242] G. Sarton: Introduction, op cit; Vol II, pp.747-8.
[2243] Ibid.

The use of Roman numerals retarded the study of mathematical theory;[2244]but, once adopted, the new decimal system was to have the most far reaching consequences, eliminating the cumbersome, traditional slow counting methods of the time. Instead of the painful operations with Roman numerals-how painful can readily be seen by trying a simple problem of multiplication or division with these characters- it was now possible to work readily with Arabic figures.[2245] Without the Arabic system of numeration, Boyer recognises, `mathematics would have been still in its cradle.'[2246]More importantly, as Boyer concludes:

`familiarity with it (the system) from childhood detracts from an appreciation of its philosophical beauty and its great practical importance. Deprived of it for a short time, and compelled to work with the inconvenient method of other systems, we should be able to form a truer idea of the advantages which this invention has conferred to mankind.'[2247]

The career of the first, greatest medieval Western mathematician, Fibonacci, is a very enlightening instance of the form and substance of Islamic influence on the Christian West. Fibonacci obtained his knowledge from the Muslims during a stay in the so called `Barbary Coast' that is North Africa where his father was for a time in charge of a Pisan trading colony in Bougie (Bejaia today), Algeria.[2248] In his contacts with Muslim traders, he (the father) realised the superiority of Arabic numerals, and to prepare his son (Leonardo) for running the family business, he sent him to a Muslim teacher of mathematics in Bougie.[2249]Subsequently Leonardo Fibonacci produced *Liber abacci* in 1202, which was, according to Sarton `the first monument of European mathematics.'[2250] A quick skip through *Liber abacci* shows indisputable filiations with Islamic precedents, concerning the types of problems addressed; the methods for their solution; terminology, and even symbolism.[2251]Fibonacci presents himself, not only in arithmetic, but also in algebra and in the theory of numbers, as carried by the current of

---

2244 W.M. Watt: The Influence, op cit, p. 63.
2245 C.H. Haskins: The Rise of Universities; op cit; p. 8.
2246 L.E. Boyer: *Mathematics, a Historical development*, New York, Henry Holt and Company, 1949, pp 29-31.
2247 Ibid.
2248 W. Montgomery Watt: The Influence; op cit; pp. 63-4.
2249 Ibid
2250 G. Sarton, Introduction, op cit, p.7
2251 A. Djebbar: *Une Histoire de la Science Arabe*; Le Seuil; Paris; 2001. p.146.

Islamic mathematics of the first period, that of the 9th-10th centuries.[2252] This conclusion is confirmed by the inclusion in his work the mathematics of Ahmed Ibn Yusuf.[2253] Ahmad Ibn Yusuf ibn Ibrahim ibn al-Daya al Misri, i. e., the Egyptian, flourished in Egypt in the second half of the 9th century and died about 912.[2254] In medieval Europe he was known as `Ametus filius Joseph.[2255] Mathematician, and secretary of the Tulunids, who ruled in Egypt from 868 to 905, he wrote amongst others, a book on proportions *Kitab al-nisba wal tanasub ("De proportione et proportionalitate")*.[2256] This work influenced mediaeval thought through Leonardo, and also Jordanus Nemorarius.[2257]This work must have reached Leonardo through the then recent translation made by Gerard of Cremona.[2258] Al-Hasib al-Misri, better known as Abu Kamil, who lived in the 10th century, perfected the algebra of al-Khwarizmi, was also one of the sources used by Leonardo.[2259]
The impact of *Liber abacci* was considerable. It became a landmark, since it laid the cornerstone of European mathematics.[2260]The earliest known abacus text is included in it (*Liber abacci* meaning `Book of the Abacus').[2261]A typical abacus text would contain problems connected with calculation of interest, simple and compound, with exchange of currencies, with distribution according to a certain ratio, plus geometrical questions about areas, volumes and land measurement.[2262] *Liber abacci's* great achievement is also in discarding the old fashioned mode of writing, thus insuring the progress of arithmetic.[2263] The age long bonds had been broken at last, and the zero and the Arabic numerals are at the basis of the modem science of calculation.[2264] It was

---

[2252] R. Rashed: Fibonacci et les mathematiques Arabes; op cit; p.146.
[2253] Ibid.
[2254] G. Sarton: *Introduction; op cit;*. vol 1; p. 598.
[2255] B. Rosenfeld and E. Ihsanoglu: *Mathematicians, Astronomers and Other Scholars of Islamic Civilisation*; Research Centre for Islamic History, art and Culture; Istanbul; 2003. p. 60.
[2256] M. Cantor: Ahmed und sein Buch uber die Proportionen; in *Bibliotheca Mathematica*, 7-9,1888.
H. Suter: *Die Mathematiker und Astronomen der Araber; 1900;* pp. 42-3.
[2257] H. Burger und K. Kohl: Zur Geschichte des Transversalsatzes usw. In *Abhdl. zur Gesch. d. Naturwiss*, 7, 47-9, 80, 1924; *ISIS*, VIII, p. 799.
[2258] G. Sarton: *Introduction*, op cit; vol 1; p. 598.
[2259] A. Mieli: La Science Arabe ; op cit; p.108.
[2260] Edward J. Jurji: The Course of Arabic Scientific; op cit; p.230.
[2261] S Cuomo: Niccolo Tartaglia: Mathematics, ballistics, and the power of possession of knowledge: *ENDEAVOUR*; 1998: pp. 31-5: p.31.
[2262] Ibid.
[2263] E.J. Jurji: The Course of Arabic Scientific; op cit; p.230.
[2264] Ibid.

Villedieu and Sacrobosco who propagated Fibonacci's mathematics to Europe, and until the 16th century at least, the generations of mathematicians did not cease relying on his writing.[2265] Fibonacci who Latinised so to say Islamic mathematics of the 9th-10th century, is well, Rashed notes, a scientist of the 15th –16th centuries, his work in all case a source for inspiration and for the renewal of Latin mathematics.[2266]

b. Astronomy:

Krisciunas, as already noted in part one in detail, observed how the general perception was that astronomical research fell into a dazed slumber following Ptolemy, not to reawaken until the time of Copernicus.'[2267] Yet, in reality, many aspects of the modern science developed during the Islamic period. Hence, in relation to the particular issue of planetary motion, Rybka observes:

`To our day, there has been no systematic study of the matter of planetary motion as dealt with by Islamic astronomers. And yet, to understand best the manner by which astronomy developed and progressed beginning in 15th century Europe, it is vital to have a precise knowledge of the Islamic contribution, whether with regard to the observation of the planets, or to the theories related to their movement. This is all the more vital, that the treatise by Peuerbach *Theoreticae Novae Planetarum*, the work which gave birth to the study of the movement of the planets in the 15th century was based on the results reached by Islamic astronomy. This work, as we know, is fundamentally based on Ibn al-Haytham.[2268] *Theoreticae Novae Planetarum* generated many commentaries, including by Albertus of Brudzewo, professor at the university of Cracow, at the end of the 15th century. At the time Copernicus studied at the University of Cracow,[2269] this commentary was the object of study, and it is from here that our future great scholar took his first knowledge concerning the structure of the universe. Thus,

---

[2265] R. Rashed: Fibonacci; op cit; p.146

[2266] Ibid. p.160.

[2267] K. Krisciunas: *Astronomical Centers of the World*; Cambridge University Press, Cambridge, 1988; at p. 23.

[2268] W. Hartner: *Oriens-Occidens;* Hildesheim; 1968; pp. 484-8.

[2269] L.A. Birkenmajer: *Stromata Copernicana;* Krakow; 1924; pp. 71-8.

his early studies were influenced by Muslim theories, most particularly by those of Ibn al-Haytham regarding planetary motion.'[2270]

Centuries even before Copernicus, it was already acknowledged by Western scholars that Islamic astronomical learning was far superior, which prompted its acquisition. Hugo of Santalla (12th century), working in Tarazona, and in close contact with Hermann of Carinthia and Robert of Chester, wrote that 'it befits us to imitate the Arabs especially, for they are as it were our teachers and precursors in this art'.[2271] For his part, Hermann laments `the low state of astronomical knowledge among his contemporaries and a reminder that true knowledge is to be found among the Arabs. Hence exists the need for translations.'[2272]The same conclusions, as seen in the preceding chapters, also reached by Petrus Alphonsi, Plato of Tivoli, and earlier by Hermann the Cripple, and Raymond of Marseilles.

It is as early as the 10th century that the strive for the acquisition of Islamic astronomical knowledge by Western Christendom began. It was done in Catalonia, Spain, and through Lorraine it spread in the Latin world. Four centuries later, Islamic astronomical works were still being translated, and astronomical thought was still developed on the Muslim models, witness Stephanus Arlandi (fl 14th) translation from Arabic into Latin of the *Sphaera solidis* of Qusta Ibn Luqa (9th century).[2273]

Three Islamic names impacted to great measure on Western astronomy: al-Battani, al-Farghani, and al-Zarqali.

Al-Battani (d. 929) was involved with the observatory that was first established in the reign of Caliph al-Mamun (ruled 813-833).[2274]Al-Battani's astronomy has been competently studied.[2275] His work on the timing of the new moons, the length of the solar and sideral year, the prediction of eclipses, and the phenomenon of parallax, anticipated, in

---

2270 E. Rybka: Mouvement des Planetes dans l'Astronomie des Peuples de l'Islam; in *Convegno Internationale: Oriente e occidente Nel Medioevo Filosofia E Scienze;* 9-15 Aprile 1969; Academia Nationale Dei Lincei; Roma; 1971; pp. 579-93; p. 579.

2271 C. Burnett, 'A Group of Arabic-Latin Translators Working in Northern Spain in the mid-twelfth Century' *Journal of the Royal Asiatic Society*, 1977, pp.62-108; at p.90.

2272 R. Lemay: Translators of the Twelfth Century: Literary Issues raised and impact created; in Medieval Philosophers; *Dictionary of Literary Biography*; Vol 115; Edited by J. Hackett; A Bruccoli Clark Layman Book; Detroit; pp. 367-89. p.378.

2273 G. Sarton: Introduction; op cit; Volume III. p.114.

2274 J. Glubb: A Short History; op cit; p.109.

2275 Such as by C.A. Nallino: *Raccolta di scritti Editi e Inediti*, Roma, 1944.

the words of Wickens, the space age.[2276] Jewish scholars: Ibn Ezra, Maimonides, and Levi Ben Gerson made al-Battani's tables and calculations the foundations of theirs.[2277] Amongst the Christians, Robertus Cestrensis (Retinensis) devised tables of the celestial movements for the meridian of London for the year 1150 after him. Albertus Magnus, Alphonso X, Regiomontanus, Nicolas Cusanus, Copernicus, and Tycho Brahe are amongst others, on whom, al-Battani, in one way or another impacted.[2278] His *Compendium of Astronomy* was used as a text-book in Europe until the 16th century.[2279] Al-Battani's observations of lunar and solar eclipses were reliable enough to be used in 1749 by the Englishman Dunthorne in calculating the secular acceleration of the mean motion of the moon.[2280]Al-Battani's late 9th century application of the principle of orthographic projection to achieve new solutions in spherical trigonometry, however, did not reach Europe until the 15th century.[2281]

Like Al-Battani, Al-Farghani (9th century) exerted a deep influence upon European astronomy almost until Copernicus' time.[2282] He also worked at the same Al-Mamun's court. His best known work *Kitab fi Harakat Al-Samawiyah wa Jaamai Ilm al-Nujum* (The book on the movement of the planets, and compendium of the science of the stars) was a manual of cosmography of thirty chapters, including a description of the inhabited part of the earth, its size, the distances of the heavenly bodies from the earth and their sizes, and much else.[2283] This and other treatises of his remained much prized in the West through Latin and Hebrew translations in the centuries to follow.[2284] At the core of the astronomical curriculum was a series of new textbooks on the sphere, modelled on the general pattern of al-Farghani's *On the Science of the Stars* and replacing Martianus Capella, Macrobius, and the Carolingian anthologies with coherent introductions to the rudiments of spherical astronomy.[2285] The translation in 1135 by John of Seville of al-

---

[2276] G.M Wickens: The Middle East; op cit; pp. 117-8.

[2277] Carra de Vaux: *Les Penseurs de l'Islam*, Paris; Geuthner, 1921.Vol 2; pp 208-13.

[2278] Ibid.

[2279] J. Glubb: A Short History; op cit; p.109.

[2280] Editorial: Islam and science: retrospect and prospect; *ENDEAVOUR; V*ol 4; pp 1-2; and 34: (editorial); p.1.

[2281]W. Hartner, `Al-Battani,' i: 512. in T.F. Glick: Islamic and Christian Spain; op cit..p.252

[2282] G. Sarton: Introduction; op cit; Vol II, p.15

[2283] R. Morelon: Eastern Arabic Astronomy, in *Encyclopaedia of the History of Arabic Science* (Rashed ed), op cit; pp 20-57; at p. 24.

[2284] G. Sarton: Introduction; op cit; vol 2; p.545.

[2285] S. C. Mc Cluskey; *Astronomies; op cit;* p.193.

Farghani's on the elements of astronomy was used by John of Hollywood for much of the materials he incorporated into his *De Sphaera* and which had a profound effect on the future development of astronomical geography during the later Middle Ages.[2286] Dante's ideas on astronomy were equally derived almost exclusively from the Latin versions of Al-Farghani; representing the astronomical and cosmological knowledge not only of his educated (not specialised) contemporaries, but also of many following generations.[2287] Al-Farghani was the first to introduce the notion of *Umbra Versa* which corresponds to our tangent.[2288] The introduction of tangents in trigonometry had a considerable importance. `That fortunate revolution in the science,' says Chasles in his *Apercu historique des methodes en geometrie*, ridding science of cumbersome operations, and included sines and cosines of the unknown, preceding similar discoveries in the West by five centuries.[2289]

The role of al-Zarqali (1029-1087) is obvious in the fact that European tables are very analogous to the Islamic, the Europeans having to obtain their first inspiration and guidance from Islamic documents.[2290] Al-Zarqali's Toledan tables (1080) found their way into Christian hands before the middle of the 12th century. The first Christian to adapt the Toledan Tables to a new place and time was Raymond of Marseilles in his Marseilles tables of c.1140. He decided to transform the astronomical tables of Al-Zarqali, which were computed for the meridian of Toledo and adapted to Muslim years, so as to arrange them for the meridian of his native city and according to years dated from `the birth of our Lord.'[2291] Then in 1149, Robert of Chester compiled the London Tables, which were derived from Al-Battani as well as Al-Zarqali. Almost a century later, in 1231, William the Englishman compiled new Marseilles Tables. William had a deep knowledge of Al-Zarqali's astronomy, but he had also become familiar with the ideas of Al-Farghani.[2292] The tables of Marseilles (based on Al-Zarqali's Toledo's tables) were also adapted to the meridians of Paris and Pisa.[2293]

2286 J.K. Wright: The Geographical Lore; op cit; p. 96.
2287 G. Sarton: Introduction; op cit; Volume III. p.111.
2288 Encyclopaedia of Islam, I, p. 698 in A. Mieli: La Science Arabe; op cit; p.88.
2289 G. Le Bon: La Civilisation; op cit; p.360.
2290 G. Sarton: Introduction; op cit; Vol II, p.15.
2291 J.L. E. Dreyer: Mediaeval Astronomy; in Toward Modern Science, op cit; Vol 1, pp 235-256; p.243.
2292 G. Sarton: Introduction; Vol II, p.15.
2293 J.L. E. Dreyer: Mediaeval Astronomy; op cit; p.243.

A lasting contribution of Islamic astronomy was to refute and correct Greek astronomy, thus laying the foundations for modern astronomy.[2294] The shortcomings of Ptolemy's *Almagest* had been recognised by Muslim astronomers, and various corrections had been proposed.[2295] Muslim astronomers corrected his measurement of latitudes and longitudes of diverse locations, and brought vital improvements to his map of the earth. Al-Farghani, for instance, relied on measurements effected at the court of Al-Mamun to make some substantial corrections.[2296]

The biggest onslaught on Ptolemy's *Almagest* was in Spain, originating with Ibn Badja and Jabir ibn Aflah and continued by the philosopher Ibn Tufail and completed under his direction by al-Bitruji.[2297]Ibn Aflah's treatise *Islah al-majisti (Correction/refutation of the Almagest)* had the deepest influence upon medieval thought through its Latin and Hebrew translations.[2298]The Latin translation was made by Gerard of Cremona before 1187; the first Hebrew translation appeared a century later.[2299] In I2I7, the astronomical work of Al-Bitruji (Alpetragius) in a Latin version *on the Sphere* was introduced into the West through Michael Scot. The controversy between Ptolemy and Aristotle, began in Greece and continued in Spain, now raised doubt as `to the unassailability of the system of the *Almagest* in the minds of the Latin Scholastics as well.'[2300] The first author in whom the influence of Al-Bitruji makes itself felt was William of Auvergne, who endorsed his system in his encyclopaedic work *De Universo.*[2301] Likewise, Buridan (14th century) was also acquainted with the work of al-Bitruji, which may have set him thinking about the difficulties of the Ptolemaic theories, for instance, with regard to the epicycles and eccentrics.[2302]

2294 G.Saliba: Critiques of Ptolemaic astronomy in Islamic Spain; in *Al-Qantara*, Vol 20, 1999; pp 3-25.
-A.I. Sabra: The Andalusian Revolt against Ptolemaic astronomy: Averroes and al-Bitruji; in E. Mendelsohn *Transformation and Tradition in the sciences*; Cambridge University Press; 1984; pp. 133-53.
L. Gauthier: Une reforme du systeme astronomique de Ptolemee tentee par les philosophes arabes du xii em siecle; *Journal asiatique*; 10em serie; Vol XIV; 1909; pp 483-510.

2295 G. Sarton: Introduction; op cit; Volume III. p.114.

2296 R. Morelon: Eastern Arabic Astronomy, op cit; p. 24.

2297 G. Sarton: Introduction; op cit; vol ii; p. 295.

2298 Ibid. p.16.

2299 Ibid.

2300 E. J. Dijksterhuis: *The Mechanisation of the world Picture*; trans C. Dikshoorn; Oxford at The Clarendon Press; 1961; p. 212.

2301 *Ibid.*

2302 G. Sarton: Introduction; Volume III. p.544.

Onto matters pertaining to the geocentric and heliocentric theories of earth, theories which Draper defines:

`by geocentric theory is meant that doctrine which asserts the earth to be the immovable centre of the universe; by heliocentric theory that which demonstrates the sun to be the centre of our planetary system, implying, as a necessary influence, that the earth is a very small and subordinate body revolving round the sun.'[2303]

The question whether the earth was at rest or not was not discussed in Europe: the earth was assumed to be at rest in the centre of the world.[2304] But in Islam, according to al-Biruni, his contemporary, the astronomer al-Sijzi, had conceived and built an astrolabe based upon the hypothesis of the earth rotation.[2305] And at least three Muslim astronomers discussed the question in the second half of the 13th century: al-Khatibi; Qutb al-Din al-Shirazi, and Abu-l-Faraj. All considered the possibility of a daily rotation. These theories together with the persistent criticism of Ptolemaic astronomy (by Jabir Ibn Aflah and Al-Bitruji, above all) helped prepare the Copernican reform of 1543.[2306]

The heliocentric theory made its way through Western Christendom slowly and dangerously, though. It was Bruno, who contributed largely to its introduction into England. He was the author of a work on the plurality of Worlds, and of the conception that every star is a sun, having opaque planets revolving around it-a conception to which the Copernican system suggestively leads to.[2307]Driven from England, France, and Germany in succession, he ventured in his extremity to return to Italy, and was arrested in Venice, where he was condemned, and burnt in Rome, on February 16, 1600.[2308]

A significant innovation was the `Gestalt switch' proposed by Copernicus: the heliocentric hypothesis that the sun rather than the earth was the stationary member of our planetary system.[2309] His borrowing from the Muslims in this respect has already been considered in the first part, but more on this is told by Isaievych and Korolec as follows.[2310]

[2303] J.W. Draper: History; op cit; Vol II; p.254
[2304] G. Sarton: Introduction, op cit; Vol II, p.46.
[2305] A. Djebbar: Une Histoire de la Science Arabe; op cit; p.74.
[2306] G. Sarton: Introduction, op cit; Vol II, p.46.
[2307] J.W. Draper: A History; op cit; Vol II; pp.257-8.
[2308] Ibid.
[2309] I. Grattan-Guiness: *The Fontana History of the Mathematical Sciences*, Fontana Press, 1997. p. 199.
[2310] I. Isaievych: George Drohobych's astronomical treatises and their Arabic sources; in The Introduction of Arabic philosophy; op cit; pp. 59-64;

Islamic astronomy entered the university of Cracow, the lectures given there relying principally on Abu Ma'Shar, Al-Qabisi, Ali Ibn Rijal (Abenrajel) of Qayrawan, Al-Kindi, Masha'Alllah, Thabit Ibn Qurra, Al-Battani, Al-Zarqali, Al-Farabi; Al-Farghani; Jabir Ibn Aflah; and Ibn Rushd.[2311] Al-Qabisi's *al-madkhal ila Sina'at Ahkam al-Nujum)* (Introduction to the science of the stars), which was translated into Latin by Johannes Hispalensis, and Abu Ma'shar's *De revolutionibus* and *Liber florum,* influenced greatly Drohobych, who first lectured in Bologna, before moving on to Cracow. There Copernicus was a student (in 1491-94). Copernicus had already studied astronomy before he even reached Cracow under another colleague of Drohobych (Nicolas Abstemius).[2312] Korolec follows minutely this line of transmission, naming masters and their teachings based on Islamic authors, until ending with Copernicus.[2313] It is one such master Adalbert de Brudzewo who taught Copernicus the critical approach to the system of epicycle.[2314]Other Islamic influences on Copernicus' study of the planets[2315]are also explained by Korolec.[2316] Copernicus, here basing his knowledge on al-Battani, says:

`In comparison with the sun, other planets are smaller bodies; that even if it is larger than Mercury, Venus can just about cover the one hundredth of a part of the Sun's diameter, as is explained by the Arab Albategnius, who considers that the Sun's diameter is ten time larger, and this is why it is easier to perceive a so little dot in the background of even the strongest light.'[2317]

Modern observatories have also been strongly influenced by Islam as summed up by Sayili:

-The observatory as an organised and specialised institution was born in Islam.

-It went through very important stages of evolution within Islam itself.

-It passed on in a rather highly developed state to Europe, and this was followed, shortly afterwards, by the creation of the modern observatories of Europe, in an unbroken process of evolution superposing upon the traditions borrowed from eastern Islam.[2318]

J. Korolec: la Premiere Reception; op cit;

[2311] J. Korolec: La Premiere; op cit; pp. 116-21. and also p. 129.

[2312] I. Isaievych: George Drohobych's astronomical treatises: pp 60-3.

[2313] Markowski: Powstanie; pp. 103-4 in J. Korolec: La Premiere; op cit; pp.112-21.

[2314] Ibid. p.121.

[2315] J. Korolec: La Premiere; op cit; p.121-2.

[2316] See also A. Brikenmajer: Mikolaj Kepernik, *O obtrotach* Warsawa; 1974.

[2317] Brikenmajer; in J. Korolec: la Premiere; op cit; p. 123.

[2318] A. Sayili: The Observatory in Islam; op cit; p.391.

Garaudy, likewise, notes that the Islamic observatories of Maragha and then Samarkand were to become the models for those of Tycho Brahe and Kepler.[2319] The Samarkand observatory (15th century), most particularly, seems to represent the high-water mark of Islamic achievement in this field of activity, and it is also probable that it constituted the most important link between Islam and Europe in the transmission of the tradition of founding observatories.[2320] There was not only parallelism and similarity between the essential features of the observatories of medieval Islam and those of modern Europe, Sayili points out, but, as the comparisons with the Samarkand Observatory indicate, there is also evidence that there was actual continuity between them, i.e, that apparently the early modern observatories of Europe grew more or less directly out of the observatories of late medieval Islam.[2321]

As far as the matter of the size of the earth is concerned, Fernel, physician to Henry II of France, supported by Magellan's voyage, had ventured so far as to measure in 1527 the size of the earth, his method being to observe the height of the pole at Paris, then to proceed northward until its elevation was increased exactly one degree, and to ascertain the distance between the stations by the number of revolutions of his carriage wheel.[2322] He concluded that it is 24, 480 Italian miles round the globe; nearly the same result as that made by the astronomers at Al-Mamun court seven hundred years previously on the shore of the Red Sea.[2323]

With respect to the subject of global time system, several methods of synchronizing different local time systems were undertaken. One is to locate one place with respect to another by survey and calculating the relation between their time bases by using the geometry of the earth. This method was used probably until around 1750; the event that was most used during the greater part of this period was the lunar eclipse. Al-Biruni gives several examples of time synchronization by means of lunar eclipses around the year 1000, in which the average error is about 6 or 7 minutes.[2324] How, and whether, Al-Biruni influenced subsequent

2319 R. Garaudy: *Comment l'Homme devint Humain*, Editions J.A, 1978. p.208.
2320 A. Sayili: The Observatory in Islam; op cit; p. 259:
2321 Ibid; p.345.
2322 J.W. Draper: A History; op cit; Vol II; p.255.
2323 Ibid.
2324 Al-Biruni: *Kitab tahdid nihayat al-Amakin*... English version: The determination of the coordinates of positions... By J. Ali; American University Press; Beirut; 1967; in R.R. Newton: The application of ancient astronomy to the study of time: in *ENDEAVOUR*;33; pp 34-9.at p.35.

works is difficult to answer here, this being one of the so many matters whereby similar findings are made in different places, but centuries apart, and where the impact of the Islamic source has not been studied, or was, but remains locked in some writing this author was unable to unearth or come across.

c. Optics:

Before summing up the Islamic impact on the Christian West in relation to this science, first and foremost, need to be outlined succinctly the decisive transformations accomplished by Islamic scholarship in the field.

Al-Kindi, followed by Ibn al-Haytham, fundamentally altered Greek theories of vision, Ibn al-Haytham demonstrating that the rays of light do not issue forth from the eye, and impinge on external things, but instead the rays of light come from external objects to the eye.[2325] `Light,' according to Ibn al-Haytham, is emitted from every self luminous source. It is `a primary emission;' but there is also secondary emission from `accidental source,' emitted `in the form of a sphere' (that is in all directions.) Both lights travel in straight lines (as al-Kindi had pointed out before Ibn al-Haytham) but the secondary would be weaker (the principle of secondary wavelets was to be proposed six centuries later by the Dutch Christiaan Huygens.)[2326] In discussing his reflection at polished surfaces, Ibn al-Haytham claimed that such a surface did not absorb light, but reflected it straight back.[2327]

Ibn Al-Haytham's merit, according to Lindberg, is no just in explaining the principal facts of visual perception, he also managed to establish the intromission theory of vision beyond all doubts and dispute for good.[2328] He `fundamentally' altered the aims and scope of the optical theory, and also managed to integrate into his theory anatomical and physiological claims of the medical theory; thus, as Lindberg notes, he was able `to draw together the mathematical, physical and medical traditions into a single comprehensive theory.... He created a new optical tradition and

---

[2325] See:
D.C. Lindberg: *Studies in the History of Medieval Optic*; London, variorum; 1983.
D.C. Lindberg, *Theories of Vision from Al Kindi to Kepler*, Chicago and London, 1976.

[2326] C. Ronan: The Arabian Science; in *The Cambridge Illustrated History of the World's science*; Cambridge University Press; 1983; pp. 201-44. p 228.

[2327] Ibid.

[2328] D.C. Lindberg: Sciences of Optics, op cit, pp 347-9.

established the aims and criteria of optics which would prevail, though not without rivals, until Kepler and beyond.'[2329]

Ibn al-Haytham's greater merit was that his findings do not depend as Draper puts it `upon mere hypothesis or supposition,' but are based `upon anatomical investigation as well as on the geometrical discussion.'[2330]He determined that the retina is the seat of vision, and that impressions made by light upon it are conveyed along the optic nerve to the brain.[2331] Experiment also allowed him to investigate amongst others the reflection of light from concave mirrors.[2332] Further achievements of Ibn al-Haytham include developing precision instruments, expounding for the first time the use of the camera obscura, and writing treatises on the halo and rainbow.[2333]

Following Ibn al-Haytham, a mass of interest fell on optics in the period 1250-1350, witness the works of Roger Bacon, John Peckham, Witelo, John of Paris, Dietrich of Freiberg, and Levi ben Gerson.[2334] How shall we account for such ubiquitous and simultaneous efflorescence? Sarton asks. The explanation is that all these scholars were drinking from the same source, which became available to them (or which they were ready to use) at about the same time.[2335] That source was the *Kitab al-Manazir* of Ibn al-Haytham known to the Latin public as *Opticae thesaurus Alhazani (*translated into Latin by Gerard of Cremona*)*, which must be listed among `the leading classics, for it influenced scientific thought for at least six centuries.'[2336] Hill states `unquestionably, the most important work on physics to reach the West in medieval times'.[2337] The Latin translation of his work remained the standard optical textbook in Western Europe until the 17th century.[2338]

The Kitab al-Manazir includes discussion of such a medley of topics as the structure of the eye, optical illusions, perspective, binocular vision, vision of outlines, shadows, and colours, the ancient catoptrics and dioptrics with new developments, atmospheric refraction, length of

---

[2329] Ibid. p. 349.
[2330] J.W. Draper: History; op cit; Vol II p.45.
[2331] Ibid.
[2332] O. Pedersen: Early Physics; op cit; p.163.
[2333] D.R. Hill, Islamic Science, op cit, pp. 73-4.
[2334] G. Sarton: Introduction; op cit Volume III. p.141.
[2335] Ibid.
[2336] Ibid.
[2337] D.R. Hill, Islamic Science, op cit, p. 224.
[2338] F. Sherwood Taylor: *A Short History of Science*; William Heinemann Ltd, London, 1939.p.82.

twilight and height of the atmosphere, apparent increase of size of the moon near the horizon, camera obscura, mirages, comets, the Milky way, rainbows, halos, etc.[2339] That is, it dealt with questions which would be now classified in at least seven different compartments, anatomy, physiology, psychology, mathematics, astronomy, physics, meteorology.[2340] The Christian, Jewish, and Muslim commentators on the Kitab were, thus, induced to discuss all these topics, and did so in various measure according to their own inclinations.[2341]

One of the matters Ibn al-Haytham studied was lenses.[2342] His explanation of the use of the retina and lens was the first truly scientific investigation in physiology.[2343]Lenses were unknown in antiquity but there are ancient references to the magnifying powers of glass globes.[2344] These have been recovered from medieval sites and were probably used as burning glasses for making fire.[2345]But it was from the properties of convex lenses from the Latin version of Ibn al-Haytham Kitab[2346] that Grosseteste developed his theory of the formation of the rainbow.[2347]After him, Roger Bacon continued his work. He judged the speed of light to be very high, comparing it to the sound of the cannon, which is heard long after the smoke is seen, and he refined the explanation of the rainbow.[2348] Using the works of Ibn al-Haytham and al-Kindi on lenses, he gave a geometrical description of the rainbow's position in the sky understanding it to be composed of a multiple of droplets.[2349] Witelo, too, looked at the phenomenon of refraction, stressed its role, in addition to reflection in the production of the rainbow arc and colours.[2350] Witelo had in his hands most of the optical pieces necessary to resolve the rainbow mystery.[2351]In establishing, thanks to careful experimental work, precise tables of refraction between different media for the different colours, he provided a precious tool for the construction of optical instruments.[2352]

[2339] G. Sarton: Introduction. Op cit; Volume III. p.141.
[2340] Ibid.
[2341] Ibid.
[2342] F. Sherwood Taylor: A Short History; p.82.
[2343] J.W. Draper: History; op cit; Vol II; p.380.
[2344] C. Singer: Short History of Scientific Ideas; op cit; p. 180.
[2345] Ibid.
[2346] At pp 170 and 152.
[2347] C. Singer: Short History of Scientific Ideas; op cit; p. 180.
[2348] M. Authier: Refraction and Cartesian `forgetfulness' in A history of Scientific Thought; M. Serres ed; op cit; pp 315-343; p.328.
[2349] Ibid.
[2350] S. Devons: Optics; op cit; p. 215.
[2351] Ibid.
[2352] M. Authier: Refraction and Cartesian `forgetfulness; op cit; p.328.

The mathematical laws of optical reflection and refraction in glass and other media were thoroughly investigated and extended by Ibn al-Haytham.[2353] He knew how to use spherical glass segments to magnify objects and was familiar with spherical aberrations and techniques to calculate the focal lengths of lenses and mirrors.[2354] Much of this knowledge was subsequently transmitted to Europe through Latin editions of his work, and especially through the texts of his Polish disciple, Witelo, and through Bacon as well.[2355]

Al-Shirazi and al-Farizi pursued the work by Ibn al-Haytham.[2356] `Qutb al-Din al-Shirazi (d. A.D 1311) was able to explain the rainbow in correct terms. He said that the rainbow `is caused by the sun's rays falling on tiny drops of water which are in the air when rain is falling, and which bring about an inner refraction of the rays and this is then passed outwards to the eye of the spectator.'[2357] Al-Farizi continued his predecessor's work on the camera obscura (later to be taken up by Leonardo da Vinci), and he put forward an explanation for refraction, suggesting that the speed of light was proportional to the density of the medium.[2358]The experiment carried out in 1849 by Jean Foucault and Hyppolyte Fizeau shows that the speed of light is proportional to the refractive index of the medium, as suggested by Huygens, finally closing a problem inaugurated centuries before by Ibn al-Haytham, and pursued by others.[2359]

Finally, Stilman refers to Jacob Bronowski, who has popularised the rise of Western technical civilisation, and who felt, that the borrowing of Islamic optics was perhaps the most important technical finding that Europe took from Islam, because the taking of optics allowed the ability to handle perspective, which gave rise to the whole Italian Renaissance.[2360]

[2353] J.A. Smith: Telescope: Encyclopaedia (Selin ed); op cit; pp. 953-4: p. 954
[2354] Ibid.
[2355] Ibid.
[2356] M. Authier: Refraction and Cartesian `forgetfulness'; op cit; p.328.
[2357] O.A. Farukh: *The Arab Genius in Science and Philosophy*; American Council of Learned Societies, Washington, D.C, 1954.p.67
[2358] M. Authier: Refraction and Cartesian `forgetfulness'; op cit; p.328.
[2359] Ibid. p. 343.
[2360] Stilman in discussion In Islam and the medieval West; K. I. Semaan; ed; op cit; pp. 152-3.

2. Medicine and Medical Sciences:

Many aspects of Islamic influence on the development of Western medical sciences have already been seen. Thus, here, it will be matters not much explored, such as pharmacy and surgery, which will receive more interest. The impact of Islamic medicine in Italy will also be looked at so as to highlight how Islamic learning evolved in certain parts of Europe, and how Islamic medicine was diffused via Italian sources.

a. Surgery:

The beginnings of modern surgery owes principally to Al-Zahrawi (936-1013) of Cordova.[2361] Al-Zahrawi's chapter on surgery from *Kitab al-Tasrif* associates both illustration of instruments, their use for particular operations, and also brings in the author's personal experience.[2362] Most of the instruments were devised and made by him, and for their overwhelming majority, they were new, their introduction and use, thus, constituting vital breakthroughs in the history of the science.[2363] Al-Zahrawi's surgical techniques were also revolutionary. For calculus in the urethra, for instance, he introduced the use of a fine drill inserted through the urinary passage.[2364] In order not to frighten patients during the operations, he invented a concealed knife to open abscesses. In the case of tonsillectomies, whilst he held the tongue by a tongue depressor, he removed the swollen tonsil holding it by a hook, and then removed it with a scissor like instrument with transverse blades, which cut the gland, whilst holding it for removal from the throat.[2365] Al-Zahrawi also pioneered the use of instruments made of iron, in opposition to the prejudices of the age, according to which every metal had some special occult property, he instead, argued that iron only ought to be employed.[2366] He attacked the disease with fire and iron,

---

[2361] See: M.S. Spink and G.L. Lewis: *Abulcasis on Surgery and Instruments*; The Wellcome Institute, London, 1973.
[2362] E. Savage-Smith: Medicine, in Encyclopaedia (Rashed ed), op cit, pp. 902-62, at p. 943.
[2363] C. Bouamrane-L. Gardet: *Panorama; op cit;* p. 232.
[2364] E.S. Smith: Medicine, op cit, pp. 945-8.
[2365] Ibid.
[2366] P. Lacroix: Science and Literature; op cit; p.147.

resorting to cauterisation with boldness (which he describes.)[2367] He also practised the difficult operation of bronchotomy, or incision of the windpipe, which modern science resorts to in certain cases.[2368] In gynaecology, he included instructions on training midwives to perform unusual deliveries, ways of extracting dead foetuses, removing the afterbirth, the design and introduction of vaginal dilators, the description of forceps, and the use of caesarean methods. Al-Zahrawi who was both an anatomist and physiologist did not implicitly accept the often contradictory authority of Ibn Sina and Galen, most particularly. He lay down as a principle that medicine and surgery should lend each other mutual assistance.[2369] And as Smith holds he, like other surgeons, displayed a sensible and humane reluctance to undertake the riskiest and most painful operations. He was aware of the discomfort inflicted on patients, which could be seen as a decisive breakthrough in the relationship between the surgeon and the patient.[2370] There is a great deal more on the accomplishments of Al-Zahrawi that can be gleaned from the excellent work by Spink and Lewis.[2371]

The surgical part of *Al-tasrif* by al-Zahrawi was translated into Latin by Gerard of Cremona, and various editions were published in Venice in 1497, Basel in 1541 and Oxford in 1778, and for centuries, it remained the manual of surgery in all early medical universities such as Salerno and Montpellier, whilst the illustrations of his instruments lay the foundations for practical surgery in Europe.[2372]

William of Saliceto (1201-77), Italian surgeon, commonly known as Saliceto or Salicet, and as Placentinus,[2373] expresses, in the words of Campbell, the native Italian renaissance combined with the Islamic teaching that was felt throughout Europe.[2374] It was from his work that Lanfrank the Frenchman borrowed, Guy de Chauliac noting how Lanfrank `wrote a book containing little else than what he got from William but changed the order;' Saliceto's work itself primarily based on al-Zahrawi.[2375]

Guy de Chauliac (1300-68), just named, has been surnamed `The Restorer' because of his having introduced the use of Arabic terms and

[2367] See Spink and Lewis: Abulcasis; op cit.
[2368] P. Lacroix: Science and Literature; op cit; p.147.
[2369] Ibid.
[2370] E. S. Smith: Medicine, op cit, p. 948.
[2371] M.S. Spink and G.L. Lewis: *Abulcasis; op cit.*
[2372] P.K. Hitti: History, op cit, p. 577.
[2373] D. Campbell: Arabian medicine, op cit; p.133.
[2374] Ibid.
[2375] Ibid.

doctrines with increased vigour into the European medical system of thought.[2376] Reading through Guy de Chauliac, just like through Saliceto, reveals the near overwhelming presence of al-Zahrawi in content, form, and methodology. Guy himself succeeded to propagate Islamic surgery through the rest of Europe.[2377] Fifty-two editions of his work were printed in Europe during the 15th and 16th centuries.[2378]

Henry of Mondeville was born in the second half in the 13th century in Normandy, and died sometime after 1335. He studied medicine and surgery in Montpellier, with Lafranchi and Jean Pitart in Paris, and also studied surgery in Italy under the direction of Theodoric Borgognon. Henry, thus, became one of the main links between Italian and French surgery; and thanks to him, and a little later to Chauliac, surgical leadership passed from Italy to France.[2379]His *Chyrurgia* is much more than a compilation, referring mainly to Hypocrates and Galen on the Greek side, but principally on Islamic authors: Ibn Masawih, Ibn Sarabi, Al-Razi, Ali ibn Abbas, Ali ibn Radwan, Ibn Sina, Ibn Rushd, Constantine the African, and of course, Al-Zahrawi.[2380]

As just noted, there are other Islamic sources of influence than Al-Zahrawi. Hence, the eminent Paduan professor Leonardo da Bertapaglia (d. c.1460) known to have practised dissections,[2381]in his *Chirurgia*, presents an arrangement of book iv of Ibn Sina's Canon and an array of Islamic poly-pharmacy and salve surgery based on the *Kullyyat* of Ibn Rushd.[2382]

The Salernitan route, discussed before, is also obvious in Roland of Parma (fl 13th century), whose *Chirurgia rolandina* is an elaboration of Roger of Salerno's *Practica chirurgiae*; and just like its sister is based primarily on Islamic surgery.[2383] The *Rolandina* was translated into Hebrew at least once; one Hebrew text is entitled *Sefer ha-habburot ve ha-negaim* (Book of ulcers and plagues). An extensive commentary on the *Rolandina* and the *practica* (by Roger of Salerno) was made in France in the second half of the 13th by four masters, and entitled *Glossulae quatuor magistrorum super chirurgiam Rogerii et Rolandi*,

---

2376 Ibid. p.176.
2377 Ibid. p.43.
2378 Ibid. p.176.
2379 G. Sarton: Introduction; op cit; Volume III; pp.866-8.
2380 Ibid. p.866.
2381 D. Campbell: Arabian Medicine; op cit; p.171
2382 Ibid. p.171.
2383 G. Sarton: Introduction, op cit; Vol II, p.653.

which shows even stronger Islamic impact than the two works commented upon.[2384]

The association of Islamic surgical sources can be traced in the works of the Englishman, Giles, also known as Gilbertus Anglicus, the author of one of the most influential medical works of the period.[2385] His *Compendium Medicinoe of Laura Anglica* (also called *Lilium* or *laurea medicinae*) follows exactly the Islamic/Salernitan tradition,[2386] but also Ibn Sina, Isaac Judaeus, Ibn Rushd, and often transcribing whole chapters of Al-Razi.[2387] Giles Compendium is divided into seven books: 1) Fevers; 2) diseases of the head, the hair, and nerves; 3) of the eyes and face; 4) of the external members; 5) and 6) internal diseases; 7) genito-urinary diseases, gout, cancer, skin diseases, poisons, etc... The surgical part (fifty chapters) of the compendium follows closely the Chirurgia of Roger of Salerno itself derived from al-Zahrawi's surgery; Gilbert emphasised the importance of the surgical treatment of cancer (as described by al-Zahrawi).[2388]
In the 14th century, Islamic surgery can be traced in England via John of Adern (c.1350), a physician and surgeon who practised the healing art in London during the middle of the century, writing on both medicine and surgery, and first to be reviving the art of surgery in England.[2389] John largely transcribed from Islamic surgeons.[2390]

A Note must be made that the possibilities of anaesthesia by inhalation were known to the physicians of Islam.[2391]Contained in the Arabian Nights, references to anaesthesia by this method was not without its effect on surgery.[2392] Theodoric of Bologna (1206-98), whose name is associated with the `soporific sponge', got his formula from Islamic sources; the sponge was steeped in aromatics and soporifics and dried, and when required for use it was moistened and applied to the mouth

---

[2384] Ibid.
[2385] Derived from G. Sarton: Introduction, Vol II, pp. 520 and 658; and J.Freind: Hist of Physick, Pt ii, pp 268-269, and footnote a.
[2386] See:
C. Burnett and D. Jacquard: Constantine the African; op cit.
M. Mc Vaugh, `Constantine the African,' *Dictionary of Scientific Biography*, vol 3: pp. 393-5.
[2387] J. Freind: History of Physick, Pt ii, pp 268-269, and footnote a.
[2388] G. Sarton: Introduction, op cit; Vol II, pp. 520 and 658.
[2389] J. Freind: The History of physick, p. ii. p. 325.
[2390] Ibid. p. 329.
[2391] T. Puschmann: *History of Medical Education*, op cit; p. 145.
[2392] D. Campbell: Arabian Medicine, op cit; p.56.

and nostrils.[2393] The `soporific sponge' of the Muslims, Campbell points out, was one of the causes of their surgery tending to rise above the level of the travelling mountebank, while on the other hand, the surgery of contemporary Latin Europe, i.e. before the time of Theodoric, tended to fall into the hands of uncultivated charlatans.[2394]

b. Pharmacy:

The Muslim influence in pharmacy, as with other sciences, goes back mainly to the 12th century. This infiltration is seen in the *Lapidary*, or *Liper lapidum*, of Marmod of Anjou (1123), and in the poem on the use of herbs entitled *Macer Floridus,*[2395] attributed to Odo of Meune (d.1161).[2396]

Beginning in the 12th century, this Islamic influence remained strong for centuries.[2397]Many influential Latin works of the `Renaissance' and thereafter are just compilations and slightly altered works of previous Muslim treatises on the subject. Belonging to these is Johannes of St Awand *Expositio Supra Nicolai Antidotarium* written in 1250 and published in Venice in 1495, 1599 and 1602; and *Conciliator and De Venenorum remediis* by Peter Albano (professor in Padua from 1306 to 1316), repeatedly printed thereafter, both based to large extents on Ibn Rushd and Al-Maradini.[2398] An important work on pharmacy in the modern sense, as Levey holds, much influenced by the works of Ibn Sina, Ibn Saraby, Al-Zahrawi and Ibn Masawaih in form and content was *Compendium aromatariorum* written by Saladin of Ascolo, a well known physician of the 15th century.[2399] Divided into seven parts, this work follows exactly Muslim categorisation of subjects: examination of the pharmacist, the qualities desired for the pharmacist, substitute drugs,

---

[2393] Ibid.

[2394] Ibid.

[2395] Note four on page 117 D. Campbell: Arabian medicine: The compilation *Macer Floridus*, which was frequently translated, describes the therapeutics of some 77 simples, was also known as *De virtutibus herbarum*, and `was the original of the oldest Scandinavian medical writing' F.H. Garrison: *Contributions to the History of medicine,* Library of Congress catalogue, New York, 1966.

[2396] D. Campbell: Arabian Medicine; op cit; p.117

[2397] M. Levey: Early Arabic Pharmacology, op cit, pp 175-6.

[2398] H. Schelenz, Geschichte der Pharmazie, Berlin, 1904, p 329, in M. Levey: Early Arabic, op cit, p 175.

[2399] M. Levey: Early Arabic, op cit, p. 175.

care of simples and compound drugs etc.[2400] Another work that also influenced European pharmacopoeias `greatly' including material from Muslim treatises on simples, substitutes, preservation of drugs, lists of little known drugs, etc, was by Ludovico dal Pozzo Toscanelli, a physician of Florence, authorised by the Florentine College of Physicians, and of which various editions were made.[2401]

The novel ideas and the data of pharmacology, which Muslims contributed to medical Europe, Levey points out, fall mainly into the following categories: 1. Theory of pharmacology; 2. diversity of *materia medica*; 3. proliferation of textual literary models; 4. botanical and other drug experimentation; and 5. purity tests for drugs. [2402] Some Western works addressed a diversity of aspects of pharmaceutical sciences; Simon de Cordo (d.1330), for instance, wrote *Synonyma medicinae*, the first dictionary of drugs and simples showing their Arabic, Greek and Latin synonyms, whilst Jacob de Dondi (1298-1359) also wrote a similar work (*Aggregator de medicinis simplicibus*) in which he makes free use of the Arabic terms.[2403]This work in conjunction with the *Synonyma medicinae* of de Cordo and the *Liber Pandectae medicinae* of Mathew Sylvaticus, were the agents through which Islamic medical nomenclature were widely spread through Latin Europe.[2404] Pharmacopoeias in all vernaculars of German, French, English and Spanish also showed Muslim influence.[2405]

Centuries after it first exerted its impact, Islamic pharmacy was still widely adopted. In the late 17th century, was made an edition of the London Dispensatory, in its list of botanicals, simples, minerals, compound drugs for external and internal uses, oils, pills, cataplasms, etc, highlight such Muslim influence.[2406]In the subsequent century, parts of the Latin version of Ibn al-Baytar *Simplicia* were printed in 1758, whilst Ibn Sarabi and Massawih al-Maradini were studied and summarized for the use of European pharmacopoeias until about

---

[2400] Ibid. p. 176.
[2401] Ibid.
[2402] M. Levey: Influence of Arabic Pharmacology on Medieval Europe; in *Convegno Internationale; op cit;* pp. 431-44. p. 432.
[2403] D. Campbell: Arabian medicine, op cit; p.165.
[2404] Ibid.
[2405] R. Folch Andreu: Influensso Italiano sull'evoluzione della farmacia,' raccolta di scritti in onore di Guilio Conci a cura di A.e. Vitolo (Pisa, 1953), pp 167-77, in M. Levey: Early Arabic, op cit, p. 177.
[2406] M. Levey: Early Arabic, op cit, op cit; p. 177.

1830.[2407]Muslim material was, in fact, used until late in the 19th century.[2408] For centuries until the early decades of the 20th, century, as Campbell was writing, the voluminous pharmacopoeias of Europe, with their tables of weights and measures, were largely based on the original Islamic ideas.[2409]One work bearing such an impact was Nicholas Praepositus' *Antidotarium (Parvum)*, which contains about 150 prescriptions arranged in alphabetical order, showing their administration and action, a work based on Islamic *materia medica* with its tables of weights and measures.[2410] This work formed the basis of later pharmacopoeias and was translated into Italian, Arabic, Hebrew, and other languages, and was the standard textbook on *materia medica* for many centuries in Europe, and numerous impressions of it were made.[2411] It is also important to note, Campbell points out, that this work contains the Arabic formula for the soporific sponge, which was used to produce anaesthesia by inhalation; this formula was later mentioned by Theodoric of Bologna who got his knowledge either from Nicolas or directly from Islamic sources.[2412]

Finally, Riddle makes the point that one possible later benefit of Islamic pharmacological theory is cogently argued by M Mc Vaugh, in `Arnal of Villanova and Brawardine's Law,'[2413] that the mathematical skills developed by the pharmacological theorists influenced the Merton College's or Bradwardine's law on motion.[2414]

c. Further Aspects of Healing and Medical Sciences:

First to mention is the study of psychical diseases and the psychical means of combating them as vastly studied by Muslim scientists.[2415] Muslims, for example, carefully studied the effects of music and even introduced its practice in some of their hospitals for therapeutic

---

2407 E. J. Jurji: The Course of Arabic. p. 249.
2408 M. Levey: Early Arabic; op cit; p. 177.
2409 D. Campbell: Arabian medicine, p.136.
2410 Ibid. p.127.
2411 For example, Venet. 1471, 1497, 1532 in D. Campbell: Arabian medicine, p.127.
2412 D. Campbell: Arabian Medicine, p.127.
2413 *ISIS* 58 (1967) pp.56-64.
2414 J.M. Riddle: Theory and Practice in Medieval Medicine: *Viator*: 5:pp 157-84; note 70; p. 174.
2415 G. Ziboorg: *A History of Medical Psychology,* W.W. Norton & Co., New York, 1941, p. 123.

purposes.[2416] It was also Al-Razi who set up an exclusive ward for the mentally ill in Baghdad. And it was the Muslims, who, as Syed explains, `brought a refreshing spirit of dispassionate clarity into psychiatry.'[2417]And as they were free from `the demonological theories' which were sweeping over the Christian world, they could make clear-cut clinical observations about such diseases.[2418] All these pioneering aspects will be found generalised centuries later in Western Christendom.

Jacquart notes how the *Liber phisionomie* of Michael Scot is the real first treatise on physiognomonie to have been composed in the medieval West.[2419] The principal innovation offered by the *Liber phisionomie* in relation to Greek tradition consists in the central role granted to the notion of complexion. The source used by Michael Scot is the second book of *Ad Almansorem* of Al-Razi.[2420] The main foundation of this second book, often transcribed separately in the manuscripts, is the determination of the complexion of an individual and each of his major organs, a determination, which is crucial in the establishment of a medical diagnosis and in delivering a treatment. The chapters which Michael Scot devotes to the indicative signs of the dominating complexion and humours are the same as in *Ad Almansorem* of Al-Razi, from which it also borrows on the meanings of dreams.[2421] Michael uses this fundamental source whilst making no reference to it as highlighted in many instances by Jacquart.[2422]As for the theme of conception, it is found in two fundamental sources used by Scot, one of them being the *De nativitabus* of Abu Bakr, which Salio of Padua translated at Toledo in 1218 at the time Scot was there.[2423]

2416 On the effects of music as observed by the Muslims see D.B. Macdonald: emotional religion in Islam as affected by music and singing *Journal R. Asiatic Society*, 195-252, 705-748, 1901; 1-28, 1902). H.G. Farmer: History of Arabian music (35, London 1929; *Isis,* 13, 375). On the medical use of music, Ahmed Issa Bey: *Histoire des Biamaristans* (Comptes rendus du Congres international des maladies tropicales, Cairo, 1929; e.g., p. 130; Isis, 14, 535). George Sarton: Introduction to the history of science, Vol II, p. 86.
2417 I.B. Syed: Medicine and Medical Education in Islamic History, in Islamic perspective; op cit; p. 55.
2418 G. Ziboorg: *A History of Medical Psychology,* op cit; p. 123.
2419 D. Jacquart: La Physiognomonie a l'epoque de Frederick II, le Traite de Michel Scot: in Micrologus (Science at the court of Frederick II); op cit; pp19-37.
2420 Ibid. p.22.
2421 Ibid.
2422 Ibid.
2423 Ibid. p.33.

Three traditions: the Greek, the Islamic, and the Western Christian, and how they dealt with a similar matter, are admirably outlined by Glick. According to Galen, the humoral imbalance which constituted illness had to be treated by administering to the patient a drug equal in strength (on a scale of four degrees) but opposite in quality to the imbalanced complexion it was supposed to cure.[2424] The problem with Galenic theory, however, was the fact that the intensive effect of a drug could not be measured quantitatively (which once more proves the lack of practicality of Greek science), and Muslim medical writers further attacked Galen on the grounds that each individual differed in complexion (thereby negating the necessity for a unified theory of pharmacology).[2425] The Muslims formulated precise mathematical relationships between a medicine's weight and its therapeutic value.[2426] Thus al-Kindi, in a treatise translated by Gerard of Cremona under the title *Quia primos*, asserted that the complexion of a compound medicine could be mathematically derived from the qualities and degrees of its component samples, and that there was a geometrical relationship between increasing quantity and degree of effectiveness.[2427]

Al-Kindi's work was conveyed to Christian physicians by Arnald of Vilanova following a methodology explained by Mc Vaugh, and taken up by Glick.[2428] Arnald who was conversant in Arabic, and made many translations (already noted,) in his treatise *Aphorismi de gradibus*, accepted al-Kindi's views on the relationship between quantity and degree in formulating dosages.[2429] He moulded these together with Ibn Rushd's notion of prime quantities, and with ideas on the role of fermentation (chemical reaction) in confecting a compound medicine from a mixture developed earlier by Peter of Spain and John of St. Armand, in order to form a unified theory of pharmaceutical action.[2430] McVaugh explains that Arnald's creativity lay not only in the pharmacological synthesis that he was able to achieve but also in the fact that he was able to make these notions intelligible to the Christian scientific community by locating them within a philosophical context relevant to dominant Western interests.[2431]

[2424] T. Glick: Islamic and Christian Spain; op cit; pp. 271-2.

[2425] Ibid. pp. 272.

[2426] Ibid.

[2427] Ibid.

[2428] Arnald of Vilanova, *Aphorismi de gradibus*, Michael R. McVaugh, ed. (Granada-Barcelona: Seminario de Historia de la Medicina, 1975), pp. 4, 22, 36-38, 56-57, 78, 81, 82, 86, 87, 91-92, 105. in T. Glick: Islamic and Christian Spain; op cit; pp. 272-3.

[2429] T. Glick: Islamic and Christian Spain; op cit; pp. 272.

[2430] Ibid.

[2431] Ibid.

d. Islamic Medicine in Italy and via Italy:

Highlighting the Italian role in medical impact serves to put emphasis on four crucial points constantly reiterated in this work:
-First, Western Christian medicine, just as all other sciences that erupted in the medieval times, bears profound and formative Islamic substance and content.
-Second, everywhere science and learning appeared in Western Christendom, they owed to agents in contact with Islamic learning.
-Third, whichever part of Western Christendom that came into contact with Islam with regard to a particular science, soon thrived in this particular science before the rest.
-Fourth, any change that occurred in Western Christendom, happened not as a result of coincidence, or recovery of something local, or ancient, but precisely soon after contact was made with Islam.

Beginning with the first point, and with Bruno da Longoburgo who flourished c.1252 at Padua, but was educated in Salerno. His main surgical work, the *Chirurgia magna,* was divided into two books each containing 20 chapters. Book I deals with wounds, fractures, luxations; ulcers; healing etc. Whilst Book II deals with eye diseases, polyps in the nose, affections of the lips, mouth, and gullet, dentistry, earache, erysipelas, oedemata, cancer, bubo, dropsy, herniae, castration, warts, haemorrhoids, stones and lithotomy, etc. Both books are written and organised on the Islamic model, and in content they are derived mainly from Islamic authors: Al-Razi, Hunain Ibn Ishaq, Yahia ibn Safyun, Al-Zahrawi, Ali ibn Abbas, Ibn Sina, Ibn Rushd, and Constantine the African. The impact of al-Zahrawi is particularly felt in surgery, especially his method of dry process of wound healing (against the traditional festering process).[2432]
In anatomy, Mondino de' Luzzi's (c.1275-1326) knowledge of anatomy is almost exclusively obtained through Islamic channels, that is, through Latin translation of Islamic works, which explains the confusion of his terminology and the number of Arabic or Arabicised terms which it contains; many such terms henceforth popularised by him.[2433]Guido da

---

[2432] G. Sarton: Introduction, op cit; Vol II, p. 1077.
[2433] Ibid. Volume III; p.843.

Vigevano (c.1280-after 1345) of Pavia's description of the veins and arteries is based largely on Ibn Sina.[2434]

With regard to general medicine, when Robert, king of Naples from 1309 to 1343, desiring to have all the un-translated Islamic works rendered into Latin and explained, he urged Dino del Garbo to write two great volumes of commentaries, one on medicine and one on surgery; hence Dino's treatise: *The Super IV fen primi canonis Avicenna.*[2435] Gentile da Foligno (d.1348) from near Perugia was very well read and may be assumed to have been acquainted with most of the medical writings available in Latin. His sources are besides Galen, Al-Razi, Ali Ibn Abbas, Ibn Sina, and Ibn Zuhr.[2436]

With regard to the second point, that is the agents of diffusion, here is seen the contribution of Gilles of Corbeil, the poet physician, (c. 1140-c.1224). His arrival from Salerno, after a short stay en route at Montpellier towards the end of the 12th century in Paris was to lead to an improvement in the study of medicine in the French capital.[2437] Gilles has long been considered as the founder and originator of medical studies in Paris; and that, in bringing advanced Salernitan medicine to Paris, he must have given a new impulse to such studies, and helped to lay the foundation for the revival of science and medicine that took place there much later in the next century.[2438]

Thirdly, the geographical/regional element. As Erbstosser notes, just like the great universities of southern France, Montpellier principally, Italian universities were not only in the vicinity of Spain and southern Italy but were also the traditional centres of the crusades and the trade with the Orient.[2439]Many Italian practitioners took part as personal physicians to kings and princes in the crusades of the 13th century and used the opportunity to extent their knowledge.[2440]Amongst these was Huggo of Lucca, also known as Hugo of Bologna, a member of a noble family who took part as a physician in a crusade in 1218. Returning in 1221, he was appointed municipal surgeon in Bologna and set up a surgical school there, introducing a series of practical innovations.[2441]

[2434] Ibid. p.846.
[2435] Ibid. p.837.
[2436] Ibid. p.849.
[2437] B. Lawn: The Salernitan questions; op cit; p. 69.
[2438] Ibid.
[2439] M. Erbstosser: *The Crusades;* op cit; p. 188.
[2440] Ibid.
[2441] Ibid.

His son, a priest, was the author of a four volume teaching manual on surgery.[2442]

Finally, the timing factor (as well as all previous three points) is found at work in the matter considered here: the lesser circulation of the blood and the role of Ibn al-Nafis in its discovery. Ibn al-Nafis made this discovery before 1288, refuting Galen's theory of circulation fundamentally, [2443] and anticipating the Spaniard Miguel Servet (1511-53) by more than 265 years.[2444] Unlike Servet, who hid his discovery in a theological treatise, Sarton notes, Ibn al-Nafis published his right where it belonged, in a commentary on Ibn Sina's anatomy, where it was perfectly proper to discuss the pulmonary vessels.[2445] It would seem there is little or no link between Ibn al-Nafis, and other Western doctors who made similar discovery centuries later, not just Servet, but also others: Realdo Colombo (1510-1559), Carlo Ruini, Andrea Cesalpino, Francois Rabelais,[2446]and William Harvey. Looking at Ibn al-Nafis' work and the others' will, first, show stunning similarities, Mieli, for instance, noting how Ibn al-Nafis' description of lesser circulation reminds strangely of that of Servet (word by word).[2447] Many modern historians claim these are purely accidental similarities. Possibly, until one comes across the other pattern observed with regard to every single other transformation that occurred in Western Christendom, which is timing, that it is precisely at the time Ibn Al-Nafis became known to the Western Christians, that suddenly took place such burst of discoveries of the blood circulation. Indeed, this happened precisely years after the Italian, Alpago, brought to Western knowledge the work of Ibn al-Nafis. Andrea Alpago of Belluno (Veneto) (born c.1440) spent some thirty years in the Near East residing for a long time (c.1487 ff) in Damascus where he was physician to the Venetian colony,[2448]and from where, by a strange coincidence, Ibn al-Nafis comes from.[2449]Alpago obtained a fluent knowledge of Arabic and translated various Islamic books into Latin, including Ibn Sina's canon. He left Damascus in 1517-20, resided a few years at Nicosia, Cyprus, then returned to Italy; teaching medicine

[2442] Ibid.
[2443] A. Whipple: The Role; op cit; pp. 47-8.
[2444] G. Sarton: Introduction; op cit; Volume III; p. 267.
[2445] *Christianismi restitutio*, Vienne, Dauphine 1553.
[2446] M. Meyerhof: Ibn Nafis; op cit.
[2447] Aldo Mieli: *La Science Arabe; op cit;* pp. 164-6.
[2448] G. Sarton: The Appreciation of Ancient and Medieval Science; op cit; p.43.
[2449] A K Chehade, *Ibn-al-Nafis, et la Découverte de la circulation Pulmonaire,* Damascus, 1955.

at Padua.[2450] He added to his translation of the Canon an elaborate Arabic-Latin glossary, which was edited by his nephew, Paolo Alpago, who had been with him in the Near East.[2451]Micheau points out that Andrea, who was in Damascus was fully aware of the latter's criticism of Galen's theory on blood circulation, to which he refers in his translation.[2452] He also, Micheau adds, transmitted his knowledge of this orally; and both he and his nephew communicated Ibn al-Nafis' theory to both Venetians and Paduans.[2453] It was, and precisely, only following the translation from Ibn al-Nafis into Latin that the new ideas on the subject of blood circulation, suddenly, made their appearance in Europe.[2454]Had Western discoverers of blood circulation, Servet, Harvey, etc, seized on Galen, who lived over fifteen centuries before, as modern Western historians claim, such discovery would have made its appearance in the West centuries before, and not precisely soon after Ibn al-Nafis was translated into Latin. Which, also, serves to reinforce the trend observed already in other matters of timing of medical breakthroughs:

-First, Salerno rose to fame in the late 11th-early 12th century, precisely following Constantine's translations.

-Second, 12th-13th century medical changes elsewhere followed precisely the translations of Islamic learning.

-Third, the development of many aspects of war surgery in Western Christendom followed precisely the return of crusader/surgeons from the East, and such developments took place precisely in parts of Western Christendom where such surgeons returned.

-Fourth, the discovery of blood circulation followed precisely the translation of Ibn al-Nafis in the 16th century.

Thus, the same pattern is obvious at different points of history in different places. Once is a coincidence, every time is a pattern. And had it been, a Greek or any other local influence which operated, it would not have followed the pattern, i.e revival of a particular subject, in a particular place, at precisely the time the Islamic factor enters play, and according to an Islamic substance. And Ibn Nafis' instance also shows clearly that it is not the Greek element within Islamic science which impacted on the Christian West, but quite the reverse, for Ibn al-Nafis built his theory in an attack on the Greek authority: Galen.[2455]

2450 G. Sarton: The Appreciation of Ancient and Medieval Science; op cit; p.43.
2451 Ibid.
2452 F. Micheau: La Transmission; op cit; pp. 417-8.
2453 Ibid
2454 Brunet; Mieli.... in A. Sayili: The Observatory in Islam; op cit; p.382.
2455 A. Whipple: The Role; op cit; pp. 47-8.

3. Nautical Sciences and Geography:

Until the 17th century or so, the Christian West and the Islamic world were somewhat equal in power. It was the new discoveries overseas, and most of all, the exploitation of the new lands that were to give Western Christendom the upper hand. Although it was a Spaniard, or more properly a Spanish venture that first led to the discovery of America, soon, in the late 16th-early 17th, the English took over; Spain, gradually eliminated from the north exerted its influence from Mexico further down the American southern continent. The impact of the settlement of those new lands by people of European stock meant that the culture and civilisation of Western Christendom now stretched over two continents (America, Europe,) and subsequently Oceania. The settlements of the new continents by the Europeans also absorbed excess numbers of Europeans, and the new continents stimulated the growth of both European industry and trade. Hence the great role of maritime explorations and discoveries, which hardly benefited the Muslims whilst they contributed considerably to them. It is this Islamic impact on nautical sciences and maritime discoveries, which is looked at here.

a. Nautical Sciences and Maritime Discoveries:

Although the great discoveries took place in the so called Modern Times (late 15th century onwards), the sources of such discoveries go to the Middle Ages, and by chance, again, principally to the 12th century. This medieval origin is raised by Balmer who notes that the development of the movable sail, the steering rudder, the compass (magnetic needle) and the spy glass (telescope), all come together between the 10th and 13th centuries to provide men with control over the seas.[2456] Gauthier Dalche also points out how by the 13th century, the Christian world found itself in an excellent place of observation to analyse geographical knowledge, mainly thanks to the translation of Islamic works, and the appearance of new tools: compass, portolans and nautical maps, and also via contacts with the Holy Land.[2457] Wright, for

---

[2456] R.T. Balmer: The Invention of the Sand Clock: *ENDEAVOUR;* 1979 (NS Vol 3):pp 118-122:p.118.

[2457] Patrick Gautier Dalche: Les Savoirs geographiques en Mediterranee Chretienne (XIIIe s).in Micrologus (Science at the court of Frederick II); op cit; pp: 75-99:p.75.

his part, devotes a book showing how the geographical lore necessary for the modern discoveries dates from the crusades time, just as his title says.[2458]

Fundamental breakthroughs in Western shipping also go back to medieval Islamic antecedents. The Muslims constructed lighter sailing ships or caravels; calked their boats with tar (known in Romance languages by the Arabic name: gatran; goudron in French and caltrame in Italian), and showed expertise in the handle sails and cables.[2459]With respect to the rig of ships, the Muslims brought to the Mediterranean the vast experience of their use in the Indian Ocean, which they dominated then.[2460] More importantly, it is in that very ocean where the lateen sail, despite its Western name, was invented.[2461]There are references to lateen sails in Arabic literature of the 9th and 10th centuries.[2462] The Muslims introduced into the Mediterranean the lateen caravel whose advantage was that it could beat against the wind, whilst the other ships could only sail before the wind.[2463]Without the lateen, the European mizzen on the three masters would have been impossible, and the ocean voyages of the great explorers could have never taken place.[2464]In the early 15th century, according to Clowes, northern ships were entirely dependent on a fair wind, and were quite unable, and never attempted, to make headway against an adverse wind; however, just before, 1500, ships had been able to make the long ocean voyages, which had resulted in Columbus' discovery of America, Diaz's doubling of the cape of Good Hope, and the opening of the Indian trade route by Vasco da Gama.[2465] European shipbuilders had adopted and developed the principles of the lateen sail, which made possible the construction of the much larger ships that were capable of crossing the vast oceans, and both Spanish and Portuguese shipwrights laboured to increase the number of mats and sails; whilst further transformations created a sufficient area of sail to propel large ships.[2466] Balmer also notes that with the use of controllable wind power for propulsion there was no longer any need for carrying hundreds of men on board ship as oarsmen, and the space they and their

[2458] J.K. Wright: the Geographical Lore; op cit.
[2459] R. Briffault: The Making, op cit, p. 205.
[2460] W. M. Watt: The Influence, op cit, pp. 19-21.
[2461] Ibid.
[2462] G.F. Hourani: *Arab Seafaring*; Khayats; Beirut; 1963; p. 103.
[2463] W. M. Watt: The Influence, op cit, pp. 19-21.
[2464] G.F. Hourani: *Arab Seafaring*; op cit; p. 104.
[2465] Clowes: Sailing ships; p.54; in G.F. Hourani: Arab; op cit; p. 104.
[2466] W.M. Watt: The Influence, op cit, pp 19-21.

provisions previously occupied could now be used for trading cargo or war materials.[2467]

The mariner's compass is subject to great debate and contention about its origins. The compass, like paper, for that matter, owes very likely to the Chinese in the first place. The first clear reference to the use of the magnetic needle in Chinese navigation appears in a sea manual written around 900 A.D., and, by the 11th and 12th centuries, floating compasses were in common use on Chinese ships.[2468] Abulafia, however, makes the point that whether with respect to the compass or other elements of Chinese origins (paper, some fruit, specialised crops...) it was still due to the Muslims that all or most of this know how arrived in Western Europe, judiciously pointing out `nor would it be easy to prove that around 1300 or even 1400 Western Europeans had much knowledge or understanding of Chinese and Indian culture, Marco Polo notwithstanding.'[2469]On this Chinese line, Watt observes that many stages had to evolve between `discovering the property of a magnetized piece of iron and producing a serviceable instrument for navigation.'[2470] He also rejects the assertion that the compass was invented by Flavio Gioia Amalfi in 1302, observing that there are references to the compass in 1187 and 1206 in Arabic literature in the year 1220, and its use on a voyage between Tripoli and Alexandria in the year 1242.[2471]Hourani, for his part, insists that the magnetic needle is mentioned as being used on Muslim ships trading between Canton-Sumatra and India in the 11th century.[2472] Watt observes that the first use of the compass by Chinese sailors is dated about 1100, but when the Europeans, during the times of Vasco de Gama, came into contact with Chinese mariners, they found them using a compass inferior to theirs, but not the Arabs', who had superior compasses as they found when they came across them in the Indian Ocean.[2473]

The transfer of the magnetic compass to the West must have occurred during the crusades, for it is mentioned for the first time in a French poem of 1190.[2474]The crusader route was obvious with Petrus of

[2467] R.T. Balmer: The Invention; op cit; 118.
[2468] J.Needham, 1960 lecture on `The Chinese Contribution to the Development of the Mariner's compass," reprinted 1970: particularly 243-44).
[2469] D. Abulafia: The Role of Trade in Muslim-Christian Contact during the Middle Ages, in *The Arab Influence on Medieval Europe*; op cit; pp. 1-24, at p. 2.
[2470] W. Montgomery Watt, The Influence, op cit, p. 20.
[2471] M. Watt: The Influence; op cit; p. 21.
[2472] G.F. Hourani: Arab Seafaring; op cit; p. 108.
[2473] M. Watt: The Influence; op cit; pp. 19-20.
[2474] G.F. Hourani: Arab Seafaring; op cit; p. 109.

Maricourt (Petrus Peregrinus), who brought knowledge of magnetism and the compass back to France from the Orient, and in 1269 wrote a treatise about magnetism in which an illustration of a compass appears for the first time.[2475] Thus, Gioia, as Watt concludes, was possibly responsible for some refinements or additions to the instrument; hence whilst the Muslims developed the instrument, the later refinements were the work of the Europeans.[2476]

Islamic accomplishments include the construction of scientific instruments of measurement and calculation such as the astrolabe, the *ruba* (quadrant), the gnomon, the celestial sphere, the sundial (and the compass.)[2477]The flat or planispheric astrolabe was an instrument greatly appreciated and perfected by the Muslims, and used as an aid to navigation up to the end of the 18th century.[2478] Its uses are outlined by Glick:

`The planispheric astrolabe, had on its front a zodiacal circle and a disc designed for a specific geographical latitude, with a stereographic projection of the equator, the tropics and the horizon. From this, various problems of spherical astronomy could be solved, the hour of the day measured, and horoscope cast. The back of the instrument was divided into four quadrants, upon which the declination of the sun with respect to its observed height could be read directly (with the use of a sight or alidade), without the observer having to consult declination tables. This aspect was of immense significance to navigation since the latitude of a place could thereby be determined by the elevation of the sun and vice versa. the quadrant with alidade also became a common surveying instrument.[2479]

The *ruba* was used for measuring the value of angles, whilst the gnomon was also used for measuring altitudes of the sun and other planets.[2480]The use of celestial sphere was to explain celestial movements; the sundial for calculating daily time and the azimuth (compass bearing); the compass for finding direction during navigation.[2481]

[2475] M. Erbstosser: *The Crusades;* op cit; p. 188.

[2476] M. Watt: The Influence; op cit; pp. 19-20.

[2477] A. Buang: Geography in the Islamic world; in Encyclopaedia (Selin ed) pp 354-6: at p.356:

[2478] H.C. King: The Planetorium: *ENDEAVOUR;* Vol 18 (1959) pp 35-44; p.36.

[2479] T.F. Glick: Islamic and Christian Spain; op cit; p.266.

[2480] A. Buang: Geography; op cit; p.356:

[2481] Ibid.

The passage of these instruments to the West has been examined already. Similarly, the Jacob's staff, a popular medieval instrument for determining planar angles, is believed to have reached Europe via Muslim sources, and may have had its origins in navigation methods used by early Muslim traders.[2482] The oldest actual description of this instrument comes from a navigator's manual, *The Mohit*, written by Sidi Ali Chelebi.[2483] Terms of key importance in navigation, such as zenith, azimuth and astrolabe, also betray the European debt to Islamic technology in the field of navigation.[2484]

Portulans (nautical charts) use in nautical science is in giving at once a much more exact image of the position of coasts and islands than all the earlier maps, besides showing in good detail the design of the coastlines.[2485]Historians agree on the difficulties related to the use and handling of cartographic evidence and nautical charts to make definite conclusions, and also agree on the decisive role played by Muslims in this particular field.[2486] Watt, for instance, observes that the nautical charts were developed by the Genoese and others from Islamic cartography.[2487] Kramers notes the exact description of the African coast in the work of al-Idrisi and also his predecessors: Ibn Hawqal and al-Bakri (d. 1094), the experience of the Islamic navigators-reflected in their geographical treatises contributing considerably to the composition of those prototypes of modern cartography, the oldest portulans.[2488] The crossings from one side of the Mediterranean to the other, or from one island to the other, according to meridians or parallels are characterised by their orientation, and their length in miles is hardly new knowledge, having already been found amongst Muslim scholars, notes Vernet.[2489] Sarton, too, explains that the origin of the sailing charts is mysterious, but tends to accept the `reality of Arabic ones' because, he explains, there were already, in the 12th century, and maybe even before,

---

2482 F.J. Swetz: Surveying: Encyclopaedia (Selin ed); op cit; p. 926.
2483 Ibid.
2484 C. Hillenbrand: The Crusades, Islamic Perspectives, op cit;.p.397.
2485 J.H. Kramers: Geography and Commerce; in The Legacy of Islam, 1st ed; op cit; pp 79-107. at p.98.
2486 See:
-D. Abulafia: The Role of trade, op cit, at p. 15.
-Henri Grosset Grange (in Collaboration with H Rouquette): Arabic nautical science, in Encyclopaedia (Rashed ed), op cit, pp 202-42.
2487 M. Watt: The Influence; op cit; p. 21.
2488 J.H. Kramers: Geography and commerce. Op cit; p. 98.
2489 Most particularly al-Bakri: Cf J. Vernet: La navegacion en la alta media, in *Settimane di studio del Centro italiano di studi sull'alto Medieoevo*, XXV, Spolete 1978, 371 ss; re-ed in *Estudios sobre historia de la ciencia medieval*, Barcelona, 1979, 431 ss.

professional pilots (mu'allim, or musta'mil markab) and writers of nautical instructions, like the three `Lions of the sea,' Sahl ibn Aban, Mohammed ibn Shadan, and Laith ibn Kahlan.[2490] Sahl ibn Aban, for instance, was a compiler of sea voyages and route books, who prepared instructions for the captains and pilots sailing to Cathay and the East Indies. He stands here as representative of a class, the members of which are generally as little known as the authors of portolani.[2491] The Islamic pioneering role is further reinforced by two written theses on the beginning of portulans.[2492]

With regard to the passage of such Islamic know how, the usual patterns as with regard to every other breakthrough or science, i.e of timing, regional contact, agents of transmission, substance, etc, are, again, at work. Many maps that might have been used on the high seas, Abulafia explains, bear resemblance to Muslim maps of the 13th century; and map makers such as Abraham and Judah Cresques in 14th century Majorca had access to Muslim geographical sources, as they were Jews who could exploit the close cultural and economic links between both Jewish communities of the Balearic Isles and those of North Africa.[2493] Another Islamic source is explained by De la Ronciere, who notes how the use of coastal charts was destined to become general in Sicily; `a rational method of navigation to be substituted for the routine of pilotage, and thus the way was prepared for the progressive conquest of the world.'[2494]The Genoese learned the arts of navigation from the Sicilians in the early 13th century and transmitted them subsequently to the Spaniards, Portuguese, French, and English; and a new science of the seas was developed upon the foundations originally laid by Sicilian Muslims and Normans.[2495]A further Islamic link is a detailed description of the coasts of the whole of the Mediterranean and the Black Sea and Africa (from Cape Spartel to Anfa), more vaguely of Western Europe, including about 1200 toponyms, compiled towards the end of the 12th century.[2496]The Italian author only gives a biographical source concerning the Bab-Al-Mundeb straight into the Red Sea, he learnt about it from a *garbini*, returning from the Mecca pilgrimage with whom he returned by boat. This author knew Arabic.[2497]

2490 G. Sarton, Introduction, op cit; vol 2; p. 39.
2491 Ibid. p.130.
2492 Consult for more details *Arabica*:Vol 1; pp 375-6.:
2493 D. Abulafia: The Role; op cit, p. 15.
2494 De La Ronciere: Marine Francaise; vol 1; 1909; p. 136 in J.K. Wright: The Geographical Lore; op cit; p. 81.
2495 Ibid.
2496 Patrick Gautier Dalche: Les Savoirs geographiques, in Micrologus; op cit; pp.85-6.
2497 Ibid.

A major route of transmission of Islamic scientific lore, including in the subjects that led to nautical discoveries, came through the 12th century translations from Arabic already examined. Such translations put at the disposal of the West astronomical tables, which are sometimes accompanied by geographical tables.[2498]From Al-Battani's tables Regiomontanus constructed the ephemerides that made possible Columbus' voyage.[2499] In 1135 John of Seville translated Al-Farghani's on the elements of astronomy, a work from which John of Hollywood borrowed much of the materials that he incorporated into his *De Sphaera,* and which thereby was to produce a profound effect on the future development of astronomical geography during the later Middle Ages.[2500]Al-Farghani said there was no difference of opinion among learned men that the universe was a sphere, and like him John of Hollywood admitted the earth was round.[2501] Kramers insists, that the geographical works of Muslim astronomers, which the Christians had translated in Toledo, contributed in the first place to the keeping alive the doctrine of the sphericity of the earth, which had been nearly forgotten in the `Dark Ages'.[2502] All Muslim geographers believed in the sphericity of the earth;[2503]and from the earliest Al-Khwarizmi (d. 863) in his *Surat al-Ard*[2504] (image of the earth) was initiated a new geography, where the world is in the form of a sphere, divided in its northern half, into seven longitudinal bands from the equator.[2505] The idea that the earth was a sphere, and that it was also very small compared to the size of the universe,[2506] inherited from the Muslims, was brought out in 1410 by Pierre d'Aily in his map of the `Imago Mundi.'[2507]This Islamic breakthrough tore down one of the most established views of the time, that the earth was flat, and the spherical shape of the earth also raised the possibility that one end of the world could be reached by sailing in the opposite direction. The impact of this is well known. Without it,

---

[2498] J.H. Kramers: Geography; op cit; pp.93-4.
[2499] R. Briffault: The Making, op cit, p. 202.
[2500] J.K. Wright: The Geographical Lore; op cit; p. 96.
[2501] Ibid. pp.151-2.
[2502] J.H. Kramers: Geography; op cit; pp.93-4.
[2503] Ernst Honigmann: Die sieben Klimata; Heidelberg 1929; *ISIS,* 14, pp. 270-6.
[2504] Al-Khwarizmi: *Surat al-Ard*, Ed. Hans v. Mzik, Leipzig, 1926.
[2505] A. Miquel: Geography, in the Encyclopaedia (Rashed ed), op cit, pp 796-812, at p. 796.
[2506] J.L.E. Dreyer: *A History of Astronomy; op cit;* p. 249.
[2507] A.S. Atiya: *Crusade, Commerce and Culture*; Oxford University Press; 1962: p.228.

Kramers recognises, the discovery of America would have been impossible.[2508]

The doctrine of the habitability of the equatorial regions of the earth, too, came into Europe in the 12th century from Islamic sources, most certainly through the translation of Al-Battani by Robert of Chester.[2509] Inasmuch as Islamic astronomers such as Al-Battani and Al-Zarqali, Sarton notes, were willing enough to accept the habitableness of every climate and to extend it to inaccessible parts of the earth, the more scientific writers such as Petrus Alphonsi, Lambert of st Omer, Robert Grosseteste, and Roger Bacon shared their indulgence, but William of Conches sat on the fence, and Megold of Lautenbach voiced his disapproval.[2510] As late as 1327 belief in Antichthons was a dangerous idea imputed to Cecco d'Ascoli, which led to his execution.[2511]

Back to Kramers and his theory on Columbus's discovery of the New World.[2512] Kramers explains that the discovery owes to the idea that the known hemisphere of the world had a centre or `world summit' which was equally distant from east, west, north, and south, referred to by Al-Battani as the `cupola of the earth' (*Qubbat al Ard* in its Arabic original), whilst Ibn Rusta (fl. 903) refers to it as the `cupola of Arin'. The word Arin itself is a misreading of the Arabic transliteration of the name of an Indian town. Adelard of Bath, Gerard of Cremona, Roger Bacon and Albertus Magnus, considered this arin theory of the highest importance; which was later to be found in the *Imago Mundi* of Cardinal Pierre D'Ailly published in 1410. *Imago Mundi* had convinced Christopher Columbus that the earth was round,[2513]and that, on the western hemisphere, opposite the summit of Arin, was another centre, much higher than the one on the eastern side, thus forming the shape of the lower half of the sphere. This inspired his sailing experience when all around him was against it. What followed his successful attempt is well known.[2514]

[2508] J. H. Kramers: Geography, op cit, p. 93.
[2509] C.H. Haskins: Studies; op cit; P. 64.
[2510] G. Sarton: Introduction. Op cit; Volume III.p.193.
[2511] Ibid.
[2512] J.H. Kramers: Geography, op cit, at pp. 93-4.
[2513] *Larousse Encyclopaedia of Modern History; from 1500 to the Present*; Ed M. Dunan; Paul Hamlyn; London; 1964; p. 32.
[2514] J.H. Kramers: Geography, op cit, at pp. 93-4.

Columbus' role in the discovery of America is hardly a fortuitous, isolated act, detached form previous forms and patterns of impact. Columbus, it must be reminded, is Genoese, and Draper notes how with ruin before them, and unwilling to yield their Eastern connections, the merchants of Genoa had tried to retrieve their affairs by war, but her practical sailors saw that she might be re-established in another way.[2515] There were among them some who were well acquainted with the globular form of the earth, and with what had been done by the Muslims for determining its circumference by the measurement of a degree on the shore of the Red Sea, and with them originated the attempt to reach India by sailing to the west.[2516] The Genoese of Seville and Cadiz were keen to invest in these enterprises, and Andalusian mariners, including many who were to ship with Columbus or who made transatlantic journeys after him, were schooled in Atlantic navigation.[2517] And it is the Genoese, as already seen, who had inherited Islamic knowledge of portulans through both Sicily and the island of Majorca, where they had a commanding presence.

The fact that it was Spain and Portugal, which led in the naval/continental discoveries is no accident of history, either. The Iberian Peninsula was under the direct influence of the Muslims for centuries, and so it directly benefited from Muslim knowledge of seafaring and diverse related sciences.[2518] This Iberian role, although pioneering, is disputed by Western historians, who, as Bensaude notes, defend the view that nautical knowledge and the use of nautical instruments had disappeared in the Peninsula, a knowledge allegedly re-introduced eventually by the 15th century Regiomontanus/Behaim Nuremberg school.[2519] Bensaude, relying on Steinschneider's earlier works, demonstrates the fallacy of such view. The idea that Iberian knowledge of instruments of Islamic origin was lost is false, for Regiomontanus knew of instruments of Iberian origin, such as the

---

[2515] J.W. Draper: History; op cit; Vol II; p.159.
[2516] Ibid.
[2517] F. Fernandez Armesto: Before Columbus: op cit; p. 203.
[2518] See for instance:
J. Bensaude: *L'Astronomie Nautique; op cit.*
-J. Vernet: *Influencias musulmanas en el origen de la cartografia nautica*, publ. de la Real Sociedad Geografica, serie B. No 289, 30 p; Madrid, 1953; *Los conocimientos nauticos de los habitantes del occidente islamico*, extrait de la Revista general de Marina, Madrid, June 1953, 15 p.
R. Briffault: The Making, op cit.
[2519] J. Bensaude: L*'Astronomie Nautique*; pp.30 fwd.

Saphae of Al-Zarqali.[2520]In a treatise by Regiomontanus on this instrument, the name of the inventor (al-Zarqali) is not mentioned, but the name is found in his pupil's work, Shoner.[2521] Regiomontanus knew the Muslim astrolabe, which he had faithfully reproduced.[2522] And there are in Nuremberg a large number of Muslim astrolabes;[2523] one is kept in the library of that city, which belonged to Regiomontanus himself.[2524] There is, more importantly, no reason for all the vestiges of Muslim science and all the treatises on the astrolabe and the quadrant, printed, or known as manuscripts, to be ignored or lost in the very country (the Iberian Peninsula) where they were made.[2525]There is, thus, plenty of evidence to show that contrary to what Western historians write, the knowledge of the Nuremberg school itself directly comes from the Iberian-Islamic heritage. And had it been a purely northern breakthrough, the question to ask should be: why did Regiomontanus not use his discoveries and instruments somewhere in northern Europe: England, France, Venice, etc, and help them make the discoveries that Spain and Portugal were to make?

The decisive role played by the Iberian-Islamic route in modern maritime discoveries is further highlighted by the pioneering role of Portugal's Afro-Asian discoveries, as is going to be seen. In the process, is also refuted the view that Portugal, independently, without any Islamic role, is behind such discoveries.

By the end of the 15th century, as tradition holds, the Portuguese had `discovered' the sea route to India, sailing down the Atlantic coast to Africa and then up the eastern coast to enter the gateway to the all important Indian Ocean, [2526] still under the control (but not for long) of Muslim and Indian fleets.[2527] This was scarcely a `discovery,' as Tibetts explains, for Islamic navigation manuals had charted these waters long before, and the coastline, albeit in the reverse order from east to west, is described in such detail in the manuals that one cannot doubt the prior

---

[2520] Ibid. p.30.

[2521] *Problemata XXIX. Saphaea nobilis instrumenti astronomici ab Joanne de Montegio;* published by Shoner (Nuremberg) 1524.

[2522] fig 1; in J. Bensaude: L'Astronomie; op cit; p. 36.

[2523] Baguette: *Die Bedeutung des Astrolabiums;* Bonn; 1909; p.18.

[2524] Astrolabio della Bibliotheca di Norimberga del Seculo XIII aopparteneva a Reggiomentano. *America da Schio* Di due astrolabii etc, Venezia; 1880; p. 58.

[2525] J.Bensaude: L'Astronomie; op cit; pp. 39-40.

[2526] See C. de Vaux: Les Penseurs de l'Islam, op cit, chapter ii, pp. 41-74.

[2527] Janet L. Abu-Lughod: *Before European Hegemony,* Oxford University Press, 1989.p.19.

circumnavigation of Africa by Muslim sailors.[2528] Muslim navigators were fascinated by the mysteries of the Western Ocean, and were making queries such as: what would happen if one tried to navigate westward? would one fall off the earth? or if one followed the African coast southward, would it end anywhere and allow one to turn eastward?[2529] Questions that prompted Muslim sailors to make adventurous journeys in the Atlantic in the 9th century.[2530] And they did so from Portugal itself, a group of Muslim sailors called *al-Mugharirrun* (the Adventurers) of Lisbon setting out for unknown lands in the 9th century through the Atlantic Ocean.[2531] An adventurous spirit, which meant the Muslims were practically and perfectly familiar with the fact that Africa might be circumnavigated.[2532] The Portuguese prince Henry the Navigator, who is credited for the Portuguese discoveries, had established a school of navigation, arguably the first technical college in the world, and encouraged his sailors to push further and further down the coast of Africa and out into the unknown Atlantic.[2533]In truth, the nautical academy set up by Prince Henry of Portugal, which prepared the way for Vasco de Gama and for `the expansion of Europe to the uttermost ends of the earth,' was placed under Muslim and Jewish teachers.[2534] Interestingly, such knowledge was even sought in the North African coast; Jean the First of Portugal retained in Ceuta (Morocco) sufficient forces to resist the attacks of the Moroccan kings, and kings of Grenade, and he turned the city into a sort of military school where able officers for war and naval sciences came to train.[2535]

In the Indian Ocean, itself, there was a deliberate Portuguese policy of gleaning from the Muslims all the information they could find about navigation and shipbuilding.[2536] Carra de Vaux points to the works on nautical instructions left by Muslim pilots at the end of the 15th century.[2537] Those instructions, de Vaux insists, served as a basis to the

---

[2528] G.R. Tibbetts: tr and ed: Arab Navigation in the Indian Ocean.... *London Royal Asiatic Society of Great Britain and Ireland;* 1981.

[2529] G.Sarton: Introduction; op cit; Vol II, p. 36.

[2530] Ibid.

[2531] Abrege par Gabriel Sionite, *Geographia Nubiensis*, Paris, 1619, p. 157, in Baron Carra de Vaux: Les Penseurs, op cit, pp. 47-9.

[2532] J.W. Draper, op cit; Vol II; p.174.

[2533] D. Cardwell: *The Fontana History of Technology*; Fontana Press, 1994; p.59.

[2534] R. Briffault: The Making, op cit, p. 202.

[2535] M.L. de Mas Latrie: Traites de paix; op cit; p.262.

[2536] A. Pacey: *Technology in world Civilization*, The MIT Press, Cambridge, Massachusetts, 1990. p.68.

[2537] The publication includes four volumes; the first two include the reproduction of the nautical instructions of Ibn Majid and Soleiman al-Mahri. The third includes the translations of the reproduced geographical parts of the manuscripts and a glossary of

Portuguese pilots of the following century. They are, in prose and in verses, and can be found in Arab manuscripts of The French National Librarie (Bibliotheque Nationale).[2538] The two main authors of such manuscripts are Ibn Majid (the author of more than thirty nautical treatises, according to Miquel)[2539] and Soleiman al-Mahri. This literature was the outcome of the two men's first hand ocean experience. Ibn Majid's *al-hawi* (the Compodium), dated 1462, just before the Portuguese arrived in the Indian Ocean, includes subjects such as wind chronology; maritime routes; coastal roads of Arabia and other places; distances between ports; latitudes of ports on the Indian Ocean and so on. His other treatise *Kitab al-Fawaid* gives useful information on the principles of nautical science, and also describes the large islands such as Madagascar, Java, Sumatra, Ceylon, etc.[2540] In the Eleventh fa'ida of this work,[2541]Ibn Majid gives detailed advice about the `monsoons (sailing seasons) in which one is compelled to travel, the intervals of the monsoons, their beginnings and ends, *showing what is good in each.*[2542] He makes explicit the break between the circuits and his omissions are as significant as his inclusions.[2543]He looks at the Arabia to India circuit, discusses the timing of departures from the Arabian coasts (Yemen, Jeddah) and notes that to reach Malabar in India such journeys must be undertaken at the end of March or the beginning of April, but in no case later than early May. The important thing was to reach India before the Indian Ocean closed.[2544]It is all this knowledge the Portuguese came across in the Indian Ocean. It was further enhanced by the fact that they had large recourse to Muslim pilots as can be amply shown in chronicles and other governmental sources.[2545] Thus, Gaspar Correia asserts that, after his first trip, Vasco de Gama brought back to Portugal Muslim pilots whom he lodged in his own house, and to whom he had recourse

---

nautical expressions. Part IV is the translations of some ancient Portuguese seafarers. `From the comparisons of these seafarers with previous Arab texts, the document says, it comes out that these have been established after Arab originals." In C. de Vaux: Les Penseurs de l'Islam, op cit, chapter ii, pp. 41-74.

2538 Ibid.

2539 A. Miquel: Geography, op cit, p. 811.

2540 C. de Vaux: Les Penseurs de l'Islam, op cit, chapter ii, pp. 41-74.

2541 G.R. Tibbetts: Arab navigation; op cit; pp. 225-242.

2542 Ibid. 225.

2543 J. L. Abu-Lughod: *Before; op cit;*.p.255

2544 G.R. Tibbetts: Arab navigation; op cit; p. 26.

2545 A.Teixeira da Mota: Methodes de navigation et cartographie nautique dans l'Ocean Indien avant le XVI siecle.in *The Global Opportunity*; edt by F.F.Armesto; Variorum; Ashgate Publishing; London; 1995; pp. 44-91. op cit; p. 52.

for the preparations of the fleet of Cabral.[2546] In 1498 Vasco de Gama sailed round the Cape to reach Mocambique; there he encountered Arab shipping and was able to secure the services of an Arab pilot to guide him along the East African coast to Mombassa and Malindi.[2547] From the latter port, another pilot helped the Portuguese ships across the ocean to South India.[2548] Albuquerque's commentaries also make many references to the widespread use of Muslim pilots, generally those embarked in 1507 at Melinde, Socotora, and Orfacao.[2549] Vasco de Gama also acquired several examples of the instruments used by Muslim navigators, and learned new navigational techniques from Ibn Majid (who acted as his pilot from the East African coast to South India.)[2550] According to Portuguese sources, this pilot was in possession of a very good sea map and other maritime instruments. Arabic sources of that time also knew the story. They state that the pilot, whom they knew under the name of Ahmad Ibn Majid, could only be induced to show the way to the Portuguese after having been made drunk. This probably fictitious story shows that the Muslims fully realised the far-reaching consequences of the coming of the Portuguese.[2551]The Islamic naval challenge to the Portuguese, when it came was too late. Western Europe's new route to Asia, Pacey tells, was now open.[2552]

b. Branches of Geography:

It is impossible to look at all aspects of Islamic geographical impact here, thus, focus is only on a couple of matters deemed of greater worth. Beginning with Western European maps, such as by Pedro Alfonso, for instance, who made a sketch map of the world, clearly derived from Muslim models which shows the navel of the world surrounded by the seven climates, the south being placed at the top.[2553] The Islamic rather than the classical heritage in this respect, is highlighted by the fact that in the Roman Empire, there were no frontiers marked by one sign, one

---

[2546]G. Correia: Lendas da India; Lisboa; 1858-1866; Vol 1; part 1; Gama ch xxii; Cabral Ch 1; in T. A da Mota: Methodes; op cit; p. 52.
[2547] A. Pacey: Technology in World Civilization, op cit; p.57.
[2548] Ibid.
[2549] In T.A.da Mota: Methodes; op cit; p. 52.
[2550] A. Pacey: Technology; op cit; p.68.
[2551] J.H. Kramers: Geography and Commerce; op cit; p.96.
[2552] A. Pacey: Technology in world Civilization, op cit; p.57.
[2553] G. Sarton: Introduction; op cit; Vol II, p.130.

reason being that the Romans lacked accurate maps which would have allowed them to define borders correctly.[2554]

Al-Idrisi's geography produced at the Norman court a complete description of the world then known to the Muslims and from other non Islamic sources, and from his own travels from Asia to England. All this knowledge was put in seventy maps, all accompanied by written description, which formed the first comprehensive work on the state of the world.[2555] On this map are hundreds of cities and geographical features, and further details summarised by Kennedy from Miller.[2556] In this map, Kennedy recognises the `Chef d'oeuvre' of Islamic cartography that inspired recent studies of particular regions on the map, which include The British Isles in Beeston (1949), Germany in Hoernerbach (1938), Spain in Dozy and de Goeje (1866), and India in Maqbul Ahmad (1960).[2557] Le Bon points how Al-Idrisi's reference to the sources of the Nile was only matched by European discoveries in the late 19th century.[2558] According to Al-Idrisi:

`The Nile has its origin from that mountain (that of the moon) from ten sources, of which five run and gather in a big lake; the others flow down from the mountain equally, from the mountain towards another large lake. From each of such two lakes flow three rivers which then gather, and then end up flowing into a very large lake, near which is a city called Tarfi.'[2559]

Islamic geography of travel and the narratives of Muslim pilgrims are far superior to the Christian ones, and their scientific value is greater, Sarton notes.[2560] Latin works `are truly childish,' according to Sarton, compared to their Muslim counterparts by Ibn Jubair of Valencia, who described his first journey to the Near east in 1183-1185; or other descriptions by another Valencian, Muhammad al-Abdari and of the Moroccan Mohammad ibn Rushaid; many sided travellers, who took pains to obtain information of various kinds and to meet famous scholars.[2561] Muslim descriptive travels date from much earlier, especially those to China in the 9th. These consist in accounts of

---

[2554] J. Fontana: The Distorted Past, Blackwell, 1995.p.12.

[2555] W.M. Watt, The Influence, op cit, p. 21.

[2556] K. Miller: *Weltkarte des Arabers Idrisi vom Jahre 1154*, Stuttgart, 1981, in E. S. Kennedy: Mathematical Geography, in the Encyclopaedia (Rashed ed), pp. 185-201; pp 199-200.

[2557] E.S. Kennedy: Mathematical Geography, op cit, p. 200

[2558] G. le Bon: La Civilisation; op cit; p. 372.

[2559] Ibid.

[2560] G. Sarton: Introduction, op cit; Vol II, p. 35.

[2561] Ibid.

Sulayman *Akhbar al-Sin wa al-Hind* (presumed 851 A.D) which were incorporated into the 10th century text of Abu Zayd of Siraf; thus centuries ahead of those of Marco Polo.[2562] Marco Polo's fame as the `first' to discover the Orient is, thus, spurious, he being simply the one whose memoirs, due to chance, were recorded.[2563] And if Chinese (Hui-Ch'an, 722 A.D) and Japanese (748 A.D) sources are to be followed, the presence of Muslim traders in Chinese ports dates from the 8th century.[2564] It is notable, however, that it was the geographical treatise of Abu'l-Fida (1273-1331), entitled *Taqwim al-Buldan*, which had a considerable reputation in the Latin West, expressed in the so many translations of it, either partial or complete.[2565] Hence, in the mid 17th century it had an unedited translation by Schickard. Gravious in 1650 published in London extracts relating to Khwarezm and Transoxonia.[2566] A Latin translation was made in Leiden in 1746 by Reiske, published in 1770 and 1771.[2567]Michaelis published the part related to Egypt; Eichhorn the one about Africa, whilst Solvet, in 1839, edited and translated The Maghrib in Algiers.[2568] Reinaud and de Slane published the complete text and half the French translation in Paris in the 1840s.[2569]

4. Technology

Examining Islamic technology and its impact in its deserved worth requires a large treatise. This is because it is necessary to look at literally every single technological change dating from the end of ancient times through the Middle Ages, and study how they relate to modern

---

2562 *Relations des Voyages faites par les Arabes et les Persans dans l'Inde et a la Chine*, ed. et tr. Langles et Reinaud, 2 vols; Imprimerie Royale; Paris; 1845.
G. Ferrand: *Relations de Voyages; op cit.*
2563 De Rachewiltz, 1971, and Dawson, 1980 for earlier travellers in J.L. Abu-Lughod: Before European Hegemony; op cit; p.29.
2564 Di Meglio, 1970: 108-109 in J.L. Abu-Lughod: Before European Hegemony; op cit; p.306.
2565 B. C. de Vaux: Les Penseurs, op cit, p. 13.
2566 J. Greaves or Gravius; (1602-52); London; 1650.
2567 J. J. Reiske; Leipzig; 1266; reprinted 1286.
2568 In Carra de Vaux: Les Penseurs, op cit; p. 13.
2569 J.T. Reinaud and Baron de Slane; Paris; 1840.
Abu al-Fida: *Geographie d'Aboulfeda*, ed. and tr. M. Reinaud. 3 vols. Paris, 1840-83.

equivalents. It will be necessary to look at various devices to piece their routes, and the names of people and places connected with them, and circumstances of their transfer between places. One will also need to fill the horrendous gaps between the Greek era and the late Middle Ages (between ten and thirteen centuries) so as to refute the now current argument that, suddenly, tens, hundreds, even, of technological innovations erupted out of centuries of darkness without any explanation. Most importantly, for every technical device and process, out of the hundreds dating from the 13th-14th century onwards, it will have to be decided whether they were known to the Greeks and Romans; or were the same as theirs, and whether they operated like theirs. If the answer is negative, then the question to ask will be: where did everything come from? Thus, is obvious the scale of the task. Here, because one is not equipped with either time or competence, all that is considered are just a couple of points, beginning with a couple of historical fallacies.

a. Fallacies Related to the History of Modern Technology:

Unlike Pacey, who does one of the remarkable jobs with regard to what he calls the dialogue of civilisations through technologies, outlining the patterns of influence and exchanges between various world entities,[2570] other historians, in their majority, stand by their usual narrow interpretations, attributing technological rise to one culture, alone, and so, perpetuate the vast array of fallacies which afflict the history of the subject.

Fallacy number one sends us back to the Greeks, and to the notion, that between the Greeks and the late Middle Ages, there was no technology, just darkness pure and simple. It seems technology leapt nearly fifteen centuries, from the Greek times to the Renaissance, unchanged. Bedini, for instance, says:

`There appears to be no longer any question, on the basis of recent research, that the mechanical clock and fine instrumentation evolved in a direct line without substantial change from the mechanical water clocks of the Alexandrian civilisation, transmitted through Islam and Byzantine.'[2571]

To answer this matter easily and quickly, recourse is made to Hill, who devotes plenty of attention to the issue. He observes that fine technology is a recognizable Muslim profession, and if any modern engineer `might

---

[2570] A. Pacey: *Technology; op cit.*

[2571] S.A. Bedini: The Role of Automata in the History of Technology; in *Technology and Culture*, Vol 5; pp 24-42; at p. 29.

refer to Greek works, he could find most of his inspiration in the works of his Muslim predecessors. A similar process that can be observed with other sciences and technologies.'[2572]
And, indeed, any good engineer, with knowledge of, and interest in Islamic history, can very easily come to the same conclusion as Hill did, that modern fine technology, in all its branches, has very little to compare with the Greek, but bears instead nearly all resemblance with Islamic sources. Curious minds can check this by picking and studying any device present in all three literatures: the Greek, the Islamic, and the modern.

A second fallacious interpretation is that Western Christendom, locked in centuries of darkness, suddenly leapt into light; by magic it would seem, a spontaneous streak of inspiration hitting Western minds that had lay dormant for ten centuries, such minds suddenly starting to devise machines left and right. Here, one leaves it to Daumas to comment on the particular colossal `genius' of Da Vinci:
`Our inadequate knowledge of the technical history of technology may in part excuse misrepresentations of the kind which one too often encounters when the general historian turns to the history of technology. But how can one explain the fact that manifest errors, corrected over and over again, are still propagated by the most conscientious and indeed renowned historians?.... for instance, how many times has the creative genius of Leonardo da Vinci been given responsibility for all the inventions of the 16th and others?
It is a melancholy thought that far from sinking under ridicule this hotch-potch of commonplaces, unchecked assertions and historical errors has passed for an original work.'[2573]

The third form of inane history, worth dwelling upon longer here, is found amongst medieval historians, who recognise the role of the medieval period, but insist technology was the brainchild of Western genius. This theory, as explained in part one, rests fundamentally on the suppression of facts and any sources of information that contradict it. Thus, going through a Clagett,[2574] Lynn White jr,[2575] Gimpel,[2576] and their

---

[2572] D.R. Hill: Engineering in the Encyclopaedia (Rashed ed), op cit, pp. 751-95; at p. 786.
[2573] M. Daumas: The history of Technology: Its limits; its methods; trans into English and notes by A. R Hall; in *History of Technology*, 1976; pp 85-112. at p.94.
[2574] M. Clagett: *The Science of Mechanics in the Middle Ages*; Madison; University of Wisconsin Press; 1959.

followers, one would come across the usual suppression of evidence, and a re-writing of history, which does away with any evidence of the Muslim role in the rise of technology. Thus, Bradford Blaine, en par with the overwhelming strata of modern historians, says:

`The sugar industry was introduced into Sicily and the Iberian Peninsula by the Arabs, but there is no indication that they initiated the use of water power in the manufacturing process. All the evidence, however, points to the fact that Christians did. Employing pounders or flat rotating grindstones, a sugar mill existed in Norman Sicily in 1176; crusaders had water powered sugar mills at work in the Middle East by the mid 13th century, and the Portuguese and Spaniards are known to have carried the technique to the Madeiras, Canaries, and West Indies.'[2577]

Then he goes on:

`Europeans learned how to make paper from the Arabs, who acquired the knowledge from the Chinese in the mid eight century. There is no proof that water power as used in the process until the second half of the 13th century, when Christian paper makers in Spain and Italy, already familiar with the hydraulic hammer from other industries, adopted the device to prepare pulp. From its origins in Italy and Spain, the paper mill spread throughout Europe during the next three centuries.'[2578]

In response to this, first, it would not occur to Blaine to note that every single breakthrough he is describing occurred in parts of Western Christendom that had the closest links with Islam geographically and historically. Second, when he holds that there is no evidence of Muslim use of water power in manufacturing, he tells a historical fallacy, which any individual can check by simply browsing through the literature on the subject, whether primary Islamic sources,[2579] or some secondary Western sources.[2580] They include tens of instances of Islamic water wheels generating power for multiple uses. Blaine could have also read Al-Biruni (d.ca 1050) describing how such water powered mills worked,

---

2575 See, for instance, Lynn White Jr: Technology in the Middle Ages, in *Technology in Western civilisation*, Vol 1, edited by M. Kranzberg and C.W. Pursell Jr, Oxford University Press, 1967; pp 66-79.
Lynn White Jr: *Medieval technology and social Change*, Oxford, 1964.

2576 J. Gimpel: *The Medieval Machine, Pimlico*, London, 1976.

2577 Bradford. B. Blaine: Mills; Dictionary of the Middle Ages; op cit; vol 8; pp. 390-5; at p. 393.

2578 Ibid.

2579 Al-Djazari: *The Book of Knowledge of Ingenious Mechanical Devices*, edited by D.R. Hill; Dordrecht, Boston, 1974.

2580 See, for instance, V. Lagardere: Moulins d'Occident Musulman au Moyen Age (9em au 15 em Siecle): Al-Andalus, *Al-Qantara:* vol 12, 1991.pp 59-118. p.60.

and how water power was used in driving trip hammers for paper mills in Samarkand and in crushing gold ores.[2581] He could have read Western sources describing the Muslim processes of manufacturing paper through a process he precisely attributes to Italians and Spaniards.[2582] Blaine could have checked his historical sources and found that he makes the same mistake others made before him, and that the process of a water wheel driving a cam shaft to operate trip hammers, which used to be thought to be a distinctly European development, has been corrected, and that evidence now points to numerous water mills in the vicinity of Baghdad, and that water power was applied to paper making in that region for two or more centuries earlier than in Europe.[2583]Blaine could have checked his historical sources, and would have found, that the Sicilian word for sugar mill is *massara*, which is Arabic, meaning precisely crushing mill, and that the Crusaders in the East followed exactly the same processes and methods as the Muslims, and introduced, again, that word `massara' to describe their mills.[2584] Blaine would have also discovered that when the Muslims disappeared from Sicily, the sugar industry died with them, and that Western Christian rulers kept seeking artisans to run their industry from the Muslim East.[2585] He could have read that it was Muslim know how which was transferred by the Portuguese to the Madeiras, the Canaries, and the modern world to run sugar industries.[2586] And, he could have looked at archaeological remains whether in Spain, or in the Muslim east, or in Sicily, to find, that, indeed, Muslims used water powered mills centuries before Western Christendom.[2587] And more can be added. Thus, for Blaine, just like the hordes of other modern writers on the history of technology to claim there is no evidence of Muslim breakthroughs in this field is simply to show ignorance of a subject they should well keep away from.

[2581] In A.Y.Al-Hassan: Technolgy; Islamic; in Dictionary of Middle Ages; op cit; vol 11; pp.636-40; at p.637.

[2582] On the paper making industry in Spain, see E.Levi Provencal: *Histoire de l'Espagne Musulmane*; Vol III; Paris, Maisonneuve, 1953.p. 185; and also C.E. Dubler: *Uber das Wirtschaftsleben*; Romania Helvetica XXII; Geneva; 1943., pp. 81-4.
See also D. Hunter: *Papermaking: The History and Technique of an Ancient Craft*; Pleiades Books; London; 1943; 1947; p. 139.

[2583]A. Pacey: *Technology; op cit;* pp. 41-3.

[2584] Taf and Thom., II; p. 368; Strehkle, p. 9; 28 in W.Heyd: Histoire du Commerce; op cit; vol 2; p. 686.

[2585] Huillard-Breholles, Hist.Dipl. Friderici II; Vol 5; pars 1; p.574. in W.Heyd: Histoire; p. 686.

[2586] A. Pacey: *Technology*. op cit; p.100.

[2587] See for instance D.R.Hill: *Islamic Science and Engineering*; op cit.

Windmills are another subject of contention with the same author and the majority of authors, too. Blaine, again, says:

`Windmills first appeared in Europe in the late twelfth century in Leicestershire in 1137... followed by rapid proliferation elsewhere. By the 1190s German crusaders were building windmills in Syria... What inspired their development is not certain.. The distinctive Western model appears to have been an independent invention, possibly suggested by the mechanical principles and efficient production associated with the familiar water mill in which the vertical wheel turned the horizontal drive shaft.' [2588]

First, once, more, we have the same issue again, that changes, suddenly, by chance, occurred in Western Christendom. Never mind, if such change happened exactly in the time of the crusades, and in connection with the Islamic East. Blaine, also, makes it seem that it was German crusaders who took the technique east rather than the reverse. His interpretation is utterly groundless, for the fact that, had he gone through literature, contemporary or from the late 19th century, he would have discovered that the windmill appeared during the rule of caliph Omar (634-44); [2589] that the windmill was carried to Syria by the Arabs in the 8th century.[2590] That it was the crusaders who copied it in the 12th century as evidence in their castles suggests.[2591] That if there are differences between the eastern windmill and the Western windmill this does not suppose independent origins, but instead, illustrates a fundamental rule of technological history, that one invention (whether the car, the computer, the aeroplane..) begins in one source, then is gradually, and at other times and other places altered to suit the place, times, local conditions etc, but the original source remains the same.

The fourth form of fallacy is represented by the likes of Ashtor, who, just like the majority of modern historians, presents the Muslims as copiers, inept at everything; their military victories accomplished against weak foes; [2592] their faith a copy of that of others; [2593] their civilisation a pale

---

[2588] Bradford. B. Blaine: Mills; op cit; p. 394.

[2589] Al-Tabari: Selection from the Annals (edit. de Goeje, Leiden, 1902, p. 1, in R.J. Forbes: *Studies in Ancient technology*; vol II, second revised edition, Leiden, Brill, 1965. p. 116.

[2590] N. Khanikoff: *Memoire sur la Partie Meridionale de l'Asie Centrale;* Paris; Martinet; 1861; p.116.

[2591] N. Elisseeff: Les Echanges Cultures entre le Monde Musulman et les Croises a l'Epoque de Nur Eddin b.Zanki (m.1174); in *The Meeting of two Worlds*; Edited by V. Goss; Medieval Institute Publication; Kalamazoo; Michigan; 1986; pp. 39-52. pp. 45-6.

[2592] E. Ashtor: *A Social and Economic History of the Near East in the Middle Ages;* Collins; London; 1976; p. 10. See also C. Hillenbrand: *The Crusades, Islamic*

imitation of others;[2594] their laws a mere reproduction of Persian and Byzantine laws,[2595] and their technology, as is going to be expanded upon a little here, a mere borrowing, which, once such borrowing ceased under the Seljuk, from the late 11th onwards, led to the collapse of Muslim civilisation. Hence, from randomly picked extracts by Ashtor, we can read:

`The technological knowledge possessed in former times by Persian and Babylonian engineers was lost.' [2596] And so:

`The execution of great constructions in Egypt at the end of the twelfth century, does not contradict the supposition of technological decline. For the citadel and the new walls of Cairo, which were constructed by order of Saladin, were built by Christian prisoners. The evidence for this is the report by Muslim eye witness, the Spanish traveller Ibn Jubayr, who says that both the workmen and the overseers were Franks. He reports what he saw, but he did not know that even the architects were Christians as revealed by the Franco-Syrian style.'[2597]

Here, referring to Imberciadori, [2598] Ashtor says:

`The contrast between technological stagnation and even decline and the great progress achieved in the same period in European agriculture is striking.' [2599]

`In the Near east technological stagnation had followed a period of great progress. Whatever the reasons of this phenomenon, it brought about the decline of many industries. The factories of Tinnis and the neighbouring towns were closed, not because of the danger a crusaders' invasion, but because they were technically inferior to the industries of Flanders and of Italy.' [2600]

Yet, evidence, once more, shows how inane Ashtor's arguments are. Beginning with his assertion that Muslims in the 12th century relied on Christian skills to erect constructions of one sort or another. Had Ashtor

---

Perspectives, Edinburgh University Press; 1999; pp. 576 fwd on how Muslim victories were only against weaker foes, or due to the Muslim adopting Western tactics.

[2593] E. Ashtor: A Social; op cit; first chapter; or see C. Brockelmann: *History of the Islamic Peoples;* trans from German; Routledge and Kegan Paul; London; 1950 reprint.

[2594] E. Ashtor: A Social; p. 22; just as nearly every modern historian tells us, as seen in the first chapter.

[2595] E. Ashtor: A Social; p. 22; just as Von Grunebaum repeatedly explains in his:
G.E. Von Grunebaum: *Islam,* Greenwood Press, Publishers, 1961.
G. Von Grunebaum: *Medieval Islam*; The Chicago University Press; 1969.

[2596] E. Ashtor: A Social; op cit; p. 245.

[2597] Ibid.

[2598] I. Imberciadori: Agricultura italiana dall XI al XIV secolo; Rivista di storia dell'agricoltura; 1971; p. 22 off.

[2599] E. Ashtor: A Social; op cit; p. 245.

[2600] Ibid. p. 247.

given the slightest attention to any Muslim work depicting the works and lives of Muslim builders and architects, he would have realised how idiotic his assertion was. Mayer's work on Muslim Architects and their Works,[2601] for instance, lists hundreds of Muslim architects, Muslims in names and in faith, who built and rebuilt many edifices, in Cairo itself and throughout the rest of the realm.

And had Ashtor checked the lives and works of Muslim scholars, he would have found that if there was one science, which thrived most after the 12th century, it was precisely technology in all its branches. Indeed the greatest Muslim engineers: Al-Jazari (fl. 1206), Qaisar (fl. 1225-49), who built the huge water wheels on the Orontes in Syria, Taqi Eddin (16th century)… all are obviously post 12th century.

More importantly, with regard to mechanical engineering and fine technology, the Muslims were far from being inept imitators, but instead, it was they who impacted decisively on modern technology. A brief look at some of the Islamic legacies shows that Muslims were the first in using segmental gears, sinking floats serving as actuators and many hydraulic devices.[2602] Al-Muradi's treatise on machines *Kitab al-asrar fs nata'ij al-afkar* (Book of secrets of the results of thoughts), dating from the 11th century, includes the usual models of water clocks and automata, but also large machines with powerful prime movers.[2603] In the Banu Musa's *Kitab of Hiyal* (Book of Ingenious Devices),[2604] completed in 850, there are descriptions of about a hundred devices, many of which reveal mastery of aerostatic and hydrostatic pressures, and the use of automatic control and switching systems.[2605] And their designs, Munro recognises, were much more sophisticated than anything that had appeared earlier; most particularly their preoccupation with automatic controls and the use of self-operating valves, timing devices, and delay systems which distinguishes their mechanical ingenuity from their predecessors (I,e: Hero and Philo).[2606] Taqi Eddin's treatise: `The Sublime Methods of Spiritual machines,' completed in 1551, contains

---

[2601] L.A. Mayer: M*uslim Architects and Their Works;* Albert Kundig; Geneva; 1956.

[2602] C.G. Ludlow and A.S. Bahrani: Mechanical Engineering during the early Islamic period; in *Chartered Mechanical Engineering*; Nov 1978; pp. 79-83. p. 83.

[2603] J.H. Munro: Technology Treatises in *Dictionary of the Middle Ages*; vol 11; pp 641-2. p. 642.

[2604] Banu Mussa: *The book of Ingenious Devices*, tr and annoted by D. R. Hill, Dordrecht: Reidel, 1979; Arabic text, ed. Ahmad Y. al-Hasan; Aleppo: Institute for the History of Arabic Science, 1981.

[2605] D.R. Hill: Arabic Fine technology and its influence on European Mechanical Engineering,' in *The Arab Influence in Medieval Europe*, op cit; p. 27.

[2606] J.H. Munro: Technology Treatises; op cit; p. 641.

descriptions and illustrations of weighing equipment, pumps, and water turbines, and various other machines.[2607]

All the devices and operations included in Islamic treatises, even those seemingly detached from modern day concern, as in Al-Jazari's treatise on the mechanical arts, completed in 1206, were in fact fundamental to the development of machine technology. Hill and Munro explain how these effects were achieved by techniques, which did not enter the general vocabulary of European machine design until the 16th century.[2608]Specifically included amongst these, are ingenious applications of conical valves, tipping buckets, and segmented gears; double acting pumps with suction pipes and the use of a crank shaft in a machine, accurate calibration of orifices, lamination of timber to minimize warping, static balancing of wheels, use of paper models to establish a design, casting of metals in closed mould boxes with green sand etc.[2609] Munro also notes how the preoccupation with automata was one of the factors that led to the development of rationalistic, mechanistic explanations of natural phenomena. The mechanically sophisticated astronomical clocks from the 14th to the 16th centuries may, indeed, well have stimulated natural philosophers into `imagining the entire cosmos as a gigantic clockwork, an attitude that was immensely fruitful in the development of modern science.'[2610] In addition, the makers of trick devices made important contributions to the development of machine design, the outcomes of which, among other things, are vending machines, mechanical calculators, and the modern computer.[2611]

Beyond their pioneering role, it was Muslim engineers who impacted directly on their successors as is seen in the following.

b. Instances of Islamic Impact:

Water mills divide primarily into two varieties: the non geared horizontal mill, powered by a horizontal wheel with paddles (the ancestor of the turbine), connected directly to the bedstone by a shaft; and the vertical mill (either overshot or undershot), whose motive force

[2607] C.G. Ludlow and A.S. Bahrani: Mechanical Engineering; op cit; p. 79.
[2608] D. R. Hill: Engineering, op cit, pp 791-2; and J.H. Munro: treatises; at p.642.
[2609] Ibid.
[2610] J.H. Munro: Treatises, op cit; p. 642.
[2611] Ibid.

is transmitted to the stone by a gearing mechanism.[2612] Both were used in the Islamic world. In places, where the banks of the watercourse were high, as for instance, along the Euphrates, at Hamma on the Orontes, at Amasia on the Yeshil Irmak (in the further eastern lands of Islam), or at Toledo, the current of the river itself was used to turn waterwheels, which produced energy for flour and paper mills; some wheels such as at Toledo being gigantic, 150 feet in diameter.[2613] The Spanish water wheels (like the Syrian), most particularly, had sophisticated internal mechanisms, the equipment of Andalusia marking `a technical advance which goes much beyond the modest history of milling,' according to Lagardere.[2614]
Hill insists that it is important to know about the origins of the horizontal wheels as they are the direct ancestor of modern day turbines.[2615] He holds that some type of horizontal wheels were unknown in Europe before the 16th century, but appeared in the 9th century treatise of the Banu Musa brothers, both descriptions, and figures show that the Banu Musa's design is the closest to the modern day turbine.[2616] Here, of course, is raised the question: did the Banu Musa impact on subsequent changes in the West? and if so, how?
Also needs answering the impact of another Islamic early breakthrough, tide mills, whose earliest known cases were in Basra; but how was the knowledge carried to Europe?[2617]

Use of waterpower dates from early in Islam, and was common in driving trip hammers for paper mills in Samarkand and in crushing gold ores, processing sugarcane, sawing timber, and raising water.[2618] One description of the Kur River dam in central Asia mentions ten water wheels in the vicinity, driving mills, but another account, written around the year 990, implies that there were also water raising wheels in operation.[2619] The reference of mills could simply mean corn mills, but a new type of mill had been introduced in Iran and Iraq for processing sugar cane, as crushing the cane and then boiling the extract were the main operations necessary for obtaining crystalline sugar.[2620] Water

---

2612 T. Glick: Islamic and Christian Spain, op cit, p. 230.
2613 G. Wiet et al: History; Op cit; P. 312
2614 V. Lagardere: Moulins d'Occident Musulman au Moyen Age (9em au 15 em Siecle): Al-Andalus, *Al-Qantara:* vol 12, 1991.pp 59-118. p.60.
2615 D.R. Hill: Islamic Science, op cit, p. 110.
2616 Ibid. pp. 110 fwd.
2617 W.E. Minchinton: Early Tide Mills: Some Problems; *Technology and Culture*; Vol 20. pp 777-86; 785.
2618 A.Y. Al-Hassan: Technology; op cit; p. 637.
2619 A. Pacey: *Technology*; op cit; p. 10.
2620 Ibid.

powered cane crushing mills are known to have existed in Basra and other places, whilst other new applications of water wheels developed by the Muslims were for fulling woollen cloth, and for preparing pulp for papermaking.[2621] Casanova shows that there was even a whole street for rice millers in Cairo.[2622] Lautensach comments lengthily on various milling operations in Spain, and on the new types of mills that may have been introduced to Spain in Islamic times.[2623]

Lagardere points out that with regard to the diffusion of water wheels, Spain was the centre of radiation, mills being mounted on diverse structures in the Ebro at Saragossa, and on the Segura in Murcia.[2624] The diffusion of water mills takes place in the Asturias in the 9th-10th centuries mainly via irrigation works and colonisation effected by the mozarab (Christians living amongst Muslims) population.[2625] The Mozarabs, Glick points out, were prominent in mill-building activities: a document of 905 describes the construction of a mill by a converted Jewish monk named Habaz, clearly of Andalusi origin, along with his own workmen.[2626] In 1032, another Mozarab, Cidi Domínguez, rebuilt some mills on the Bernesga River.[2627]

Wind-power was widely used in Islam to run millstones and also to draw up water for irrigation.[2628] Its use came early during the reign of Caliph Omar (634-44).[2629] Windmills were widespread east of the Islamic land, most particularly in `Sedjestan,' where the people, according to Al-Masudi use wind to operate their mills and raise water from wells.[2630] Al-Istakhri, too, notices how the wind blows without interruption and operates mills erected everywhere.[2631] Al-Qazwini

---

2621 Ibid.

2622 P. Casanova: Essai de Reconstitution de la ville d'al Fustat ou Misr; *Memoires de l'Institut Francais d'Archeologie Orientale*; xxxv; 1919.p.155.

2623 H. Lautensach: *Maurische Zuge im geographischen Bild der Iberischen halbinsel*; Bonn; 1960; p. 81.

2624 V. Lagardere: Moulins d'Occident p.61.

2625 Ibid. p.63.

2626 T. Glick: Islamic and Christian Spain; op cit; p. 222.

2627 Ibid.

2628 G. Wiet et al: History; op cit; p.312.

2629 Al-Tabari: Selection from the Annals (edit. de Goeje, Leiden, 1902, p. 1, in R.J. Forbes: *Studies in Ancient technology*; vol II, second revised edition, Leiden, Brill, 1965. p. 116.

2630 Al-Masudi: Meadows of Gold, vol ii, p. 80; in Carra de Vaux: Les Penseurs, op cit, p. 191.

2631 Cited by Yaqut: Dictionary of Persia, p. 301, in Carra de Vaux: Les Penseurs, op cit, p. 191.

Al-Istakhri (10th century): *Das Buch der Lander*, tr. A.D. Mordtmann. Hamburg, 1845.

describes how corn is ground by the operation of such windmills.[2632] Contemporary drawings of Islamic windmills exist, too, such as by al-Dimashqi,[2633] who offers very good descriptions of such wind powered corn mills, supplemented with sketches and explanatory notes.[2634]

Khanikoff describes a windmill in Seistan:

`A millstone is attached to the end of a wooden cylinder, half a metre wide, and 3.5 to 4 metres high, standing vertically in a tower open on the north east side to catch the wind blowing from this direction. The cylinder has sails made of bundles of ush or palm leaves (which reminds of the modern European windmill), attached to the shaft of the axle. The wind, blowing into the tower, exerts strong pressure on the sails, so turning the shaft and millstone.'[2635]

The windmills were erected on substructures built for the purpose, or on the tower of castles or on hilltops. They had two chambers, an upper chamber for the millstone, and a lower one for the sails. The walls of the lower chamber were pierced by four vents with the narrower end towards the interior, like the loopholes of a fortress so as to direct the wind on to the sails, and increase its speed.[2636] A wheel driven by the sails-six or twelve in number and covered with fabric, turned the upper millstone.[2637]

Abundant references to windmills in all corners of Islam hardly deterred Ashtor, just as many others, from holding that:

`Windmills had been introduced by German crusaders in Palestine, but they did not come into use elsewhere.'[2638]

Lynn White Jr and others claim that windmills were never diffused in Islam, nor did they impact on the West[2639]

And yet, such an impact exists, and one seizes on this instance to show how the same factors of timing and routes of diffusion (as for other areas of influence) are at work again.

First, timing. Every single source (including White and his followers) accepts that windmills appeared in Europe in the 12th century. Lagardere traces them to areas where water-power was scarce, windmills used as

---

[2632] Al-Qazwini, *Works* (ed. Wustenfeld, Cottingen, 1849, vol II, p. 134.) in R.J. Forbes: Studies, op cit, p.116.

[2633] Al-Dimasqui: *Manuel de la Cosmographie Arabe*, tr. A.F. Mehren, Amsterdam. 1964.

[2634] Al-Dimashqi: M*anuel;* p. 246, in R.J. Forbes: Studies; op cit; p 117.

[2635] Khanikoff cited in G. Wiet et al: History; op cit; p. 312.

[2636] D.R. Hill: Islamic Science, op cit, p. 116.

[2637] T.K Derry and T.I Williams: *A Short History of Technology*; Oxford Clarendon Press, 1960, p. 254.

[2638] E. Ashtor: A Social and Economic History; op cit; p. 308.

[2639] Lynn White Jr: Technology in the Middle Ages; op cit; p. 77.

an alternative imported from the land of Islam in the later parts of the 12th century.[2640] Hill, too, recognises the absence of windmills in Europe before the end of the 12th century, observing that even if European mills differed from those of the Muslims in their design, the principle came from Islam.[2641]Carra de Vaux further substantiates this Islamic 12th century origin, pointing out that in Europe, the oldest text in relation to windmills is a French act of 1105 granting a religious community the right to establish one of these apparatuses, called *molendinam ad ventum* (moulin a vent in French: windmill in English).[2642]

As for the routes of influence, there were two, the usual: Spain and the East during the crusades, both routes, by some coincidence, opening to the Christian West precisely in the 12th century, and precisely when the windmills appeared in Western Christendom. Had it been any other source of influence, say local, such windmills would have appeared centuries earlier. And windmills are yet another amongst the countless other innovations that suddenly struck Western Christendom at the same time, out of nothing. And just as other transformations, by some pure coincidence, it would seem, windmills followed precisely the same routes as the rest, i.e those under Islamic influence. Mieli, who sees no doubt in the Islamic source,[2643] notes how the diffusion of this technology was very rapid in the Mediterranean islands and on the coastal shores of that sea, and also Sicily.[2644] He does recognise the Eastern route via Syria during the Crusades.[2645]For Gille, windmills seem to have followed the same route as paper did: Tarragone (Spain) in the 10th, then the European west: Arles: 1162-1180; Normandy: 1180; England: 1182; and Ypres: 1197.[2646] Needham is of the opinion that by the 16th century the Islamic horizontal windmills had become well known in Europe; surely a westward transmission from Christian Spain originally derived from Muslim Spain.[2647] Wiet et al recognise such Islamic origin through the Iberian peninsula, but earlier, via 10th century Catalonia; and through the eastern route via the Greek Islands, and other

---

[2640] V. Lagardere: Moulins d'Occident. op cit; p.60.

[2641] D.R. Hill: Islamic science, op cit; p. 116.

[2642] Cited in Magasin Pittoresque, t. XX, 1852, p. 50. In Baron Carra de Vaux: Les penseurs op cit, p. 190.

[2643] A. Mieli: La Science Arabe; op cit; p.118.

[2644] Ibid.

[2645] Ibid.

[2646] B. Gille: Le Machinisme au Moyen age: *Archives Internationales des Sciences;* Vol 6; pp 280-6; P. 283.

[2647] In A.Y. Al-Hassan: Technology: Islamic; Dictionary of Middle Ages; op cit; vol 11; pp. 636-40;p. 637.

Mediterranean regions where water supply was not adequate for milling.[2648]
Later diffusion is explained by Forbes, holding that wind-power was a dominant feature of the Egyptian sugar cane industry, and thence travelled to the West Indies when experts from Egypt were lured to help and establish the first sugar plantations there.[2649]

The Islamic impact in civil engineering is illustrated by a brief look at the role of the qanat system, that is the underground water system, which conducts water from a source to a distant location.[2650] A series of vertical shafts, resembling but not acting as wells, are constructed along the line of the qanat to allow access for maintenance and removal of spoil.[2651] The qanat system allows the protection and sound management of water from evaporation.[2652] The word `qanat' in Arabic is said to be the same as the English word `canal' which was initially used to mean a pipe, or tune or tunnel carrying liquid.[2653]Qanat technology spread to Europe, and qanats were used in Spanish provinces such as Catalonia and Madrid,[2654] and are still a major source of water use in Cyprus and the Canary islands.[2655] Some abandoned qanats have been discovered in Central Europe, in Bavaria and Bohemia.[2656] The qanat system has survived to this day in many parts, including modern Spain, and diverse parts of the South American continent, where it had a substantial impact on the local farming.[2657] Today one can see them in Central America: they are the oil qanats.[2658]
Deep drilling techniques, which, in view of the number of references made to them, also had an Islamic diffusion; to judge by the interval

---

2648 G. Wiet et al: History; op cit; p. 350.
2649 In A.Y. Al-Hassan: Technology- Islamic; at p. 637.
2650 P. Guichard: Mise en valeur du sol et production: De la `revolution agricole'aux difficultes du bas Moyen Age; In Etats et societes (J.C.Garcin et al ed); op cit; pp. 175-199; p. 181.
2651 K. Sutton: Qanats in al-Andalus; the continued presence of Moorish irrigation technology in the Campo Tabernas, Almeria; Spain; *The Maghreb Review*; vol 26; 1; 2001; pp. 69-78; at p. 70.
2652 P. Guichard: Mise en valeur; op cit; p.181.
2653 A. Pacey: Qanats: Encyclopaedia (Selin ed); op cit; p. 832.
2654 J. Oliver Asin: Historia del nombre Madrid; Madrid; 1959; in P. Ward English: The origins and Spread of Qanats in the Old World; in *Production and the Exploitation of Resources*, edited by G. Morony; Ashgate Variorum; pp. 273-284, at p. 281.
2655 P. Ward English: The origins and Spread of Qanats; at p. 281.
2656 H. Klaubert: Qanats in an area of Bavaria-Bohemia; *Geographical Review*, 57; pp. 203-12; in P. Ward English: The origins and Spread of Qanats at p. 281.
2657 K. Sutton: Qanats; op cit; pp 72 fwd.
2658 L. Bolens: Irrigation: Encyclopaedia (Selin ed); op cit; pp. 450-2..

between the mention by al-Biruni, writing in the early 11th century, and the first European documentation, again another 12th century manifestation, at Artois in 1176.[2659]

Medieval Europe possessed many elaborate devices for indicating time or for striking the hours, and many still survive in the towers of town halls. One earliest such device was a clock sent by Harun al-Rashid to Charlemagne in 807. With this clock, while the hours were being struck on a cymbal, an appropriate number of windows in the case were opened, a knight came out of each window and went back in again, and the windows closed.[2660]

Muslim astronomers had devised some nice instruments for the measurement of time. And among the Muslim works translated by order of King Alfonso was an anonymous one on the construction and use of the candle clock, translated by Samuel Ha-Levi.[2661]

More specifically on the *Libros de saber de astronomia*, written in the 13th century for King Alfonso, and based principally on Islamic sources, Isaac ibn Sid (ben Cid) describes five time-measuring devices.[2662] The clocks described are:

1.A sundial divided into quadrants, to be used with a table of declination of the sun. 2.The "Palace of Hours," a cupola on the interior walls of which the hours of daylight were marked by sunlight shining through a progression of windows. 3.A clepsydra, wherein water whose flow is regulated by a siphon turns an astrolabe. 4.A candle clock whose indicator is moved by a counterweight regulated by the candle. 5.A compartmented cylindrical mercury clock (also a clepsydra).

The mercury and water clocks are conceptually the most important because they had astrolabes for dials and were therefore true chronometers rather than devices, which illustrated the movement of the heavenly spheres.[2663] The mercury clock, most particularly, Glick insists, indicates that the Muslims had known the principle of weight-driven mechanical clocks two centuries before it was appreciated in the Latin West.[2664] This clock, which had an antecedent in the Toledo clock

---

[2659] L. Bolens, `l'eau et l'irrigation', p. 71; Ibn Bassal, `Libro de agricultura, pp 223-6 (trans); Needham, `Central Asia and the History of Science', p. 138. in T. Glick: Islamic and Christian Spain; op cit; p. 238.

[2660] Annales Fuldenses, ca.901.' There is an edition by G.H. Pertz (editor), Hahn's, Hannover. 1826. in R.R. Newton: The application of ancient astronomy to the study of time: *ENDEAVOUR*; Vol 33: pp 34-9 at p.35

[2661] G. Sarton: Introduction, op cit; Vol II, p. 764

[2662] T. Glick: Islamic and Christian Spain; op cit; p. 244.

[2663] Ibid.

[2664] Ibid.

built by al-Zarqali, was a perpetual motion machine which, as the mercury flowed from compartment to compartment, rotated an astrolabe dial, set for Toledo, where Alfonso the Wise maintained his observatory, once every twenty-four hours.[2665]

The mechanical clock was invented in Western Europe towards the end 13th century, its mentor, certainly, coming from the ranks of the makers of the water clocks.[2666] The verge escapement made the mechanical clock possible, but all its other features-weight-drive, automata, gear trains and segmental gears-were present in Islamic water clocks.[2667] It is highly probable that these ideas were transmitted from Islam to the European makers of water clocks, an Islamic influence on the genesis of the mechanical clock, which, therefore could be postulated.[2668]

The Islamic impact in industrial technology will receive focus under the next heading, thus, here, one instance will suffice. In terms of the sophistication of individual machines, notably for textile processing, and in terms of the broad scope of its technology, Western Christendom was still a backward region, which stood to benefit from its contacts with Islam.[2669]Surviving specimens of silk fabric show that thread produced in the Islamic countries (and Europe) was always twisted, to make it stronger, whereas Chinese manufacturers seem to have avoided this because fabric woven from twisted thread was stiffer and less lustrous, which hence points to a non Chinese invention of mechanical devices for twisting thread.[2670] There is, indeed, an Islamic description of a silk twisting machine dating from just before 1030; the experience of this machine possibly leading to a distinctive approach to spinning other textile fibres, and may ultimately have contributed to the invention of the specifically European type of spinning wheel known as the Saxony wheel.[2671]

[2665] S Pérez, Personalidad cieníifica de Alfonso X; S A. Bedini: "The Compartmented Cylindrical Clepsydra," *Technology and Culture*, 3 (1962), 116-117; J. M. Millás Vallicrosa, Estudios sobre Azarquiel (Madrid-Granada: C.S.I.C., 1943-1950), pp. 6-9. In T. Glick: Islamic and Christian Spain; op cit; pp 244-5.
[2666] D. Hill: Clocks and watches: in Encyclopaedia (Selin ed) pp 208-11 at P.210.
[2667] Ibid.
[2668] Ibid.
[2669] A.Pacey: *Technology*; op cit; p. 44.
[2670] Ibid. Preface, p.24.
[2671] Ibid.

C. Resolving Gaps in the History of Technological Transmission:

Here are raised instances of unexplained matters in the history of technology, and also possibilities of influence, which need exploring. First a machine attributed to the Banu Musa that was not included in the Book of Ingenious Devices, but can be found in a separate manuscript.[2672] Although the manuscript does not include any illustrations, a figure of a German work of the year 1650 shows fundamentally the same system. Hill notes how the air supply system (shown at the right) is cruder than that of the Banu Musa, and that the Banu Musa machine was very sophisticated both hydraulically and mechanically.[2673] The matter to answer, of course, is whether there are ways of transmission between the Banu Musa (9th century) and the 17th century German device.

Hollister Short points to the origin of the suction lift pump, which he says is even more heavily veiled.[2674]The first evidence of its existence comes in a sketch of about 1425. It occurs in a collection of drawings of machines and devices composed by Mariano Taccola (1382-post 1453) (*De Ingeneis*).[2675]Hollister Short goes:

`The radically different nature of these two species of pump, the force pump and the suction lift pump, will now be clear. As has been mentioned already, it has proved a matter of extreme difficulty to propose a convincing conceptual route from the un-pierced piston of the Greeks to the active water column and valued piston of the late medieval period. The literature is virtually silent on the matter. The difficulty as one can see, arises in part from the fact that evidence of sufficiently early date that might throw light on the genesis of the suction lift pump has not so far been discovered. It is only with work of Mariano Taccola in the 1420s that the first drawings become available.'[2676]

[2672] Banu Mussa, *Al-Ala allati tuzammar bi -nafsiha*, Arabic text ed. L. Cheikho, al-Machriq, 9, (1906), pp 444-56; English translation by H.G. Farmer, The Organ of the Ancients, London Reeves, 1931, pp 88-118, in D.R. Hill: Arabic fine technology, op cit, pp 31-2.

[2673] Ibid, p. 32.

[2674]G. Hollister Short: On the origins of the suction lift pump: *History of Technology;* 1993: pp 57-75: p. 58.

[2675]Taccola's book: *De Ingeneis*: compl in 1433: in the form of four books. De machinis (where some drawings repeated from De Ingeneis) was completed in 14449 and consisted of 10 books of machines (Scaglia: Mariano Taccola: De Machinis 2 Vols. (Wiesbaden, 1971) Vol I presents the Latin and English translation; Vol 2: is a facsimile reproduction of the 10 books). in G. Hollister Short: On the origins; op cit; p. 58.

[2676] G. Hollister Short: On the origins; p. 61.

Thus here is the need to find the routes and manners for the changes made to the device between the Greeks and the 15th century. The same can be also done for so many other devices in the same situation.
The other matter to resolve is how did al-Jazari impact on Western Christendom. Winder makes the point that:
`on the basis of available scholarship we are forced to believe that al-Jazari's work,[2677]with the various pictures and diagrams that profusely illustrate it, did not transmit such important advances as conical valves to the European cultural revolution known as the Renaissance. If this transfer did not, in fact, take place, one must wonder why it did not, since al-Jazari's work appeared relatively early in medieval Islam, at a time when cultural transference from East to West was at its height. No compelling solution to the mystery suggests itself. Revived interest in Arab Islamic technology may, in time, produce one.'[2678]

Picking on the last point, Hill concludes that as research proceeds, firmer evidence for the transmission of Islamic fine technology into Europe can be provided.[2679]He suggests the routes for such transmission, Spain, of course, but also Sicily, Byzantium, and Syria during the Crusades.[2680]
On this matter of routes of transmission, Munro suggests the court of Alfonso X the Wise at Seville.[2681]Alfonso commissioned the translation of a number of Islamic scientific treatises, including works on the design of astronomical instruments, which are contained in the *Libros del saber de astronomia and the Dos libros de las armellas*. The treatise on machines by Al-Muradi (fl 11th century) *Kitab al-asrar fi nata'ij al-afkar* (Book of secrets of the results of thoughts) was also copied at Alfonso's court around 1266. Al-Muradi's work, Munro notes, includes large machines with powerful prime movers, resembling subsequent European treatises more than any other.[2682] How did such models travel from Alfonso's court to subsequent, mainly Italian sources, remains to be answered. It must be stressed that the same manuscript available at Alfonso's court is now in Florence at the Bibliotheca Laurenziana.[2683]
Oddly enough, this is precisely the route followed by a certain Brunetto

---

[2677] Ed D.R. Hill: *The Book of Knowledge of Ingenious Mechanical Devices*, Dordrecht, Boston, 1974.
[2678] R.B. Winder: Al-Jazari, in *The Genius of Arab Civilisation;* J.R. Hayes ed; op cit; p. 188.
[2679] D. R. Hill: Engineering, op cit, p. 795.
[2680] D. R. Hill: Arabic Fine Technology, op cit, pp 41-2.
[2681] J.H. Munro: Treatises; op cit; p. 642.
[2682] Ibid.
[2683] D.R. Hill: Islamic; op cit, p 142.

Latini, a Florentine envoy, who also resided at Alfonso's court at the time, and who was very much interested in the scholarly activities there, and who returned to his Florentine origins subsequently.[2684] And, oddly enough, soon after his return, technological innovations flourished in northern Italy.

Ludlow and Bahrani have also pointed out, that there are large possibilities still awaiting in the mass of the thousands of Islamic manuscripts dormant in the European and North American libraries.[2685] In some such manuscripts can be found many of the answers to problems raised here, and others not looked at.

[2684] F. Reichmann: *The Sources; op cit.* p.203.
[2685] C.G. Ludlow and A.S. Bahrani: Mechanical, op cit, p. 79.

3. TRADE, INDUSTRY AND FARMING

The awakening of the Christian West in trade, industry and farming in the Middle Ages highlights and confirms many crucial points made previously:

First, the impact of the 12th century translations in the awakening of such activities is inexistent, or shallow at best, which proves that the generally held theory in Western history that the 12th century renaissance of the Christian West owes to the translations of Greek science is ridiculous.

Second, the changes in these areas highlight, once more, that all changes that took place in the Christian West at the time were not due to fortuitous conditions, or to local factors, or to the recovery of lost heritage, but form part of a larger ensemble of changes, that affected each and every area of learning, science, economy, art, culture, and civilisation as a whole.

Third, as this chapter will confirm, these transformations, just as every other transformation that took place in the 12th-13th century, did so only once contact with Islam was made, and bears obvious Islamic resemblance.

Fourth, this chapter also confirms previously observed patterns that it was principally the parts of Western Christendom that had contacts with Islam that were first transformed in the particular fields they were in contact with Islam. This is most particularly relevant to the Italian cities, which were the most important traders with Islam, and which, by some coincidence, once more, were the first in Western Christendom to show major transformations in industrial crafts, techniques, and also trade mechanisms and banking.

1. Trade

It is the generalised Western historians' distorted writing on the role of Islam and its civilisation, which keeps forcing the issue to be discussed, and with respect to every matter. In respect to trade, hence, it is impossible to deal with the Islamic impact without having to address the issue of the Pirenne theory, first.

a. The Pirenne Theory:

In the early 1930s, Pirenne held in his *Muhammad and Charlemagne* that the advance of Islam led to the collapse of economic activity around the Mediterranean, thus driving Europe into the dark ages.[2686]In more detail, he said:

`European civilisation formed around the Mediterranean by the successive work of Egypt, Syria, Phoenicia, Greece and Rome. The latter, the last worker of an admirable work, has gathered in one single state all the people it was the inheritor. The empire founded by it, including all, is thus an Empire that was essentially Mediterranean.'[2687]

Pirenne goes on:

`From Byzantium, Asia Minore and Egypt Jewish merchants, but above all Syrian merchants continued their supply of it (the West) with luxury goods, rich cloth, and fine wines. By their intermediary it received the gold that was necessary for its currency and the papyrus that was used by copyists and clerks of chancelleries.'[2688]

Until:

`Islamic invasion of the Mediterranean, to my opinion, it is to this event which must be attributed the cut which separates Antiquity of European history from that which we call usually under the name of the Middle Ages. In closing the sea and in isolating by this the one from the other the West and the Orient, it had put an end in fact to this Mediterranean unity, which had constituted for thousands of years the most striking character, and the condition itself of traditional development of civilisation in that part of the world.'[2689]

Thus, for Pirenne, the advance of Islam in the east and south in the late 7th century destroyed the cultural and religious unity of the Mediterranean, and killed the Roman world. An Islamic irruption, which led to a two century disruption of economic and commercial contacts between the Middle East and Western Europe, hence forcing economic activity to shift from south to north, giving rise to the Dark Ages. Thus, here,

---

[2686] H. Pirenne: *Mohammed and Charlemagne*; F. Alcan; Paris-Bruxelles; 7th edition; 1937.

[2687] H. Pirenne, Mahomet et Charlemagne. Revue Belge de Philosophie et d'Histoire 1, 1922, 77-86. in *Bedeutung Und Rolle des Islam Beim ubergang Vom Altertum Zum Mittelalter*, Paul Egon Hubinger: ed; Darmstadt, 1968. pp. 1-9. p. 1.

[2688] Ibid. p. 7.

[2689] Henri Pirenne: Un contraste economique. Merovingiens et Carolingiens, Revue Belge; 2, 1923, 223-35. in Bedeutung; op cit; pp. 10-22; p.10.

unlike previous matters, it is not just that Islam had no role in the positive changes which took place in medieval Western Christendom (learning, universities, birth of modern science, development of art and architecture...), but also that Islam destroyed Western civilisation.

Pirenne's theory became and remained a convenient foundation for his followers to see in the Islamic advance of the 7th-8th century an explanation to Europe's centuries of darkness, a convenient theory which earned Pirenne great fame.[2690] For Wiet et al, for instance:
`Reference must be made here to the views brilliantly put forward by the great Belgian historian Henri Pirenne.'[2691]
Pirenne had been `spreading the good word,' Coville says,[2692] delivering lectures world wide, explaining how it was Islam, instead of the `Barbarian' invasions of three centuries before (late fifth AD) that had broken a hitherto cohesive and prosperous civilization.

Pirenne's theory was flimsy, though, mainly based on the fact that imports of gold and papyrus had `disappeared' during the Islamic advance. And so it hardly resisted the tests of time and more solid challenges. Some scholars do not accept that the Carolingian period was, economically speaking, a period of regression, but believe, to the contrary, that there were more commercial transactions during this than in the preceding era. Others are in agreement with Pirenne with regard to economic regression in the Merovinigien period, but do not accept that the domination of Islam on the Mediterranean basin as its main cause.[2693]

Amongst such latter scholars is Perroy, who outlines the main defects of Pirenne's theory by first demonstrating that Islam as a faith had no problem with trade. To the contrary, the Prophet was a trader; his followers crossed the world from The Sudan to the Volga, from China to Madagascar to trade; and it was, in fact, Islam that awakened Western trade[2694] (more on which further on). Besides, explains Perroy, the decline of trade between east and west of the Mediterranean was

---

[2690] Hence, on May 18, 1938, in his honour, was held in Brussels (Belgium), a solenal academic session, which was attended by the Belgian king, Leopold II.
[2691] G. Wiet et al: *History of Mankind; op cit*; p.5.
[2692] A. Coville, les Commencements du Moyen Age d'apres Henri Pirenne, *Journal des Savants,* 1938, 97-104, at p.97.
[2693] P. Lambrechts: Lcs Theses de Henri Pirenne sur la fin du monde Antique et les debuts du Moyen Age, in Bedeutung; op cit; pp 32-57. p. 34.
[2694] E. Perroy: *Le Moyen Age*, Presses Universitaires de France, 1956. p.113-4.

anterior to Islam, and in the period in question, the 8th century, Byzantium kept its trade with its possessions of Southern Italy and the Adriatic. Moreover, if there was little traffic beyond that limited sector, it was related to the internal evolution of the West and to monopolistic policies pursued by Byzantium.[2695] Perroy, finally, notes, that the passage from gold to silver between 650 and 700 is neither a sign of the collapse of civilisation as believed by Pirenne, nor it is of a definitive exhaustion of the stocks of gold of the Occident.[2696]

Further attacks on Pirenne came amongst others from Lopez, Lombard and Genicot.[2697]Lopez points out that gold did not become scarcer after the Muslim advance, but instead, in the 8th century and after, both Muslim coins and their imitations seem to have been fairly common.[2698] Lopez also refers to Sabbe (an earlier follower of Pirenne) to highlight that the trade of Oriental purple-dyed and embroidered cloths was never interrupted in Western Europe, and the diminished use of Oriental cloths among the laymen (if there was a diminution) was largely due to fashion change.[2699]

Taking the opposite view from Pirenne, Lombard affirms that the Muslim advance, occurring at a time of exhaustion in Europe, re-established and amplified international commerce and contributed to the recovery characterizing the Carolingian Empire, and that Muslim currency in particular infused new blood into commercial relations.[2700] Lombard goes even further, holding that it was the Muslim advance, which led to the West regaining contact with Oriental civilisation and, through the Muslims with the major world movements in trade and culture. `Whereas the great barbarian invasions of the fourth and fifth centuries,' Lombard holds, `had caused an economic regression in the West under the Merovingian and Carolingian dynasties, the creation of the new Islamic Empire brought with it an astonishing development in this same area.'[2701]

Genicot, too, referring to Ganshof, notes that the ports of Provence (France) had not stopped their activity from the 8th to the 10th

---

[2695] Ibid.

[2696] E. Perroy: Encore Mahomet et Charlemagne. Revue Historique 212, 1954, 232-238. in Bedeutung; op cit; pp. 266-275. p.267.

[2697] For an excellent summary of articles devoted to the thesis and its criticism see *Bedeutung op cit;*.

[2698] Cf.Bloch, p.13 ff., with bibl in Robert S. Lopez: Mohammed and Charlemagne: A Revision. Speculum 18, 1943, 14-38. in Bedeutung; op cit; pp. 65-104. p.92.

[2699] Cf. Sabbe, op cit.. in R. S. Lopez: Mohammed. p. 99.

[2700] M. Lombard: l'Or Musulman au Moyen Age, in *Annales ESC* (1947): 143-160.

[2701] M.Lombard: Quand l'Islam Brillait de Mille feux; op cit.

century,[2702]and suggests that the decline of the exchange economy could have other causes than the Muslim irruption, especially the state of anarchy of the Frank monarchy after Dagobert.[2703]
And for Lopez to conclude:
`If neither the `disappearance' of papyrus nor that of gold currency is connected with a sudden regression in trade caused by the Arab conquests, the thesis of Pirenne has little support left.'[2704]

Pirenne's theory is further undermined by the fact that historians, who looked at the domestic history of various parts of Europe noted the decline taking place in the Roman empire even earlier than the 5th; the decline that gripped the Christian West, thus, taking place centuries before Islam was even born. Some historians, i.e Lewis, have even noted that Muslim control of the Mediterranean did not begin in the 7th or 8th century, as Pirenne stated, but did in the late 9th and early 10th centuries;[2705]a five century gap between European decline and Islamic rise in the area, which makes Pirenne's theory untenable.

Rather than the Muslims causing the decadence of trade, facts, instead, prove that modern trade, in all its foundations, owes to Islam, just as the following shows.

b. The Islamic Fundamentals of Trade:

Basing himself on a diversity of sources, Cahen writes:
`Let us first rid ourselves of an idea that Pirenne himself seem to have had, namely, that Arabs and Islam are marked by a kind of native impotence in economics and trade.[2706] No matter what modern developments have been, the Arabs, as far as back as pre-Islamic times, organised trade caravans which were at least inter-regional, reaching as

---

2702 F.L. Ganshof: *Note sur les ports de Provence du viii au x siecle,* in *Revue Historique*, t. CLXXXIV, 1938, p. 28. in L. Genicot: Aux Origines de la civilisation in Bedeutung; op cit; pp. 105-19. p.106.
2703 L. Genicot: Aux Origines; pp 105-119.
2704 R. S. Lopez: Mohammed and Charlemagne; op cit; pp 97-8.
2705 A.R. Lewis: The Moslem expansion in the Mediterranean, A.D. 827-960: pp 23-29 in *The Islamic World and the West*; Ed: A. R. Lewis; John Wiley and Sons; London; 1970. p.23.
2706 Since it would be impossible to list here a bibliography of this immense subject, Cahen points out, he judiciously recommends Rodinson: *Islam and capitalism;* Paris, 1966.

far as Syria.[2707] Through the Yemen, they were in contact with the Indian Ocean's traffic. Islam was born in a mercantile milieu. Muhammad was a merchant and was not troubled by it. Several of his companions were merchants, and if evidently certain practices of the surrounding states were unknown to them, the reverse was perhaps also true.[2708] In any case there was no question of a basic Muslim incapacity to trade.'[2709]

If any historical fact confirms the great capacity of Muslims to trade, it is the fact that anywhere Muslims set foot they fostered trade. Garaudy observes how agrarian communities based on the Savannah or forest evolved in the 8th century into great empires, a consequence of large scale trade in the geographical area where Islam was present, from Cadiz to China.[2710] In Africa, indeed, it was Islam, which legated the concept of special consideration to traders and trading; and even more importantly, created a trading class.[2711] It imposed contractual laws, hence stimulating institutional as well as legal foundations, not just for trade, but for the whole of society. And, of course, it forbade the practice of usury.[2712]Elsewhere, Muslim shipping was prominent throughout the Indian Ocean, and as early as 750, merchants from the Persian Gulf made the long voyage to China. After 1100, Indian cotton goods and Chinese porcelain were reaching very remote Indonesian islands (whose main exports were spices) and distant African ports (whence came ivory and gold.)[2713]Then, only the Muslim Arabs and Muslim South Asians who led the trade with China had such a background and their efforts enabled them to extend their enterprises into the Malay Archipelago.[2714]Their reach was remarkable when one considers the shipping and navigational conditions of the time.[2715]Eventually, the Muslims stimulated Chinese merchants themselves to develop better ocean-going shipping to trade in the region

---

[2707] See A. Udovitch: At the Origins of the Western Commenda, in *Speculum* 37 (1962): pp. 198-207.

[2708] Synthese in A. R. Lewis: *Naval Power and Trade in the Mediterranean, 500-1100*; Princeton University Press; 1951.

[2709] C. Cahen: Commercial Relations; op cit; at p.3.

[2710] R. Garaudy: *Comment l'Homme devint Humain*, Editions J.A, 1978. p.271.

[2711] J. Spencer Trimingham: *The Influence of Islam upon Africa*; Longman, Librairie du Liban; second edition 1980; at p 38; and p.51.

[2712] Ibid.

[2713] A. Pacey: *Technology*, op cit; p.12.

[2714] Wang Gungwu: Transforming the Trading World of Southeast Asia[i] at http://hometown.aol.com/wignesh/5Wanggungwu.htm

[2715] Ibid.

as well.[2716]Such achievements testify to the way commercial vigour could fashion and enhance civilisation when trade flourished freely and attracted the active participation of local elites.[2717]Which, Abu Lughod notes, contradicts the views that Eastern cultures provided an `inhospitable environment for merchant-accumulators and industrial developers.'[2718]

And rather than destroying trading lines between the East and the Christian West, as Pirenne and his hordes of followers hold, `The Arabs,' Lopez writes, `masters of an empire extending from the Gulf of Gascony to beyond the Indus, involved in commercial enterprises reaching into Africa and Baltic Europe, brought East and West together, as never before.'[2719]Indeed, Muslims had trading posts in Sind and Gujarat, near Bombay, and by the end of the 11th century, and Muslim merchants are known to have set up permanent establishments in Hungary, all facts testifying to `the zeal and ability with which Muslim society could call upon in commercial matters.'[2720] A zeal, which finds greater illustration with the huge Muslim coin finds in and around Scandinavia, the result of a trade dating from about the year 800 in which the Viking carried skins, swords, amber, honey, walrus ivory (elephant ivory was scarce then), flacons and slaves across Russian lands as far as Byzantium, or crossing the territory of the Khazars, on towards the Caspian and to Baghdad.[2721] It was during periods when this trade slackened-as a result of the crisis in the Caliphate-that the Vikings devoted themselves to looting and piracy.[2722]

Islam did not just revive and stimulate trade, it also set and built the very fundamentals and mechanisms of modern trade, eventually inherited by the West, and we have today, and in every single respect, as is explained in the following.

Udovitch insists on the fundamental point that it is Islamic law and the customary practice in the Muslim world, which provided merchants and traders with the commercial techniques to structure and facilitate trade

---

2716 F.Hirth and W.W. Rockhill. 1911; Ibn Batuta. 1983: *Travels in Asia and Africa, 1325-1354*. London; in Transforming the Trading World.

2717 Van Leur 1955; Hall 1985; Briggs 1951; Dumarcay 1985; Stierlin 1984 in Transforming the Trading World.

2718 Janet L. Abu-Lughod: *Before European Hegemony*, op cit; p.364.

2719 G. Wiet et al: History; op cit; p.161

2720 Ibid. p.163.

2721 J. Fontana: *The Distorted Past*; Blackwell, 1995. p.37.

2722 Ibid.

and exchange.[2723] Long before the West, Udovitch adds, Muslim merchants had at their disposal accepted legal mechanisms for extending credit and for transferring and exchanging currencies over long distances.[2724] The `Hawala' (in Arabic), *suftaja* (in Persian), or letter of credit, allowed a merchant to advance or transfer a sum of money to a business associate at some distant place with `the full confidence that the transfer would be expeditiously accomplished.'[2725] The letter of credit was regularly used to avoid carriage of large amount of capital over large stretches of land.[2726] Chance, Braudel holds, has preserved letters of Jewish traders of Cairo from the times of the first Crusade (1090s), which show that all methods of, and instruments of credit, and all forms of trade associations were known already, and were not invented subsequently in Europe as was asserted by many.[2727] Some such letters of credit were for the huge sum of 40,000 dinars in the Saharan oasis of Sijilmasa, and many examples of such letters found at Cairo Genizah,[2728]confirm that these instruments of credit were always scrupulously and strictly honoured;[2729]just as regulated by the Islamic religious text.[2730]

Derived from this form of transactions is the cheque. Cheque, in Arabic *Saqq*, is as Udovitch highlights, `functionally and etymologically the origin of our modern checks.'[2731]The use of saqq was borne out of the need to avoid having to transport coin as legal tender due to the dangers and difficulties this represented; the bankers took to the use of bills of exchange, letters of credit, and promissory notes, often drawn up as to be, in effect, cheques.[2732] At the city of Basra, in Iraq, by the mid-11th century, anybody could deposit their assets with a changer or banker who handed over a receipt. Any subsequent purchase was then made by means of a draft on the banker, who honoured it when presented by the vendor. `Such drafts on bankers were the merchants' exclusive currency.'[2733] In

[2723] A.L. Udovitch: Trade, in the *Dictionary of the Middle Ages*; op cit; vol 12; pp. 105-8; at p. 106.
[2724] Ibid.
[2725] Ibid.
[2726] Louis Massignon: L'Influence de l'Islam au Moyen Age sur la formation de l'essor des banques Juives; *Bulletin d'Etudes Orientales* (Institut Fr de Damas) Vol 1; year 1931: pp 3-12.; p. 7.
[2727] F. Braudel: *Grammaire des Civilisations*; Flammarion, 1987. p.96.
[2728] See S.D. Goiten: A Mediterranean society; op cit.
[2729] A.L. Udovitch: Trade; op cit; p. 106.
[2730] Quran: ii.282; iv.33.
[2731] A. Udovitch: Trade; op cit; p. 106. See also A. Udovitch: *Bankers Without Banks; The dawn of Modern Banking*; N. Haven; Yale University Press; 1979.
[2732] L. Massignon in G. Wiet et al: History; op cit. at p.336.
[2733] Ibid.

promoting the concept of the bill of exchange-sakk, or cheque-the Muslims, thus made the financing of commerce, especially inter-continental trade, feasible.

The development of modern banking has its early origins in the Abbasid court, under Harun al-Rashid (9th century), where under a highly developed system, a Muslim businessman could cash a cheque in Canton on his bank account in Baghdad.[2734] The main role was played by Jewish bankers who, in the entourage of both Caliph and ministers in Baghdad, were entrusted with the keeping of both the jewels of the crown and prisoners of the state.[2735] The title of Court bankers (*Jahabidhat al-Hadra*) was granted by the state chancellery under Caliph Muqtadir to two or three Jewish bankers in Baghdad.[2736]In fact the development of international banking,[2737] Massignon explains, has origins with that Jewish element serving the Abbasid Caliphate in the 9th century.[2738]That was about five centuries before a banking system of worth appeared in Western Christendom.[2739]
Islamic banking impacted directly on the West via the commercial transactions between the East and the Christian world.[2740]The Jewish communities took their practice from the Muslim milieus into that of their communities in the Christian West, especially as Jewish bankers associated themselves with others from their own community[2741] to form groups of investors willing to support large ventures that included regular caravan journeys and maritime expeditions to Africa, India and China.[2742]

2734 J. Glubb: A Short History; op cit; p.105.
2735 Passion d'al-Hallaj; Paris, 1922, 1922, p. 266 in L Massignon: L'Influence de l'Islam; op cit; p. 3.
2736 H.Sabi, *Kitab al-Wuzara*, ed. Amedroz, Leyden, 1904 in L Massignon: l'Influence. p.5.
2737 See also:
W. Fischel: The Origins of Banking in Medieval Islam: *Journal of the Royal Asiatic Society (JRAS)*; 1933; pp 339-52.
2738 L. Massignon: l'Influence de l'Islam; op cit; p. 4.
2739 Ibid.
2740 See:
-D.Abulafia: The Role of Trade in Muslim-Christian contact during the Middle Ages in *The Arab Influence in Medieval Europe*; op cit; pp 1-24.
-M.Amari: *I Diplomi arabi del reale archivio Fiorentino*, Florence, Lemonnier, 1863.
- M.L. de Mas Latrie: *Traites de Paix et de Commerce, et Documents Divers, Concernant les Relations des Chretiens avec les Arabes de l'Afrique Septentrionale au Moyen Age*, Burt Franklin, New York, Originally Published in Paris, 1866. p.xv.
2741 Jacob Mann: *Responsa des geonim*, Mesopotamiens, ap.Jew. Qart Rev., 1917-1921, in Louis Massignon: L'Influence de l'Islam; op cit; p. 6.
2742 L. Massignon: L'Influence de l'Islam. p. 6.

Paper money was first adopted in north China by the end of the 11th century and in the Chin and Southern Sung territories it was in regular use by the 12th century, although it still coexisted with metal coins.[2743] Some paper money was printed in Chinese and Arabic in 1294 at Tabriz via block-printing, a method also of Chinese origin.[2744] We have a contemporary account of it by a Persian historian who lived in Tabriz.[2745] As with paper, it was the Muslims, who traded directly with the West, who both generalised the use of, and spread of this Chinese invention.

There is an Islamic powerful form of influence with regard to weights and measures, too. The smallest weight Muslims used in trade was the grain of barley, four of which were equal to one sweet pea, called in Arabic carat; which is still in use as a unit of weight, and of precious metals as being so many carats fine.[2746] Most of the common Arabic units found their way into one or all of the Iberian romance languages.[2747] As early as 989, the *qaf'iz* (a measure of weight) appeared in Catalonia as the kaficio, and later the *qadah* (a large measure for grain) became alcadafe in Castilian, alcadafe in Portuguese, and cadaf or cadufa in Catalan.[2748]

Muslim coinage, as in Spain, was reputed for its purity and design.[2749] Spanish currency consisted of the Dinar (of gold), which was equal to two dollars (early 20th century value); the dirhem (of silver), equal to twelve cents; and various small pieces of copper that fluctuated in value.[2750] Whatever the means of transfer, numismatic data shows that coins moved between al-Andalus and Europe during the 8th, 9th 10th and early 11th centuries.[2751] Bates also notes how the Normans of Sicily struck Arabic gold quarter dinars (called taris by the Italians) for nearly a century after their conquest of the island, whilst Christian France, just as

---

[2743] J. L. Abu-Lughod: Before European Hegemony; op cit; p.333.

[2744] G. Sarton: *Introduction; op cit;* Vol II, p. 764. D. Hunter: *Papermaking: The History and Technique of an Ancient Craft*; Pleiades Books; London; 1943; 1947; p.474.

[2745] G. Sarton: Introduction, Vol II, p. 764.

[2746] J.W. Draper: A History; op cit; Vol II; p.44.

[2747] O.R. Constable: *Trade and Traders in Muslim Spain*; Cambridge University Press; 1994. p. 47.

[2748] J. Vallve: Notas de metrologia hispano-arabe II, Medidas de capacidad; in *Al-Andalus* 42; 1977; pp. 91-8.

[2749] S.P. Scott: History, vol 2; op cit, p.636.

[2750] Ibid.

[2751] O.R. Constable: Trade and Traders; op cit; p. 39.

Spain and Italy, also used and imitated the gold coins of the Almoravids (called maravedis).[2752]

Thus have been made clear aspects of how Islam pioneered and impacted on fundamental elements of modern trade. The current Western historical interpretation, though, is that it was not from Islam that modern trade derives but from Western Christian genius, more precisely, Italian genius. Setting aside the fact that the developments just looked at come centuries prior to similar ones made by the Italians, this issue of pioneering and impact is now looked at from another set of angles so as to refute this generalised Western historical interpretation.

c. The Italian Role:

Abu Lughod points out how during the so-called Dark Ages of Europe, the Italian ports never lost their continuity nor their connections with the East.[2753] The Italian port towns of Genoa and Venice, in particular, maintained an intense trade with Anatolia as well as with the Fertile Crescent, Egypt, and North Africa, and because of that were able to learn from their eastern counterparts many of the institutional arrangements that facilitated long distance and cross-societal trade.[2754]Only few Western historians, she notes, have paid adequate attention to these Eastern precedents, whilst the like of Max Weber have often credited the Italians with unique business creativity, which they hardly deserved, although they did make crafty use of the lessons they learned. But they were subsidiary to the Middle East.[2755]

The reason why the Italians pioneered with regard to trade is precisely because they, not other parts of Western Christendom, had the most trading links with the Islamic world whether in North Africa, or in the East. In the Maghrib, for instance, in the 12th century, the Pisans, Florentines, Genoese, Venetians, and Sicilians had trade establishments in the main city ports from Tripoli in the east to Ceuta in the West.[2756]With the East, Amalfi, principally, traded with Syria, [2757]whilst

---

2752 M.L. Bates: Mints and Money: Dictionary of the Middle Ages; op cit; vol 8; pp-421-5; at p. 423.
2753 J.L. Abu-Lughod: Before European Hegemony, op cit; p.67.
2754 Ibid.
2755 Ibid.
2756 M.L. de Mas Latrie: Traites de Paix; op cit; pp. 64; 89 and 91.
2757 C. H. Haskins: The Renaissance; op cit; p. 21.

Pisa, Genoa and Venice had monopoly over Eastern trade in the wake of the crusades.[2758]Thus, it is little surprise, that it is the very cities, which traded with the Islamic world that pioneered and dominated every aspect of Western Christian trade, in form and in substance. And how, when, where, and in what form they picked and transmitted some fundamental aspects of modern trade from Islam is now considered.

Many expressions, which are today part of the Western vocabulary and international trade have an Arabic origin, expressions such as arsenal, Magasin, traffic, tariff, douane (customs), aval, etc. The impact is not just, as has been the practice on the part of most historians/specialists of Islamic culture, to mention them whilst passing, or see them in their linguistic form only, but much more than this. The true impact is their establishing fundamentals upon which the whole modern system of trade works. No need here to dwell too long on a word such as traffic, for instance, from *tafriiq*, meaning `distribution,' which is the basis for exchanges. Today, the focus of the World Trade Organisation is on the concept of free movement of goods as the basis of prosperity. 'Magazine', for example, particularly in the sense of a storehouse for goods, comes from the Arabic; the Arabic plural *makhazin* being adopted as a singular by the Italian traders of the late Middle Ages (e.g. Genoa or Venice), either direct from an Arabic-speaking country like Egypt or, more likely, from Turkey or Persia, where Arabic plurals were often used as singulars.[2759] Then, from Italian *magazzino*, it passed into Old French as magazin (modern *magasin* = 'shop') and thence to English.[2760] Nowadays, of course, it is most familiar in the sense of a 'storehouse' and as a miscellaneous weekly or monthly periodical.[2761] Magasin carries the notion of storage; the magasins for centuries acting as the bases for all European/Jewish trade dealings in and out of the Islamic land. Around and from the magasins evolved maritime activity, money exchange, road transport, etc. Reference to De Mas Latrie shows that all Western Mediterranean republics, Italians, without exception, owned permanent establishments in Muslim coastal towns, entertaining

[2758] See, for instance, W. Heyd: *Histoire du commerce; op cit.*

[2759] G. M. Wickens: `What the West Borrowed from the Middle East,' in *Introduction to Islamic Civilisation*, ed by R.M. Savory, Cambridge University Press, Cambridge, 1976. pp 120-5; at p. 121.

[2760] Ibid.

[2761] Ibid.

councils and envoys to safeguard their interests and manage their businesses, and expand their trade.[2762]

Another borrowing of fundamental importance is the English word 'arsenal' derived from Italian *arsenale*, itself derived from the Arabic expression *dar as-sina'ah*, 'craft-house, workshop'.[2763] Wickens appropriately makes the following point:
`The non-expert might well be sceptical here: were there no workshops in the West, and could the word 'arsenal' really come from a word looking so different? The answers are fairly straightforward. In the first place, while Western craftsmen in the early Middle Ages were certainly capable of making weapons and building vessels, they lacked (and often suffered for lacking) really large-scale centralized organization of these activities until it was introduced from the Middle East. The linguistic jump is not so great as it seems: when terms are borrowed in this way, one of the commonest casualties is the initial, imperfectly heard consonant: hence the disappearing 'd'. As to the inserted 'l' in 'arsenal', this was probably an attempt to cope with the heavy Arabic guttural while still giving the word a satisfactory Italian sound to finish with.'[2764]

The concept of wealth creation relies on a fundamental element: risk. Without risk in search of profit, no venture is undertaken; and no investment is made. The concept of risk comes from the Arabic `Rizk' (bounty), which is even more enticing than profit. In no culture, would economic venture and bounty seem so closely associated than in the Islamic. In tracing the history of commerce, and wealth creation, Peter Jay seized on this particular element to highlight the decisive role of the Islamic civilisation in expanding international trade by associating the concepts of risk taking and bounty, and the role of the Italians in seizing on the concept.[2765] The notion of `rizq' has a powerful psychological impact, stimulating the search for wealth through association of bounty with economic venture. Islam, thus, replaced the fulfilment of localized needs with profit through large commercial exchanges; and the search for higher profit demanding increased risk taking. The fundamental reason why risk of capital is the child of Islam is simple: Islam forbids the hoarding of money for the sake of lending it in return of interest on it. Interest is banned in Islam. Thus, for any Muslim with money, the need is

---

[2762] M.L. de Mas Latrie: Traites de paix; op cit; p.84.
[2763] G.M. Wickens: What the West; op cit; p. 123.
[2764] Ibid.
[2765] P. Jay: The Road to Riches; BBC; August; 2000 (seen by this author).

to invest it in person, or via another party.[2766] This way, capital is always circulating rather than being static, thus, maximizing its uses. By forbidding interest on loans, Islam also makes available, and freely, the required capital for the risk takers. There is no heavy burden upon the investor having to borrow at high interest, or having to repay crippling interest on loans. Without dwelling on this, today, one of the major, if not the major reason of Third World poverty is debt servicing. There are, of course, other crippling factors for the Third World: administrative inefficiency, incompetence, wars etc; yet, the amount of money such poor countries have to disburse every year (out of their export gains) to repay not their loans, just the services on such loans, means they have little chance of getting out of the poverty-dependency trap. By forbidding usury, Islam not only removes this burden, it also kills the easy avenue for enrichment, and makes business investment the one way to derive profit, which hence promotes productive ventures in industry, trade and farming.

Already noted is how Islam provides a legal basis to commercial transactions.[2767]Amari has also gathered 84 original documents, 41 diverse pieces all related to the Maghrib, many in duplicate and original contemporary text, relating to exchanges between Muslims and Christians,[2768] the oldest dating from 1150.[2769] Islamic procedures from earlier times were adopted by Western counterparts, Wiet et al noting how oral precedents became committed to standardised written forms; notarial practice evolving in Italy in the 11th century and spreading through southern France and Spain from the middle of the 12th, affording private individuals the opportunity, of which they were not slow to take advantage, of ensuring legal validity for their smallest transactions.[2770]

The strong Italian presence in the East during the crusades, which will be considered under the next heading, contributed to considerable extent to transfers of similar sort. Some such transfers included rationalised calculating methods for book keeping and the introduction of a simplified system of payment in the shape of cheques and bills of exchange.[2771] All these individuals examples were so favourably received in the merchants' own cities that the most important spheres of

---

[2766] See for instance: A. Udovitch: Credit as a mean of investment in medieval Islamic trade; *Journal of Economic and Social History of the Orient* (JESHO); 1967; pp 260-4.

[2767] A.L. Udovitch: Trade, op cit.

[2768] M. Amari in *I Diplomi arabi del reale archivio Fiorentino*, Florence, Lemonnier, 1863.

[2769] M.L. de Mas Latrie: Traites de paix; op cit; p.xv.

[2770] G. Wiet et al: History; op cit; p.474.

[2771] M. Erbstosser: *The Crusades;* p. 202-3.

social life there were given a stimulus which significantly accelerated their historical progress.[2772]

The transfer of the Arabic numeral system and accounting via Leonardo Fibonacci is one of the most endearing instances of how commercial contact with Islam affected not just mathematical sciences in Western Christendom but also commercial practice. To illustrate this point, return must be made, again, to the links the Italians had with the Muslims, this time in North Africa. The Almohad ruler Abd-El Mumen had in the years 1153 or 1154 concluded with the Republic of Genoa a treaty to secure peace and good rapports between their subjects,[2773] whilst in 1166, were passed treaties between the Almohads and Pisa; Abu Yakub Yusuf, son of Abd-El Mumen, giving back the Pisans the franchises and possessions they had before in Africa.[2774] In the 12th century, the Pisans, Florentines, Genoese, Venetians, Sicilians all had trade establishments in the main city ports of the Maghrib including the Algerian city of Bejaia.[2775] Genoa had in 1164 appointed a regular official at Bejaia to supervise trade there; he, perhaps the first `colonial official' of modern times.[2776] Pisa immediately followed suite. The Pisan office had an important repercussion on European culture, for in 1175 its holder was one Bonacci.[2777] It was his son Leonardo (c. 1170-1248) who was to show himself the most gifted mathematician of the Middle Age.[2778] Leonardo Fibonacci's father had discovered during his trading exchanges with the North African coast the superiority and advantages of the Arabic numerals for commercial purposes.[2779] Hence Leonardo was sent there to learn at the hands of Muslim masters the system.[2780]In his father's warehouse Leonardo first heard of the use of Arabic numerals in which the value of the digit is decimally related to its position.[2781]This is our modern way of reckoning. At that time only the Roman system of numbering was known in Europe, and all calculation was with the abacus. Leonardo wrote *Liber abacci* in 1202 where he advocates the Arabic system, which was the first European

---

[2772] Ibid.
[2773] M.L. de Mas Latrie: Traites de paix; op cit; p.47.
[2774] Manrangone, *Chron. Pis*, edit. Bonaini. in M.L. de Mas Latrie: Traites de paix; op cit; p. 48.
[2775] M.L. de Mas Latrie: Traites de paix; op cit; pp. 64; 89 and 91.
[2776] C. Singer: The Earliest Chemical Industry; op cit; p. 85.
[2777] Ibid.
[2778] Ibid.
[2779] W. Montgomery Watt: *The Influence of Islam; op cit;* pp. 63-4.
[2780] Ibid.
[2781] C. Singer: The Earliest Chemical Industry; op cit; p. 85.

scientific appreciation of the method.[2782] In his *Liber abacci* Leonardo gives, amongst his examples, a method for calculating the capacity value of alum in a cargo.[2783] Thus the essential notation of modern mathematics, as of modern commerce, arose directly from the trade between Pisa and Bejaia.
Arabic numerals were first used in Europe precisely around that time by notaries charged with drawing up commercial contracts for use in the Islamic world.[2784] The progress of such numerals in the Christian West was slow; but eventually they made their way there. What their history also proves is that it was not the Italians who carried expertise to the Muslims but quite the reverse.

A further Italian link in the development of the administrative/financial structures of Western Christendom, this time, via Norman Sicily, is with regard to the development of the English exchequer. This matter having already been seen, here thus, it is briefly reminded, that this is yet again another development taking place in the 12th century. Coincidentally, it happens just when Thomas Brown (Qaid Brun), whose former service with King Roger in Sicily in *Regis Secretis*, i.e: the *Diwan or Doana de Secretis,*[2785]is transferred to England. It was he who introduced the Exchequer to Henry II's England after he left Sicily at the accession of William the Bad (1154).[2786] The origin of the Exchequer and its Pipe Rolls, may have its beginning in the Sicilian *duana* (Arabic *diwan,*) which was largely staffed by Muslim officials, kept voluminous registers, and `seems plainly to go back to Islamic antecedents.'[2787]
However, there remains the manner of calculating, and here must be added another element of impact, again, taking place in the 12th century, and again, owing to Islamic sources, and this is the use of the abacus.[2788] It is worth reminding that it was Adelard of Bath who wrote treatises on the subject (in the 12th century), continuing on the traditions of earlier men (Gerbert and Hermann of Reichnau, both of them, as chapter one of

---

[2782] Ibid.
[2783] Ibid.
[2784] D.Abulafia: The Role of Trade; I; in C. Hillenbrand: *The Crusades, Islamic Perspectives*, Edinburgh University Press; 1999.p.397.
[2785] W. Stubbs: Select Charters Oxford, 1895, p. 190. in E-Jamison: The Sicilian Norman Kingdom in the Mind of Anglo-Norman Contemporaries; *Proceedings of the British Academy*, Vol 24. pp 237-285.P.250
[2786] R. Briffault: The Making, op cit, p. 212; R. L. Poole: The Exchequer; op cit. p. 118 onwards.
[2787] C.H. Haskins: *The Normans in European History*; New York, 1966; p. 229.
[2788] R.L. Poole: The Exchequer; op cit; pp. 50-61.

part two has shown, were imbued and inspired by Islamic learning, just as Adelard was). Adelard also spent time in Norman Sicily, and must have familiarised the English with the early rudiments of the Islamic (Arabic) system of calculation, setting an idea into motion, but far from resolving the problem. The development in the 12th century exactly leads to the Muslim/Sicilian source for the simple reason that the system does require people with knowledge of Islamic accounting or use of decimals. It would have been impossible for English born people to master the use of accounting based on such Islamic sources, for at the time, the Christian West was devoid of those who could handle Islamic methods of calculation. Bresc notes, indeed, how the Normans never refrained from using Arabic extensively, and the shortage of well read personnel explains why, still, in 1240, functions of the Duana Secretis are filled with Muslim scribes.[2789] If this is to prove something, it proves that it is impossible for anyone not learned in Arabic to run the administration of the Normans in Sicily. Thus, how come, Qaid Brown (Brun) (Thomas Brown,) supposedly an Englishman, should travel from England to run Sicilian administration as modern Western history holds. Qaid Brun, thus, rather than being an Englishman returning to his country after a stay in Sicily, was in reality a Muslim Sicilian, coming to England to run the English exchequer, thus, proving that such expertise travelled from Sicily to England rather than the reverse.

Finally, Islamic literature in the field of trade influenced subsequent Western literature, and by `coincidence', the Italian, first. Al-Dimashqi's 11th century guide: *Kitab al-Ishara (The Book of Guidance)*[2790]begins with an essay on the true nature of wealth and then proceeds to discuss the necessity of money; how to test a currency; how to evaluate commodities; their prices; how to discern good from defective merchandise; investment in real estate; handicrafts and manufactures; advice for sales people; the advantages of business; the different types of merchants and their duties; how to avoid fraud; how to keep records, wealth protection, and so on and so forth....[2791] By some coincidence, Al-Dimashqi's *Kitab* shows a very close relationship in technique and approach to the subsequent

---

2789 H. Bresc: Mudejars des Pays de la Couronne d'Aragon et Sarrasins de la Sicilie Normande: le Probleme de l'acculturation; In *Politique et Societe en Sicile; XII-Xv em siecle*; Variorum; Aldershot; 1990; pp. 51-60. at p. 58.

2790 Al-Dimashqi: *Mahasin al-Tijara*; trad. H.Ritter, Ein arabisches handbuch der handelswissenschaft; in *Der Islam*; vol VII; 1917; pp 1-91.

2791 R.D. Mc Chesney: Ad-Dimashqi in *The Genius of Arab Civilisation*, J. R. Hayes Editor; Source of Renaissance, Phaidon, 1976. p 206.

Pegalotti's *Practica della Mercatura.*[2792] A great deal of the merchandise referred to in the two manuscripts are the same, and so is a lot of the technical terminology, including the advice to businessmen, and so are many of the forms of business relationships.[2793] (The two manuscripts are available for checking).

2. Crafts and Industries

Lopez notes, that amidst the agents of economic revival of the West from the 10th century onwards, half oriental cities, which never slept: Venice, Amalfi, Salerno, and Bari, occupy the first rank.[2794]The same Italian cities, that traded with Islam and imported Islamic trade mechanisms, playing the overwhelming part in the introduction of Islamic skills in crafts and industry in the Christian West. The inventory of industries further on will highlight this. However, just as with sciences, or other skills, the concourse of skilled Muslims and other Christians who lived under the Muslims was also necessary to this transfer. Hence, the focus, first, on the agents of transfer (the Italians and Muslim craftsmen), before is seen the passage of some crafts and industries from Islam to the West.

a. Italian Cities and Muslim Craftsmen as Agents of Diffusion:

The fundamental reason why the Italian cities were first to convey most crafts and early industries (just as trade mechanisms) to Western Christendom is simple: they were the most powerful Christian presence on Islamic soil on the economic front. It follows the same pattern observed throughout this work, that each and every region that made contact with Islam was first to change, and it changed in whatever aspect it took from Islam. Lorraine sought and brought astronomy and mathematics from Islam, and changed precisely in such sciences; Salerno got the Islamic medical lore, and rose precisely in that field; when England borrowed astronomy (through Walcher, Adelard, Petrus) or administration (from Sicily), these were the very precise subjects it

---

[2792]N. Stilman in discussion seminar of published articles Islam and the medieval West; In K. I. Semaan; edt; op cit p. 152.
[2793] Ibid.
[2794] R Lopez: Les influences Orientales; op cit; p. 597.

pioneered; when Cracow focused on astronomy, and its lectures made Islamic astronomy a basic requirement for graduates and masters, it produced a Copernicus; and when the Italians, not the French, nor the English, traded with Islam, not the French, nor the English, but the Italians, precisely, witnessed the advances in their trade. And it is absolutely the same with regard to craft and industries. As the Italians were the closest industrial partners to Islam in North Africa, and those who took over Muslim industry and trade in the East following the success of the crusades, it is absolutely no surprise at all, as is going to be shown now, that they were the first to develop crafts and industries in the West, and that they held the ascendancy for centuries to come in the field. The only competition they will encounter at some point will come, not surprisingly, from the nation which was the closest to Islamic industries and crafts: Spain.

The Italian presence in the Islamic land, whether west or east of the Islamic realm, during the Middle Ages, was very powerful. Italian cities held the most extensive Western Christian links in North Africa, as highlighted by De Mas Latrie.[2795] The Venetians followed the Pisans and the Genoese, and soon, under the patronage of the pavilions of the great maritime cities, were also involved the small ports of Liguria and Dalmatia, and the rich merchants of Tuscany and Lombardy.[2796] Sicilians, Sardinians, like the Venetian, without neglecting Morocco, were, like the Genoese and the Pisans, in continuous business rapport and interest with Tunis and `Oriental Mauritania.' In Tunis, Bejaia, and El-Mehdia, there was a large Venetian presence, the Venetians even having changing offices, and public writers.[2797] The republic of Florence, at the same time as it built its navy, developed its textile and silk industries, and sent consuls and ambassadors.[2798] Genoa and Pisa, as noted above, already had their special representatives, and some impact through these extensive links has already been seen.

It is, however, the place of the Italians in the East, which is of greater interest in this section. Italian cities were the most important intermediaries between East and West, already preceding the

[2795] M.L. de Mas Latrie: Traites de paix; op cit.
[2796] Ibid. p.84.
[2797] Ibid. p.89.
[2798] Pagnini: *Della decima di Firenze*, Vol II, p. 39, 187, etc; in M.L. De Mas Latrie: Traites; pp. 84; also preface; pp. 37; 48-9; etc.

crusades.[2799] The `treasures' which converged on Alexandria by sea and land `from the two Indies, the two Ethiopias, and Arabia'[2800]were re-distributed to the Western countries through the representatives, established in that city, of the merchants principally of Venice, Amalfi, Pisa and Genoa.[2801]It was, however, the crusades (launched in 1095), which were to play a central role in putting the Italians not just in contact with Muslim trade and industry in the East, but in control of such Muslim trade and industries, the Italians simply taking over Muslim crafts and industries as they found them. This take over has its origins in the crusades themselves. A major reason behind the crusades was the great desire of the Italian cities of Pisa, Genoa, Venice, Amalfi to extend their rising commercial power, and capture Islamic wealth for themselves.[2802] Once the Normans captured Sicily from the Muslims (1060-1091), and Muslim rule was partly broken in Spain (1085f), the western Mediterranean was freed for Christian trade; the Italian cities grew richer and stronger, and planned to end Muslim ascendancy in the eastern Mediterranean.[2803]They participated greatly with their fleets in the assistance of the crusades, often such fleets playing a decisive part. It was the Genoese ships of the Embriaco brothers which brought the Crusaders provisions and supplies for the war, and it was to Genoese sailors that the chroniclers attribute the success in the capture of Jerusalem.[2804] In 1099, the Doge of Venice set out with a fleet to open up a new and profitable trade with all the coast, and to win privileges for his city, by aiding to conquer Caesarea and Arsuf, Haifa, Tyre and Ascalon.[2805] From Rhodes came letters in November, 1099, announcing the approach of these important allies; and in the June that followed Godfrey, the crusader leader, made treaty with them.[2806]If from the 24th of June until 15th August, the Venetian fleet would aid his army, he promised the Doge a third part of every city taken, and a church and market in every town, and half the spoil, and safety for the crew of any ship wrecked on the coast; an alliance ratified on 18th of July.[2807] The Genoese fleet equally played a great part in the taking of Caesarea

---

[2799] R.S. Lopez in A.R. Lewis: The Moslem expansion in the Mediterranean, A.D. 827-960: pp 23-29; in *The Islamic World and the West (*A. R. Lewis ed) op cit; p.30.

[2800] William of Tyre: *Historia*, book XIX, in G. Sarton: Introduction; Volume III. p.229.

[2801] G. Sarton: Introduction; Volume III. p.229.

[2802] W. Durant: The Age of faith, op cit; p.586.

[2803] Ibid.

[2804] Z. Oldenbourg: The Crusades; op cit; p. 295.

[2805] C.R. Conder: *The Latin Kingdom.* Op cit; p. 72.

[2806] Ibid.

[2807] Ibid.

(1101), Tartus (1102), Acre and Jubail (1104) and Tripoli (1109).[2808] Pisa and Venice played further part, too; the Pisan fleet besieging Lattaquieh in 1099,[2809] whilst Venice lent its fleet in 1110 against Beirut and Sidon, most particularly;[2810] and in 1123, a large Venetian squadron inflicted a severe defeat on the Egyptian fleet, allowing the Crusaders to take Tyre the following year.[2811] Then, once conquest was achieved, because of their very nature, or location all along the coast, the Crusader kingdoms would have never lasted without the support of the powerful Italian fleets supplying them with goods and fighting men.[2812]

Although they were gratified for such assistance, Genoa, for instance, having the honour of seeing its deeds engraved in letters of gold in the Church of the Holy Sepulchre itself, the Italians were never content with that alone. The Genoese assistance earned them a third of the booty, and trading quarters in every town they had helped take.[2813] After the capture of Tripoli, the Genoese earned themselves a street in that city, and the whole town of Jebail.[2814] Bertram the second count, in 1109, granted the Genoese a third of the port of Tripoli, and the rocks of islands near it, and free trade in the province.[2815] The Genoese quarter in Antioch consisted of at least thirty houses, a church and a set of buildings used as warehouses and stores.[2816] In helping capture Tyre, the Venetians earned themselves a quarter of the city, and a district of their own in every crusader city.[2817] Tyre became in fact the main settlement of the Venetians.[2818] A few years later we find the Venetians settling in Tripoli, and later in Jebail.[2819] The Pisans owned property in Tripoli towards the close of the century,[2820] and were strongly present in Acre.[2821] There was also a powerful Pisan colony in Antioch, one of its members (Stephen) best known as a translator.[2822] All in all, the whole coastland of Syria and Palestine, and other major centres of trade, were under Italian

---

[2808] R.H.C. Davis: *A History of Medieval Europe*; Longman; London; 2nd ed; 1988. p. 271.
[2809] Z. Oldenbourg: The Crusades; op cit; p. 295.
[2810] R.H. C. Davis: A History; op cit; p. 271.
[2811] Z. Oldenbourg: The Crusades; op cit; p. 295.
[2812] Ibid; p. 295-6.
[2813] R.H.C. Davis: *A History; op cit;* p. 271.
[2814] Z. Oldenbourg: The Crusades; op cit; p. 296.
[2815] Regesta, nos 55; 84. In C.R. Conder: The Latin Kingdom; op cit; p. 87.
[2816] M. Erbstosser: *The Crusades;* op cit; p. 131-2.
[2817] Z. Oldenbourg: The Crusades; op cit; p. 297.
[2818] M. Erbstosser: *The Crusades;* op cit; p. 131-2.
[2819] C.R. Conder: *The Latin Kingdom; op cit;* p. 87.
[2820] Ibid.
[2821] M. Erbstosser: *The Crusades;* op cit; p. 131-2.
[2822] C.H. Haskins: Studies; op cit.

control: Genoa in Antioch, Laodicea, Caesarea, Acre, Jafa, Jerusalem, Beirut; Pisa in Jafa, Laodicea, Tyre, Jerusalem, and Acre; Venice in Sidon, Tyre, Tripoli, and Jerusalem.[2823]

The established Italian colonies in Palestine and Syria contributed immensely to the transfer to the West of new crafts, techniques, new methods of building, and new ideas in the useful arts.[2824]Indeed, the Italians have now become the owners of industries, which were once in Muslim hands, and the products, and skills and know how of such industries, directly passed under their control. Thus, little surprise if woodwork and metal work, as well as the manufacturing of glasses, which required varied knowledge, which was unknown during the Crusade times, was soon borrowed and spread into Europe.[2825]The glass-works of Tyre served as models to those of Venice, and from Syria were in 1277 passed on the secrets of Syrian glass-making to Venice.[2826] The finding of glass objects in former crusader castles, such as Montfort, objects which were executed following the traditional enamelling techniques of the Islamic East, but which show purely Western subjects, constitute links with later Venetian work.[2827] The diverse crafts, to be seen under arts further down, were also acquired, to the largest measure, in the same manner from the East. When subsequently the local Sicilians lost the skills for sugar manufacturing, Emperor Frederick II sent to Marshall Ricardo Filangieri (an Italian obviously) in Tyre for the supply of new skills.[2828] Even in coinage, with their so called `Tyre Dinars' the Crusaders imitated Muslims from the middle of the 12th century for over a hundred years.[2829]

Other than the Italians, Muslim craftsmen were agents of transfer of many crafts and industrial skills. In conflict, at all times in history, whether during the crusades, or during the Second world War, and even

---

[2823] M. Erbstosser: *The Crusades;* op cit; p. 131-2.

[2824] C. Singer: East and West in Retrospect; in C.J. Singer et al: *History of Technology*; 5 vols; vol 2; Oxford at the Clarendon; 1956; pp 753-77; p. 764.

[2825] G. Le Bon: La Civilisation des Arabes; op cit; p.259.

[2826] A. Y. Al-Hassan; D.R. Hill: *Islamic Technology; op cit;* p. 33

[2827] R.Ettinghausen: Muslim decorative arts and painting, their nature and impact on the medieval West; in *Islam and the Medieval West*; ed S. Ferber; State University of New York at Binghamton; 1975. pp. 5-26. p. 19.

[2828] Huillard-Breholles, Hist.Dipl. Friderici II; Vol 5; pars 1; p.574. in W.Heyd: Histoire; p. 686.

[2829] Ibn al-Qalanisi; Gibb; 48; Ibn Taghribirdi; Nujum; v; 150 in C. Hillenbrand: The Crusades, Islamic Perspectives, op cit;.p.398.

under the harshest foe, i.e the Mongols or Timur Lang,[2830] one class is always spared total annihilation: people with practical know how. And so were Muslim craftsmen during the wars between Christianity and Islam. In the midst of war, or following conquest, Muslim craftsmen carried the bulk of transfer of skills from one culture into the other. The skilled Andalusi workforce, for instance, with its well developed industries and sophisticated agriculture, had much to offer to the rural and less technologically developed northern kingdoms, Constable notes.[2831] The role of such craftsmen had dramatic repercussions on any part of Western Christendom they were carried to. The transfer of Muslim ceramic experts between Spain and other parts of Western Europe directly led to the rise of Western gold lustre ceramics, for instance.[2832] Prior to such transfer, imported pieces from the Islamic land seemed to be located `in some exotic distant land.'[2833] All changed, when in the 14th century Muslim experts moved from Malaga (still under Islamic control) to the suburb of Manises (near Valencia), then under Christian control, and began to produce lustre-ware; `the surrender of this professional secret to a Western land governed by Christians had taken place,' Schnyder notes.[2834] Manises soon developed into a leading centre in the art of lustre faience, so much so, in 1383 its gilded and expertly painted products enjoyed such an excellent reputation that the Franciscan monk Eiximenes, author of a eulogy to Valencia, was able to write that even the Pope, the Cardinals and the Princes of the world were among its admirers.[2835]Then from there, the skills spread northwards. Pottery decorated with the emblems of important Italian, French and Spanish personalities were to follow;[2836] and the golden ceramics from Valencia achieved their widest distribution to the furthest reaches of Europe.[2837]And wherever `the brilliant examples of the artistic ability of Valencia arrived, they served as guidelines and ideals, strongly influencing the Italian Majolica art of

---

[2830] Timur Lang, for instance, when he destroyed Damascus and mass slaughtered its population only spared the artisans, whom he took to Samarkand his capital. In D. Whitehouse: Glass; *Dictionary of the Middle Ages*; op cit; vol 5; pp. 545-8. at p. 547.
[2831] O.R. Constable: Trade and Traders; op cit; p. 4.
[2832] R. Schnyder: Islamic ceramics: A Source of Inspiration for Medieval European Art; in *Islam and the Medieval West*; S. Ferber edition; op cit; P. 34 fwd.
[2833] Ibid. p.34.
[2834] Ibid.
[2835] M. Olivar Davdi: *La ceramica trecentista en los paises de la corona de Aragon,* Barcelona; 1952; pp. 118 fwd
[2836] A Wilson Frothingham: *Lustreware of Spain,* New York; 1951;, pp. 15-78.
[2837] R. Schnyder: Islamic Ceramics; op cit; P. 34.

the 15th Century.[2838] After the established relations between Manises and Avignon during the years 1362-64, we hear in 1382-85 of a certain Jehan de Valence who was employed in the service of the Duc de Berry and who produced painted faience tiles in Poitiers and in Bourges (in France).[2839]

The superiority of Muslim skills is further substantiated by the fact that everywhere under Christian rule, Muslim craftsmen were keenly sought after. In Spain, as the re-conquest proceeded, Muslims, masters of great skills were allowed to retain their functions and serve the new crown; alongside builders, paper and textile makers, manufacturers of iron, they represented expertise of a diverse sort.[2840] Glick notes, that, in general, Christian rulers made concerted efforts to keep Muslim owned industries going, particularly those crafts deemed to be Islamic specialities.[2841] Thus, in 1251 Jaime of Aragon allowed the potters of Jativa to practise their craft on the annual payment of a bezant for every oven.[2842] The same Jaime encouraged the continuity of the paper industry in Jativa and supported it by forbidding the making of paper by Muslims elsewhere in the kingdom of Valencia, whilst Alfonso X ordered in 1281 that no pottery works were to be built in Cordoba unless in the Muslim style.[2843] Groups of Muslim workers were enticed from their homes by royal or seigniorial privilege and settled en masse elsewhere, to develop particular industries.[2844] Muslim craftsmen, dye-masters, boatmen on the Ebro River, leatherworkers, and providers of many kinds of service shared their hamlets and urban quarters.[2845] Equally the barons and landlords, in Spain, valued both Muslims' work ethic and the income it brought, and they tried to protect this investment against church and townsmen.[2846] Muslim expertise was so critically needed that when in Murcia Muslim weavers departed en masse, the silk industry was destroyed, and fulling mills had to be converted by new Christian owners to rice husking.[2847] Also both Valencian and Sicilian Muslims served in the respective royal armies as contingents; and both

---

[2838] Ibid.

[2839] M. Olivar Davdi: La ceramica trecentista; op cit; p. 135 fwd.

[2840] N. Smith: *A History of Dams,* The Chaucer Press, London,1971, p .103.

[2841] T.F. Glick: Islamic and Christian Spain; op cit p. 223.

[2842] J.F. Riano: *South Kensington Museum Art handbooks. The Industrial Arts in Spain*; London; 1879; p. 163.

[2843] T.F. Glick: Islamic and Christian Spain; op cit p. 223.

[2844] Ibid. p. 224.

[2845] R. I. Burns: Muslims in the Thirteenth; op cit; p.65.

[2846] Ibid. p.63.

[2847] T.F. Glick: Islamic and Christian Spain; p. 223.

manufactured valued weapons for the Christian armies.[2848] Muslim craftsmen of Sicily under Christian rule contributed to the same spread of crafts and techniques as Muslims did in Spain. Frederick II had large numbers of Muslims transported and exiled to Lucera, and they took with them their own arts and crafts.[2849] At the fall of Lucera fifty years later, the conquering Angevin transported back to Naples various such Muslims for their service.[2850] In the crusader East, European artisans who had settled in the cities of the crusader states were unable to exercise any lasting influence worth mentioning.[2851] In the process of sugar production, for instance, the Crusaders found that the Syrians were not just expert at growing sugar; they also mastered the technique of crushing it under presses, extracting the juices, concentrating the substance on fire, then drying it out slowly into sugar.[2852] The Crusaders took over the industry, and followed precisely the Muslims system of production, using the same Muslim terminology.[2853] At Acre, they used Muslim prisoners in the manufacture of sugar.[2854] Large numbers of Eastern Muslims craftsmen, skilled in many other trades, were also carried to Europe by their new crusader masters on their return;[2855] and their impact will be particularly obvious in the following chapter on arts and architecture.

It is worth adding another point here, raised by Stock, who points out, that it may be, that Bernard of Tiron, a wandering preacher who died in 1117, founded a house specifically as a haven for craftsmen, but the real model for change came once again from Islam, in which the status of the artisan had changed from that of the slave to that of the free labourer.[2856] The artisan scientist, who was considered an aberration in the ancient world, was more a norm in Islam, artisans playing a leading part in the transfer of techniques throughout the highly mobile Muslim world.[2857] The importance Muslims granted their craftsmen or instrument makers is also noted by Sarton `in the extravagant praise' lavished on the

---

[2848] R. I. Burns: Muslims in the Thirteenth; op cit; p.101.
[2849] A. Lowe: *The barrier and the Bridge*, G. Bles, London, 1972; p.92.
[2850] Ibid.
[2851] M. Erbstosser: *The Crusades;* op cit; p. 131.
[2852] Jacques de Vitry in W. Heyd: Histoire; vol2; op cit; pp. 685-6.
[2853] W. Heyd: Histoire; op cit; vol 2; pp. 685-6.
[2854] Michaud-Reinaud: Bibliotheque des croisades; IV; p. 126; in W. Heyd: Histoire; op cit; pp. 685-6.
[2855] J.H. Harvey: `The Origins of Gothic Architecture,' *Antiquaries Journal* 48 (1968), pp. 91-4.
[2856] B. Stock: Science, Technology, op cit; p. 31.
[2857] Ibid. pp. 21 and 31.

instrument maker: Badi al-Astrulabi.[2858] Both this attitude to the artisan and his status were eventually transferred to Christendom.[2859]Which is also a defining landmark in the rise of industry in the West.

b. The Industrial Legacy:

In this outline, mainly due to space considerations, many industries, which could have been seen under different headings, are grouped together under one heading. These include primarily those grouped under earthenware and chemical industries.

Textile industries:

Documented evidence of 916 at the monastery of San Vincente of Ovideo shows a considerable amount of Arabic expressions describing textile products and items of clothing.[2860] These coincide exactly with the introduction of cotton manufacture for the first time into Europe by the Muslims in both Sicily, but most of all in Spain under Abd Errahman III (912-961). He, Abd Errahman, also established extensive manufactures of silk and leather.[2861] Scott emphasises most particularly the strength and delicacy of texture of the products, and the extraordinary permanence of the dyes employed in the fabrics.[2862]Le Bon is categorical that it is from Islamic Sicily that the art of cloth dyeing spread to Europe.[2863]Sicily seems to have shared the same expertise as is often the case with most manifestations of Islamic civilisation. On the island, the textile factories of Palermo, which had fame under the Muslims carried on under the Normans, of which remnants survive in the regalia of Roger II, preserved in the Treasury of the Holy Roman Empire in Vienna.[2864] In the middle of the 12th century, silk industry seems still restricted to Sicily alone, and from there it spread to other regions in the course of the 13th century.[2865] It spread to

---

[2858] G. Sarton: Introduction, op cit, vol 2; p.13.
[2859] B. Stock: Science, op cit, p. 21.
[2860] Aguade Nieto, S., *De la sociedad arcaica a la sociedad campesina en la Asturias medieval*, Universidad de Alcala de Henares, 1988, p. 156.
[2861] J.W. Draper: History; op cit; Vol II; p.386.
[2862] S.P. Scott: History, Vol II,; p.589.
[2863] G Le Bon: La Civilisation; op cit; p.233
[2864] J.D. Breckenridge: The Two Sicilies; op cit; p.54
[2865] M. Erbstosser: *The Crusades;* op cit; p. 186.

central and northern Italy, Provence and finally to northern Germany.[2866]Lucca became the great centre of the silk trade but Bologna, Venice, Augsburg, Ulm and other cities also raised silk worm or produced silk fabrics.[2867]

Carpet manufacturing played a major part in furthering Islamic crafts and skills, and also in sharpening Western tastes. It was Eleanor of Castile who brought woven carpets to England in 1255 on her marriage to the future Edward I.[2868] Gradually the once muddy and straw covered floors left way to carpets as we have today. The Islamic impact stretched further in geographical terms, to the far north, one of the oldest extant Oriental carpets, dating from the early 15th century, was found in the village church of Marby in northern Sweden, and there is a whole category of Scandinavian adaptations of Oriental textiles, some of them of Islamic derivations.[2869]

From the East, Islamic textile products introduced, not just linguistic expressions, but also new varieties of cloth and ideas, such as Damask (from Damascus), Fustian from Fustat and Muslin (from Mosul) in which the respective types of textiles were believed to be manufactured.[2870] Further legacy in the field, that associates names and objects, includes cotton, divan, sofa, and mattress, as well as baldachin.[2871]

In respect to technological breakthroughs within the industry, Pacey notes that, along with paper, the magnetic compass, and other innovations, a new type of loom was one of the innovations which appeared in Western Europe soon after 1150.[2872] Such textile technology was already in existence in Muslim Spain centuries before appearing in the rest of Western Christendom. The early phase lasting from 825 to 925 was marked by two interesting technological innovations, one of them being the horizontal loom, which appeared, together with the use, well in advance of Christian Europe, of silk thread,[2873] as in the shroud

---

[2866] Ibid.
[2867] Ibid.
[2868] John Sweetman: *The Oriental Obsession*; Cambridge University Press, 1987; p.5.
[2869] R. Ettinghausen: Muslim Decorative arts; op cit; p. 14.
[2870] C. Singer: East and West in retrospect; op cit; p. 764.
[2871] R. Ettinghausen: Muslim Decorative arts; op cit; p. 15.
[2872] A. Pacey: *Technology*; op cit; p. 38.
[2873] J. Zozaya: Material Culture in Medieval Spain; in V.B. Mann; T.F. Glick; J. D. Dodds: *Convivencia; Jews, Muslims, and Christians in Medieval Spain;* G. Braziller and the Jewish Museum; New York; 1992; pp. 157-74; p. 159.

of Ona, Burgos (datable to sometime around 925.)[2874] The implications are clear: the horizontal loom was already in use in Al-Andalus at least three centuries before the rest of Europe, giving rise to a weaving industry there.[2875]

Thanks to Pacey's erudition, it is possible to outline the history of impact in this area, and accept with him, that although, in the use of non human energy, Europe in 1150 was the equal of the Islamic and Chinese civilisation, in terms of the sophistication of individual machines, however, notably for textile processing, and in terms of the broad scope of its technology, Europe was still a backward region, which stood to benefit much from its contacts with Islam.[2876] A few years before 1150, the first cotton cloth to be woven in West Africa was produced, development indicating that new areas were being drawn into technological dialogue due to events in Spain and nearby areas of Africa.[2877] Migration of people with relevant skills was a possible explanation for the different diffusion of many techniques.[2878] Documentation of the equipment used is non existent, but deductions can be made from a distribution map of different types of loom in Africa prepared by a specialist on ethnic textile traditions.[2879] If we take only the looms used for weaving cotton, and exclude types thought to derive from later European influence, the distribution coincides almost exactly with the areas, which were under Islamic influence by 1150 or soon after; and the vertical cotton loom used in the Mali region of West Africa, and operated only by women, was of a type also found in North Africa.[2880] It is possible that looms of this type were in use as early as 1150, and that they were introduced into Mali about then as a result of trade with North Africa.[2881]In Europe, a new type of horizontal loom was introduced, notably in the Low Countries for weaving woollens, and its great advantage over earlier European looms was that some operations (such as raising and lowering heddles) could now be controlled by foot pedals, thus leaving the weaver's hands free to pass the shuttle forward and backward; the idea of pedal operation possibly

---

[2874] For the horizontal loom, see: M. Returece: El templen:, primer testimonio del telar horizontal en Europe?' Bolletin de Arqueologia medieval; 1 (1987); pp. 71-7.

[2875] J. Zozaya: Material Culture; op cit; p. 159.

[2876] A. Pacey: Technology; op cit; p. 44.

[2877] Ibid. p. 38.

[2878] Ibid.

[2879] H.L. Roth: *Studies in Primitive Looms;* 1918; Reprinted Bedford; England; Ruth Beam; 1077; p. 63.

[2880] A. Pacey: *Technology*; op cit; pp. 39-40.

[2881] Ibid.

derived from Islamic weaving.[2882] However, whilst in Iran, Syria, and parts of East of Africa, when pedals were used, the operator sat with his feet in a pit below a fairly low slung loom, in the West, the whole mechanism was raised higher above the ground on a more substantial frame, precisely like looms of this type, which were very widely used in the Islamic part of Spain by 1177, and it was probably from here that they were first adopted in Christian Europe.[2883]

Earthenware:

We call porcelain, Sarton explains, that kind of ceramics of which the substance is vitrified and more or less translucent.[2884] Porcelain was invented by the Chinese, who were the first to see the advantage of baking ceramics at very high temperatures; in such circumstances certain ceramic wares- a mixture of kaolin and fusible feldspar-would necessarily be vitrified and remain translucent.[2885] The earliest foreign account of Chinese porcelain is that given by Sulaiman the Merchant (9th century).[2886] Like paper, the compass, and much else, the Muslims soon were to borrow, adapt, develop, before conveying to the West this Chinese product. In the production of Porcelain in Baghdad, potters developed a white opaque tin-glaze composed of powdered potash-glass, oxides of lead and tin, and salt-in which to dip the once fired vessel, the result was a surface on which a brush could paint most delicate work.[2887] The ceramics of Baghdad, and later Cairo, to which Baghdad potters migrated in the 11th century, inspired imitation in Spain and Italy, and eventually the production of faience.[2888]

Lustre, like tin glaze, reached Spain before 1154, when al-Idrisi says that lustre-ware was produced in Aragon and exported.[2889]Two centuries earlier, in the period lasting from 825 to 925, Muslim Spain was already marked by two interesting technological innovations, the horizontal loom mentioned above, and glazed pottery, which came into use, with

---

2882 Ibid. p. 41.
2883 Ibid. p. 41.
2884 G. Sarton: Introduction, op cit; Vol II, p. 409.
2885 Ibid.
2886 Ibid.
2887 T.K Derry and T.I Williams: *A Short History of Technology*; Oxford Clarendon Press, 1960.P. 93.
2888 Ibid
2889 For the early history see A. W. Frothingham: *Lustreware of Spain*; New York; 1951; 1-6; in J Sweetman: The Oriental Obsession, op cit; p.35.

the appearance of the first Eastern forms, as well as pottery with different colours on the same piece.[2890] Polychrome textiles seem to arrive at the same time as polychrome pottery with which it shared both colours and decorative motifs; cosmopolitan trends beginning to become commonplace in 10th century Andalusia.[2891]The Andalusian new type of pottery was unknown to Christian Spain, and also in the rest of Europe.[2892] The Spanish Muslims must therefore have had access at low cost to the production of the acids necessary for making glazed pottery.[2893] After the 13th century re-conquest, the skill known as `golden pottery' was located only in the region that was still Muslim, the Grenada enclave, precisely at Malaga, where Muslim potters as they did after the re-conquest, coated vessels with an opaque tin glaze or enamel as a base for painted decoration.[2894] Malaga became a norm for the quality of excellent faience.[2895] Output of lustre, as already detailed above, spread to Manises near Valencia, examples of which were also found in England before 1400.[2896] Much earlier than that, in fact, in 1289 a Spanish ship brought Islamic lustre pottery to queen Eleanor, and in 1303 lustre pieces are recorded in Sandwich, Kent.[2897] Islamic tin glaze (and, to a notable though lesser extent, lustre) were to influence Italian maiolica.[2898] It is obvious that Italy, geographically placed between Islamic influences coming direct from the eastern Mediterranean and those coming from Spain to the West, would be the catalyst; hence between the 13th and 16th centuries developed in Italy the tin glazed earthenware called *maiolica*, which provides a major channel for the dispersion of Islamic motifs.[2899] The name maiolica (if not derived from Malaga, Arabic Maliqa)[2900] points to the influence of the trade with Valencia in Spain via Majorca.[2901] Durant explains that the Italians called the material majolica, changing r to l in their melodious

---

2890 J. Zozaya: Material Culture in Medieval Spain; op cit; p. 159.
2891 Ibid.
2892 Ibid.
2893 For distilling pots using polychrome glazing and Chinese colouring techniques, see C. Bosh Ferro and M. C. Gomez: Formas ceramica auxiliares: anafes, arcaduces y otras, in *Il Congreso de Arqueologia Medieval Espanola;* 2: 491-500.
2894 W. Durant: The Age of Faith, op cit; p. 849.
2895 R. Schnyder: Islamic Ceramics; op cit; P. 34.
2896 J Sweetman: The Oriental Obsession; op cit; p.37.
2897 R.A. Jairazbhoy: Oriental Influences in Western Art; Bombay 1965; p. 43 in J Sweetman: The Oriental Obsession;.p.5.
2898 J Sweetman: The Oriental Obsession;.p.5.
2899 Ibid. p.39.
2900 R. Schnyder: Islamic Ceramics; op cit; P. 34.
2901 J Sweetman: The Oriental Obsession; op cit; p.39.

way.[2902] The world maiolica is even used with the meaning of a metallic lustre in the 1530s by the potter Giorgio of Gubbio, a master of lustre painting: the usage is confirmed by the influential potter and writer the cavaliere Cipriano Piccolpasso of Casteldurante, in his *Tre Libri dell'Arte de Vasaio* (three books of the Potter's Art) compiled about 1556-9.[2903] The same writer, incidentally, gives prominence to arabesques, *rabeschi*. Islamic motifs and the use of tin-glaze were to be passed to France in the faience of that country and to Holland and England in the 17th century.[2904]

An early 14th century text by al-Khashani, explains the manufacture of faience, the ingredients needed, their mixtures, the kiln process and implements, the methods of glazing and decorating, as this was done in his own native place, Kashan, in Iraq Ajami (or Jibal).[2905] This account, according to Sarton is especially valuable because it is based on actual and traditional practice and also because it is unique of its kind in world literature until the 16th century, with the earliest Italian account by Piccolpasso (c.1557).[2906] Little surprise, once more, if the successor to the Muslim author is precisely the Italian, confirming trends and patterns observed above. And also the Italian writer succeeding his Muslim predecessor by two centuries, thus, highlighting the Islamic, rather than the Italian, pioneering role.

Glass Industry:

The glass industry thrived in Egypt and Syria. In both countries, lamp shades were made in glass adorned with medallions, inscriptions, or floral designs. Syrian glasses had a far reaching reputation feeding the tastes and the homes of wealthy Western households with glass products of a diversity of shapes and usages.[2907] Aleppo and Damascus were important centres according to many witness; and so was Hama.[2908] Going through the inventories of the time, Heyd notes, can be found

---

[2902] W Durant: The Age of Faith, op cit; p. 849.
[2903] R.J. Charleston ed: World ceramics (1968); p. 155; in J Sweetman: The Oriental Obsession; p.39.
[2904] J. Sweetman: The Oriental Obsession; C1:p.39.
[2905] It was found recently by Helmut Ritter in two Hagia Sophia MSS (Nos 3614 and 3613) of a treatise on precious stones and perfumes: *Kitab jawhir al-Arais.*
[2906] G. Sarton: Introduction; op cit; Volume III. p.179
[2907] Instances in Labarte: Inventaire du mobilier de Charles V; p. 240 and sub in W. Heyd: Histoire; op cit; vol 2 ; p. 710.
[2908] D. Whitehouse: Glass in *Dictionary of the Middle Ages*; op cit; vol 5; pp. 545-8.

bottles, goblets plates of glass, painted or decorated `on the Damascus manner.'[2909] Egypt continued to produce vessels of all qualities, particularly at Al-Fustat, where excavations yielded immense quantities of glass ranging in date from the 8th century to the later Middle Ages.[2910] In Spain, it was Ibn Firnas, who in the 9th century, introduced the art of glass manufacturing and who taught the artisans the technique of putting the clay in the oven.[2911]

The transfer to the Christian West of this industry took place mainly during the crusader period. The Venetians acquired large manners of skills from the Syrians and Egyptians with whom they were in close contact during the crusades.[2912] The Christians pilfered Syrian coloured glasses believing they were cut from precious stones, whilst Venice imported from Tyre all the pieces of broken glass, and misshapen bits so as to melt them down in the early stages of the glass industry in that city.[2913] Heyd highlights the role of the Jews of Tyre, who have from one generation to the other exerted amongst the Venetian colony of that city their trades in glass making, and through them much influence was exerted.[2914]Glass making was introduced from Islamic Syria to Venice following a treaty between a local ruler and the Doge of Venice in 1277.[2915] Venetian craftsmen also used Eastern enamelling techniques, and they also copied forms of decoration, especially the ever popular application of rows of pearls and of scale patterns.[2916]
Formulas of eastern inspiration designed to strengthen or to colour glass also circulated in Christian Spain; several such formule found in the Lapidario of Alfonso X.[2917]It would not be surprising to find many such aspects circulating in the northern Italian city of Florence in the 14th century on the same pattern as other ideas and innovations taken from the same court of Alfonso by the Florentine ambassador Brunetto Latini back to Florence.

[2909] Labarte; in W. Heyd: Histoire; op cit; vol2 ; p. 710.
[2910] D. Whitehouse: Glass; op cit; pp. 546-7.
[2911] E. Levi Provencal: L'Espagne Musulmane; op cit; p. 184.
[2912] M. Ilg in W. Heyd: Histoire; op cit; p. 710.
[2913] M. Lombard: *The Golden Age of Islam*; tr by J. Spencer; North Holland Publishers; 1975. pp.188-9.
[2914] W. Heyd: Histoire; op cit; p. 710.
[2915] A. Pacey: Technology, op cit, p.50.
[2916] R. Ettinghausen: Muslim Decorative Arts; op cit; p. 19.
[2917] Alfonso X: *Lapidario,* Maria Brey Marñio, ed. Madrid; Castalia, 1968, pp. 204-205 (chaps. 259, 269).

Djebbar notes how Islamic glass industry led to advances in glasses (for vision) and optical sciences (telescopes).[2918]There is more on such links to be found in Selin's edited encyclopaedia under various entries.[2919]

One of the raw materials used to make glass was known in Syria as `Al-Qali'. This was potash, and the fact that the world passed into European languages as `alkali' is symptomatic of the transfer of a considerable body of chemical knowledge from the Islamic world,[2920] through books as well as in connection with processes of glass making.[2921]

Chemical Industries:

In this particular area, the works of Jabir and Al-Razi, their experimental work above all, set the foundations to many industrial applications we have today. Here, there is no need to go into the pharmaceutical aspect of the matter as this has been considered elsewhere (more can also be found in the works of Levey and Meyerhof.)[2922]
Jabir (late 8th-early 9th) describes the preparation of sulphide of mercury, oxides, arsenics, and many other substances, besides making applications with industrial implications, including the refining of metals, dyeing of clothes, the use of manganese in glass making, use of pyrites etc.[2923] Al-Razi's (d.923-924) *Secret of Secrets* describes processes which can be identified in their modern equivalent of distillation, calcination, crystallization etc. In al Al-Razi's *Secret of Secrets*[2924] are methods for the smelting of metals, the sublimation of mercury, the preparation of caustic sauda, the use of Mercury Ammonium Chloride solution as a dissolving reagent, and the preparation of Glycerine from Olive Oil. From al Razi and Jabir's corpus was derived the study of the corrosive properties of salts and the introduction of two new materials, sal ammoniac (ammonium chloride) and salpeter (potassium nitrate), ultimately to lead to the discovery of

---

2918 A. Djebbar: Une Histoire; op cit; pp 347-9.
2919 H. Selin Editor: *Encyclopaedia; op cit.*
2920 Al-Hassan and Hill: *Islamic Technology*, 1986, p. 153.
2921 A. Pacey: Technology, op cit, p.50.
2922 M. Levey: *Early Arabic Pharmacology*; E. J. Brill; Leiden, 1973.
M. Meyerhof: `Esquisse d'histoire de la pharmacologie et de la botanique chez les Musulmans d'Espagnc,' *al-Andalus* 3, 1935, pp. 1-41.
2923 G. Anawati: Science, in The Cambridge History of Islam, op cit, pp 741-79, at p. 776.
2924 See E.J. Holmyard: *Makers of Chemistry*; Oxford at the Clarendon Press, 1931.

the mineral acids.[2925] These acids were valuable agents for industrial applications.[2926] Nitric acid became familiar in the West from the 14th century; and was used for the separation of silver and baser metals, which it dissolved, from gold.[2927]The separation could also be effected by aqua regia, a mixture of nitric and hydrochloric acid obtained by adding sal ammoniac to nitric acid, which dissolves gold.[2928] The impact of such developments on modern industry can be gleaned in Multhauf origins of chemistry.[2929] Singer also delivers a good study on the early association of chemistry and industry.[2930]

The Muslims legacy can be also found grouped in medieval written collections, one of them being *Liber Sacerdotum,* which contains over 200 recipes, some of them, certainly dating from pre-Islamic times, but the substance of the work comes from the translated Islamic lore. It includes recipes for gilding or silvering, such as how to give a golden texture to glass.[2931]Hill also notes that works by many Muslim chemists included recipes for products that had both industrial and military uses.[2932] Hassan al-Rammah a Syrian (d. 1294) wrote a treatises on the art of war in general, which also includes pyrotechnic recipes, notably methods of preparing and purifying saltpeter.[2933]

The origins of the petrol industry go back to the Islamic times.[2934]The Muslims extracted crude petroleum (naft) and distilled it for both military and domestic uses. There exists many descriptions of the distillation process in al-Razi's Book of Secrets. From his experiments he obtained distillates (called white naft,) which he used to `soften or loosen' some solid substances, such as certain gems and minerals. Al-Razi also used oil lamps (naffata) to heat chemicals gently in his chemical and medical works. Besides crude and distillates, the Muslims also produced asphaltes, particularly in Iraq, where Qir (pitch) and Zift (asphalt), were produced and exported.

2925 R. P. Multhauf: The Science of Matter. Edited by D. C. Lindberg: Science in the Middle Ages; op cit; pp. 369-390: p.376
2926 D.R. Hill: Islamic Science; op cit; p. 88.
2927 C. Singer: *Short History of Scientific Ideas to 1900*, op cit; p. 184
2928 Ibid.
2929 R.P. Multhauf: *The Origins of Chemistry*; Gordon and Breach Science Publishers; London, 1993.
2930 C. Singer: *The Earliest Chemical Industry*; The Folio Society; London; 1958.
2931 Ibid. p. 66.
2932 D.R. Hill: Islamic Science, op cit, p. 85.
2933 G Sarton: Introduction, op cit; Vol II, p. 767.
2934 D.R. Hill: Islamic Science, op cit, pp 87-8.

The medieval Western Christian treatise of *Mappae Claviculae,* most certainly incorporated some later contributions by Adelard of Bath, which include interpolated information on methods of naval warfare used by the `Saracens,' and other military instructions, and descriptions of Muslim methods of building with oil and pitch.[2935]
It is needless here to go into all the uses and applications of oil, whether for domestic or industrial purposes that can be found in our day.

The scale of the Islamic impact on the West is visible in the very chemical vocabulary, Singer pointing out how the early medieval Latin language had no adequate technical vocabulary.[2936]The translators therefore merely transliterated words from their Arabic or Hebrew form, thus Latin technical words full of Semitic expressions: antimony, cinnabar, marcassite, realgar (red sulphide of mercury), tutya or tutty (zinc oxide) and zircon.[2937] New substances such as *sal ammoniacum* (ammonium chloride,) and other words: bismuth, borax, calamine, natron, talc, and tartar; the names of many dyes: alizarin, alkanet, aniline, carthamine, carmine, crimson, fustic, henna, kermas, lac (modern lake), saffron, and sandal wood.[2938]

The Paper Industry:

Paper was possibly one of the most important of all accomplishments in the history of humanity, but just like Arabic numerals, this innovation because so ordinary, its true implications have never been adequately seized. Before paper, writing was done on papyrus, skins, and even stones; scarcity of parchment made books extremely costly to produce.[2939] To find a substance capable of replacing parchment, and similar to papyrus, was going to render immense services to the diffusion of learning.[2940]

Paper, originally, was taken by the Muslims from the Chinese; a craft they developed into a major industry.[2941]The paper-making process is

---

[2935] L. Cochrane: Adelard of Bath; op cit; p. 37.
[2936] C. Singer: *The Earliest Chemical Industry*; op cit; p. 52.
[2937] Ibid.
[2938] Ibid.
[2939] R. Briffault: The Making, op cit, p. 206.
[2940] G. Le Bon, La Civilisation des Arabes. Op cit; p.381.
[2941] For more accounts on the growth of the industry see:

explained by Hunter, primarily, that the Muslims employed linen as a substitute to the bark of the mulberry tree for their paper, and to beat the cleansed rags to a pulp, a trip hammer was put to use, and improved method of maceration, which was invented by the Muslims.[2942]
In Baghdad were built many paper mills, and from there, the industry spread to Syria and Palestine, and made the way West. Africa saw its first paper mill built in Egypt around 850; a paper mill was then built in Morocco, from there, of course, it was to reach Spain; 950 being the date of the earliest use of paper in Spain.[2943]The centre of fabrication was Xatiba, near Valencia, but ruins of early mills in Spain could also be seen on Cordoba's river bank, and some in working order could still be seen at Al-Qantara.[2944]

The first written reference to paper in the Christian West seems to be in the pseudonymous Theophilus Presbyter's "The Art of the Painter" (first half of the 12th century).[2945] In the 12th century French pilgrims who visited St Vincent de Compostela took back with them scraps of paper to France, considering them objects of immense curiosity.[2946]
The shift in production from Islam to Western Christendom took place in the 13th century when Valencia was captured from the Muslims (in 1238.) During the 13th century, paper was exported to Sicily from both Barcelona and Valencia.[2947] The Valencian exports doubtless originated in Xativa, where the Muslim community received royal support for the continued production of paper; and virtual monopoly in the kingdom of Valencia, but also prohibition against producing paper anywhere but in Xativa, this was probably indicative of the deliberate concentration of that industry there.[2948] In Christian Spain, the gathering of rags for the paper industry was a profession in itself, as evidenced by a grant by the King of Aragon in 1287, empowering two citizens of Menorca to search

-J. Pedersen: The Arabic Book, op cit.
-M. M. Sibai: *Mosque Libraries:An Historical Study*; Mansell Publishing Ltd: London; 1987.
2942 D. Hunter: Papermaking; op cit; p.139
2943 Ibid. p.470.
2944 Al-Idrisi in J. Pedersen: The Arabic Book, op cit, p. 64.
2945 F. and J. Gies, *Cathedral, Forge, and Waterwheel* subtitled "Technology and Invention in the Middle Ages". Harper Perennial, 1995; p. 127.
2946 W.M. Watt: l'Influence de l'Islam; op cit; p.36.
2947 T. Glick: Islamic and Christian Spain; op cit; p. 242.
2948 M. Lombard: L'Islam, p.191; Madurell, Paper a terres catalanes, ii:963-8; Valls i Subira, `Caracteristiques del paper,' pp 319-321; etc in T. Glick: Islamic and Christian Spain; p. 242.

for cloth scraps with which to make paper.[2949] From Spain and Sicily paper making spread to Christian Spain and Italy.[2950]

The Italian pioneering in paper production within Western Christendom owes once more to the impact of the crusades. When the mastery of the sea fell to the Italian republics, which had given first assistance to the crusades, Western tradesmen purchased from the Levant paper called *charta damascena* for which was used as a raw material rags of linen, and there were many ways to colour it.[2951]This Italian-Eastern connection is found in the name for paper *carta cuttonea*, derived from the Arab word for linen, *kattan.*[2952] Paper sold in the south of Europe was taken north to cities and fairs, and soon the Italians started producing paper themselves, in 1250 near Ancona was set up a centre to supply Europe with paper.[2953] In 1293 was set up the first paper mill in Bologna.[2954] Germany followed suite in the late stages of the 14th.[2955] Down to the close of the Middle Ages, though, the most important paper making centres were in North Italy.[2956]

Typically, just as in the Islamic model, the West almost immediately began to use water power to process the pulp.[2957] Indeed, when paper making spread from the Muslim world into other parts of Europe, the process of pounding fibres into pulp was always carried out mechanically, with a water wheel driving a cam shaft to operate trip hammers.[2958] It used to be thought that this was a distinctly European development, however, it is now known that there were many water mills in the vicinity of Baghdad, and that water power was applied to paper making in that region for two or more centuries earlier than in Europe.[2959]

2949 M. Levey: *Medieval Arabic Book making and its Relation to Early Chemistry and Pharmacology*; Philadelphia: American Philosophical Society, 1962, p. 10.
2950 T.K Derry and T.I Williams: A Short History; op cit; p. 232; W. M. Watt: L'Influence; op cit; p.36.
2951 N. Elisseeff: Les Echanges; op cit; p.46.
2952 F. Reichmann: *The Sources of Western Literacy;* Greenwood Press; London; 1980. p.205.
2953 N. Elisseeff: Les Echanges; op cit. p.46.
2954 D. Hunter: Papermaking; op cit; p.474.
2955 R. Garaudy: *Comment l'Homme devint Humain,* Editions J.A, 1978. p.207.
2956 T.K Derry and T.I Williams: A Short History; P. 232.
2957 J. Mokyr: *The Lever of Riches* subtitled "Technological Creativity and Economic Progress". Oxford, 1990; p. 41.
2958 A. Pacey: *Technology; op cit;* p. 41-3.
2959 Ibid.

The importance of paper for the diffusion of knowledge is incalculable, of course.[2960] The Europeans of the Middle Ages only wrote, and for very long, on parchment, papyrus having passed out of general use, and paper not yet having been introduced into the West.[2961] Parchment was both expensive and rare, hence a serious obstacle to the multiplication of written works; so scarce, Le Bon notes, the monks took the habit of erasing the works of the great scholars of Greece and Rome to replace them with their homelies.[2962] Hence without the Muslims, most masterpieces of Antiquity, which are presented to us as having been well preserved, would have been lost.[2963] Thanks to the abundance of paper, just as previously under Islam, book production changed from a craft into a manufacture. Hence, in this respect, as Pedersen remarks, the Muslims accomplished a feat of crucial significance not only to the history of the Islamic book but also to the whole world of books.[2964]

Manufacture of paper was also to prepare the way for the invention of printing.[2965] Without paper, Hitti explains, printing from movable type, invented in Germany around the middle of the 15th would not have been successful, and without paper and printing, popular education in Europe, on the scale it developed, would have been impossible.[2966]

3. Farming

On the Muslim role in agricultural development, Cherbonneau holds: `it is admitted with difficulty that a nation in majority of nomads could have had known any form of agricultural techniques other than sowing wheat and barley. The misconceptions come from the rarity of works on the subject... If we took the bother to open up and consult the old manuscripts, so many views will be changed, so many prejudices will be destroyed.'[2967]

[2960] R. Garaudy: Comment l'Homme; op cit; p.207.
[2961] C.H. Haskins: The Renaissance; op cit; p.75.
[2962] G. Le Bon: La Civilisation des Arabes; p.381.
[2963] Ibid.
[2964] J. Pedersen: *The Arabic Book,* tr. G. French Princeton University Press; 1984, p. 59.
[2965] T.K Derry and T.I Williams: A Short History; op cit; P. 231.
[2966] P.K. Hitti: History of the Arabs, op cit, p. 564.
[2967] A. Cherbonneau: *Kitab al-Filaha* of Abu Khayr al-Ichbili, in *Bulletin d'Etudes Arabes*, pp 130-44; at p. 130.

So many prejudices, which can be easily found with many authors such as Ashtor who says:
`The numerous accounts of these activities do not point to technological innovations within the irrigation system, which the Muslim rulers had simply taken over from their predecessors. The records in the writings of the Arabic historians show that those who drained the swamps and dug the canals were the Nabateans, not Arabs.' [2968]
`The information which the Arabic authors provide us in the methods of agricultural work, besides the irrigation canals and engines, is rather scanty. But collecting these records from various sources one is inclined to conclude that the Arabs did not improve the methods of agricultural work. There is only slight evidence of technological innovations in near eastern agriculture throughout the Middle Ages, whereas the history of European agriculture is the story of great changes and technological achievements.'[2969]

This picture of inept Muslim farmers, shared by the overwhelming majority of historians is contradicted by historical evidence. In fact, an Islamic agricultural revolution preceded its European counterpart by at least six centuries, Muslims pioneering in many areas that were later on to be identified with the European agricultural revolution.[2970]It was also from Islam that many such pioneering elements were to transfer to Western Christendom as will be amply shown in this section.

Before looking at such impacts, it is worth making a brief outline of Islamic early accomplishments in farming. Artz tells us that the great Islamic cities of the Near East, North Africa, and Spain were all supported by an elaborate agricultural system that included extensive irrigation and an expert knowledge of agricultural methods, which were the most advanced in the world.[2971] The Muslims knew how to fight insect pests, how to use fertilizers, and they were experts at grafting trees and crossing plants to produce new varieties, and by these means areas that have since become lands of low agricultural production were

---

[2968] E. Ashtor: A Social; op cit; p. 46.
[2969] Ibid. p. 49.
[2970]For accounts on the Muslim agricultural revolution, see for instance:
-A.M. Watson: *Agricultural Innovation in the Early Islamic World*; Cambridge University Press; 1983.
-A.M. Watson: `The Arab Agricultural revolution and its diffusion,' *The Journal of Economic History* 34 (1974): pp. 8-35.
-T. Fahd: Botany and Agriculture, in the Encyclopaedia (Rashed ed) pp 813-52.
[2971] F.B. Artz: The Mind; op cit; pp. 149-50.

able, in early Islam to support huge populations.[2972] Cereal yields in Egypt according to Von Sivers were around 10 for 1, yields, which will only be obtained in Europe at the end of the 17th century.[2973] In Muslim Spain, such was the quality of product some wheat could keep for a century in adequate storage conditions.[2974] In Sicily, agriculture remained in Muslim hands under Norman rule, and was, according to Scott `carried to the highest perfection.'[2975] There, every plant or tree, whose culture was known to be profitable and which could adapt itself was to be found in the gardens and plantations; records were kept of the crops produced in each district; the methods of their disposition and the prices they brought were noted on the public registers; the breeds of horses, asses, and cattle were improved; and the greatest care was taken of them; and food, which after experiment was found to be the most nutritious, was adopted.[2976] Bolens, thus, concludes that Islamic farming represented: `a culmination of a unique balance derived from a deep love for nature… a relaxed way of life, ecological balance, and the acquisition of knowledge of many `civilized traditions.'[2977]

Gardens and gardening, for pleasure, experimentation, or as subsidiary economic outlet, used to form an integral part of Islamic life. In Algiers, a visitor once counted 20,000 gardens, and all around the city grew all sorts of fruit trees; great varieties of flowers, and all sorts of plants; fountains abounded, and in these gardens, on the lush greenery, families used to come and find enjoyment and solace.[2978] In Spain, writers speak endlessly of the gardens and *lieux de plaisance* of Seville, Cordova and Valencia, the last of which was called by one of them ``the scent bottle of al-Andalus.'[2979] Market gardens, olive groves, and fruit orchards made some areas of Spain—notably around Cordova, Granada, and Valencia—"garden spots of the world." The Island of Majorca, won by the Muslims in the 8th century, became under their husbandry `a

---

[2972] Ibid.

[2973] In P.Guichard: Mise en valeur du sol et production: De la `revolution agricole'aux difficultes du bas Moyen Age; In *Etats et Societes* (J.C. Garcin et al edition); Vol 2; Presses Universitaires de France; p.2000; pp. 175-99; at p. 184.

[2974] E. Levi Provencal: *Histoire de l'Espagne Musulmane*; Vol III; Paris, Maisonneuve, 1953. p. 272.

[2975] S.P. Scott: History; op cit; vol 3; p. 42.

[2976] Ibid.

[2977] L. Bolens: `Agriculture' in *Encyclopaedia* (H Selin ed); op cit; pp 20-2, p. 22.

[2978] In G.Marcais: Les Jardins de l'Islam; in *Melanges d'Histoire et d'Archeologie de l'Occident Musulman;* 2 Vols; Alger; 1957; pp 233-44; p. 241.

[2979] H. Peres: *La Poesie Andaluse en Arabe Classique au Xiem siecle*; Paris; 1953; pp. 115ff.

paradise of fruits and flowers, dominated by the date palm that later gave its name to the capital.'[2980]

The picture that emerges, according to Watson, is that of `a large unified region which for three or four centuries, and in places still longer, was unusually receptive to all that was new,'[2981] and also was `unusually able to diffuse novelties;' and more crucially: `both to effect the initial transfer which introduced an element into a region and to carry out the secondary diffusion which changed rarities into commonplaces.'[2982]To accomplish this, attitudes, social structures, institutions, the economy, infrastructure, science all played their part; and not only in farming, but also in other spheres of the economy, and outside the economy; all `touched by this capacity to absorb and to transmit.'[2983]

How Islamic civilisation diffused all such green science to the Christian West is what focus is on here.

a. Introduction and Diffusion of New Crops:

In the words of Wickens, Spain received (apart from a legendary high culture), and what she in turn transmitted to most of Europe, were all manner of agricultural and fruit-growing processes, together with a vast number of new plants, fruit and vegetables that we all now take for granted.[2984] These new crops included sugar cane, rice, citrus fruit, apricots, cotton, artichokes, aubergines, saffron... whilst others, previously known, were developed further.[2985] To these can be added roses and peaches, strawberries, figs, quinces, spinach, and asparagus, hemp, the mulberry and the silk worm.[2986] Muslims also brought to that country rice, oranges, sugar cane and cotton;[2987] sub-tropical crops such as bananas and sugar cane were grown on the coastal parts of the country,[2988] many to be taken to the Spanish colonies in the Americas subsequently. Also owing to the Muslim influence, a silk industry

[2980] W. Durant: The Age of faith; op cit; p. 298.
[2981] A. Watson: Agricultural innovation, op cit, p.2
[2982] Ibid.
[2983] Ibid.
[2984] G.M. Wickens: What the West borrowed; op cit; at p. 125.
[2985] M. Watt: *The Influence; op cit* pp 22-23.
[2986] F.B. Artz: The Mind; op cit; pp 149-50.
[2987] A. Pacey: *Technology, op cit* p. 15.
[2988] E. Levi Provencal: *Histoire de l'Espagne Musulmane*; op cit; p.283.

flourished, flax was cultivated and linen exported, and esparto grass, which grew wild in the more arid parts, was collected and turned into various types of articles.[2989] In Sicily, Lowe holds, practically all the distinguishing features of Sicilian husbandry were introduced by the Muslims: citrus, cotton, carob, mulberry, sugar cane, hemp, date palm, saffron... the list is endless.[2990] `It would make a whole book, and not the least interesting,' Carra de Vaux insists, on the history of flowers, plants and animals that had come from the Orient, and which are used in agriculture, pharmacy, gardens, luxury trade, and arts.'[2991] Carra de Vaux lists tulips (Turkish: tulpan,), hyacinths, narcissi of Constantinople, Lilacs, jasmine of Arabia, and roses of Shiraz and Ispahan; peaches of Persia, the prunes of Damascus, and figs of Smyrne. Also listed are the sheep of `Barbary', goats, Angora cats, Persian coqs; products used for dyeing.[2992] De Vaux then dwells on what he sees `one of the great glories' of the Arab world: the pure blood Arab horse, stressing the Arab care and expertise.[2993]

Agents of such diffusion were many and diverse. Muslim rulers, such as Abd Errahman III (912-961), promoted the culture of the sugar cane, rice, and the mulberry.[2994] The Yemeni element, benefiting of long learned know how and skills in their country of origin, as they settled in Spain, brought with them their irrigation techniques, laws and administration, and also new crops and systems of more intensive land use.[2995] Watson also speaks of thousands of mostly unknown individuals from many levels of society who moved plants over shorter or longer distances for many different reasons. Whether `Great or humble, they unwillingly collaborated in a vast undertaking that was to enlarge considerably the range of useful plants available over a large part of the known world. They also prepared the stage for still further migration of these same plants in the early modern era.'[2996]

Crucial to such a diffusion was the frontier-less, unified land of Islam, which allowed crops (rice, hard wheat, sugar-cane, watermelon, spinach, lemons, citruses…) to be taken from India and Persia to the

---

[2989] W. Montgomery Watt: The Influence, op cit, pp 22-3.
[2990] A. Lowe: *The Barrier and the Bridge*, Published by G. Bles, London, 1972; p. 78.
[2991] Baron Carra de Vaux: *Les Penseurs de l'Islam*, op cit; vol 2, at p. 306.
[2992] Ibid. pp 309-19.
[2993] Ibid. pp. 329-36.
[2994] J.W. Draper: History; op cit; Vol II; p.386.
[2995] T. Glick: Irrigation. In A. Watson: Agricultural Innovation; op cit; p. 80
[2996] A.M. Watson: Agricultural innovation; op cit; p.89-90.

Near East and North Africa, and to Europe. Many crops were probably found on the Indian sub-continent, such as the province of Sind, where the Muslims had a foot-hold.[2997] Oman may have been a halfway-house in which new plants were acclimatised before being passed farther to the north and, of course, further west.[2998] The eastern part of the Islamic world was thus `the gateway' through which passed on their westward journey all the crops, with the exception of the tropical ones, then across the Maghreb, into Spain, and Sicily, and from one Mediterranean island to another.[2999]

The progress of a number of crops in their journey West can be looked at. Chalots, first, which derive their name from Ascalon (Cepa Ascalonia), and were imported during the crusades.[3000] Spinach was imported first to Spain, where it was largely witnessed in the 11th century, from whence it was diffused to the rest of Europe.[3001] It was one of the earliest such crops to be received into Europe, but it did not appear until the 13th century when it seems to have made rapid progress.[3002] Aubergines, which spread into Italy in the 14th century, came from Muslim Spain.[3003]Sorghum, too, is mentioned in Italy by the late 12th and 13th centuries, by which time it had arrived in the south of France.[3004] Sour oranges and lemons appear to have spread slowly through parts of Italy and Spain in the 13th and 14th. Hard wheat probably appeared in the 13th.[3005] The Romans had imported rice but had never grown it on a large scale, and it was the Muslims who started growing it on irrigated fields in Sicily and Spain, whence it came to the Pisan plain (1468) and Lombardy (1475).[3006] Other crops which the Muslims either introduced or intensified, include the mulberry tree and

---

[2997] Ibid. p.79-80.

[2998] Ibid.

[2999] Ibid. p.80.

[3000] J. Andre: *l'Alimentation et la Cuisine a Rome;* Paris; 1961; p. 20.

[3001] M. Rodinson: Les Influences de la Civilisation Musulmane sur la Civilisation Europeene Medievale dans le Domaine de la Consommation et de la Distraction: l'Alimentation; in *Convegno Internationale: op cit;* pp. 479-99. p.484.

[3002] Crescentiis bk vi 55; 103 in A. Watson: agricultural; op cit; pp. 81-3.

[3003] D. Bois: Les Plantes almentaires chez tous les peoples et a travers les ages; vol1; Paris; p. 355.

[3004] Crescentis bk iii 7; V.Niccoli: Saggio storico; Turin; 1902; p. 189; J.J Hemardinquer: l'Introduction du Mais; 1963; pp. 450-1 in A.M.Watson: Agricultural; op cit; p. 81-83

[3005]G. Alessio: Storia linguistica; 1958-9; pp. 263-5; M. Gual Camarena: Vocabulario del commercio medieval; Tarragona; 1968; p. 422; in A. Watson: Agricultural; op cit; pp 81-3.

[3006] R.J. Forbes: Studies, op cit, p. 49.

saffron; the first was necessary for silk worm husbandry and industry; the second, appreciated in cooking, and also in the medical sciences.[3007]

Greater information on the passage of crops from Islam to Western Christendom, and their impact on both farming and local manufacturing, can be gleaned by looking at the particular instances of sugar and cotton.

The Muslims developed the cultivation of sugar on a large scale.[3008]By the 10th century sugar cane was cultivated all over North Africa (as in other places east), from where, it crossed into Spain.[3009]There it was cultivated and sugar produced according to all crafts of the trade.[3010]Then the Muslims acclimated the crop in Sicily.[3011]The name `massara' which is given to sugar mills in Sicily is of course of Arabic origin. Before the crusades, parts of the West, thus, already had sugar production. Early in the crusades, the Europeans took over regions where sugar was produced, such as Tripoli, the first place where they came across the crop, and where they enjoyed it with delight.[3012]Other Eastern regions where the crusaders came across the crop include Tyre; Sidon; and Acre. William of Tyre speaks enthusiastically of the great sugar plantations of Sur.[3013] When the Crusaders took possession of the country, they were very careful to maintain production which brought them considerable wealth, such as the Lord of Tyre, who enriched himself thanks to his sugar plantations.[3014] The Syrians were great experts at refining the product through an elaborate process to extract sugar.[3015]The Crusaders followed exactly the same processes and methods as the Muslims, and adapted the same terminology in the manufacturing process, using massara to describe their mills.[3016] At Tyre, this industry was so prosperous that Frederick II asked for workers to be sent to Palermo as the local Sicilians had lost the skills; the request

[3007] P.Guichard: Mise en valeur; op cit; p. 178.
[3008] W. Heyd: Histoire; op cit; p.684
[3009] R.Dozy: *Le Calendrier de Cordoue de l'Annee 961*; Leyden; 1873; p. 25; 41; 91.
[3010] Ibn al-Awwam: Livre de l'Agriculture; Trad Clement Mullet; Paris 1864. I; 365 and ff; and preface; p. 26.
[3011] M. Amari: *Storia dei Musulmani in Sicilia*; op cit; II; p. 445.
[3012] Alb. D'Aix; ed Bongars; p. 270. in W. Heyd: Histoire du commerce; op cit; p.685.
[3013] Historia, XIII, 3; in medieval French translation in Paulin Pari's edit., vol I, p. 480. The Sur of William of Tyre is Tyre. See also E. Dreesbach: *Der Orient*; (Dissertation); Breslau; 1901; pp. 24-8.
[3014] Burchard in W.Heyd: Histoire; op cit; p. 686.
[3015] Alb. D'Aix; ed Bongars; p. 270. Jacques de Vitry; p. 1075; 1099. in W. Heyd: Histoire du commerce; op cit; p.685.
[3016] Taf and Thom., II; p. 368; Strehkle, in W.Heyd: Histoire; p. 686.

was made to the Marshall Ricardo Filangieri.[3017] At Acre itself, Muslim prisoners were used for the making of sugar.[3018]After the fall of the Latin states in the East, the plantations and production of sugar were transferred to Cyprus.[3019]The land became covered with sugar cane plantations, especially around Baffo and Limisso, under the direct control of the local rulers themselves.[3020] The Cornaro, an illustrious Venetian family, possessed in the Limisso region vast plantations, whilst the Knights of Rhodes possessed vast farms on the Colossi lands.[3021]Here, again, it was Muslim craftsmen, Syrian specialists, who were imported to Cyprus to advise on sugar production.[3022] Between the years 1400 and 1415, about 1,500 Muslims were captured by the Cypriots from the Sultan of Egypt; the King of Cyprus refused to return these on the grounds that they were essential for the cultivation of sugar cane.[3023] Muslim expertise also spread elsewhere. Marco Polo mentions Egyptian technical consultants teaching their methods of sugar refining to the Chinese in the second half of the 13th century.[3024]

The progress of cotton, Watson observes, owes mainly to the fact that wealthy people copied what had become the manner of dress of many Egyptians.[3025] The fashion set by the rich was sufficiently widespread, and hence the demand for cotton was great enough to induce some landowners and peasants to experiment with its cultivation.[3026] Thus cotton moved from Egypt farther west, across North of Africa into Spain and to successive Mediterranean islands.[3027] Manufacture of cotton was first introduced into Europe by the Spanish Muslims during the rule of Abd Errahman III.[3028] One of the most valuable Spanish applications of cotton was in the production of cotton paper.[3029] Xativa, as already noted, was the centre of the paper industry in Spain. The adoption of cotton as a material for the fabrication of this article of commerce is said to be due to `the practical genius' of the artisans of Xativa, who

---

3017 Huillard-Breholles, Hist.Dipl. Friderici II; Vol 5; pars 1; p.574. in W.Heyd: Histoire; p. 686.

3018 Michelant-Reinaud: *Bibliotheque des Croisades*; IV; p. 126 in W. Heyd: Histoire; op cit; p. 686.

3019 See Herquet: *Konigsgetalten des hauses Lusignan*; Halle; 1881; pp 165-70.

3020 Sanuto Diari; X; 106; Mas latrie: III; 27; 88 in W.Heyd: Histoire; op cit; p. 687.

3021 Ibid.

3022 E. Ashtor; 1981: 105 in J.L. Abu-Lughod: Before European Hegemony.p.246.

3023 A. Watson: Agricultural; op cit; Note 20; p. 211.

3024 J.L. Abu-Lughod: Before European Hegemony.p.246.

3025 A.M. Watson: Agricultural innovation; op cit; p.102.

3026 Ibid.

3027 Ibid.

3028 J.W. Draper: History; op cit; Vol II; p.386.

3029 Ibid.

produced great quantities of paper, much of which, in texture and finish will compare not unfavourably with that obtained by the most improved process of modern manufacture.[3030]From Spain, cotton manufacture spread across Europe between the 12th to the 15th century as far as England, particularly in the form of fustian, a cheap cotton cloth with a linen warp, which derives its name from the Cairo suburb of Fustat.[3031]

The dependency upon Islamic skills in these agro-industries is most particularly obvious. Any loss of Muslim expertise in one part of Western Christendom drives the rulers to urgently request for expertise from anywhere Muslims could be found. Hence, in Sicily, following the upheavals that affected the island in the mid to late 12th century,[3032] the skills of growing henna, indigo and refining sugar had disappeared as Muslims took flight from the land they cultivated and some left the island altogether. Frederick II, for instance, had to send to the Levant for `duos hominess qui bene sciant facere zuccarum' (two men who can manufacture sugar).[3033] Similarly, in the Christian kingdom of Valencia, it seems that the farming of both cotton and sugar cane had disappeared after conquest of the place from the Muslims in 1238, and following the dispersal of its Muslim population, since Jaime II sent to Sicily for `duos sclavos sarracenos quorum alter sit magistro cotonis et alter de cannamellis' as well as for the seeds of cotton and sugar cane.[3034] In Spain, the Muslims, until their expulsion in the early 17th century, surely met the demands and needs of specialised crops, and the effects suffered by Spanish faming following such expulsions are widely acknowledged.[3035]

Understandably, many crops (and techniques and skills associated with them), that began their life in Europe, found their way to the European colonies of Spain and Portugal. Silk production was taken from Grenada to Mexico by Hernan Cortes, and was developed there by the Viceroy

---

3030 S.P .Scott: History; op cit; vol ii; P. 387.

3031 T.K Derry and T.I Williams: A Short History; op cit; P. 98.

3032 See N. Daniel: The Arabs; op cit; pp. 148 fwd; for the relentless depredations suffered by the Muslims, and their forced emigration from their lands and farms.

3033 Historia diplomatica v 573; 575 in A. Watson: Agricultural; op cit; Note 2; p. 185.

3034 J.E. Martinez Ferrandon: *Jaime II de Aragon;* 2 vols; Barcelona; 1948. Vol II; pp. 19-20.

3035 See for instance, H.C. Lea: *The Moriscos of Spain;* Burt Franklin; New York; 1968 reprint; p.379; S.P. Scott: History; op cit; vol 3; p. 320; S. Lane-Poole: *The Moors in Spain;* Fisher Unwin; London; 1888. pp.279-80.

Antonio de Mondoza, who himself came from Grenada.[3036] Many other sub-tropical crops such as bananas and sugar cane grown on the coastal parts of Spain also found their way there.[3037] Pacey notes, that it was the organization of the sugar plantations which was novel at this time, and both cultivation methods and cane processing technology used by Europeans in Madeira and later on the Caribbean islands had been acquired from the Islamic world, and from Sicily.[3038] Morocco had an important sugar industry during the 15th century, and the north Moroccan town of Ceuta was invaded by the Portuguese in 1415, just a few years before the colonization of Madeira began, and Morocco was probably one source of information concerning sugar technology, such as cane crushing mills.[3039]The plantations on Madeira proved to be highly lucrative, and exports to Europe expanded fast. By 1493 there were eighty `factory managers' responsible for sugar production on the island.[3040]

The Islamic direct transfer of crops to Africa is enlightening in many respects. The spread of Islam on the continent caused the converted to begin to wear clothes-as religion enjoined, which in turn stimulated the growth of cotton in many places to meet fast rising demand.[3041]It was the Muslims who introduced sugar cane into Ethiopia, and who made the East African island of Zanzibar famous for its high quality sugar.[3042] Other crops were diffused by the Muslims on the continent in medieval times as reported by both Muslim travellers and by the Portuguese later in the 15thcentury.[3043] It is almost certain that in medieval times West Africa received other than cotton and sugar cane, colocasia, bananas, plantains, sour oranges and limes, Asiatic rice and varieties of sorghum, which were all decisive in impact since the range of crops previously available was extremely limited.[3044] Most of the crops were probably brought from the Maghrib over the caravan routes which crossed the

---

[3036]R de Zayas: *Les Morisques et le Racisme d'Etat*; Les Voies du Sud; Paris, 1992. p.200.

[3037] E. Levi Provencal: Histoire, op cit, p.283.

[3038] A. Pacey: Technology in world Civilization, op cit; p.100.

[3039] Ibid.

[3040] Ibid.

[3041] V. Monteil: Le Cotton chez les Noirs, in *Bulletin du Comite d'Etudes Historiques et Scientifiques de l'A.O.F.* IX (1926); pp. 585-684; R.Mauny: Notes historiques autour des principales plantes cultivess en Afrique occidendate; in *Bulletin de l'Institut Francais d'Afrique Noire;* Xv (1953); pp. 684-730; pp. 698 ff.

[3042] A. Pacey: Technology, op cit, p. 15.

[3043] A. Watson: Agricultural; op cit; p. 81.

[3044] Ibid.

Sahara.[3045] There is also linguistic evidence pointing to a Muslim introduction for a number of crops; the names of several of the new crops in the languages of the interior of West Africa seem to be derived from Arabic names.[3046] Mauny notes that before agriculture became established in this region, gathering of wild fruit, leaves and roots were main products for subsistence.[3047] Many of the indigenous crops also gave little nutrition in relation to the amount of land or labour required.[3048]The transformation of modes of living following such transfers was, thus, far reaching.

Finally, it is worth highlighting that the crops introduced by the Muslims had major impact on the local economies to this very day. It had been said, Sarton, insists, that the gardens and orchards of Spain were the best part of her Islamic heritage,[3049]whilst Gabrieli notes that the crops which the Muslims introduced remain up to the present day one of the foundations of the Sicilian economy.[3050]The new plants also created many changes in consumption and land use.[3051] These plants became the sources of new fibres, foods, condiments, beverages, medicines, narcotics, poisons, dyes, perfumes, cosmetics, and fodder as well as ornamental objects.[3052]

b. Other Aspects of Islamic Impact:

As Watson notes:
`In the vast literature of irrigation history may be found assertions which tend to minimise or even discredit, the contribution of early Islamic times to the development of irrigated agriculture, particularly in Spain, North Africa and the Levant. Thus Ribera Y Tarrago, writing in a long tradition which belittles the Muslim legacy in Spain, argues that the irrigation system of the Huerta of Valencia is pre-Islamic, principally on

---

3045 Ibid. p.82.
3046 J.M. Dalziel: *The Useful Plants of West Tropical Africa*; London; 1948; pp. 122; 305-6 etc.
3047 R. Mauny: *Tableau geographique de l'Ouest Africain au Moyen Age*; Dakar; 1961; pp. 228-33.
3048 A.M. Watson: Agricultural Innovation; op cit; pp 81-2.
3049 G. Sarton: The Appreciation; op cit; p.131.
3050 F. Gabrieli: Islam in the Mediterranean World; in *The Legacy of Islam*: 2nd ed. Ed J. Schacht with C.E. Bosworth. Oxford Clarendon Press, 1974. pp 63-104, at P. 76.
3051 M. W. Dols: Herbs; in Dictionary of Middle Ages; op cit; vol 6; pp. 184-7; p. 186.
3052 Ibid. at pp. 185-6.

the ground that it does not resemble the undoubtedly Muslim system in the region of Marrakech![3053] In North Africa, Gauckler following the previous practice of European scholars writing on the region, assigned virtually all the ruined irrigation works of Tunisia to the Romans,[3054] an error the enormity of which was finally pointed out in Solignac, whose careful work is a model of this kind of investigation.[3055] In Libya, the qanawat (underground tunnels) of the desert were attributed by Beadnell to the Romans,[3056] whereas they are almost certainly Islamic. Again, for the Levant, one reads in Benvenisti that `with the Arab conquest a period of decline and decay in irrigated agriculture began.'[3057] Such assertions need not be taken seriously. To prove for a particular region whether in early Islamic times irrigated agriculture had progressed beyond its classical antecedents requires very careful analysis, and the results may not be unambiguous.'[3058]

And, the following serves to confirm Watson's conclusions.

Irrigation:

Conservation and scrupulous management of water in the civilisation of Islam is evident in scholarly theory, all of the *Kitab al-Filahat* (book of agriculture), whichever their geographical origin, insisting meticulously on the deployment of equipment and on the control of water.[3059] Serjeant also notes that a considerable part of Islamic legal books is devoted to water law-which has hardly been studied in Europe to any appreciable extent.[3060]The same Islamic attention and care for the resource is obvious on the ground, and it led to many Islamic breakthroughs in the field of irrigation as the following amply shows.

[3053] J. Ribcra: *Dissertaciones y opusculos*, 2 vols, Madrid, 1928. vol 2; pp. 309-13.

[3054] P. Gauckler: *Enquete sur les Installations hydrauliques Romaines en Tunisie;* 2 Vols; Paris; 1901-2.

[3055] A. Solignac: Recherches sur les installations hydrauliques de kairaouan et des Steppes Tunisiennes du VII au Xiem siecle, in *Annales de l'Institut des Etudes Orientales*, Algiers, X (1952); 5-273.

[3056] H.J. Beadnell: An Egyptian Oasis; London; 1909; p 167 fwd.

[3057] M. Benvenisti: *The Crusaders in the Holy Land*; Jerusalem; 1970; P.263.

[3058] A. Watson: Agricultural; op cit. Note 34, pp. 193-4.

[3059] L. Bolens, Irrigation in Encyclopaedia (Selin ed), op cit, pp. 450-2; at p. 451.

[3060] R. B. Serjeant: Agriculture and Horticulture: Some cultural interchanges of the medieval Arabs and Europe; in *Convegno Internationale; op cit;* pp. 535-41. p. 537.

One of the first Islamic contributions was to make considerable improvements to the irrigation system legated by the Romans,[3061]some important developments taking place in the Western Mediterranean.[3062] The Muslims devised new techniques to catch, channel, store and lift the water, besides making ingenious combinations of available devices,[3063] adapted to specific natural conditions.[3064]They also introduced techniques in river drainage, and irrigation by systems of branch channels with an efficient distribution of the available water.[3065] Other Islamic accomplishments are studied by Glick.[3066] Such changes cheapened irrigation, and consequently brought into production lands previously impossible or uneconomic to irrigate.[3067] Irrigated fields, in turn, yielded as many as four harvests yearly,[3068] which, as in Spain, laid the foundations for the country's prosperity.[3069]

The Yemenis certainly played a leading role in many such innovations. Of all Arabia, Serjeant notes, the Yemen is the province which has the most highly developed irrigation systems, terraced mountain sides running from the top to the foot of high mountains, great masonry cisterns, and skill in the control of flood waters that may be unequalled.[3070] So many south Arabians, to judge by their names, Tujibi, Himyari, Kindi, Ma'afiri, settled in Spain that is attractive also to think that they may have influenced the development of the mountain districts of Spain.[3071]

The earliest agents of diffusion of Islamic techniques to neighbouring Christian parts, however, were the Mozarabs. It is they who diffused waterwheels which they carried as early as the 9th and 10th century in the Asturias.[3072]Other elements of this Mozarab influence are also prevalent in 887 in the documentation of the Monastery of San Vicente de Ovideo, with expressions relating technical terms from Andalusia

---

3061 W.M. Watt: l'Influence; op cit; p. 32.

3062 R.J. Forbes: *Studies in Ancient Technology*; vol II, second revised edition, Leiden, E.J Brill, 1965, p. 49.

3063 T. Glick: Islamic and Christian Spain; op cit; D.R. Hill: Islamic Science; op cit; etc.

3064 E. Levi Provencal: *Histoire de l'Espagne Musulmane*; op cit, p. 279.

3065 R.J. Forbes: *Studies in Ancient technology*; op cit; p. 49.

3066 T. Glick: *Irrigation and Hydraulic Technology: Medieval Spain and its Legacy*, Variorum, Aldershot, 1996.

3067 A.M. Watson: Agricultural innovation, op cit, p. 104.

3068 T. Glick: Islamic and Christian Spain, op cit. P. 75.

3069 D.R. Hill: *Islamic Science*; op cit; p. 161.

3070 R. B. Serjeant: Agriculture and Horticulture; op cit; p. 537.

3071 Ibid.

3072 V. Lagardere: Moulins d'Occident Musulman; op cit; p.63.

referring to agricultural techniques of irrigation in the Valley of the Nalon.[3073]

Muslims, themselves, played a leading role, too, in such diffusion. Following the Christian re-conquest of Spain in the 13th century, all Christian farmers had to do, for generations and centuries to follow, Liazu tells, was to widen the irrigation system and the land reclamation techniques inherited from the Muslims.[3074] Reclaiming lands taken from Muslims or from a hostile nature, would not have been possible without Islamic know how in mastering irrigation, nor without the use of skilled Muslim labour.[3075] Generally, Islamic irrigation systems, Glick points out, were maintained intact, and in the case of large, interlocking regional systems with long canals and complicated distribution procedures, the Christians had to take pains to learn the customs from the indigenous population.[3076] In the Crown of Aragón the procedure was for a nobleman to hold an inquest at which Muslim irrigators would explain how the system worked and then to issue an ordinance continuing the customary arrangements.[3077] Thus in 1106 Fortún Aznárez issued a disposition concerning the distribution of the water of the Irués canal, near Tarazona, based on how the water "used to run in the time of the Moors and as he discovered the truth ... from old Moors."[3078] The document then describes the system of turns among hamlets on the canal, the word for "turn" expressed with the Arabism `adowr.' The canal was administered by Muslim style officials: the çavacequias (sâhib al-sâqiya) (The master of the canal) of the city of Tarazona and the local alamis (from Arabic amîn), who oversaw the day-to-day functioning of the canal.[3079] The `Syrian-style' distribution system continued unchanged, and in many towns along the eastern coast, a standard stipulation was that water distribution arrangements should continue as they had been "in the time of the Moors."[3080]

A Muslim legacy of note is the noria (a water-raising device using chains and buckets), which had revolutionary consequences upon agricultural productivity. Because it was relatively inexpensive to build

---

[3073] Aguade Nieto, S., *De la sociedad arcaica a la sociedad campesina en la Asturias medieval*, Universidad de Alcala de Henares, 1988, p. 156.
[3074] Jean Guy Liauzu: Un Aspect de la reconquete de la valee de l'Ebre au XI et Xii siecle: l'Agriculture irriguee et l'heritage de l'Islam: *Hesperis Tamuda*:Vol 5 (1964):pp 5-13: p.13.
[3075] Jean Guy Liauzu: Un Aspect de la reconquete; p.13.
[3076] T. Glick: Islamic and Christian Spain; op cit; p. 100.
[3077] Ibid.
[3078] Ibid.
[3079] Ibid.
[3080] Ibid. p. 101.

and simple to maintain, the noria enabled the development of entire huertas that were intensively irrigated.[3081] In Cordoba, al-Shaqundi (13th century) speaks of 5000 norias (possibly including both lifting and milling devices) on the Guadalquivir.[3082] Some are still in use, to this day, as at La Nora, six km from the Murcia city centre, where although the original wheel has been replaced by a steel one, the Muslim system is otherwise virtually unchanged.[3083] The big water wheels at Toledo also date back to the Muslims. This heritage was eventually taken over by the Christian conquerors who diffused it widely in their colonies.[3084]
The noria had a much wider impact as Glick explains. Because of its universality, the noria became the model and point of reference for all geared machines.[3085] In a treatise on clocks prepared for Alfonso the Wise, Isaac ibn Sid (Ben Cid) first describes the construction of a main wheel, by fashioning four arms to be assembled in the form of a cross, "just like norias are made;" the equalizing and bell wheels are then to be constructed in the manner of an aceña, the paradigm of a dentate wheel (cena=tooth in Arabic).[3086]

Also inherited from the Muslims is their strict system of water management. All disputes and violations of laws on water were dealt with by a court-whose judges were chosen by the farmers themselves, this court named The Tribunal of the Waters, which sat on Thursdays at the door of the principal mosque; ten centuries later, the same tribunal still sits in Valencia, but at the door of the cathedral.[3087] Landowners sit every Friday outside the cathedral of Valencia and there complaints are heard by judges, and nothing is written down, which so exactly corresponds to how customary law in irrigation is managed in Arabia.[3088] The Christian conquerors have also kept Muslim legislation in matters of irrigation as shown by various documents, such as document No 101 `hec est carta del agua de Hyruese... como deve andas at como andava en tiempo de Moros'.[3089]

[3081] T. Glick: Islamic and Christian Spain; op cit, p. 74.
[3082] Al-Saqundi: Elogio del Islam espanol, p. 105; in T. Glick: Islamic, op cit, p.75.
[3083] D.R. Hill: Islamic Science, op cit, pp. 97.
[3084] R.J. Forbes: Studies in Ancient Technology; vol II; op cit.p. 49.
[3085] T. Glick: Islamic and Christian Spain; op cit; p. 238.
[3086] J A Sánchez Pérez: La personalidad cieníifica y los relojes de A1fonso X el Sabio; Murcia: Academic Alfonso X el Sabio, 1955, pp. 21-4 in T. Glick: Islamic and Christian Spain; op cit; p. 238.
[3087] S.P. Scott: History, op cit; vol 3; pp 602-3.
[3088] R. B. Serjeant: Agriculture and Horticulture; op cit; p. 537.
[3089] Jean Guy Liauzu: Un aspect; op cit; p.9

Another Islamic legacy to our day are the so many engineering structures.[3090] Muslim dams had hardly had any repair in a thousand years,[3091] still meeting the irrigation needs of Valencia, requiring no addition to the system.[3092] According to Oliver Asin's *Historia del nombre,* Madrid seems to have presented a good case for the Muslims having made it possible to develop what has become the city of Madrid by introducing a sort of qanat system to supply the district with water.[3093]Parts of this apparently still exist, and Asin links the actual name Madrid to it.[3094] Linguistically, there is a considerable amount of Arabic words in the Spanish vocabulary related to irrigation; expressions such as: Acequia: canal of irrigation; Alberca: Artificial reservoir. Aljibe: Container; arcaduz: water conduct; Azuda: water wheel; almatriche: canal; alcorque: hole dug in front of tree for irrigation purpose....[3095] And the same legacy is noted in Sicily, philology allowing the tracing of Arabic etymology to Sicilian vocabulary related to irrigation.[3096]

Farming Techniques:

Muslim farmers raised productivity mainly thanks to the introduction of higher yielding new crops and better varieties of old crops, which made possible more specialised land use, and more intensive rotation; besides extending and improving irrigation, and spreading cultivation into new or abandoned areas, and developing more labour intensive techniques of farming.[3097] Again, old Eastern tradition, Yemeni above all, is responsible for improved soil management, `garden agriculture', which Glick notes, imposes the necessity of cultivating in such a way as to preserve the maximum amount of moisture in the soil.[3098]Which hence adds the ecological dimension. Soil rehabilitation, Bolens notes, was particularly cared for, and preserving the deep beds of cropped land from erosion was `the golden rule of ecology,' and was `subject to

[3090] D.R. Hill: Islamic Science, op cit, p. 224:
[3091] S.P. Scot: History; op cit; vol 3; p. 602.
[3092] N. Smith: *A History of Dams,* The Chaucer Press, London,1971. p.93.
[3093] R. B. Serjeant: Agriculture and Horticulture; op cit; p. 537.
[3094] Ibid.
[3095] See A. Castro: The Structure of Spanish History; p. 98 fwd.
[3096] H. Bresc: Les Jardins de Palerme; in In *Politique et Societe en Sicile; XII-Xv em siecle*; Variorum; Aldershot; 1990; pp. 55-127; p. 67.
[3097] A. Watson: Agricultural Innovation, op cit, pp 2-3.
[3098] T.F. Glick: Islamic and Christian Spain; op cit; p. 75.

scrupulous laws.'[3099] Fertilisers were also used according to a well advanced methodology;[3100] soils classified and enriched by various methods (other than by fertiliser use), which included ploughing (normal and deep), hoeing and digging.[3101] The rotation of crops, which in subsequent centuries was deemed a crucial factor in the English agricultural revolution had a wide practice, and together with new crops and better irrigation, multiplied yields by three.[3102] This comes about through the joint knowledge of plants and soils, the mastery of botanical and edaphic science.[3103] Hence, in Andalusia, well before the era of the English physiocrats of the 1800s, Bolens says, this agricultural revolution was closely based on high levels of knowledge of the life sciences and on a love of nature which was the common gift of both the Islamic and the Hebraic tradition.[3104]

This Islamic science transferred straight to its Christian successors. In Sicily, farming know how, in its wide variety, shows a direct Islamic influence visible in the use of Arabic terminology. Notary acts of the 14th-15th centuries related to sugar farming and horticulture highlight the powerful Arabic presence (in italic), terms such as catusu: *Qadus* (pipe of cooked clay); Chaya: *taya* (hedge, or garden wall); Fidenum: *fideni* (sugar cane field); Fiskia: *fiskiya* (Reservoir); Margum: *marja* (inundated field); Noharia: *nuara* (irrigated cottage garden); Sulfa: *sulfa* (advance of credit granted to farmers); etc.[3105] To this day Malta and Gozo preserve such Islamic influence, the more technical the jargon, the more purely Arabic the terms become.[3106]

The Muslims alos brought new instruments that made it possible to grow the new crops, which would otherwise have been impossible with the typically classical agricultural methods.[3107] And this legacy is obvious in the technical jargon as well. To take a glance at the philological correspondences alone, Serjeant points out, *-aretrum* the plough is obviously related to the Arabic root *haratha*, *sulcus* a furrow to the word *saliq*, and *iugum* a yoke with *ingerum* an acre (though less than an English acre) is evidently the same word as South Arabian *haig*

[3099] L. Bolens: Agriculture, in Encyclopaedia (Selin ed), op cit, pp. 20-2; at p. 22.
[3100] T. Glick: Islamic, op cit, p. 75.
[3101] Derived from A.M. Watson: Agricultural, op cit, chapter 23.
[3102] T.F. Glick: Islamic and Christian Spain. p. 78.
[3103] L. Bolens: Agriculture: in Encyclopaedia (Selin ed); op cit; p. 22:
[3104] Ibid.
[3105] H. Bresc: Les Jardins de Palerme; in *Politique et Societe; op cit*; p. 81.
[3106] R. B. Serjeant: Agriculture and Horticulture; op cit; p. 536.
[3107] R.J. Forbes: Studies, op cit, p. 49.

a yoke of oxen or, by extension, an acre, the amount they can plough in a day.[3108]

New Forms of Land Exploitation:

Islam, Watson points out, freed the countryside from many arrangements which were `economically retrograde.'[3109] Equally, Lowe observes that Muslim rule in Sicily was an improvement over that of Byzantium as the latifondi were divided among freed serfs, and small holders, and agriculture received the greatest impetus it had ever known.[3110] Thanks to a Muslim custom, uncultivated land became the property of whoever first broke it, thus encouraging cultivation at the expense of grazing.[3111] New modes of production brought more agricultural land and labour, as well as their product, into the market place, and the forces of competition thus released were intensified by laws rewarding innovators.[3112] Immamudin quotes from the documents of the School of Arabic Studies in Madrid the type of contract entered into by cultivators and landlords for the bringing of waste land (what would in Arabic be called *mawat*) under cultivation.[3113]Immamudin also cites examples of share cropping contracts (one would call these *muzara'ah, musaqah,* etc. in Arabic) that bear close resemblance to examples given in the standard Arabic law-books, and such forms of contract as those studied by Serjeant, and which too are applicable today.[3114] This highlights the advanced Islamic conditions in comparison with Europe, where, England excepted, only began to abolish the feudal system late in the 18th century.

The Muslim tax system contributed to such and other improvements; low rates of taxation helped keep alive a class of smaller, independent landowners and a relatively prosperous peasantry.[3115] Prior to Islam, taxes crippled both effort and innovation, pushing the tendency for large estates to dominate the countryside and for the peasantry to be enserfed.
The Muslims also introduced a legal corpus in irrigation to protect individual rights, and applied lower rate of taxation for land watered by

---

[3108] R. B. Serjeant: Agriculture and Horticulture; op cit; p. 535.
[3109] A. Watson; Agricultural innovation, p. 115.
[3110] A. Lowe: The Barrier; op cit; p. 78.
[3111] Ibid.
[3112] A. Watson; Agricultural Innovation, op cit; p. 115.
[3113] In R. B. Serjeant: Agriculture and Horticulture; op cit; p. 541.
[3114] Ibid.
[3115] A. Watson: Agricultural innovation, p. 115.

the Noria than by hand, leading to the prevalence of small holdings of share-croppers and free farmers, as opposed to the latifundia of antiquity with their scores of slaves.[3116]

Experimental Farming and Botanical Gardens:

It has been seen above how Muslims managed to bring in new crops, adapt them and diffuse them. They were able to do so mainly thanks to experimental botanical gardens. These were often in the charge of leading scientists such as Ibn Bassal (fl 11th century) and Ibn Wafid (b. 997-d. ca 1074). These gardens, according to Watson, were places `where business was mixed with pleasure, science with art.'[3117]And these urges acted as strong stimuli for he adaptation of crops from one place into another. Abd Errahman I (rule began in 756), who was fond of flowers and fruits, planted a beautiful garden in imitation of the Rusafah Villa of Damascus, a summer country residence between Palmyra and the Euphrates valley where he had lived for long with his grand father Hisham.[3118] Gradually, experimental gardens became part of a network which linked together the agricultural and botanical activities of distant regions, and so played a role of great importance in the diffusion of useful plants. Only many centuries later did Europe possess similar botanical gardens which acted as the same kind of medium for plant diffusion.[3119] The earliest botanical gardens in Europe appear to have been planted by Matthaeus Sylvaticus in Salerno (c.1310) and by Gualterius in Venice (c.1330); other places followed centuries later; Pisa: in 1543; Padua, Parma and Florence in 1545; Bologna in 1568; Leyden in 1577; Leipzig in 1580; Konigsberg in 1581; Paris (le Jardin Royal du Louvre) in 1590; Oxford in 1621 etc.[3120]

[3116] Ibid. chapter 21; pp 114-6.

[3117] Ibid. chap 22.

[3118] S.M. Imamuddin: *Muslim Spain;* Leiden; E. J. Brill; 1981. p.85.

[3119] A. Watson: Agricultural innovation, op cit, chap 22.

[3120] See: A. Chiarugi: Le date di fondazione dei primi orti botanici del mondo,' *Nuovo giornale botanico italiano* new ser. LX (1953) 785-839; A.W. Hill: The History and function of botanical gardens; *Annals of the Missouri Botanical Garden;* II (1915) 185-240; 195 fwd; F. Philippi: *Los jardines botanicos*. Santiago de Chile; 1878; etc.

Farming/Husbandry Manuals:

Back to the Yemeni contribution to observe how the famed Calendar of Cordova, which regulates farming activity throughout the year is once more based on Eastern origins, The Yemen having a calendar in use for agricultural and activities as reported by al-Hamdani, about 900.[3121]

With regard to Muslim farming manuals, it is generally accepted that, with rare exceptions, they seem to have been mostly translated in the 19th century into Western languages to have any impact on the revival of Western farming. Included amongst these late translations is a treatise on horses, horse riding, and veterinary matters by Abu Yusuf *Kitab al-furusiyeh,* and a veterinary treatise by Abu Bakr, which were translated into French by Perron.[3122]
There are, however, medieval translations of Muslim works, which relate to farming and animal husbandry, or zoology. These include *De animalibus* of Ibn Sina by Michael Scot, which, in the 13th century, introduced in the West important zoological texts.[3123]The *Majmu fi'l Filaha* (Compendium of farming), attributed to Ibn Wafid (Abenguefith) but in fact a work by Al-Zahrawi, had two translations of it in romance languages, Catalan[3124]and Castilian.[3125]This work had great influence on the `Renaissance' work of agronomy, the A*gricultura General* of Gabiel Alonso Herrera (d. c. 1539). The 11th century farming treatise by Ibn Bassal of Toledo, which in its abridged form was published at Tetuan in 1955, was translated into Castilian in the Middle Ages.[3126]

There are a number of issues raised when looking at the translation of a particular treatise: *Kitab al Filaha (Book of Agriculture)* of Ibn al-Awwam (fl. End 12th century). It was translated into Spanish early in the 19th century by Don Josef Antoine Banqueri.[3127] A French translation in

---

3121 R. B. Serjeant: Agriculture and Horticulture; op cit; p. 538.
3122 *Le Naceri: Traite complet d'hippologie et d'hippiatrie*, Paris, 1852-1860, 3 vol.
3123 J. L. Gaulin: Giordano Ruffo et l'art veterinaire: in Micrologus; op cit; pp 185-198: p.187.
3124 The medieval Catalan version can be found in the Bibliotheque Nationale of Paris; Number 93 by A. Morel Fatio, *Catalogue des manuscrits espagnols et des manuscrits Portugais*, Paris, 1982; pp. 332-3.
3125 Text in Castilian edited by J.M. Millas Vallicrosa: La traduccion castellana del Tratado de Agricultura' de Ibn Wafid; *Al-Andalus;* 8; 1943; pp. 281-332.
3126 R. B. Serjeant: Agriculture and Horticulture; op cit; p. 540.
3127 *Libro de agricultura*, ed. J. A. Banqueri (Madrid, 1802).

the second half of the 19th followed,[3128] as the treatise was of particular interest in Algeria (as it was in Spain).[3129] This treatise by Ibn al-Awwam has 34 chapters covering 585 plants, explaining the cultivation of more than 50 fruit trees, making observations on grafting, soil properties, manure, plant diseases and their treatments, irrigation, affinities between trees, animal husbandry and bee keeping.[3130] It seems it had no earlier impact than the 19th century. And yet, Lopez asks what, for instance, will a comparative study of farming manuals of Ibn al-Awwam and Pietro de Crescenzi give.[3131] Pietro dei Crescenzi, born in Bologna (1230-33 died in 1320) is an Italian writer on husbandry. Although citing Ibn Sina, Al-Razi; Ishaq al-Israili, Ibn Sarabi,[3132] he still makes no mention of Ibn al-Awwam. The two works are extremely similar, though. This, hence, raises matters similar to those raised in preceding chapters on whether Islamic works, even if apparently not translated, were still copied in `an unofficial' manner. Sarton points out that translation was not absolutely necessary, for there remained in Spain until the beginning of the Renaissance a goodly number of people who could read Arabic.[3133] Furthermore, it has been shown that Fray Gabriel Alonso Herrera, who wrote *Agricultura general*, has in his text many correspondences of Ibn al-Awwam, and he actually studied in Grenada and often alludes to the Grenadan Moors.[3134]

Knowledge included in Islamic farming manuals often found itself transferred straight onto the ground, or other practical manifestations. In Sicily, Bresc notes, can be found many techniques described or suggested in the contracts of the 14th and 15th century also found in Muslim farming manuals.[3135] Many ploughing methods to prepare the soil, the use of fertilisers, planting, etc, are also shared by both Islamic farming manuals and practice on the island.[3136] Equally the plants grown in Sicily are well elaborated upon in Muslim farming manuals, a rich

---

3128 Ibn Al-Awwam: *Le Livre de l'Agriculture* d'Ibn al-Awwam, tr. from Arabic by J.J. Clement-Mullet, Vol. I, Paris 1864.
3129 J. Vernet and J. Samso: Development of Arabic Science in Andalusia, in *Encyclopaedia (Rashed ed)* pp 243-76; at p 263.
3130 Carra de Vaux: Les Penseurs... op cit, pp. 300-6.
3131 R Lopez: Les Influences Orientales; op cit; p. 621.
3132 G. Sarton: Introduction; op cit; Volume III; p.813.
3133 G. Sarton: The Appreciation; op cit; p.131.
3134 R. B. Serjeant: Agriculture and Horticulture: op cit; p. 541.
3135 H. Bresc: Les Jardins de Palerme; op cit; p. 69.
3136 Ibid.

variety which, most importantly, contrasts with the absolute dearth of crops of northern European gardens.[3137]

Note must be made, here, of the work by Attie[3138] on Islamic manuscripts at the Bibliotheque Nationale de Paris as an extremely useful source for primary and secondary sources to enlighten on some of the issues presented here.[3139]

Final Words:

The Islamic impact on Spain and Portugal had universal dimensions due to the later impact these two countries had on the American continent North and South, introducing crops and techniques. In Africa equally, the Islamic impact is considerable. These remain themes for other studies.

3137 Ibid. p. 71.

3138 B. Attie: Les Manuscripts agricoles Arabes de la Bibliotheque Nationale de Paris; *Hesperis Tamuda*; Vol 10; 1969; pp. 241-61.

3139 See: Casiri: *Bibliotheca arabico-hispana*; Madrid; 1760.

4. ARCHITECTURE, ART AND CULTURE

For centuries during the Middle Ages, Lethaby says, what filled the minds of makers and listeners were `Mahomet, Caliphs and Emirs, Arabs, Turks, and Saracens who had nothing white but their teeth; Spain, Africa, Egypt, Persia; Cordova; Toledo; Seville; Palermo; Babylon, and Alexandria with its harbours and ships...'[3140]

Fascination, which eventually turned to imitation; imitation Rodinson observes, that was reinforced by the perception of the superiority of such civilisation; a model to imitate, at least on the cultural and scientific levels.[3141] Often the imitation hardly answering any new needs, just satisfying old ones but according `to new modalities which bear the mark and the prestige of the civilisation from which the borrowing is made (the Islamic).'[3142]

Eagerness for imitation by artists and architects, too, and lasting until fairly recently as noted by Sweetman:

`Owen Jone's masterly exposition of the geometrical complexities of Moorish patterns: or William de Morgan's patient researches into Persian glazes… the calm and fascinated interest of Christopher Wren, more than 100 years before the Royal pavilion, in the relationship between `Saracenic' style of architecture and Gothic.'[3143]

How Western Christendom imported and adopted the superior Islamic model in arts and architecture, culture and civilisation is looked at here. By no means will this chapter, just as the others, claim to be faultless or comprehensive. In the particular field addressed here, Islamic architecture, arts, culture, and their impact, years of work and thousands of pages will be needed to give them their due worth. This is beyond this author. Also, many sources will be cited in this chapter, but many good ones will be for one reason or another missing.[3144] For a quick and

[3140] W.R. Lethaby: Medieval Architecture: in *The legacy of the Middle Ages*, edited by C.G. Crump and E.F Jacob: Oxford at the Clarendon Press, 1969 ed, pp 59-93. p. 63.

[3141] M. Rodinson: les Influences de la Civilisation Musulmane sur la Civilisation Europeene Medievale dans les domains d la Consommation et de la Distraction: l'Alimentation. In *Academia nazionale dei Lincei*; op cit; pp 479-99; at p.482.

[3142] Ibid. p.482.

[3143] John Sweetman: *The Oriental Obsession*: Cambridge University Press, 1987; p.6.

[3144] For some good works not used here, see for instance:

-E. Male: *Art et artistes du Moyen Age*; Paris 1927; pp. 30-88.

-G.Marcais: *Manuel d'Art Musulman*; Paris; 1926.

-H.Terrasse: *L'Art hispano mauresque des origines au 13em siecle;* Paris; 1933.

-M.Gomez Moreno: *Iglesias mozarabes*; Madrid; 1919.

-E. Lambert: L*'Art gothique en Espagne aux 12 et 13em siecles*; Paris; 1931.

informative source on Islamic art and architecture and their impact, is advised to look at the following site:
http://www.islamicart.com/main/architecture/impact.html

1. Architecture

Focus in the following will be on the central matter of this whole work: that Islamic influences on Western architecture are obvious, and make historical sense; however, any time modern Western historians suppress such an influence, and offer other explanations for such changes, a number of causes and origins become the foundation for such changes. Seen in isolation from each other, such explanations can look fairly unchallengeable as their authors have enough specialised knowledge of their subject to drown the argument in infinite detail, and to refer to each other to assert scholarly legitimacy. When, however, all changes are put together, two major findings are made:
First, the tens of causes for such changes as given by such historians are conflicting with each other, and are also historically untenable. Secondly, all such changes, especially once facts suppressed (by mainstream Western historians) are re-established, show exactly the same patterns observed already with regard to other subjects repeating themselves. Hence, in the case here, changes in architecture and construction that took place in the West, in any place, and at any time during the Middle Ages, show the same substance (Islamic forms/models/techniques), timing (precisely following contact with Islam,) agents (Muslim masons), geography (in close vicinity to Islam), etc.

In the following, first is raised, albeit briefly, the matter of historical inconsistency once the Islamic role is suppressed, and then is looked in greater detail at the Islamic impact, which replicates the same patterns of influence already observed for all other changes.

a. Raising Issue with the Denial of Islamic Influence:

Even the largest buildings of Carolingian times, such as the Palace and Chapel of Charlemagne at Aachen (792-805), Harvey observes, had roofs of relatively small span.[3145] No outstanding competence in the designing of centring or scaffolding was called for, the details of architectural design were either closely copied from Roman or Byzantine work or were extremely crude.[3146]Churches, together with imperial palaces were the other major buildings standing, and churches in the early Middle Ages were roofed with wood, which was ill suited to a troubled epoch, with the ever present risk of fire, and also the problem of wood scarcity.[3147]Problems of roof construction dominated the development of architecture.[3148] It is unlikely that before 1000 there was a single stone building in the whole duchy of Normandy beyond a few unimpressive fortresses.[3149] Defences and castles were wooden structures, and patched with rudimentary mortars; no castle prior to the 12th century is preserved to our day.

Fairly dramatic changes in Western construction suddenly began in the 11th century. The beginning of a new competence in design on a much larger scale can be seen, most particularly with Santiago de Compostela (northern Spain) begun about l075, and the new church of the monastery of Cluny started I088 and finished in 1121.[3150] In secular buildings the capacity to build on notable scale is most particularly obvious with the great hall of William Rufus at Westminster, built in I097-99 and measuring 238 by 68 feet the largest room in Europe for well over a century.[3151]

This sudden upsurge without previous local antecedents drives Harvey to conclude that the new energy infused into Western art came from outside the area of north Western Europe.[3152] Byzantium is the source for such revolution mainstream Western history answers, K. J Conant, one amongst such many historians holding such view.[3153]Yet this is a misconception, whose sources are partly raised by Briggs:
`that it may be that the Church has fostered for centuries a belief that our `Romanesque' and Gothic buildings rose from the ashes of imperial

3145 J. Harvey: The Development of Architecture, in *The Flowering of the Middle Ages*; ed J. Evans; Thames and Hudson; 1985; pp. 85-105; at p. 85.
3146 Ibid.
3147 G.Wiet et al: History; op cit; p. 357.
3148 Ibid.
3149 N.F. Cantor: *Inventing the Middle Ages*, The Lutterworth Press, Cambridge, 1991. p.270.
3150 J. Harvey: The Development of Architecture, op cit; at p. 85.
3151 Ibid.
3152 Ibid.
3153 Ibid. p. 88.

Rome, or that pedantic humanists of the Renaissance are to blame for our misconceptions.'[3154]

Misconceptions, which can be partly challenged on the usual ground: why is it that such an impact did not happen earlier, closer to Byzantium, or within Byzantium itself?

The Byzantine argument with regard to architectural developments is untenable on other grounds:

First, medieval architecture was a major advance on Roman building techniques.[3155]The new techniques conflict with what is found in Byzantium, where the arch, one of the substantial innovations in medieval Western Christian architecture, often remained what it had been in the Roman Empire, a concretion held together by mortar.[3156]

Second, Byzantium, itself, gradually derived its skills from Islam; Theophilus, according to Bury, was stimulated in his building enterprises by what he had heard of `the splendour of the palaces of Baghdad.'[3157]Oriental influences on Byzantium continued to operate throughout the Abbasid period, and were `one of the ingredients of Byzantine civilisation.'[3158]

Third, it was Byzantium which, in 1064, benefited from the largest intake of Muslim craftsmen following the taking of Barbastro by the Franco-Norman army, whose `cultural booty' included 7000 men sent to Byzantium.[3159] Why should superior Byzantium need such craftsmen if it exported skills rather than imported them?

Fourth, even places that ought to be influenced by Byzantium due to their proximity to it more than to Islam, exhibited the Islamic impact. Whether during the Romanesque, Gothic and even Renaissance Italy, Grabar explains, it was the Islamic influence, which certainly played a part in developing certain architectural motifs there.[3160] The bichromy of masonry in churches in Siena and in Pisa, the towers of San Gimignano and the complex surfaces of official and secular monuments in Venice (even some details in San Marco), Grabar notes, are just a few examples

---

3154 M.S. Briggs: Architecture, in *The Legacy of Islam*, 1st ed; op cit; pp 155-79: pp155-6.

3155 G. Wiet et al: History; op cit; p. 357.

3156 Ibid.

3157 J.B. Bury: Summary for Chapter V, in *The Cambridge Medieval History*, Edited by J. R. Tanner, C. W. Previte; Z.N. Brooke, Vol IV; 1923.at p.152.

3158 Ibid.

3159 M R Menocal: The Arabic Role; op cit; p.27; J. Harvey: The Development; op cit. p. 86.

3160 O. Grabar: Islamic Architecture and the West, Influences and Parallels; in Islam and the Medieval West (S. Ferber ed); op cit; pp. 60-6; p. 63.

of tastes and techniques derived from the Muslim world.[3161] Islamic influences are also recurrent, even if harder to extract, in the Russian art of the Middle Ages and even in the pre-Petrine Kremlin, where ltalianate and Oriental motifs are often inter-mixed with local traditions.[3162]
Fifth, the places that witnessed the earliest and most dramatic changes in Western Christendom are precisely the places that experienced other earliest changes, such as in arts, as to be seen further on, and they were the ones nearest to Islam, or in contact in one way or another with Islam: northern Spain, southern France, churches of the order of Cluny...[3163] and these places are the furthest geographically and culturally from Byzantium.

Whilst the Byzantine source does not make historical sense, the Islamic source is much easier to establish. It jumps to the attention, for the same patterns observed before with regard to every other subject come into play again and again.

b. Matters of Impact:

Looking at the Romanesque style shows, and precisely, that its evolution in Western Christendom coincides with the time of contacts with Islam; it bears the same substance and forms; and it also takes place precisely in the closest geographical parts to the Islamic land, and precisely alongside the pilgrimage routes towards Spain. Staying with the last point, first, it seems fairly clear, Grabar explains, and it makes historical sense that, as the great pilgrimage routes of the Romanesque period were established, contact with Spain became the norm for many actual or potential patrons and taste-makers in Romanesque Europe.[3164] Themes and motifs were carried from south to north, the Islamic Andalusian influences obvious to various degrees in the Rousillon, Languedoc, Poitou, Auvergne, most particularly, and occasionally found in Burgundy or the Provence.[3165] These consist of architectural details, horseshoe arches, polylobes, masonry of stones of alternating colours, roll corbels, impost blocks, certain kinds of vegetal ornament, and a

3161 Ibid.
3162 Ibid.
3163 M.Gomez Moreno: *Iglesias mozarabes*; Madrid; 1919.
3164 O. Grabar: Islamic Architecture; op cit. p. 62.
3165 Ibid.

tendency in some monuments to cover entire surfaces with ornament.[3166] Lambert, too, insists that Romanesque architecture of South West France, the old Aquitaine, show intricate resemblances with those of North and North West Spain, including the multi-lobed arch seen in a crowd of churches such as that of Saintonge and of l'Angoumois, at Echebrune, at Rioux, at Thouars, Chalais, Montmoreau, Plassac, Mouthiers and many more.[3167]And playing a leading part in the changes was a group of Christians living amongst the Muslims, the Mozarabs, whose contribution became highly visible in the erection of churches in northern Spain at the end of the 10th century, and the beginning of the 11th.[3168]

In the subsequent Gothic period (post 12th century), again, changes are strictly linked to Islamic influence, Wren, for instance, wrote:
`This we now call Gothic manner of architecture... tho' the Goths were rather destroyers than builders I think it should with more reason be called Saracen style.'[3169]
The Islamic source is substantiated by the fact that we find, again, the same patterns of influence seen in previous chapters, three main ones dominating in this instance: such changes bearing the same Islamic substance; the timing of such sudden construction skills appearing in Western Christendom, precisely following the return of the first crusaders from the East; and also, once more, involving craftsmen of Islamic origin. These three elements are seen in turn, focus here placed on the second, timing.
It is from Islam, indeed, that Western architects acquired the pointed arch, which was to become the symbol and chief mark of gothic style.[3170] Sarton points out, that the term `ogival architecture' referring to one of its most striking characteristics, the use of pointed arches- is somewhat misleading, because Gothic architects did not invent the pointed arches, nor the ribbed vaulting used for many centuries before by the Muslims.[3171]

[3166] Ibid. pp. 62-3.
[3167] E. Lambert: l'Art Hispano Mauresque et l'Art Roman; in *Hesperis*; Vol 17; pp 29-42.p. 36-7.
[3168] Ibid.
[3169] Christopher Wren who wrote (in his history of Westminster Abbey, 1713) in Sir Banister Fletcher: A *History of Architecture*: 18th edition, revised by J. C. Palmes; The Athlone Press, 1975; p. 415.
[3170] J. Harvey: *The Master Builders: Architecture in the Middle Ages*: Thames and Hudson, London, 1971. p.28.
[3171] G. Sarton: Introduction; op cit; vol 2; p.334.

It is generally agreed that Western Christian Gothic was born in the 12th century.[3172] The appearance of the ribbed cross vault, an Eastern invention, is seen at Durham cathedral for the first time in the West; and it is a very strange coincidence if indeed, Harvey notes, if it be a coincidence at all, that the first known ribbed vault in the West (1104) should have been built within the five years that succeeded the taking of Jerusalem (1099).[3173] It can hardly be a coincidence that the great campaign known as the First Crusade had just taken place, and there is no doubt, as a result of the experience gained on the Crusades and especially through interrogating local craftsmen that many skills were acquired.[3174] In the East, the Crusaders and their followers were, indeed, exposed to new ideas, which had had an important influence on them.[3175] Of particular interest were the style and construction methods employed by the Seljuk Turks (who were the main crusaders' foes), such as after the earthquake in 1114 the bridge at Misis was likely to have been repaired using pointed arches to replace the rounded ones of an earlier bridge constructed in the time of Justinian.[3176] It was in Anatolia (the Seljuk heartland) that skilful masons were using techniques that were subsequently employed by the Crusaders in their own buildings.[3177]The new arches were similar to those of the bridge at Dyar al-Bakr across the Tigris, near to a mosque where the Seljuk Turks (in 1117-25) used arches of the type soon to be familiar in the West.[3178] Coincidently, as Cochrane notes, Queen Matilda commissioned the first stone-built bridge in England, at Stratford-le-Bow, before 1117, and that it was of a type never before seen in England.[3179] Within a few years of 1100, fine masonry had reached England; not only were the stones better cut, but they were of larger size, implying the existence of improved cranes and hoists, and the mortar joints were now very fine, so that a chronicler commented upon Bishop Roger's buildings at Old Sarum, begun in 1102, that the stones were so accurately set that the joints were not seen and the whole work might be thought to be cut out of a single rock.[3180]Schnyder also says, that as we are able to trace the

---

[3172] J.H. Harvey, The origins of Gothic Architecture, in *Antiquaries Journal* 48 (1968). pp 87-99. D Talbot Rice: *Islamic Art;* London, 1965, pp 59, 86-89, 165-8. L. Cochrane: Adelard of Bath, op cit, pp. 63-4; 68-9.
[3173] J. Harvey: The Master Builders; op cit; pp. 28-9.
[3174]J. Harvey: The Development of Architecture, p. 88.
[3175] L. Cochrane: Adelard of Bath; op cit; p. 35.
[3176] J. Harvey quoted here by L. Cochrane: Adelard of Bath; op cit; p. 35.
[3177] L. Cochrane: Adelard of Bath; op cit; p 35.
[3178] J. Harvey quoted here by L. Cochrane: Adelard of Bath; op cit; p. 35.
[3179] L. Cochrane: Adelard; op cit; pp 35-6.
[3180] J. Harvey: The Development of Architecture, op cit; p. 88.

decisive renewal in brick architecture to the period shortly after the first great crusades to the East, it would appear correct to assume that `the impulse which led to the rapid development of brick architecture in Europe came from the East.'[3181] `Coincidentally,' with this development, improvements in forming and firing were also introduced.[3182]
It is supposed that returning Frankish engineers from 1099 onwards might have returned equipped with fresh knowledge of structural expedients, and that, again, a proportion of Eastern prisoners of outstanding capacity were brought back to the West, at least one such prisoner, 'Lalys' built Neath Abbey and is said to have been architect to Henry I.[3183] Also, it must be added, amongst the armies that the Occident sent for centuries to the Orient were also to be found workers of all sorts, arm craftsmen, architects, and builders, whose sojourn in Syria was long enough for them to acquire the knowledge they needed.[3184]

Evolving on precisely the same lines, and betraying the same patterns of influence are Western castle fortifications, taking place not centuries before, but perfectly coinciding with the returning crusaders. Philip of Alsace, count of Flanders, completed the castle of Ghent on his return from an expedition to Palestine (1176-8), and modelled it on the fortress of Toron (between Tyre and Acre); and Richard Coeur de Lion, when he built the Chateau Gaillard after the Third Crusade, took his inspiration from the Krak des Chevaliers.[3185] In Syria and Palestine the military orders learnt to build much stronger and more elaborate castles.[3186] Briggs amply demonstrates how contact of East and West during the Crusades (and during the later Middle Ages) contributed influences on castle architecture.[3187]The Crusaders found excellent military architecture at Aleppo, Baallbek, and elsewhere in the Islamic East, learned there the uses of machicolated walls, and took from their foes many an idea for their castles and forts.[3188] In these, the main fortifications were enclosed by a series of circular walls, all set with turrets, rounded to prevent mining at the angles and arranged with lines

---

3181 R. Schnyder: Islamic Ceramics; op cit; p. 30.
3182 Ibid.
3183 J. Harvey: The Development of Architecture, op cit; p. 88.
3184 G. Le Bon: La Civilisation des Arabes; p.259.
3185 G. Wiet et al: History; op cit; p.361.
3186 E. Wright, General editor: The Medieval; op cit; p. 102.
3187 M. S. Briggs: Architecture; op cit; p.179.
3188 W. Durant: The Age of Faith; op cit; p. 271.

of fire that allowed each of them to protect others from enemy assault.[3189]

Heavy machinery appears on the Western Christian sites, and also precisely, following the return of the first crusaders from the East; 1100 highly suggestive of the direct importation of Muslim machinery brought back by returning crusaders from their victorious campaign.[3190] Which somehow explains that in the opening years of the 12th Century, the period was characterised by a new ability to produce really fine worked ashlar; the use of larger stones implying better cranes and hoists, and by the evident self reliance of industrial masters.[3191] The Palatine Abbey of Durham, Winchester new cathedral of St Sivithum, and the gigantic church and monastery as that of Bury St Edmunds well exemplify the new ability to think and build big.[3192] These new techniques contrast markedly with those of 20-30 years before in the Christian West, where nothing happened for centuries before; now, out of nowhere, a sudden revolution, which could be seen throughout Western Europe, bearing all the marks of external impact, and not the result of slow evolution in traditional skills.[3193]There can be no mere coincidence in the fact that exactly such skills had existed among the stonemasons of the Near East for centuries and that at this very date the great campaign known as the first crusade had just taken place.[3194]And once more, it ought to be reminded, that in some cases, following the crusades, the workmen accompanied their new masters when they returned to Europe.[3195]

If we linger with fortifications, and change time and place, we find again the same patterns of Islamic influence at work; focus in this instance on substance, and agents of transmission who are the same as with all other changes, i.e Muslim craftsmen, or Christian craftsmen living amongst Muslims (Spanish Mozarabs in this case).

In 10th century Muslim Spain, the art of fortification at the Castle of Gormaz, shows skills unequalled elsewhere in Western Europe.[3196]Similar skills in military architecture also seen at Tarifa, de Banos de la Encina, and even in the 9th century at the Alcazaba de Merida, through stone

[3189] E. Wright general editor: The Medieval; op cit; p. 102.
[3190] J. Harvey: *The Master Builders; op cit; p.*24.
[3191] Ibid. p.18.
[3192] Ibid.
[3193] Ibid.
[3194] Ibid. p.27.
[3195] L. Cochrane: Adelard of Bath; op cit; p 35.
[3196] J. A. Gaya Nuno: Gormaz, Castillo califal, in *al-Andalus;* VIII, 1943, pp. 431-50.

masonry, construction design, etc.[3197] Sobriety of architectural lines, rational use of space, reaching for the highest standards make this defence architecture, in the words of Levi Provencal, eloquent proof of both the military powers of the Muslims, and the considerable means which could be mustered to erect strategic ensembles of the sort.[3198]The Alcazar at Seville and the Alhambra at Grenada were fortresses and palaces combined.[3199] The Islamic substance of impact can also be traced to the vocabulary, the abundance of Arabic terms which relate to the various parts constituting a castle, and found in the Castilian Middle Ages: adarve, acitara, atalaya, etc, for parts of the castle such as: the front wall, the tower, external tower etc.[3200]

The early, and possibly earliest Christian Western fortresses on the Islamic Spanish model were the work of artisans certainly prominent among Mozarab immigrants in León. The defences of 10th century Zamora were built by masons (alarifes), presumably Mozarabs, from Toledo.[3201] When Alfonso VI of Castile (1073-1108) captured Segovia from the Muslims he built there a castle-fortress on the plan of the Alcazar of Toledo.[3202]Centuries forwards, in the same country, Muslim masons were employed in Christian buildings as bricklayers or carpenters, and the majority of the building force is likely to have been of Muslim origin, or trained by those with experience of Muslim architecture.[3203] The Muslim master mason who built the castle of Alandroal for the military order of Avis in 1298 left an inscription testifying his achievement.[3204]In 1368, Charles le Mauvais (the bad) of Navarre granted to the Mudejares of Toledo a remission of half their taxes for three years for their assistance during his wars, especially in fortification and engineering, which, again, shows that the conquering

---

[3197] E. Levi Provencal: Histoire de l'Espagne; op cit; Vol III; p.511.
[3198] Ibid. p.64.
On Islamic military fortification in Spain, see G. Marcais: Manuel d'Art musulman, I, op cit; p. 248-252; H. Terrasse: l'Art hispano-mauresque, op cit; pp. 143-62.
[3199] W. Durant: The Age of Faith; op cit; p. 271.
[3200] See: L. Torres balbas, Los adarves de las ciudades hispano-musulmanas, in *al-Andalus*; XII, 1947, pp. 164-93.
[3201] T. Glick: Islamic and Christian Spain; op cit; p. 222.
[3202] W. Durant: The Age; op cit; p. 892.
[3203] J. F. O' Callaghan: The Mudejars of Castile and Portugal in the Twelfth and Thirteenth centuries: in Muslims under Latin Rule; J.M. Powell ed; op cit; pp 11-56: pp. 26-7.
[3204] Ibid.

race depended on Muslims for the higher branches of applied knowledge.[3205]

Staying with Muslim masons, we find that throughout the medieval period, they played the central role in the erection of many structures and edifices, and changes in construction techniques took place precisely after the arrival or acquisition of such masons. Thus, following the taking of Barbastro (1063-4), several thousand Muslim prisoners were sent to France, 1500 to Rome and those to Constantinople already mentioned; among these presumably was the Muslim corps of engineers which had defended Barbastro.[3206]Such craftsmen possessed a degree of technical skill unknown north of the Alps and the Pyrenees.[3207] This and the Norman conquest of Muslim Sicily (1060-1091) were decisive factors in the rise of the new architecture, which coincides exactly with such events.[3208]The change that took place in England (cited above) also follow exactly the Norman line. In Sicily itself, the Capella Palatina was built in 1132, the church of the Martorana in 1136, La Ziza in 1154, and La Cuba in 1180, all show strong Islamic influence, abounding in pure Islamic features.[3209] Muslims, as already lengthily explained in previous chapters, had remained on the island until the late 13th century, and were appreciated for their skills and know how. Nothing obscures the fact that movement of craftsmen and builders could have taken place between Sicily and other parts of the Norman realm as seen with respect to other aspects. Such contacts between Normans and `Saracens' help explain the ambitious architectural programme which became manifest in northern France and in England, concludes Harvey.[3210] It is also said by Dulaure, in his Histoire de Paris, that Muslim architects assisted in the construction of Notre Dame.[3211]
After the capture of Cordova (1236) by the Castilians, Muslim masons and carpenters were compelled to work for a specified period every year on sacred structures and in return were exempted from paying taxes.[3212] The new churches retained such features as cupolas, decorations of

---

[3205] Fray Jayme Bleda, Cronica de los Moros, p. 877 (Valencia, 1618). In H.C. Lea: *A History of the Inquisition in Spain*, vol 3; The Mac Millan Company, New York, 1907. p.317.
[3206] J. Harvey: The Development; p. 86.
[3207] Ibid.
[3208] L. Cochrane: Adelard of Bath; op cit; p. 64.
[3209] M. S. Briggs: Architecture, op cit; pp. 167-9.
[3210] J. Harvey: The Development, op cit; p. 86.
[3211] S.P. Scott: History; Vol II; op cit; p. 569.
[3212] Ibid.

intersecting arcades, or techniques like polychrome brick patterning.[3213] Construction was, indeed, and largely in Mujedar (Muslims under Christian rule) hands; the legacy of Mujedar architecture, and also a boast of Aragonese towns today, remnants of major tourist attraction.[3214] Later on, architects from Grenada were employed by Castilian monarchs in the construction of palaces, and even by orthodox prelates in the ornamentation of cathedrals.[3215]Muslims assisted in the construction of some of `the noblest piles of the Peninsula,' Scott puts it; the walls of great monasteries, the windows of lofty spires, exhibiting the engrailed and horseshoe arches of the Muslim.[3216] Islamic skill in the chiselling of the intricate designs which cover the fronts of `magnificent' cathedrals; a chapel in the grand metropolitan church of Toledo, the seat of the primate of Spain, dating from the 13th century, is a beautiful specimen of such art.[3217]

An interesting instance dating from the 14th century needs mentioning here. One of the last French strongholds in Gascony to yield to the English during the early years of the war (mid 14th century) was la Reole. The townsmen offered to surrender. The English accepted these terms of surrender, but the commander of the castle, Sir Agos de bans, preferred to retire into the castle with his soldiers, where `great quantities of wine and other provisions' would enable them to continue the struggle. The English then moved against the castle and

`erected all their machines against it; but they did little mischief, for the castle was very high, and built of a hard stone. It was erected a long time since by the Saracens, who laid the foundations so strong, and with such curious workmanship, that the buildings of our time cannot be compared to it. When the earl found his machines had no effect, he commanded them to desist; and as he was not without miners in his army, he ordered them to undermine the ditches of the castle, so that they might pass under. This was not, however, soon done.'[3218]

As with other changes, pilgrimage and trade had their impact on construction skills, too, and again, the same patterns observed elsewhere, remarkably reproducing themselves with great ease. 9th

---

[3213] D. Matthew: *The Norman Kingdom of Sicily*; op cit; p.91.
[3214] R. I. Burns: Muslims; op cit; p.65.
[3215] S.P. Scott: History; op cit; Vol II, p.222.
[3216] Ibid. p.569.
[3217] Ibid.
[3218] The Chronicles of Froissart, tr. J. Bourchier, Lord Berners (London: D.Nutt, 1903), vol i, pp 269-74, in E Perroy: *Le Moyen Age*, Presses Universitaires de France, 1956. pp. 245-6.

century Islamic impact can be seen at the church of Germigny des Pres, via many Muslim features, possibly an outcome of early contacts, via pilgrims to Spain.[3219] The cathedrals of the Midi were situated upon routes followed by thousands of pilgrims and borrowed architectural motifs from the mosques of the Peninsula.[3220] The same Muslim skills, obvious in Spain, are found in many of the finest ecclesiastical edifices in France: the churches of Maguelonne, in the Cathedral du Puy, and in the ancient abbeys of Provence and Languedoc.[3221] It seems fairly clear and makes historical sense, Grabar explains, that as the great pilgrimage routes of the Romanesque period were established, contact with Spain affected change in Romanesque Europe.[3222]

Cairo, whose influence on Italian cities extends to the striped facades of marble buildings in Pisa, Genoa, Siena, Florence, and other Italian cities, is a good example of how trading links with the East during the Middle Ages impacted.[3223]It is very likely that merchants and travellers returned with memories of Islamic lands rather than workers and, as a result, one encounters the small consistent detail.[3224]

Staying with the role of pilgrims, and looking at a specific development in Western construction, the so-called Perpendicular style, highlights precisely the same patterns once more. The so-called perpendicular style must be regarded as a specifically new creation, produced about 1330 by William Ramsey, who was a master mason from a Norwich family who was in time to be the king's chief mason south of Trent, from 1336 until he died in London during the Black Death of 1349.[3225] The Perpendicular made its first appearance in or very soon after 1330, a new style attributed by Western historians to the lack of skills subsequent to the Black Death of 1348-49, when so many of the older generation of artists died.[3226]This is historically untenable, for this style had appeared fifteen years before the pestilence even began, signs of such style seen first in works with which William Ramsey was associated, the south cloister of Norwich Cathedral designed about 1324, and the new cloister and chapter-house for St Paul's Cathedral in

---

3219 J. Strzygowski: *Origins of Christian Church Art*; Oxford, 1923; p. 64.
3220 E. Male: l'Art et les artistes du Moyen Age; 1927; in J.W. Thompson: The Introduction of Arabic Science; op cit; p.193.
3221 S.P. Scott: History; Vol II; op cit; p. 569.
3222 O. Grabar: Islamic Architecture and the West; op cit; p. 62.
3223 M. S. Briggs: Architecture, op cit; p.176.
3224 O. Grabar: Islamic architecture; op cit; pp. 63.
3225 J. Harvey: The Development of Architecture, p. 101.
3226 Ibid.

London begun by him in 1332.[3227] Inspiration comes not from the Black Death as historians generally put it, but from the Islamic East. Something very closely akin to the earliest 'squeezed hexagons' of Perpendicular tracery, Harvey says, is found in Muslim buildings in Egypt dating from the early 13th to the early I4th century.[3228] Associated with other features of Perpendicular character, such as vertical members running up to cut the curve of an arch, these forms are found in Cairo in the Mausoleum of Mustafa Pasha (1269-73).[3229]
How did this style come to England? As with other changes, the pilgrim route is the answer. Pilgrims, including artists, were visiting Egypt within the relevant period is shown by the itinerary of Simon Simeon and Hugh the Illuminator, Franciscans from Ireland who went to the Holy Land in 1323.[3230] They went through Egypt; in Alexandria, for instance, Simon noted that `Saracens, Christians, Greeks, Schismatic (Copts) and `perfidious Jews' dress all much alike.[3231] It is not without interest, that the unique manuscript of this narrative first belonged to Simon Bozoun, prior of Norwich in 1344-1352, and though such a travel-book could not itself have influenced the course of art, as Harvey insists, it may be significant that documents of this kind were collected at major cathedral monasteries like Norwich.[3232] The English Perpendicular style was only adopted in few buildings designed by English architects in Scotland, Ireland and Calais[3233], which proves that the skills were external, and not from within Western Christendom, for had the latter been the case, independent, unrelated manifestations of such style (as of others,) could have been seen in other centuries, in other places, and detached from any Islamic source, or point of contact.

Looking at the matter of Islamic impact from another angle, that of translations, will yield similar conclusions. In the same way sciences advanced thanks to the translation effort, construction techniques did the same, relying on the new mathematics. Scott notes how the great importance attached by the Muslims to mathematics was unrivalled at the time.[3234] There is, indeed, a considerable body of mathematics, much of it Islamic deployed in design and architecture of both Spain and

---

[3227] Ibid.
[3228] Ibid.
[3229] Ibid.
[3230] Ibid.
[3231] N. Daniel: *The Arabs and Medieval Europe*; op cit; p.226.
[3232] J. Harvey: The Development of Architecture, p. 101.
[3233] Ibid.
[3234] S.P. Scott: History; op cit; vol II, p.559.

Portugal.[3235] Ozdural notes how mathematicians, who taught practical geometry to artisans, played a decisive role in the creation of patterns in Islamic art, and also in designing buildings.[3236] Mathematicians gave instructions and advice on the application of geometry to architectural construction.[3237]The mathematical input is obvious for instance, in the proportioning of the arches; a simple method of establishing a commensurate system of proportions throughout a building was well known; and the system had the advantage of deriving its ratios from the perfect square, a favoured shape in Islamic buildings century after century.[3238]The passage of Islamic mathematics to the Christian West has already been well looked at. Just as Islamic mathematics impacted on commerce, it impacted, and with other sciences, on construction techniques, opening a vast array of possibilities, as here outlined by Lacroix:

`As a proof of the forward state of the exact sciences in the Middle Ages, it would be sufficient to instance a Roman basilica or a Gothic cathedral. What immensity and depth of mathematical calculations; what knowledge of geometry, statics, and optics; what experience and skill in execution must have been possessed by the architects and builders in hewing, carving, and fitting the stones, in raising them to great heights, in constructing enormous towers and gigantic belfries, in forming the many arches, some heavy and massive, others light and airy, in combining and neutralising the thrust of these arches which interlace and hide each other up to the very summit of the edifice-all as if the most complicated science had humbly made herself the servant of art, placing no obstacle in the way of its free development!'[3239]

The best evidence of Islamic impact is its enduring character on the architecture of Western Christendom for centuries after the medieval era. One of the earliest proponents of the Islamic origin of many Western architectural innovations was of course Sir Christopher Wren (1632-1723), who had commented that Gothic should be called `Saracenic'.[3240] Wren was himself influenced by the Islamic style, Sweetman telling how the Royal Society for Natural Philosophy of

---

[3235] I. Grattan-Guiness: *The Fontana History of the Mathematical Sciences*, Fontana Press, 1997.176

[3236] A. Ozdural: Mathematics and Arts: Connections between Theory and practice in the Medieval Islamic world; in *Historia Mathematica*; 27 (2000); pp. 171-201; at p. 171.

[3237] Ibid. p. 172.

[3238] L. Cochrane: Adelard of Bath; op cit; p. 69.

[3239] P. Lacroix: Science and Literature in the Middle Ages; op cit; p.77.

[3240] In Cochrane: Adelard of Bath, op cit, p. 64.

London, formed in 1661, came to include amongst its members (from 1682) the eminent traveller and expert on Islamic matters, Sir John Chardin, and Sir Christopher Wren (possessor of one of the most gifted and questioning minds of the age,) who had interesting ideas on the subject, which is evident in his writing.[3241] Evelyn records (30 August 1680) that he and Wren met John Chardin, the French traveller, and questioned him about the East.[3242] Wren was also in touch with Dudley North, a Turkey merchant and an authority on Turkish life, about a technical point of Turkish dome construction.[3243] George Sandys's *Relation*, published over 60 years earlier but reaching its seventh edition in 1673, had possibly contributed to Wren's interest in Islamic buildings.[3244] The book had described the mosques of Constantinople as `magnificent... all of white Marble, being finished on the top with gilded spires that reflect the beams they receive with marvellous splendour' and had proceeded to a detailed account of Hagia Sophia.[3245] Amongst Wren influences are Islamic minarets, especially those of `the graceful type found, in Cairene buildings,' which may have influenced the design of the later Renaissance *campanili* of Italy, and hence some of Wren's fine city steeples.[3246] And just as Muslim architects had begun to realise the possibility of using dome and minaret in contrast, Wren also did use some dome and towers so effectively in contrast at St. Paul's.[3247]

Another instance of later impact occurs in 17th century Turin, where the Baroque architect Guarini created a type of intersecting ribs for several churches which are strikingly reminiscent of those of Cordova and its descendants in Spain.[3248] Guarini's manual with drawings of his own monuments was published in 1686 and made its way to Spanish America where it is supposed to have influenced the design of a number of Mexican churches as well.[3249]

Closer to us, in the UK, Oriental motifs made their appearance in the architecture of railway stations, just as they did, more prominently in seaside piers, bandstands, kiosks and garden pavilions.[3250] Muslim arches

---

3241 John Sweetman: The Oriental Obsession; op cit; p.47.
3242 Ibid. p.53.
3243 R. North: Lives of Francis North; 1826 ed; iii; p. 42 in J Sweetman: The Oriental; op cit; p.53.
3244 J. Sweetman: The Oriental; p.53.
3245 Ibid.
3246 M. S. Briggs: Architecture, op cit; p.174.
3247 Ibid.
3248 O. Grabar: Islamic Architecture; op cit; p 63.
3249 Ibid.
3250 J. M. Mac Kenzie: *Orientalism, History, Theory and the Arts*; Manchester University Press; 1995: p.xx.

were used at railway entrances,[3251] and it is interesting to see the engineer Robert Stevenson (1772-1850) giving the elegance of a Mughal minaret to his beautiful lighthouse at Girdleness, near Aberdeen (1833).[3252] The 1888 Glasgow exhibition, which was mounted in Joseph Paxton's great Kelvingrove park opposite the tenement was known as `Baghdad by the Kelvin' because of its strikingly Orientalist architecture.[3253]

2. Arts

`For over 1,300 years,' Ettinghausen says, `the worlds of Islam and of Europe have been in more or less constant, dynamic relationship, and often tense confrontation. But in spite of violent denigration of the Muslim religion and its Prophet (as seen in chapter one), the West has had nothing but admiration for the arts of the Near East. It manifested itself in the association of whatever was available of this art with its most revered institutions, whether sacred or mundane, and in artistic borrowings of one type or another by the West from the East.'[3254]
Not everything, though, was borrowed from Islam. Far from it, in fact. In Islamic art, there is no sanctified iconography of the Prophet of Islam paralleling that of Christ, the Holy Family, and of the saints, within the iconographic repertory of the Roman Catholic or the Greek Orthodox Church.[3255] Besides, as Ettinghausen holds, Awn Ibn Abi-Juhayfah reported that:
`The Prophet forbade men to take the price of blood or the price of a dog, or the earnings of a prostitute, and he cursed the tattooing woman and the woman who had herself tattooed, the usurer, and the man who let usury be taken from him, and he cursed the painter.'[3256]
Hence the painter at the same level as usurer, and the earnings of the prostitute. Everyone, on the other hand, knows the elevated value of painting in Western culture.

[3251] F.D. Klingender: Art and the Industrial Revolution; 1968; p. 124; in J. Sweetman: The Oriental; op cit; p. 111
[3252] J. Sweetman: The Oriental Obsession; C3; p.111.
[3253] J. M. Mac Kenzie: *Orientalism, op cit;* p.xx.
[3254] R. Ettinghausen: Muslim Decorative Arts; op cit; p. 13.
[3255] R. Ettinghausen: The Character of Islamic Art; in The Arab heritage (N.A. Faris ed); op cit; pp 251-67; at p. 256.
[3256] Ibid. p. 257.

The Islamic artistic influence on the Christian West did, however, take place, and in many aspects as the following outline will show. This influence is not, in fact, just purely artistic as most, if not all, previous studies have shown. Instead, it was crucial to the development of many early crafts and industries of Western Christendom, which aimed at reproducing Islamic objects and models. This is one of the main points that will be focused upon in this outline. Another point of focus, once more, is with regard to the patterns of influence, which repeat themselves, and are the same as other changes observed elsewhere. Before looking at these points, first it is looked at how Islamic art and aesthetics stimulated both admiration and artistic reproduction.

a. Islamic Art: Admiration and Artistic Reproduction:

Medieval Western Christian admiration for Islamic arts and aesthetics is symbolised by the long list of Islamic art objects found amongst Western collections. Hence amongst the earliest in the British Museum in London is an Irish bronze gilded cross dating from the 9thcentury with a glass paste in the centre which has the Arabic phrase: `Bismillah' (in the name of God) in Kufic letters, and in the Musee de Cluny at Paris, there is a silk fabric which came from the tomb of Bishop Bernard de Laccare, which contains Arabic inscriptions: La Illaha Ill Allah, Muhammad rasul Allah (There is no God but God, and Mohammed is his messenger).[3257] The *tapis Sarrasinois* (Muslim carpet) became known in Louis IX's France, and in 1277 there were trade privileges for it in Paris.[3258] In the 14th century, woven Islamic hangings were prized in Arras, whilst silks were a precious part of church treasuries: a cope from Mamluk Egypt inscribed in Arabic with the words `the learned Sultan' was in St Mary's Church, Danzig, early in the same century.[3259] Equally the Medici collection of Islamic objects formed the nucleus of today's holdings of the Bargello Museum in Florence, and infiltration of Islamic motifs and objects into Western Europe was the result of the thriving late medieval trade with Mamluk Egypt and of the acquisitive instincts of the great Italian aristocratic families.[3260] In the 18th century, another craze, Kufic coins (8th-early 11th century,) highly coveted items in north-

---

[3257] M. A. Marzouq: Influences of the Arabian art on the European Medieval arts: in *The Islamic Review;* March 1970; pp 23-9; p.27.

[3258] John Sweetman: The Oriental Obsession; op cit; p.5.

[3259] R.A. Jairazbhoy; Oriental influences in J Sweetman: The Oriental Obsession; p.5.

[3260] C. Hillenbrand: The Crusades, Islamic Perspectives, op cit;.p.406.

eastern Europe in the early Middle Ages, now appeared in large numbers in many places around the shores of the Baltic Sea, in the Scandinavian countries, in Northern Germany, and in Russia.[3261] These finds instigated serious research and a fairly large literature, such as George Jacob Kehr Leipzig monograph in 1724, considered the first scholarly book on Muslim numismatics[3262] and also of Muslim archaeology in the widest sense.[3263] By the end of the century catalogues of coin collections could be found in various parts of Europe: The Museum Cuficum Borgianum in Rome, the Museo Naniano in Padua, the Royal Library in Cottingen, and the Stockholm collection, which culminates in Fraehn's systematic classification of Muslim coins.[3264]

Most of these Islamic objects and others were no mere objects for collection, but were, instead, best symbols of a civilisation that was once both sophisticated and superior. The appreciation of Islamic superior science has also been acknowledged by most, if not all, the contemporary learned amongst Western Christians. This civilisation, however much feared, was, thus, bound to give rise to admiration and envy, surely, and was also to be imitated to large measure, including in the artistic field. Lethaby insists that it was inevitable, that with the Muslim revival of learning, the acquaintance with Arabic numerals, trigonometry, astrology and philosophy, that the arts would have had their share of influence.[3265] Ettinghausen also maintains that Eastern arts were so popular in the West because there was specifically no Muslim iconography or overt religious symbolism, which would have been offensive to the Christian mind.[3266] `The innocent blandness of the various quadrupeds and birds,' and arabesques, made the objects on which they were portrayed fully acceptable, even for the wrapping of a sacred relic or the carpeting of the altar steps.[3267] The ready acceptance of Islamic objects and arts, obviously, was their obvious aesthetic quality, their harmony, opulence, and often the great richness of their colours.[3268] But more importantly, a further asset, especially in the early

---

[3261] R. Ettinghausen: Islamic Art and Archaelogy: in *Near Eastern Culture and Society*; Ed by T. Cuyler Young: Princeton University Press, 1951: pp 17-47; at p.21.
[3262] L.A. Mayer: *The Rise and Progress of Moslem Archaeology* (in Hebrew), Jerusalem, 1935.
[3263] R. Ettinghausen: Islamic Art; op cit; p.21.
[3264] L. Mayer: The Rise; op cit, pp 6-7.
[3265] W.R. Lethaby: Medieval Architecture; op cit; p. 63-4.
[3266] R. Ettinghausen: Muslim Decorative Arts; op cit; p. 14.
[3267] Ibid.
[3268] Ibid.

periods, was the high degree of technical skill evident in the execution, far surpassing anything possible in the West.[3269]

The admiration for Islamic arts and aesthetics was such that no exception was ever taken to the use of the Arabic script, which was widely used. It can be found on the halo of the Madonna, along the edges of the garments worn by saints, on cathedral doors, and on every other Possible surface.[3270]It was noteworthy during the reign of Henry II when a new type ornamentation of Muslim and Arabic in character appears in the carvings of English architecture.[3271] In the church of the Martorana built by George of Antioch for a convent of Greek nuns in Palermo, the Arabic inscription runs round the base of the tiny dome, which actually translates a Greek hymn.[3272] And although Arabic writing had a symbolic meaning in the Muslim world, and certain formulas contain religious invocations, the West apparently did not understand it as such.[3273]

So endearing was the Islamic artistic influence, such an influence spilled beyond the post medieval period, thriving even at the height of the so-called Renaissance. Hence, the Reception of a Venetian Embassy in Damascus, attributed to the school of Bellini in the early 16th century, was by an artist who was familiar with the topography and monuments of Damascus.[3274]Turkish costume and Muslim dress in general attracted immense interest, in 1587 an unknown European artist producing a volume of watercolour drawings of `Turkish, Moorish and Persian figures,' which in turn provided the models copied by Rubens in his Costume Book in about 1600.[3275] The Frenchmen Tavernier and Chardin were so moved by their experiences in the East that they publicly wore, on their return to Europe, the Eastern dress that they had acquired at first hand, and King Louis XIV's interest also encouraged the issue of popular engravings of Persian subjects, which included details of costume and architecture.[3276] In England, under the later Stuarts, as under the Tudors, the brilliance of Islamic textiles and the captivating

---

[3269] Ibid.

[3270] A. de Longperier: 'L'Emploi des caracteres arabes dans l'ornamentation chez les peuples Chretiens de l''Occident,' *Revue archaelogique,* ii (1845), pp. 696-706; in R. Ettinghausen: Muslim decorative Arts; op cit; p. 14.

[3271] W.R. Lethaby: Medieval Architecture; op cit; p. 63-4.

[3272] J. D. Breckenridge: The Two Sicilies; op cit; p. 53.

[3273] R. Ettinghausen: Muslim Decorative Arts; op cit; p. 14.

[3274] Blair and Bloom at http://www.islamicart.com/main/architecture/impact.html

[3275] In J. Sweetman: The Oriental Obsession: op cit; p.32

[3276] Ibid. p.48.

intricacy of the arabesque found a happy correspondence with existing tastes and also made notable contributions to them.[3277]Rembrandt, too, was collecting Eastern objects, including miniatures, costumes and metalwork, some two decades, it seems, before copying, in the 1650s, original Mughal miniatures in his possession in Amsterdam.[3278] Rembrandt also owned a collection of several dozen Mughal and Deccani paintings, which he copied.[3279] Sweetman also notes how, subsequently, with the concourse of Muslim calligraphy line-along with many other influences, Celtic art-became part of `a highly charged decorative language,' which led to Art Nouveau.[3280]

The appreciation of Islamic arts in Western culture finds expression in the many sources that sought to revive such a place even after the Islamic impact had dimmed. Hence Ettinghausen notes an early 19th century awakening of interest in the artistic monuments of Islam, especially in buildings, the first country to arouse such interest and instigate a sizeable literature being Spain.[3281]James Cavanah Murphy pioneered this upsurge in *Arabian Antiquities of Spain*, a book which expresses enthusiasm for everything Islamic, including buildings, their decoration and inscriptions. Other writers also active in Spain in the first half of the 19th century include A. de Laborde, Girault de Prangey, J. Goury, and Owen Jones.[3282]At about the same time, other writers in their discussion of Sicilian monuments included the Muslim remnants.[3283]The outstanding figure in this group remains Frederich Sarre (1865-1945), who, from 1896 wrote about 200 books and articles, which cover the Islamic impact from Spain to India, and that includes architecture, painting, the minor arts, and also forerunners of Muslim art and its relationship with European and Far eastern arts and crafts.[3284]Sarre even fixed the exact historical and geographical place of whole groups of

[3277] Ibid. p.71.
[3278] Ibid. p.32.
[3279] Blair and Bloom at: http://www.islamicart.com/main/architecture/impact.html
[3280] J. Sweetman: The Oriental Obsession; Preface: XVI.
[3281] R. Ettinghausen: Islamic Art; op cit; p.23.
[3282] A. de Laborde: *Voyage pittoresque et historique de l'espagne*, Paris, 1806-1820; G. de Prangey: *Monuments Arabes et moresques de Cordoue, Seville et Grenade....* Paris, 1836-9. Idem, essai sur l'architecture des Arabes et des Mores en Espagne, en Sicilie et en Barbarie, Paris, 1841; J. Goury and O. Jones: *Plans, elevations, sections et details of the Alhambra ......* London, 1842-5.
[3283] R. Ettinghausen: Islamic Art; op cit; p.23.
[3284] J.H. Schmidt: *Frederich Sarre*, Schriften, Berlin, 1935.

objects and monuments.[3285]Belonging to the same era is William Richard Lethaby (1857-1931), who became the first Principal of the Central School of Arts and Crafts, London, who Sweetman notes, as an Arts and Crafts man concerned to propagate standards of example and method across the whole field of design `sensed to the full Europe's debt to the lands of `Caliphs and Emirs, Mahomet, Arabs, Turks and Saracens'.[3286]

Islamic art and aesthetics impacted so strongly, that early Islamic objects bearing them, from objects prized for decorative purposes, soon turned into imitated Western objects, thus providing the foundations for some of the most successful early Western Christian crafts and industries as the following shows.

b. The Impact of Islamic Art and Aesthetics on Early Western Crafts and Industries, and Sources of Influence:

The preceding outline has avoided troubling itself too much with instances of Islamic medieval influences for the simple reason that it seeks to use such instances in the following to highlight three main points, which are amongst those central to this work:
-The crucial role of Islamic influence in the awakening of the Christian West, here in the field of early crafts and industries courtesy of the Islamic artistic influence.
-The substance of such early crafts and industries, which was Islamic.
-The re-occurrence of the same patterns, routes and means of influence observed already with regard to other changes, thus highlighting, once more, that all changes occurring in medieval Western Christendom, whatever their nature, go back to one and single source: the Islamic.

Beginning with earthenware objects, in their wider definition here, which occupy one of the leading places in both Western arts, crafts and early industries, highlighting how admiration led to unrestrained imitation. The crusades, first, and then Spain, were the principal sources of influence.
Let us suppose, says Schnyder, that you had joined the powerful crusade movement in one of the northern countries, and had passed the important point, Constantinople, and had safely reached the goal of the

---

3285 In R. Ettinghausen: Islamic Art; op cit; p. 30.
3286 W.R. Lethaby: Medieval Architecture; op cit; p. 63. in J. Sweetman: The Oriental Obsession; op cit; p.203.

undertaking: the Holy Land.[3287] `There you would very soon have noticed that the material, clay, played quite a different and far more significant role than at home. In fact, you would not at first have recognized certain clay products as such and would have suspected that they had been made of some far more precious material. The potters in the coastal countries along the eastern Mediterranean were able to employ various techniques which made it possible for them to give their products such brilliance that the eye would have been deceived.'[3288] Such products soon found their way to the Christian West for decorative purposes. The Vatican, for instance, owns an Egyptian splash-ware vessel once used as a reliquary, and a white carved semi porcelain cup preserved for its rarity as the chalice of San Girolamo.[3289] Islamic lustre-painted bowls, prized for their colour and brilliant surface, were embedded in the walls of some Italian churches;[3290]such as with the so-called *bacini,* flat, round, glazed vessels which for colouristic effects are set into the fabric of some Italian churches, whether in the facade or the campaniles, and there is little doubt that wares from different Muslim countries, especially Egypt and the Maghrib are prominently displayed among them.[3291]

Local demand, and acquired skills via Muslim craftsmen, soon played their part in stimulating a local Western Christian production of these same objects, and here the Spanish route played a central role. Schnyder shows how Muslim skills passed on first from Muslim Malaga to Christian Manises in the neighbourhood of Valencia, before passing North to Italy, and also to France.[3292]With the latter, this took place after relations were established between Manises and Avignon during the years 1362-64, when we hear in 1382-85 of a certain Jehan de Valence who was employed in the service of the Duc de Berry and who produced painted faience tiles in Poitiers and in Bourges (in France).[3293] The same technique used to produce the tiled floor, which the Prince of Burgundy had made in 1391 for his castle in Hesdin by `Jehan le Voleur' and Jehan de Moustier, after drawings by the court painter Melchior Broederiam.[3294]The challenge posed by the ceramics of

---

[3287] R. Schnyder: Islamic Ceramics: A source of inspiration; op cit; p. 27.

[3288] Ibid.

[3289] M.D. Whitman: Ceramics; Dictionary of the Middle Ages; op cit; vol 3; pp. 238-40; at pp. 238-9.

[3290] Ibid.

[3291] R. Ettinghausen: Muslim Decorative Arts; op cit; p. 18.

[3292] R. Schnyder: Islamic Ceramics: A source of inspiration; op cit; p. 34.

[3293] M. Olivar Davdi: La Ceramica trecentista; op cit; p. 135 fwd.

[3294] Ibid; p. 137; M. Dehlinger, "Les Incunables de la Faience Francaise 'a Poitiers et a Bourges," *Memoires de la Societe 'des Antiquaires de l'Ouest*, 16, (1940), pp. 3-41.

Valencia producing amazing results in the French centres.[3295] The more direct Islamic influence, of course, as Ettinghausen notes, particularly of its Hispanic-Muslim varieties with their tin glazes and *sgraffito,* or lustre decorations, can be seen in the nascent Italian pottery production, which was soon to enjoy such an extraordinary flowering.[3296]Small bowls, vases, pots, and the drug jars called *albarelli, as* well as specific decorative motifs, were also readily taken over, and the artistic effects of the techniques which had originated in the Near East and had been developed in Spain were still further refined in the different Italian centres, but, Ettinghausen rightly points out, before long they turned to a figural imagery quite alien to the East and with it a specifically Western type of pottery came into being.[3297]

Textile products of Islamic origin, first, served diverse decorative uses. There are numerous surviving examples of early medieval Islamic silks such as the famous 10th century Buwayhid Suaire de St. Josse from the Pas-de- Calais, or the Holy Coat of Jesus in the Trier Cathedral.[3298] This is also the case of the 'Veil' of Caliph Hisham II (976-1013) (Muslim Spain), which is possibly part of a dress given as a battle trophy to the Church of San Esteban in San Esteban de Gormaz, and the same applies to the great Almohad textiles of the 12th Century.[3299]Such was the appreciation of Islamic decorative models that when at the end of the Middle Ages and during the early Renaissance painters wanted to represent the Madonna in a worthy garment, they often adorned her robes with border designs in which Arabic writing was imitated.[3300]
In the 12th-13th centuries, an important development took place as the Islamic textile patterns were taken over by European weavers who paraphrased them freely, albeit on a reduced scale; first to be copied, the Sasanian-type roundels with pairs of animals were copied in Lucca and Regensburg, then there followed ogival composition schemes and

---

[3295] R. Schnyder: Islamic Ceramics: A source of inspiration; op cit; p. 34.
[3296] B. Rackham, *Guide to Italian Maiolica;* London, 1933, pp. 1-2, 8, 82, idem, *Catalogue of Italian Maiolica;* London, 1940, in R. Ettinghausen: Muslim Decorative Arts; op cit; p. 18.
[3297] R. Ettinghausen: Muslim decorative Arts; op cit; p. 18.
[3298] W.B. Denny: Rugs and Carpets; in Dictionary of Middle Ages; op cit; vol 10; pp. 546-552; at p. 548.
[3299] L. May, *Silk Textiles of Spain. Eighth to Fifteenth* Century (New York, 1957), pp 14-17; in R. Ettinghausen: Muslim Decorative Arts; op cit; p. 16.
[3300] R. Ettinghausen: Islamic Art; op cit; p.18

geometric tile patterns which were woven in `Mudejar patterns of Chinese derivation.'[3301]

The Oriental carpet as we know it, Ettinghausen says, is assumed to have been brought to the Near East by the Seljuk Turks when, in the middle of the 11th century they moved west from their Central Asian homes, the patterns undoubtedly further developed in Anatolia in the 12th-13th centuries.[3302]Two types of association are attached to carpets in Europe from the High Middle Ages on, Denny observes, as furnishings for the altar area in churches, and as accoutrements for the thrones of royalty; in each case, carpets are identified with sanctity, wealth, and power.[3303] By the 12th-13th century, carpets are represented in ever-increasing numbers in Italian paintings.[3304] When depicted in European paintings, these carpets are often shown as floor coverings under the feet of the Madonna or before the throne of a king or pope, or they are seen hanging from windows as colourful decorations displayed on feast days.[3305]
In the late Middle Ages the rugs and carpets were adapted to large commercial carpets;[3306]and in the 15th century began the European carpet mania that led to the westward flow of thousands of carpets; such a popularity of these works, eventually leading to imitations of the Middle Eastern carpets being created not only in Spain but in England and in central Europe as well.[3307]

Fairly everything else followed the same pattern, whereby attraction to the Islamic object is followed by its Western `production'. Thus, briefly, here, the Damascus inlaid metal work was imported to Europe, and became the source when the idea of copper plate printing arose.[3308]

3301 O. Von Falke, *Kunstgeschichte der Seidenweberei,* ii, Berlin, 1913, figs. 261-74, 293-6 (Italy), 308-16 Regensburg, 371-9 (Spain), 351-2, 354-5 (Chinese influence). In R. Ettinghausen: Muslim Decorative Arts; op cit; p. 16.
3302 R. Ettinghausen: Muslim decorative Arts; op cit; p. 16.
3303 W.B. Denny: Rugs and Carpets; op cit; p. 548.
3304 R. Ettinghausen: Muslim Decorative Arts; op cit; p. 16.
3305 W.B. Denny: Rugs and Carpets; op cit; p. 549; R. Ettinghausen: Muslim Decorative arts; op cit; p. 16.
3306 W.B. Denny: Rugs and Carpets; op cit; p. 551.
3307 Ibid.
3308 C.R. Conder: The Latin Kingdom; op cit; p. 334.

There is, in Venice, the establishment of a workshop of Muslims producing versions of Mamluk metalwork tailored to Italian taste.[3309]

Glass objects found their way to Western decorative places, in churches, cathedrals, palaces, etc, the most celebrated of the ecclesiastic treasures in St Stephen's in Vienna being an enamelled Syrian pilgrim bottle of about 1280, thought to contain earth from Bethlehem which was saturated with the blood of the Innocents.[3310] The Venetian glass industry, as the previous chapter amply showed, took its origin in the imitation of Syrian art; and the materials were brought from Syria.[3311]

Book binding also impacted in similar fashion. Many affluent Muslims had bibliophile inclinations, and appreciated calligraphy and paid handsomely for sumptuous bindings.[3312]The craft of bookbinding was highly developed and specialised in fine leather (Cordovan, Moroccan), which was embellished with gold tooling.[3313]The first mention of a gilding process occurs in a North African technical handbook pertaining to the arts of the book, written between 1062 and 1108, while the first gold-tooled binding for an Almohad sultan of Morocco dates from 1256.[3314]Western Christendom acquired the skills from Islam, but substituted cardboard for wood as the core material for the covers, and then the gilding of the leather, especially by means of a hot tool.[3315] The earliest known Western use of this technique is Italian and dates from 1459,[3316] and the history of the craft in its most creative period, the second half of the 16th century, cannot be understood without taking Muslim bindings into special consideration.[3317]

The Western `re-production' of Islamic objects, just as with all other changes seen in previous chapters, occurred precisely via the same sources of influence. The earliest, without a doubt, and quite logical, is the usual Mozarab source. The Mozarabs were Christians living

---

[3309] S.J. Auld: Kuficising inscriptions in the work of a gentile da Fabriano; *Oriental Art*; 32/3; 1986; pp. 245-65.

[3310] R. Ettinghausen: Muslim decorative Arts; op cit; p. 19.

[3311] C.R. Conder: The Latin Kingdom; op cit; p. 334.

[3312] F. Reichmann: *The Sources of Western Literacy;* Greenwood Press; London; 1980. p.206.

[3313] Ibid.

[3314] R. Ettinghausen: Muslim Decorative arts; op cit; p. 20.

[3315] R. Ettinghausen: Near Eastern book covers and their influence on European bindings; *Ars Orientalis*; 3; 1959; pp. 113-31; R. Ettinghausen: Muslim decorative arts; op cit; p. 20.

[3316] A. R. A. Hobson, 'Two Renaissance Bindings,' *The Book Collector,* vii (1958), 265-6; R. Ettinghausen: Near Eastern Book Covers; op cit;121-2.

[3317] R. Ettinghausen: Muslim decorative Arts; op cit; p. 20.

amongst Muslims in Spain, and being the earliest, nearest, and most powerful link between both cultures, they were bound to be the first transmitters of Islamic influences. Their influence was felt as early as the 9th-10th century in the Asturias, most notably in the Churches of Valdedios and San Martin de Salas.[3318] The Romanesque art in France came from Spain during the great part of the 11th century via Mozarab monasteries, and not the least important which spread the Road of Saint Jacques through which many French passed through Aragon, Navarre, Castile and Leon to get to Compostelle.[3319] In the 11th and 12th centuries, the French could have directly come across Islamic works through their participation to the re-conquests of Castile and Aragon; but the resemblances of Mozarab art with Muslim Spain explain that as much as that French participation of the re-conquest the borrowings of French Romanesque art from Islam.[3320]The combined Mozarab-pilgrim-French southern participation in the wars in Spain, meant that the South of France, with places such as Toulouse, becoming the centre of an Orientalizing type of Romanesque art.[3321]Other forms of Islamic art in the south of France are seen at Le Puy, some remarkable carved wooden doors bearing Kufic inscriptions applied in ornamental ways, and this use of Kufic decoration spread later, even as far as England.[3322]

The Sicilian-Italian route, equally, imposes itself as a major source of influence. The early Sicilian rulers, Roger II, in particular, had been vastly encouraging to Islamic artistic creation. The Islamic legacy was in the architectural and decorative style of early Norman churches, as well as in the minor decorative arts of the Norman period.[3323] The suburbs of Palermo, like the Zisa, whose name derives from the Arabic al-Aziz, "the Splendid",[3324] highlight the Islamic influence. The columns of the Cathedral of Palermo were sculptured with floral ornaments, interspersed with inscriptions in Kufic characters.[3325] The doors of the church of the Martorana were carved by local craftsmen, recalling the skills of the Muslims who wrought the fantastic ceiling of Roger's own Palace Chapel.[3326] The roof structure and ceiling of the nave of the

---

[3318] V. Lagardere: Moulins d'Occident Musulman; op cit; p.63.
[3319] E. Lambert: l'Art Hispano Mauresque et l'Art Roman; in *Hesperis*; Vol 17; pp 29-42.pp. 32-3.
[3320] Ibid.
[3321] W.R. Lethaby: Medieval Architecture; op cit; p. 63-4.
[3322] Ibid.
[3323] A.L. Udovitch: Islamic Sicily; in *Dictionary of the Middle Ages*; 11; p.263.
[3324] J. D. Breckenridge: The Two Sicilies; op cit; Breckenbridge: p. 55.
[3325] S. P. Scott: History of the Moorish Empire; op cit; p. 26.
[3326] J. D. Breckenridge: The two Sicilies; op cit; p. 53.

Chapel are the work of Muslims, decorated with paintings of Oriental style illustrating Eastern legends and fables.[3327] Islamic influence persisted even under William 1 (The Bad) (ruled 1154-1166), the heir to Roger II.[3328] He built a number of retreats in the outskirts of Palermo, the geometric structuring of the design suggesting a relation to woven textile patterns, a frequent means of transmission of ornamental motives during the Middle Ages.[3329] Frederick II, for his part, through his encouragement, stirred the diffusion of Muslim arts from Sicily to Lombardy.[3330]
For centuries, also, Italy, to the north, had the largest collections of Islamic art in Europe, a legacy of the vigorous trade between East and West.[3331] The Italian `Oriental' strongholds are highlighted by Sweetman who notes the strategically placed presence of medieval and Renaissance Venice, continuously purveying Eastern design to the rest of Western Europe.[3332]Muslim artists settled in Venice played a great part in introducing into Europe technique of filling depressed parts with gold tints, decorations of wood covers with enamel or warded ivory, or inlaid with gold, silver, or gems etc.[3333]

And, of course, the crusade route, once more. Textiles, metalwork, even glass and ceramics, hitherto part of trade, during the crusades became almost automatic items of the loot brought back from the East.[3334] Islamic artistic influences on Western architectural decorations were re-produced motifs found on objects.[3335] In the wake of the first crusade, for instance, is a striking development in the field of architectural ceramics and bricks used to construct decorative patterns.[3336] The art of faience decoration began to show its influence on the ceramic work of France in the 12th century, when Arabic letters were imitated on the enamel tiles of St Antonin.[3337] The production of decorative floors first appears in the second half of the 12th century in Northern France and

---

[3327] Ibid.
[3328] Ibid. p. 55.
[3329] Ibid.
[3330] G. Sarton: Introduction; op cit; Vol II, p.575:
[3331] C. Hillenbrand: The Crusades, Islamic Perspectives, op cit; p.406.
[3332] J. Sweetman: The Oriental Obsession; op cit; p.3.
[3333] W. Durant: The Age of Faith, op cit; p. 908.
[3334] O. Grabar: Islamic Architecture and the West; op cit; p 60.
[3335] Ibid.
[3336] R. Schnyder: Islamic Ceramics; op cit; p. 29.
[3337] C.R. Conder: *The Latin Kingdom; op cit;* p. 333.

bordering areas and flourished at the beginning of the 13th century.[3338] `It would seem that quite suddenly,' Schnyder notes, `masters appeared who were able to refine the surface of their architectural ceramic products not only with a white engobe, a covering of white fired clay, but also with a simple lead glaze.'[3339]
Which is precisely the same conclusion made with regard to other sudden changes: castle fortification, arches, bridge construction, hospitals, windmills, etc, which occurred precisely at the same time, on the same models, and from the same source.

The Islamic source is further reinforced by the fact that changes, which occurred subsequently, in their substance, or agents, were Islamic, besides the timing of such changes, which occur precisely when such Islamic link is established.[3340] And this is also evident with cultural influences as can be seen now.

3. Culture

Lewis observes that during most of the period 622-1492, Western European civilisation was definitely inferior to the Islamic, and was, in comparison to it `underdeveloped.' This did not just mean, he explains, the average upper class Muslim felt superior to most Western Europeans (merchants, warriors, scholars, or priests,) it also helps explain why, for centuries, Western Europeans were eager to copy many facets of Muslim culture.[3341]The most important period of passage, however, once more, as Le Bon stresses, is the 12th and 13th century period, when, in his words, the luxury of the Orient with respect to the military, manner of dress, and home interior, passed West.[3342]Many other forms of cultural influence also passed in that same period as the following will underline. Before considering some such passages, however, it is important to dwell a little on two important matters:

[3338] A. Lane: A *Guide to the Collections of Tiles,* Victoria and Albert Museum, London; 1960, p. 27ff.; E. Eames, *Medieval Tiles,* British Museum, London (1968).
[3339] R. Schnyder: Islamic Ceramics; op cit; p. 29.
[3340] See J.Sweetman: The Oriental Obsession.
[3341] A.R. Lewis: *The Islamic World and the West*; op cit; p.vii.
[3342] G. Le Bon: La Civilisation des Arabes; op cit; p.259.

-First, The parameters by which Western Christendom allowed some of the Islamic culture to filter through.
-Second, a comment on the expression: luxury in a Muslim context.

On the fist point, as Menocal points out, political enmity towards the Muslims on the part of the `entrenched establishment,' never succeeded in mitigating the seductiveness of such Islamic culture and its numerous attractions for many who emulated them and believed they had much to offer.[3343] However, because of the sort of relationship that existed between Muslims and Christians, it was a relationship that is most likely to produce anxiety, both antagonistic and dependent, loathed at one level but inescapably influential at many others, the culture of a world `damned by one's faith yet seeming to be rewarded by God with affluence and often with stunning military victories.'[3344]
Glick comments on the conflicting elements related to Islamic cultural impact. Factors influencing selectivity were varied: economic demand, the market for stylistic innovation, a desire for new knowledge all contributed to climates favourable to innovation; hostility, warfare, and religious difference contributed to a climate that may have been inimical to borrowing, but only selectively so.[3345]Competition with an enemy can be a powerful stimulus to cultural innovation. If the barrier is strong enough, such imitation may not be consciously acknowledged; rather, a process of reinvention may take place within the recipient culture.[3346]
Summing up, Letourneau, notes that however hostile in principle to Muslim Spain, Christian Spain would not stop imitating it because the civilisation of al-Andalus was richer and more sophisticated than that of the states of Barcelona, Aragon, Navarre, Castille, Asturies, and Leon, pursuing that, similarly Muslim Sicily and Ifriqyia appeared as fabulous territories, rich and full of luxury to the Italian population.[3347]

The second point, talking of luxuries in relation to Islam sounds misplaced. The concept of excessive material wealth or luxury has no place in Islam. The idea of the Day of the Judgement `has always imbued Islam with a humbling spirit,' Ettinghausen reminds us.[3348] In view of the pending hour of reckoning, moral deeds have much higher

---

[3343] M.R. Menocal: The Arabic Role; op cit; p.65.
[3344] Ibid. p.54.
[3345] T. Glick: Islamic and Christian Spain; op cit; p. 285.
[3346] Ibid.
[3347] R. Letourneau: l'Occident Musulman du VII a la fin du 15 siecle: *Annales de l'Institut d'Etudes Orientales*, Alger, Vol 16, 1958, pp 147-176.p.160.
[3348] R. Ettinghausen: The Character of Islamic Art; op cit; p. 255.

value than earthly goods with which to embellish life, and artfully made objects of daily life, are only symbols of worldly splendour or ostentatious luxury, which can easily corrupt.[3349] The Hadith (Islamic tradition), thus, states:

`he who drinks from gold and silver vessels, drinks the fire of hell,'

Hence Islam shuns luxury, and never found ground for jewelled, gold or silver vessels, even within the mosque, for the greater glory of God; thus, there is no parallel whatsoever to the sumptuous objects in the church treasuries of the Christian Middle Ages.[3350] Islam, Ettinghausen insists, was amply satisfied with the humblest materials, such as brass, clay, plaster and brick; cheap material such as stucco used to decorate even the mirhab, the focal point of the mosque, when the wealth of the community could have provided the most costly material.[3351] The accumulation of wealth as in the treasuries of the Fatimids is an exception, and ample evidence for the ebbing morale of the slowly degenerating dynasty.[3352]In contrast, the second Caliph of Islam, Omar (634-44), owned but one shirt and one mantle, patched and re-patched; lived on barley bread and dates, and drank nothing but water; slept on a bed of palm leaves, hardly better than a hair shirt,[3353] and this while the immense treasures of Byzantium and Persia were spread at his feet after both had been vanquished.[3354]Thus, no beakers of precious metal could be used at the courts of the Muslim state, and earthenware was called to the fore to fulfil the needs of the highest ranks of Muslim society.[3355]

Having, thus, cleared two major issues in relation to the Islamic cultural impact, such impact is looked at in terms of its wider definition, with regard to some dominant aspects, but by no means all aspects.

a. Imitation in War and Peace:

At war, first, the Islamic impact took a variety of forms. Defence and castle fortifications have been dealt with already; the point raised here, relates to Arabic vocabulary carrying concrete meaning, here the term 'barbican', ie a tower guarding a gate or a bridge, derived form the

---

3349 Ibid.
3350 Ibid.
3351 Ibid.
3352 Ibid.
3353 W. Durant: The Age of Faith; op cit; p.189.
3354 J. Glubb: A Short History; op cit; p.84.
3355 R. Ettinghausen: The Character; op cit; p. 255.

Islamic compound meaning 'gatehouse' or 'house on the rampart'.[3356]Barbican survives for a London underground station, close to the old London Wall, the object itself disappeared with the widespread use of modern artillery.[3357]
Many changes came from the Islamic west, from Spain, from where was borrowed by Christians the Islamic ribât or frontier fighting "monastery" (inherited from the Almoravids, who swept into Spain in the late 11th century,) and its reinvention as the crusading military order.[3358] In land combat, the Islamic tactics of charging the enemy followed by sudden retreat, the Arabic *Karr wa farr* acquired a great prestige, and was adopted by Christian armies in Spain, who gave it the equivalent of *de torna fuye.*[3359] Norman/Sicilian mechanical and military arts were spread from Sicily to Italy, including the weapons used by Muslim engineers at the sieges of Syracuse and Alexandria.[3360]
The Eastern influence, of course, due to the crusades, was much wider. The use of the tunic for the rider and cloth for his steed, worn on top of the armour, was adopted from the Orient; this, originally, was intended to give protection against the sun but was regarded later as a part of knightly apparel.[3361] Amongst other transfers can be cited the bearing of blazons, also began in Syria during the Crusades, and, which appeared among Turks and Latins alike.[3362] This change took place precisely at the end of the 11th century, when the European knights began to carry coats of arms, these being imitated from Islamic models, the point of this at first was to assist identification of the knights when they were in armour.[3363] This soon led to the development of family coats of arms, and numerous symbols indicate the Orient as the beginning of this tradition.[3364] The music of the army included horns and trumpets, the pipe, the timbrel, the harp, and the nacaires or metal drums, also all borrowed from the East.[3365]

[3356] G.M. Wickens: What the West; op cit; p. 123.
[3357] Ibid.
[3358] On the ribât see A. Castro: The Spaniards, p. 473; Glick and Pi-Sunyer, "Acculturation as an Explanatory Concept in Spanish History," p. 152. in T. Glick: Islamic and Christian Spain; op cit; p. 285.
[3359] J. Olivier Asin: in *al-Andalus*., XV, 1950, p. 154.
[3360] A. H. Miranda: The Iberian Peninsula, op cit, p. 438.
[3361] M. Erbstosser: *The Crusades;* op cit; p. 202.
[3362] C.R. Conder: *The Latin Kingdom; op cit;* p. 175.
[3363] M. Erbstosser: *The Crusades;* op cit; p. 202.
[3364] Ibid
[3365] Rey: Colonies Franques; III; 2; Pietro de la Valle (Bohn's Chronicles of Crusades; p. 389; note) in C.R. Conder: The Latin Kingdom; op cit; p. 177.

Changes in warfare, the increased importance of archers and infantry forces, for example, also resulted from experience gained in the Orient and were then employed under different conditions in the fighting of the 13th and 14th century in Europe as well.[3366] The evolutions of cavalry, the adoption of lighter armour, also exhibited the effect of the pervading Islamic influence. Especially noted here, the role of the Seljuk, the first and main opponents to the first crusaders until the mid 12th century, and their influence in military terms could have been stirred by the admiration of their military prowess. At the battle of Dorylaeum, a Christian witness says:

`I speak the truth, which no one can deny: that if they had always been steadfast in Christ's faith and in Christianity, if they had wished to confess on triune Lord, and if they had honestly believed in good faith that the Son of God was born of the Virgin, that he had suffered and rose from the dead and ascended into heaven in the presence of his disciples, that he has sent the perfect comfort of the Holy Spirit, and that he reigns in heaven and on earth; if they had believed all this, it would have been impossible to find people more powerful, more courageous, or more skilled in the art of war. By the grace of God, however, we defeated them.'[3367]

Many of the Turkish military commanders in Syria and Palestine in the early 12th century, such as Il Ghazi, Tughtegin and Zangi, had come to prominence, and they must have passed on many of the features of the Seljuk military system to the independent rulers of the Levant.[3368]

The Muslim legacy was also in sea warfare, which refutes the general mistake found in historical writing, that the Muslims had little, or no interest in the sea. The very word Admiral, the symbol of sea power, derived from the French *amial* (the 'd' was inserted at some stage under the impression that the name had something to do with the 'admiration' due to this exalted rank); the French *amial* deriving through Spanish, from the Arabic *amir al*-'commander of the…'[3369] The Arabic term itself does not necessarily refer to a naval commander but to a high-ranking officer generally. Here was an innovation, Wickens points out, of enormous strategic importance, `for supreme commanders, apart from kings, were not a normal feature of Western campaigning for many

---

[3366] M. Erbstosser: *The Crusades;* op cit; p. 202.

[3367] Brehier: Gesta Francorum; iii; 9; in J.A. Brundage: *The Crusades*; The Marquette University Press; 1962; p. 51.

[3368] C. Hillenbrand: The Crusades, Islamic Perspectives, op cit; p.444.

[3369] G.M. Wickens: What the West; op cit; p. 123.

centuries, reliance being placed instead on the old anarchic system of Germanic-Frankish loyalty to the band-chieftain or boat-captain.[3370]

The Islamic tradition of generosity at war, Le Bon notes, gave birth to chivalrous acts, which all people of Europe followed later.[3371] The Chronicle of Salerno tell of the siege of Salerno in 871 contrasting Christian desperation with Islamic chivalry, suggesting some spirit of rivalry, an almost sporting element which prefigures, if it does not actually caricature, a later phase of chivalry.[3372] The treatment of Levantine Muslims at the time of the Frankish conquest resembled, in general terms, that of the Muslims in Spain, but the massacres in the Levant were often more ferocious, probably because most Crusaders-unlike many Spaniards had never encountered Muslims.[3373] The crusaders, Oldenbourg explains, eventually adopted the Oriental mentality that their countrymen from Western Christendom were to accuse them of later, that is a new tolerant spirit, having discovered that the Muslims were just ordinary humans, and that all that was needed was some common sense to cohabit side by side.[3374] The Muslim historian/warrior, Usama comments that amongst the Franks are those who have become acclimatized and have associated long with the Muslims, and who are much better than the recent comers from the Frankish lands.[3375]A few years after his accession to the throne, Baldwin I, the crusader leader, as Oldenbourg notes, was `already on the political chessboard of Middle Eastern politics, an Oriental prince not so different from the Turkish and Arab emirs of Syria... and bowing to the customs of local diplomacy and courtesy, just as though he had been born in the country.[3376] Following him, Tancred and Baldwin of Le Bourg adopted the same attitude.[3377] The crusaders were also initially bewildered at the array of non-Catholic beliefs they encountered in the Levant, and soon evolved the realistic policy of letting each group observe its `law' which, as far as the Muslims were concerned, was the law of `detested Muhammed.'[3378]`We can readily understand,' Owen

---

3370 Ibid.

3371 G. Le Bon: La Civilisation des Arabes, op cit; p.37.

3372 N. Daniel: The Arabs and Mediaeval Europe; op cit; p.70.

3373 J. Prawer: *Crusader Institutions*, Oxford; 1980; p.90, n.21.

3374 Z. Oldenbourg: The Crusades; op cit; p. 492.

3375 P.K. Hitti: *An Arab-Syrian Gentleman and Warrior in the Period of the Crusades. Memoirs of Usamah ibn Munqidh*, Columbia University, New York, 1929. p. 169.

3376 Z. Oldenbourg: The Crusades; op cit; p. 478.

3377 Ibid.

3378 B. Z. Kedar: The Subjected Muslims of the Frankish Levant, in: Muslims under Latin Rule, 1100-1300, J.M. Powell, Editor; op cit; pp 135-174.p.161

observes, `that the crusader, with no imputation on his good faith or his religious perspicacity, might occasionally return from Palestine with a more impaired faith in the Dogmas of Ecclesiastical Christianity, and a higher respect for the miscreant paynim than before his enterprise he could have thought possible.'[3379]

Courteous and chivalrous relations, it seems, had also been established during the third crusade between Salah Eddin and Richard who as a boy had been brought up in Aquitaine, in the south of France, where the influence of Islamic culture had been strong.[3380] The ease of Richard's relationships with Salah Eddin was doubtless largely due to the growing extension `of Arab manners in Western Europe. In the same manner today, a Syrian or Iraqi diplomat would mingle easily with Americans in the United States, if he had been educated in the American University of Beirut,' notes Glubb.[3381] Glubb, according to whom, the Muslim code of chivalry, retained by the Spaniards for centuries after the fall of Granada, passed over into France and to England, where it ultimately formed the basis of our codes of sport and fair play.[3382]

Away from the field of war, the Islamic affairs and manners of state also impacted in a diversity of forms, at some stage or another finding their way to Western Christendom. Under Caliph Mehdi, was introduced an innovation in the form of a wazeer, or chief minister, who was the head of the government, which, of course, centuries later brought the position of Prime Minister.[3383] Al-Kindi, in the 9th century, wrote short treatises dealing mainly with ethics and political philosophy, such as on *Morals, On facilitating the paths to the virtues, on the warding off of griefs, on the government of the common people*, and *account of the intellect*.[3384] Myers expands on the impact such literature was to have.[3385] The Islamic impact can be seen in the organisation of the state, its institutions and regulatory bodies. Christian Spain reintroduced a central Islamic institution, the *Muhtasib* (the state inspector), an office that had fallen into desuetude in late Islamic times, in the revivified form of the *Mustasaf*, with its traditional jurisdiction

[3379] J. Owen: *The Skeptics of the Italian Renaissance;* Swan Sonnenschein &Co; London; 1908. p. 29.
[3380] J. Glubb: A Short History; op cit; p.179.
[3381] Ibid.
[3382] Ibid. p.292.
[3383] Ibid. p.99.
[3384] E. A. Myers: *Arabic Thought*; op cit; p. 11.
[3385] Ibid. pp. 11 fwd.

but armed now with a standard, written code to execute.[3386] In the East, during the crusades, the same institution was adopted, the regulation of the markets put by the crusaders under an official called a *mathesep*, from the Arabic *Muhtassab*. [3387] He had charge of the standard weights and measures, inspected streets and bazaars, and regulated the trade of bakers, butchers, cooks, and corn merchants, dealers in fried fish, in pastry, in butter, oil, and in various drinks, and also the native alcohols, the native doctors, oculists, and chemists, the horse surgeons, grocers, money changers, and hawkers, the cloth merchants, tanners, shoemakers, goldsmiths, blacksmiths, and tinsmiths, the slave market, and the market for horses and mules.[3388]

The Islamic impact with regard to state regulations for medical practice, university studies;[3389] the preparation of drugs as well as the relations between doctors and apothecaries,[3390] have all been considered previously to warrant any more space here.

Muslim rulers management of public affairs in Spain was the most competent in the Western world of that age, maintaining rational and humane laws, effective administration and a well-organized judiciary.[3391] The conquered, in their internal affairs, were governed by their own laws and their own officials, whilst towns were well policed; markets, weights and measures were effectively supervised, and a regular census of population and property was kept.[3392] It is from that era, in nearly every respect, Letourneau notes, that dates a large Castilian vocabulary borrowed from Arabic to describe administrative functions, technical details, and other facts of civilisation.[3393] Over a six-hundred-year period, Glick observes, the borrowing of terms related to social and administrative institutions by the Christians in Spain was pre-eminent in the process, an indication, in the first two periods, of the modelling of a less highly structured society after a more highly structured one.[3394]

[3386] R.I. Burns, Islam under the Crusaders, p 240 in T. Glick: Islamic and Christian Spain; op cit; p. 296.

[3387] C.R.Conder: The Latin Kingdom; op cit; p. 173.

[3388] Rey: Colonies Franques; p. 63; in C.R. Conder: The Latin Kingdom; p.173.

[3389] G. Sarton: Introduction, op cit, vol 2; p. 576.

[3390] See: Sir Thomas W. Arnold: Muslim Civilisation During the Abbasid Period; in *The Cambridge Medieval History*, Cambridge University Press, 1922 (1936 reprint):Vol IV: Edited by J. R. tanner, C. W. Previte; Z.N. Brooke, 1923. pp 274-298; at p.279. G.E. Von Grunebaum: *Medieval Islam*, The University of Chicago Press, 1954; at pp. 165; and 217-8.

[3391] W. Durant: The Age of faith, op cit; p.297.

[3392] Ibid.

[3393] R. Letourneau: l'Occident Musulman du VII a la fin du 15 siecle: *Annales de l'Institut d'Etudes Orientales*, Alger, Vol 16, 1958, pp 147-176.p.160.

[3394] T. Glick: Islamic and Christian Spain; op cit; pp. 297-8.

b. Home Comfort and Elegant Living:

De Zayas notes that the streets in Islamic towns and cities are narrow, and homes rise against each other, like scrambling, so small, and very simple seen from the outside; and yet inside, there is a great meticulousness and extreme cleanliness; so much so that the occupants take off their shoes at the entrance.[3395] Great care was taken in medieval Islam to make due provision for the cleanliness, occupation, and amusement of the inhabitants, through pipes of metal, came water, both warm and cold, to suit the season of the year, running into baths, whilst in niches, where the current of air could be artificially directed, hung dripping alcarazzas.[3396]

High standards, of course, were to be found in mosques, such as those of Cairo, in their hundreds, each of them with its pool for ceremonial ablution, all perfectly clean, and lit by numerous lamps, which amazed the visitors.[3397] Muslim `oratoires', unlike Gothic chapels, of course, distinguished themselves in the entire absence of sculpture, painting or gilding, and yet remaining beautiful in the simplicity of white unpainted plaster.[3398] And no less astonishing and unexpected, Savage observes, were the numerous fountains of water scattered throughout the great city, and the beauty of exotic flowers and strange trees.[3399]

It is in the East, primarily, during the crusades, that the Western Christians discovered such art of living of which at home they could only have had the remotest idea in the form of stories, and travellers' tales.[3400] Soon, they adopted such ways of living one such being becoming accustomed to living in the cities.[3401] Crusader knightly and mercantile classes also acquired similar tastes to those of the Muslims, which shows in the interior of their houses, judging by the precious enamel painted glass beakers and glazed pottery fragments excavated at

---

[3395] R de Zayas: *Les Morisques et le racisme d'etat;* Les Voies du Sud; Paris, 1992; p.205

[3396] J. W. Draper: A History; op cit; Vol II; p.32.

[3397] The latest edition of the *Saint Voyage de Jherusalem*, which gives the story of Ogier's journeying, is that Edited by F. Bonnardot and A.H. Longnon: in *Societe des Anciens textes Francais*, Vo X, Paris, 1878. in H.L. Savage: Fourteenth century Jerusalem; op cit; p.211.

[3398] H.L. Savage: Fourteenth Century Jerusalem; op cit; p.211.

[3399] Ibid.

[3400] Z. Oldenbourg: The Crusades; op cit; p. 476.

[3401] M. Erbstosser: *The Crusades;* op cit; p. 135.

Crusader sites.[3402] Carpets, curtains, exquisite furniture, vessels of porcelain and glass, and other objects could be found in the dwellings of every crusader; only the richest princes of Europe were accustomed to luxury of this order.[3403] It is a fact that the courts of Western princes presented a spectacle which deserved to be called Oriental (as indeed, it was, the fine carpets and fabrics and even golden ornaments nearly all imported from the East.)[3404] The palace of the lords of Ibelin in Beirut is described in the chronicle as a splendid building; marble used for the floors, ceilings and walls, and was employed to such an advantage that the floors, for instance, conveyed the impression of water rippled by the wind, whilst mosaics on the walls provided additional decoration.[3405] An object of particular magnificence was the fountain with its marble ornamentation in the centre of the house, the purpose of this was to provide a kind of air conditioning for the rooms; whilst large windows looked over the sea and on to gardens which surrounded the entire palace.[3406] Even if not all of the crusaders possessed such establishments as this, much less was still enough to convince travellers from Europe of the difference between this and their own material life style.[3407]

Though the climate continues to be praised, Christian Andalusia never speaks to us with that sort of lush, rich voice of Muslim times.[3408]In those Muslim times, according to Draper:

`Under the shade of cypresses cascades disappeared; among flowering shrubs there were winding walks, bowers of roses, seats cut out of the rock, and crypt-like grottoes hewn in the living stone. Nowhere was ornamental gardening better understood; for not only did the artist try to please the eye as it wandered over the pleasant gradation of vegetable colour and form-he also boasted his success in the gratification of the sense of smell by the studied succession of perfumes from beds of flowers.'[3409]

Dreesbach insists that the passages from the French literature of the crusading period which describe the Orient show that the things which impressed themselves on the minds of historian and chronicler and poet

---

[3402] E. Baer: Ayyubid metalwork with Christian images; Leiden; 1989; p. 4 in C. Hillenbrand: The Crusades; Islamic Perspectives, op cit; p.388.
[3403] M. Erbstosser: The Crusades; op cit; p. 135.
[3404] Z. Oldenbourg: The Crusades; op cit; p. 476.
[3405] M. Erbstosser: *The Crusades;* op cit; p. 135.
[3406] *Ibid.*
[3407] Ibid.
[3408] F Fernandez Armesto: *Before Columbus:* MaC Millan Education; London, 1987; p.68.
[3409] J.W. Draper: History; op cit; Vol II; p.33.

were the richness of gardens and orchards.[3410] The description of Syria in William of Tyre's history tells of the neighbourhood of Damascus `where there are great number of trees bearing fruits of all kinds and growing up to the very walls of the city and where everybody has a garden of his own.'[3411] `Dunayat (in northern Syria) lies on a vast plain, surrounded by sweet smelling plants and irrigated vegetable gardens,' according to crusader account.[3412] `Long indeed would be the list of early Islamic cities which could boast huge expanses of gardens,' Watson holds.[3413]

Much of this passion for greenery, gardens and also flowers, eventually travelled west. Carra de Vaux lists the flowers that came in from the East, including tulips (Turkish: tulpan,) hyacinths, narcissi of Constantinople, Lilacs, jasmine of Arabia, and roses of Shiraz and Ispahan.[3414] Subsequently, due to Turkish influence, a mania grew for carnations and tulips, Tulipomania developing into one of the more intriguing phenomena.[3415] The plant was brought to Vienna by Count Ogier de Busbecq, ambassador to Suleyman the Magnificent, in 1554, and reached Holland about 1560.[3416] The interest was also shared by Italy: Francisco Caetani, Duke of Sermoneta, appears to have had the remarkable total of 15,147 tulips in his garden by the 1640s.[3417] In France the Huguenots, who were garden conscious, took the plant with them when driven to other countries by persecution, and helped to popularise it.[3418] In the 1680s it was among the flowers of the Serial when it caught the attention of the Englishman Sir George Wheler who, with other amateur botanists, brought home specimen.[3419] Ceramic decoration also provides many examples of 17th century interest in Levantine flowers such as carnations or, most notably, tulips, especially familiar to travellers who visited the Serail gardens at Constantinople.[3420]

[3410] Dreesbach: Der Orient; 1901; pp. 24-36, in J. K. Wright: The Geographical Lore; op cit; p. 238.
[3411] Historia; XVII, 3; Paulin Pari's edit; vol ii; p. 141 in J. K. Wright: The Geographical Lore; p. 239.
[3412] M. Erbstosser: *The Crusades;* op cit; p. 130.
[3413] A. Watson: Agricultural, op cit, p.117.
[3414] Baron Carra de Vaux: Les Penseurs; op cit; pp 309-19.
[3415] See W. Blunt: *Tulipomania;* Penguin; 1950.
[3416] J. Sweetman: The Oriental Obsession; op cit; p.50.
[3417] G. Masson: Italian Flower Collectors' gardens; in *The Italian Garden*; Dumbarton Oaks; Washington; 1972; p. 77 in J. Sweetman: The Oriental Obsession; p.50.
[3418] J. Sweetman: The Oriental Obsession; p.50.
[3419] R. W. Ramsey: Sir George Wheeler; 1650-1724; in Trans Royal Soc; 1942; pp. 1-38; in J. Sweetman: The Oriental Obsession; p.50.
[3420] J. Sweetman: The Oriental Obsession; op cit; p.50.

The Muslims, Draper observes, `religiously cleanly, it was not possible for them to clothe themselves according to the fashion of the natives of Europe, in a garment unchanged till it dropped to pieces of itself, a loathsome mass of vermin, stench, and rags.'[3421] And that `No Arab who had been a minister of state, or the associate or antagonist of a sovereign, would have offered such a spectacle as the corpse of Thomas a Becket when his haircloth shirt was removed.'[3422] It is from the Muslims, Draper pursues, that was inherited the use of `the often changed and often washed under garment of linen or cotton, which still passes among ladies under its old Arabic name.'[3423] Christian pilgrims to the holy sites in the East were shocked to notice, in particular, the adoption of Oriental clothing amongst the established crusaders.[3424] Silk burnous and turban were the normal attire for the crusaders, made of exquisite oriental cloths, of course, and richly embroidered as was the custom of the country.[3425]The older crusaders were also regarded by the newly arrived as having turned effeminate in contact with the East, effeminate because they had got into the habit of taking frequent baths, using scents, wearing shirts of fine cloth, and sleeping in sheets.[3426] The palaces had a constant supply of piped water; whilst the ordinary crusaders used the public baths if they did not possess one of their own.[3427] The arriving pilgrims were astonished to see how jealously guarded were the wives of the older crusaders by their husbands, and even more shocked to see that the same ladies were wont to use the public baths two or three times a week, likewise in accordance with local customs.[3428] Speculation about loose morals may have been based on this, although there was no real foundation for it.[3429]One item necessary for the bathing, soap, obviously has an Islamic origin, hard soap, an Islamic development later imported into Europe. It was made using olive oil, *al-Qali* (alkali), and sometimes *natron* (sodium carbonate); David of Antioch (Dawud al-Antaki) giving one recipe.[3430]

3421 J.W. Draper: History; op cit; Vol II; p.33.
3422 Ibid.
3423 Ibid.
3424 M. Erbstosser: *The Crusades;* op cit; p. 135.
3425 Ibid.
3426 Z. Oldenbourg: The Crusades; op cit; p. 476.
3427 M. Erbstosser: *The Crusades;* op cit; p. 135.
3428 Ibid. p.136.
3429 Ibid.
3430 In A. Y. Al-Hassan; D.R. Hill: *Islamic Technology;* op cit; pp.150-1.

Medieval Islamic literature abounds with all sorts of information devoted to other forms of care for the body. In the 19th volume of *Al-Tasrif,* al-Zahrawi, devotes a complete chapter to cosmetology; cosmetics seen as a definite branch of medication (*Adwiyat al-Zeenah*). He describes the care and beautification of hair, skin, teeth and other parts of the body, dealing also with perfumes, scented aromatics and incense, includes under-arm deodorants, hair removing sticks and hand lotions; methods for strengthening the gums and bleaching the teeth, and so on and so forth.[3431] Many such new usages found their way to the Christian West following the translation of the work by Gerard of Cremonna.

One of the translations by Constantine the African is the *Kitab al-Aghdiya* (the book of diets) by Ishaq b. Sulyman al-Israeli (d. 932), who was established in Al-Qarawan.[3432]The treatise is dedicated to the Archbishop of Salerno, Alfanus, who often complained to Constantine about his stomach troubles. Constantine is surprised not to have found anything on the matter in the works of the Greeks. He says he derived his own work from the elegant conclusions reached by the diverse authors of Al-Qayrawan.[3433] Later, towards the 12th-13th century, *Kitab minhag al-bayan fima yastamiluhu l'insan*, which is a treatise on diets by the Baghdad doctor, Yahia Ibn Jazla (d. 1100), was translated partially into Latin, by a certain Jombobinus of Cremona,.[3434] This work had a large influence through a translation made by Charles of Anjou, King of Naples, in 1289-1309, a manuscript which reached France before the end of the 14th century.[3435]

The impact of Islamic dietetics is often illustrated in the form of tables, which are called *tacuinum sanitatis* (from the Arabic word taqwim); these being mainly derived from the translations of Ibn Jazla and Ibn Butlan.[3436] Salernus composed such medical treatises, one of which in tabular form may have been inspired by the *Taqawim* of Ibn Butlan and

---

[3431] Mainly derived from the following sources:
-S.K Hamarneh and G. Sonnedecker: *A Pharmaceutical View of Albucassis Al-Zahrawi in Moorish Spain,* Leiden, coll. Janus, suppl. 5, 1963.
-M. Levey: Early Arabic, op cit.

[3432] A. Mieli: La Science Arabe; op cit; p. 23; pp 119 subsequent.

[3433] N.L. Leclerc: *Histoire de la medecine*; op cit; p. 365.

[3434] M. Rodinson: Recherche sur les documents arabes relatifs a la cuisine; *Revue des Etudes Islamiques;* 1949; pp. 95-165; p. 111. n. 3.; p. 102; n. 4.

[3435] M. Rodinson: Romania et autres mots arabes en Italien; *Romania;* 71; 1950; pp. 433-49; pp. 445 and subs.

[3436] See for instance: L.Delisle: Traits d'Hygiene du Moyen Age; *Journal des Savants;* 1896; pp 518-40.

Ibn Jazla.[3437]The popularity of Islamic dietetics even allowed the word *taccuino* in the current Italian language in the sense of almanach, agenda.[3438]

Food recipes were frequently the compositions of the eminent Muslim scholars, al-Kindi (b. 803), for instance, not considering it beneath his dignity to become the author of a work on cookery, giving a menu for each day of the year.[3439] An anonymous author of the Almohad dynasty also wrote a recipe book called *Kitab al-Tabkh fi-l Maghrib wal Andalus.*[3440] And with Ibn al-Awwam, the 12th century agronomist,[3441] according to Armesto, `we seem transported into a world of epicene contentment, in which he mingles aromatic vinegars, concocts foie gras and happily devises recipes to please his sybaritic King.'[3442]
The first recipe books of the West generally date from the 13th century with two small treatises by the Danish Harpestraeng (d.1244), but all recipes bear the name `sarasines.' And they refer to `saracen' sauces, cooked meat, etc. There are recipes for chicken cooked with pomegranates (la Romania; la lomania (recipe of meat with lemon juice; la sommachia: a chicken dish with almonds; etc.[3443]
The Islamic Eastern-crusade influence is also strong, offering many examples of Franks, who in the East only ate oriental foods;[3444]being served meals consisting of various exotic dishes flavoured with a diversity of spices.[3445]In contact with the East, the crusaders learnt to despise the meagre and plain meals of their own countries, many amongst them going as far as refusing to eat pork, and there is no lack of remarks to this effect, notes Erbstosser.[3446] Many of the old literary sources indicate that there was a certain pride on the part of the European feudal lords in possessing only Egyptian cooks, just as in being attended only by Oriental physicians.[3447]In the East, the crusaders also learnt to eat from vessels of metal or precious woods.[3448] In this

---

3437 G. Sarton: Introduction, op cit; Vol II, p.135.
3438 M. Rodinson: Les Influences de la Civilisation Musulmane; op cit; p.490.
3439 G. Wiet et al: History; op cit; p. 320.
3440 See for recipes included in V. Lagardere: La Riziculture en Al Andalus (VIIIem-Xvem siecles), in *Studia Islamica*, vol 83, 1996, pp 71-87.
3441 *Libro de agricultura*, ed.J. A. Banqueri; Madrid, 1802.
3442 Felipe Fernandez Armesto: Before Columbus; op cit; p.68.
3443 M. Rodinson: Les Influences de la Civilisation Musulmane; op cit; at pp 491-3.
3444 Ibid. p.482.
3445 Z. Oldenbourg: The Crusades; op cit; p. 476.
3446 M. Erbstosser: *The Crusades;* op cit; p. 135.
3447 Ibid.
3448 Z. Oldenbourg: The Crusades; op cit; p. 476.

they were following the patterns established elsewhere as by William II of Sicily (1166-1189) who took a Muslim as his head cook.[3449] He was not alone, for the leading figures of Europe had at their service foreign cooks.[3450] A Catalan cookery book, *Libre de Sent Sovi,* kept amongst manuscripts of the end of the 14th and early 15th century, was written under the dictation of someone named Pedro Felipe (a strong man, and good cook) who had been at the service of the English king, Edward II.[3451]Thus, Mediterranean cooking progressing to the north of Europe; and there are many other instances like this one.[3452]

There is a considerable number of ordinary delights, which also have Eastern origins. Yoghurt is Turkish through and through (though other Middle Eastern countries make a similar preparation); but all the promotional literature in the West insists on its origin in Bulgaria or some other part of the Balkans.[3453] European cooking of the medieval period and Renaissance makes abundant use of milk of almonds, but also of cream and butter and oil of almonds.[3454] This ingredient is neither found in Greece nor Rome, whilst Muslim works make very many references to oils of almonds.[3455] As for all forms of paste, there is nothing more illuminating on the subject than the work by E. Sereni, which sums up the use of pasta, in all its variety, that has been borrowed by the Italians and Spaniards from the Muslims.[3456] Ice cream was diffused to the rest of the world from Sicily, and is yet another Islamic legacy, whose early production used to take place in cool caves on the island.[3457] Also courtesy of the East, the delectation of coffee, tea and chocolate became commonly established in Europe by 1700 whilst they were almost unknown a century earlier.[3458] Coffee houses in Marseilles and Venice fostered the habit, and soon after 1650 one opened in St Michael's Alley, Cornhill, London, the `Pasqua Rosee's Head,' named after the servant whom a Turkey merchant had brought back with him to

---

[3449] M. Rodinson: Les Influence de la Civilisation Musulmane; op cit; at p.482.
[3450] Ibid. p 488.
[3451] L. Faraudo de Saint Germain: *El `Libre de Sent Sovi.'* Recetario de cocina catalan medieval; Boletin de la Real Academia de Buenas Letras de Barcelona; 24; 1951-2; pp. 5-81.
[3452] M. Rodinson: Les Influences de la Civilisation Musulmane; op cit; p.488.
[3453] G.M. Wickens: What the West borrowed; op cit; p. 124.
[3454] Austin: *Two 15th Century Cookery Books*; index; s.v.risschewes; p. 143; in M. Rodinson: Les influences; p. 492.
[3455] M. Rodinson: Recherche; op cit; p. 16.
[3456] E.Sereni: Note di storia dell'alimentazione nel Mezzogiorno; Cronache meridionali; Napoli; Anno V; no5; maggio 1958; pp. 353-77.
[3457] A. Carluccio: Food Programe on the BBC (1994-5) (seen by this author).
[3458] J. Sweetman: The Oriental Obsession; op cit; p.49.

England.[3459] By 1700 there were probably about 500 coffee houses in London.[3460] Also were born coffee and chocolate-pots of ceramic and silver of the long spouted ewer shapes developed long before in both China and Persia, but indissoluble part of the Islamic metal-ware tradition of the 13th and 14th centuries.[3461]

Outlining such Islamic influences in parts of Christian Spain, Levi Provencal notes: `The `mozarabization' of Spanish Leon and Castile, which accentuated with time, will affect all marks of life, and even every aspect of the spoken language, from institutions, to home furnishing, to clothing, and all personal outer signs.'[3462] And to `the Saracens,' are indebted many of the personal comforts,' concludes Draper.[3463]

c. Literature and Polite Literature:

When coming across the literature of 18th century Europe, one reads with great fascination about the Literary Salons of France in particular, where the leading aristocracy conversed in endless disputations with the French intellectual elites, the likes of Voltaire, for instance. A wonderful, typically Western/French manifestation, born in the century of enlightenment, it would seem. And yet, again, written history proves so misleading in comparison with true history.

Early rulers and ruling elites of Islam, despite the shortcomings of some, led in this movement, which, with the exception of Frederick II of Sicily, Europe only caught up with in the 18th century. `Never before and never since', admits Briffault `on such a scale has the spectacle been witnessed of the ruling classes throughout the length and breadth of a vast empire given over entirely to a frenzied passion for the acquirement of knowledge. Learning seemed to have become with them the chief business of life. Caliphs and emirs hurried from their Diwans to closet themselves in their libraries and observatories. They neglected their affairs of the state to attend lectures and converse on mathematical

---

3459 In 1652, according to the memory of John Aubrey; Life of sir Henry Blount; Brief Lives; 1949; p. 26 in J. Sweetman: The Oriental Obsession; p.49.
3460 J. Sweetman: The Oriental Obsession; p.49.
3461 Ibid.
3462 G Moreno, Iglesias mozarabes, p. p 121-5; in E. Levi Provencal: Histoire; op cit; p.217.
3463 J.W. Draper: History; op cit; Vol II; p.33.

problems with men of science.'[3464] The Spanish Caliphs, Draper notes, emulating the example of their Asiatic compeers, and in this strongly contrasting with the popes of Rome, were not only the patrons, but `the personal cultivators of all the branches of human learning, one of them being the author of a work on polite literature in no less than fifty volumes, whilst another wrote a treatise on Algebra.[3465]

The literary salons developed around the learned caliphs and their scholarly companions, and became meeting places for literary and scholarly exchanges of ideas. Nakosteen says that those attending the salons were hand picked, and were instructed as to the style of dress they should wear and required to follow certain strict rules of general dignity and bearing, such as absolute silence when the Caliph spoke.[3466] Everyone was required to use a refined language, in quiet measured voice, whilst interruptions were not allowed.[3467]

The one early ruler of Western Christendom who followed on this line was Frederick II of Sicily, who was, of course, the ruler most imbued in Islamic culture. His court was a thriving debating society of learned scholars of all faiths.[3468] "The mingling of the Orient and Occident at the Sicilian court is nowhere better illustrated than in Frederick II's own work, *De arte Venandi cum Avibus,*" writes Van Cleve.[3469] In this work one feels that all Frederick's scholarly efforts, the results of his correspondence and learned discussions with men from all corners of the earth, found their ultimate repository.[3470]

Frederick is also one of the great heroes of Dante's *Purgatorio*, Dante risking his fate for the cause inspired by Frederick's legacy: "Boccaccio said of Dante that he would have been ill able to create his work had he not been a Ghibelline."[3471] Dante saw Frederick's "Sicilian" poetry as the source of vernacular Italian verse, and evoked the spirit of the Southern court as the perfect home for the civilized man: "Those who were of noble heart and endowed with graces strove to attach themselves to the majesty of such great princes (Frederick and his son Manfred); so that, in their time, whatever the best Italians attempted first appeared at the court of these mighty sovereigns."[3472]

3464 R. Briffault: *The Making of Humanity*, op cit; p 188.
3465 J.W. Draper: History; Vol II; op cit;p.34.
3466 M. Nakosteen: *History of Islamic Origins; op cit;* p.48.
3467 Ibid.
3468 M. R. Menocal: *The Arabic Role;* op cit; p.61.
3469 In J.D. Breckenridge: The Two Sicilies; op cit; p.57.
3470 C.H. Haskins: Studies; op cit; 265.
3471 In J. Breckenridge: The Two Sicilies; op cit; p. 58.
3472 Ibid.

Dante, himself, was strongly influenced by Islamic culture. Although he, personally, did not know any Arabic, his teacher, Brunetto Latini, who had been with the Florentine embassy at the court of Alfonso the Wise in 1260, was familiar with some aspects of Islamic culture and showed some knowledge of Islamic beliefs.[3473] Dante may also have met his Florentine compatriot, the Dominican missionary Ricaldo da Montecroce (d.1320) who spoke Arabic and was familiar with the literature.[3474]Dante's main source of astronomical knowledge was the Elements of al-Farghani, which he had studied very thoroughly in the Latin translation as *(Elementa astronomica, or Liber aggregatione scientiae stelarum, or Liber de aggregationibus stellarum).*[3475] This very elementary work had been Latinized in 1134 by John of Seville, and later by Gerard of Cremona; the Latin text was even translated into French and the French text was translated into Italian by Zucchero Bencivenni in 1313.[3476] Of course Dante had no need of translations into the vernacular, as he knew Latin as well as Italian. He quoted Al-Fraganus or his book only twice (in the Convivio, book 2), but he used him repeatedly, possibly using John's translation.[3477]

Other than poetry, all literary genres: fiction, romance, chivalry, etc, have been cultivated by the `Arabs,' admits Le Bon.[3478] The earlier literature of Italy bears ample trace of Oriental influence; poetry was certainly affected by Sicilian model and later Provencal devices.[3479] Literary, philosophical, and military adventurers were perpetually passing; and thus the luxury, the taste, and above all, the chivalrous gallantry and elegant courtesies of Muslim society found their way from Granada and Cordova to Provence and Languedoc.[3480] Also to southern France spread the manners and ways of Islamic Spain, such as poetic disputations, carried to perfection among the Troubadours; the Provencal also learning to employ jongleurs.[3481] A large number of miscellaneous Arabic or Oriental analogues have also been traced in the Canterbury tales, especially in the Knight's tale, the Franklyn's, the Merchant's, the Man of Law's, the Pardoner's, the Manciple's and

---

3473 F. Reichmann: *The Sources; op cit.* p.203.
3474 Ibid.
3475 G. Sarton: Introduction. Op cit; Vol III; p.484.
3476 Ibid.
3477 Ibid.
3478 G Le Bon: La Civilisation des Arabes, op cit; p. 351.
3479 H. G. Farmer: *Historical Facts for the Arabian Musical Influence*; Verlag; Hildesheim; 1970: p. 17.
3480 J. Draper: History; op cit; Vol II:p.34.
3481 M. R. Menocal: *The Arabic Role; op cit.*

others.[3482] The sudden appearance of a fictional literature is evidence of Europe's natural links with the other cultures that derive from the ancient sources of the Near East.[3483] Ibn Tufayl (c. 1110-85), of Spain, wrote *Hayy ibn Yaqzam* (The Living son of the awake), the story of Hayy, who was brought up in isolation by a gazelle... then he receives a visitor, Asal, from an inhabited island etc...The work was translated in the 17th century by E. Pococke, and is said to have been among the influences which led to Defoe's Robinson Crusoe.[3484]

When the Muslim libraries boasted tens of thousands of volumes, some hundreds of thousands, European libraries, even the most renowned, such as the Sorbonne in Paris and the Vatican libraries, had just few hundreds volumes.[3485] Santa Maria de Ripoll reached its height under Abbot Oliva (1008-46), with a catalogue of its notable library of two hundred and forty six titles.[3486] Most libraries had less than a hundred; Cluny, one of the best, had 570 volumes in its 12th century catalogue, a remarkably large and complete collection for its time.[3487] Western Medieval libraries were, of course, not public libraries, for there was no reading public, nor were they lending libraries such as came into existence at the universities.[3488]
It is in the 12th century, once more, that we see a transformation in Western Christendom; the universities-or rather, their college halls-began to have libraries precisely then.[3489] A development that arrived via the usual routes: Spain, Sicily and the crusades. The French King, St Louis (1214-1270), who went on the crusade in the East, for instance, taking example of what he saw in Palestine, began to encourage the collection of books in libraries.[3490]Many of the books that served as foundation for such early Western libraries were, of course, Islamic books, witness Daniel of Morley, who about 1200, brought to England from Spain `a precious multitude of books.[3491]The university of Naples had a large collection of Muslim works as the popularity of Frederick with the Muslim princes of the East gave him exceptional facilities for

---

3482 N. Daniel: The Arabs; op cit; p.306.
3483 Ibid.
3484 R. Fletcher: *Moorish Spain;* Phoenix; London; 1992; p. 132.
3485 John F. D'Amico: `Manuscripts,' op cit, pp. 11-24.
3486 C.H. Haskins: The Renaissance; op cit; p.41.
3487 Ibid. p.43.
3488 Ibid. p.85.
3489 W. Durant: The Age of faith, op cit; p. 909.
3490 C.R. Conder: The Latin Kingdom; op cit; p. 320.
3491 C.H. Haskins: Studies; op cit; p. 100.

the acquirement of literary treasures.[3492] He, in turn, made Naples University an academy for translations from Arabic into Latin, and had copies of such translations sent to Paris and Bologna.[3493]
Islamic libraries also inspired in their organisation and management.[3494] Whether in book lending, cataloguing, librarianship, and general library management, the methods adopted and introduced by the Muslims can be seen even today. Equally, it was the Islamic profession of Warraq, plural warraqueen, or book-shop keepers, which developed considerably in the Muslim East in the 9th century onwards, following the development of the paper industry,[3495] which served as the foundation for future similar professions in the West, that is of both book sellers and makers.

A final word on the major tool of Islamic civilisation, its language: Arabic. From the end of the 8th century to the end of the 11th, Sarton insists, the intellectual leaders had been most of them Muslims, and the most progressive works had been written in Arabic; during these three centuries the Arabic language was the main vehicle of culture.[3496] Arabic, which, Leopold Von Ranke observes, leaving Latin aside, is the most important of all the languages of the world for universal history.[3497] Montgomery, too, in the *Haverford Symposium*, asserts that Arabic has had the most unique development and spread of all the tongues of the earth and that only within the last two centuries has English come to rival it.[3498] For centuries, the prestige of Arabic was such that not just the translators of Muslim science (Gerard of Cremona, Robert of Chester, John of Seville…), but every single man of learning of Western Christendom had to be knowledgeable of it. Arnold of Villanova (d.1311), for instance, mastered Arabic, and in his enthusiasm for Islamic medicine translated a series of its important works into

---

[3492] S.P. Scott: History; op cit; vol 3; p.44.
[3493] De Lacy O'Lcary: Arabic Thought; op cit; p. 281.
[3494] O. Pinto: The Libraries of the Arabs during the time of the Abbasids, in *Islamic Culture* 3 (1929), pp. 211-43;
-R.S. Mackensen: `Background of the History of Muslim libraries.' *The American Journal of Semitic Languages and Literatures* 51 (Jan 1935) 114-125, 52 (Oct 1935) 22-33, and 52 (Jan 1936): 104-10.
-R.S. Mackensen: `Four Great Libraries of Medieval Baghdad.' *The Library Quarterly* 2 (July 1932): pp. 279-99.
[3495] See: J. Pedersen: The Arabic Book; op cit.
[3496] George Sarton: Introduction; op cit; Vol II, p.109.
[3497] P.K. Hitti: America and the Arab heritage; op cit; p.5.
[3498] Ibid.

Latin.[3499] Erbstosser points out how words of Arabic origin are very numerous in the scientific sphere; almost all the names of constellations and the basic terms of astronomy, for instance, coming from Arabic.[3500] The place of Arabic goes even further, Arabic symbolising all that was sophisticated, and superior; `material wealth and comfort for Western Europeans, must have at times appeared to go hand in hand `with the ability to read Arabic,' Menocal says.[3501]Such was the impact of the language, the Christian figure, Alvarus (9th century), bitterly reacted:

`Who is there among the faithful laity sufficiently learned to understand the Holy Scriptures, or what our doctors have written in Latin? Who is there fired with love of the Gospels, the Prophets, the Apostles? All our young Christians… are learned in infidel erudition and perfected in Arabic eloquence. They assiduously study, intently read and ardently discuss Arabic books…. The Christians are ignorant of their own tongue; the Latin race does not understand its own language. Not one in a thousand of the Christian communion can write an intelligent letter to a brother. On the other hand there are great numbers of them who expound the Arabic splendour of language, and metrically adorn, by mono-rhyme, the final clauses of songs, better more sublimely than other peoples.'[3502]

No matter, centuries, on, such was the appeal of Arabic, even Alvar Fanez, the lieutenant of the Cid, who fought the Muslims bitterly early in the 12th century, signed his name in Arabic.[3503]

Finally, briefly returning to one major issue raised by this work, the gradual suppression by Western history of Islamic achievements, one after the other, as here noted by Dawson with regard to the rise of Provencal culture. This new culture was the result of influence of Islamic civilisation, as was accepted by Western scholars up to the early 19th century.[3504] After that, not due to scientific reasons, but due to nationalist tendencies, Dawson says (although he could have added other motivations,) modern Western historians suppressed the Islamic

---

3499 R. I. Burns: Muslims in the Thirteenth Century Realm of Aragon: Interaction and Reaction, in *Muslims under Latin Rule (*J.M. Powell: ed) op cit; pp 57-102: at pp.90-1.
3500 M. Erbstosser: *The Crusades;* op cit; p. 185.
3501 M. Rosa Menocal: The Arabic Role; op cit; p.63.
3502 Alvari Cordubensis Indiculus Luminosus in Migne, *Patrologia Latina* 121, cols. 555-6. Quotation in English from R. Dozy: *Spanish Islam: a history of the Muslims in Spain;* trans: F.G. Stokes; London; 1913; p. 268.
3503 Sebold: Glossarium Latino-Arabicuml in H. G. Farmer: Historical facts; op cit; p. 29.
3504 C. Dawson: Medieval; op cit; pp. 222 fwd.

influence, and insisted on the independent and native origin culture.[3505] Dawson, referring to older sources,[3506] highlights the resemblance with Islamic elements, and the lack of resemblance with anything Western, besides insisting that at the time of impact, whilst Muslim culture was glittering, Western Christendom was `almost barbarian' to exert such sort of impact.[3507] Yet, in a same and similar pattern as with regard to all other medieval changes, all such obvious points were done away with by Western historians, the Islamic influence suppressed, and new, odd, countless, even conflicting forms of origin, made the end product of our modern history of civilisation.

Concluding Remarks:

Mac Kenzie,[3508] just as Le Bon,[3509] a century before him, noted that in the process of European imperialist domination of Islamic countries, whole chunks of Islamic culture were removed, which betrays both contempt and admiration for the civilisation of the occupied. Several artists were members of official diplomatic, scientific and military expeditions, even present at acts of imperial aggression.[3510] Some extolled the virtues of French rule in North Africa and bought property there to capitalise upon it themselves. Many, however, went further in the looting of antiquities of all sorts, robbing tombs, buildings etc, and in this respect, just as Nochlin put it, some of the artists distinguished between visual beauty and moral quality; the moral superiority of the West, able to preserve while the East destroyed, justifying such plunder.[3511]

And just as was plundered material Islamic culture and civilisation, today, as this work amply showed, is plundered the Islamic intellectual legacy and its impact on civilisation.

Two centuries ago, Chateaubriand, although no keen admirer of Islam, still, on his Middle Eastern journey of 1806-7, concluded that:

[3505] Ibid.

[3506] Dawson refers here to J. Andres: *Origine, progressi e stato attuale d'ogni letteratura*; 17282-99.

[3507] C. Dawson: Medieval; op cit; pp. 223.

[3508] J. M. Mac Kenzie: Orientalism; op cit; p.53.

[3509] G. Le Bon: la Civilisation; op cit; p. 466 ff.

[3510] J. Mac Kenzie: Orientalism; op cit; p.53.

[3511] Nochlin in J. M. Mac Kenzie: Orientalism; p.53

`The Bedouins, though now decadent, are descendants of a great civilisation.'[3512]

It is the image of decadence, which now shrouds that of greatness that once was; image reinforced by both iniquitous Western historical writing and corrupt, inept, Muslim leadership.

[3512] Chateaubriand in J. Sweetman: The Oriental Obsession; op cit; p.79.

Conclusion

At an International Congress of Orientalists, in 1883 (Leyden), Dr Tien of England stated that `Only those who are blinded can deny the Muslim scientific contribution.'[3513]

> `For indeed it is not the eyes that grow blind,
> but it is the hearts, which are within the bosoms, that grow blind.'
> Qur'an 22:46.

[3513] Bulletin d'Etudes Arabes; Vol 3 (1943); p.68.

Select Bibliography

-D. Abulafia: *Commerce and Conquest in the Mediterranean, 1100-1500*, Variorum, 1993.

-J L. Abu-Lughod: *Before European Hegemony,* Oxford University Press, 1989.

-Adelardus Von Bath, *Die Quaestiones Naturales*, c.6, ed. M. Muller (*Beitrage zur Geschichte der philosophie des Mittelalters*, xxxi.2; Munster, 1923.

-D.A. Agius and R. Hitchcock ed: *The Arab Influence in Medieval Europe*; Ithaca Press, Reading, 1994.

-N. Ahmad: *Muslim Contribution to Geography* Lahore: M. Ashraf, 1947.

-S. M. Z Alavi: *Arab Geography in the Ninth and Tenth Centuries*, Published by the Department of Geography, Aligrah Muslim University, Aligrah 1965.

-R. Allen: Gerbert Pope Silvester II; *The English Historical Review*:Year 1892: pp 625-68.

-A. Amari: *La Storia dei Musulmani di Sicilia,* 3 vols, (1933-9) Revised 2nd edition by C.A. Nallino, Rome.

-M.Amari: *I Diplomi Arabi del Reale Archivio Fiorentino*, Florence, Lemonnier, 1863.

-F F Armesto: *Before Columbus*: MaCMillan Education; London, 1987.

-T.Arnold and A Guillaume ed: *The Legacy of Islam;* 1st edition Oxford; 1931.

-F.B. Artz: *The Mind of The Middle Ages*; 3rd ed revised; The University of Chicago Press, 1980.

-A.S. Atiya: *Crusade, Commerce and Culture*; Oxford University Press; London; 1962.

-S Athar ed: *Islamic Perspectives in Medicine*; American Trust Publications, Indianapolis, 1993.

-Ibn al-Athir: *Al-Kamil fi'l Tarikh;* 12 Vols; ed C.J. Tornberg; Leiden and Uppsala; 1851-76.

-Ibn Al-Awwam: *Le Livre de l'Agriculture* d'In al-Awwam, tr. from Arabic by J.J. Clement-Mullet, Vol. I, Paris 1864.

-Al-Bakri: Descriptions de l'Afrique Septentrionale; in *Journal Asiatique*; 5th series; XII.

-L. G. Ballester et al ed: *Practical Medicine from Salerno to The Black Death*; Cambridge University Press; 1994.

-Banu Musa: *The Book of Ingenious Devices*, tr and annoted by D. R. Hill, Dordrecht: Reidel, 1979; Arabic text, ed. Ahmad Y. al-Hasan; Aleppo: Institute for the History of Arabic Science, 1981.

-Jose Rubia Barcia ed: *Americo Castro, and the Meaning of Spanish Civilisation.* University of California Press, Berkeley, 1976.

-Ibn Bassal: *Libro de agricultura*, Jose M.Millas Vallicrosa and Mohammed Azinan eds, Tetuan: Instituto Muley al-Hasan, 1953.

-Ibn Battuta: *Travels in Asia and Africa;* tr and selected by H.A.R. Gibb; George Routledge and Sons Ltd; London, 1929.

BBC Television; London.
-J. Bensaude: *L'Astronomie Nautique au Portugal*, Meridian Publishing, Amsterdam, 1967.
-Issa Bey: *Histoire des hopitaux en Islam*; Beirut; Dar ar ra'id al'arabi; 1981.
-L. Bolens: L'Eau et l'Irrigation d'apres les traites d'agronomie Andalus au Moyen Age (XI-XIIem siecles), *Options Mediterraneenes*, 16 (Dec, 1972).
-H.Bresc: *Un Monde Mediterraneen: Economies et Societe en Sicile*, 1300-1450: 2 vols, Rome-Palermo, 1986. vol 2.
-H. Bresc: *Politique et Societe en Sicile; XII-Xv em siecle*; Variorum; Aldershot; 1990.
-R. Briffault: *The Making of Humanity*, George Allen and Unwin Ltd, 1928.
-E.G. Browne: *Arabian Medicine*; Cambridge University Press, 1962.
-T. Burckhardt: *Moorish Culture in Spain*, George Allen & Unwin, London; 1972.
-C. Burnett: *Adelard of Bath*, Warburg, London, 1987.
-C. Burnett: *The Introduction of Arabic Learning into England*; The Panizzi Lectures, 1996; The British Library; 1997.
-C. Burnett and D. Jacqart: *Constantine the African*, Brill, 1994.
-C. Burnett ed: *La Connaissance de l'Islam dans l'Occident Medieval*; Variorum; 1994.
-C.E. Butterworth and B.A Kessel ed: *The Introduction of Arabic Philosophy into Europe*; Brill; Leiden; 1994.

-C Cahen: l'Histoire economique et sociale de l'Orient Musulman medieval; *Studia Islamica*Vol 3 (1955) pp. 93-115.
-*The Cambridge Medieval History*, Vol IV: Edited by J. R. tanner, C. W. Previte; Z.N. Brooke, 1923.
-*The Cambridge History of Islam*, vol 2, edt P.M. Holt, A.K.S. Lambton, and B. Lewis, Cambridge University Press, 1970.
-D. Campbell: *Arabian Medicine and its Influence on the Middle Ages*; Philo Press; Amsterdam; 1926.
-Barron Carra de Vaux: *Les Penseurs de l'Islam;* Geuthner, Paris, 1921; vol 2.
-A. Castro: *The Structure of Spanish History*, English translation with revisions and modifications by Edmund A.King. Princeton: Princeton University Press, 1954.
-A.Castro: *The Spaniards. An Introduction to Their History.* trans. Willard F. King and Selma L. Margaretten. Berkeley, The University of California Press, 1971.
-A K Chehade: *Ibn an-Nafis*, Institut Francais, Damas, 1955.
-A. Cherbonneau: *Kitab al-Filaha* of Abu Khayr al-Ichbili, in *Bulletin d'Etudes Arabes*, vol 6 (1946); pp 130-144.
-L. Cochrane: *Adelard of Bath,* British Museum Press, 1994.
-M.L. Colish: *Medieval Foundations of the Western Intellectual Tradition 400-1400*; Yale University Press; 1997.
-C.R. Conder: *The Latin Kingdom of Jerusalem;* The Committee of the Palestine Exploration Fund; London; 1897.

-M.A.Cook ed: *Studies in the Economic History of the Middle East*; Oxford University Press; London; 1970.
-Y Courbage, P Fargues: *Chretiens et Juifs dans l'Islam Arabe et Turc*, Payot, Paris, 1997;
-K.A.C. Creswell: *Early Muslim Architecture*, 2 Vols, 1932-40.
-K.A.C. Creswell: *A Short Account on Early Islamic Architecture*; Scholar Press; 1989.
-A.C. Crombie ed: *Scientific Change;* London, 1963.
-A.C Crombie: *Science, Optics and Music in Medieval and Early Modern Thought*; The Hambledon Press, London, 1990.

-N.Daniel: *The Arabs and Medieval Europe*; Longman Librarie du Liban; 1975.
-N.Daniel: *Islam and the West*; Oneworld; Oxford; 1993.
-C.Dawson: *Medieval Essays*: Sheed and Ward: London; 1953.
-M.L. De Mas Latrie: *Traites de paix et de Commerce, et Documents Divers, Concernant les Relations des Chretiens avec les Arabes de l'Afrique Septentrionale au Moyen Age*, Burt Franklin, New York, Originally Published in Paris, 1866.
-*De Toulouse a Tripoli*, Colloque held between 6 and 8 December, 1995, University of Toulouse; AMAM, Toulouse, 1997.
-T.K Derry and T.I Williams: *A Short History of Technology*; Oxford Clarendon Press, 1960.
-B.G. Dickey: *Adelard of Bath*, unpublished Thesis, University of Toronto, 1982.
-*Dictionary of the Middle Ages*; J.R. Strayer Editor in Chief; Charles Scribner's Sons; New York; 1982 fwd.
-*Dictionary of Scientific Biography;* Editor Charles C. Gillispie; Charles Scribner's Sons, New York, 1970 fwd.
-Al-Dimasqui: *Manuel de la cosmographie arabe*, tr. A.F. Mehren, Amsterdam. 1964.
-Al-Dimashqi: *Mahasin al-Tijara*; trad. H.Ritter, Ein arabisches handbuch der handelswissenschaft; in *Der Islam*; vol VII; 1917; pp 1-91.
-A. Djebbar: *Une Histoire de la Science Arabe*; Le Seuil; Paris; 2001.
-A Djebbar: Mathematics in Medieval Maghreb; *AMUCHMA-Newsletter* 15; Universidade Pedagógica (UP), Maputo (Mozambique), 15.9.1995.
-B.Dodge: *Muslim Education in Medieval Times*; The Middle East Institute, Washington, D.C. 1962.
-D. C. Douglas: *The Norman Achievement*; Eyre and Spottiswoode; London; 1969.
-R. Dozy: *Spanish Islam: A History of the Muslims in Spain*; trans: F.G. Stokes; London; 1913.
-J.W. Draper: *A History of the Intellectual Development of Europe*;Vol I; Revised edition; George Bell and Sons, London, 1875.
-J.L.E. Dreyer: *A History of Astronomy from Thales to Kepler*; Dover Publications Inc, New York, 1953.

-C.E. Dubler: *Uber das Wirtschaftsleben*; Romania Helvetica XXII; Geneva; 1943.
-P.Duhem: *Le System du Monde*; Paris; 1914.
-D.M. Dunlop: *Arab Civilisation 800-1500 A.D*, Longman Group Ltd, 1971.
-W. Durant: *The Age of Faith*, Simon and Shuster, New York; 6th printing; 1950.
-Al-Duri: *Tarikh al-Iraq*; Baghdad; 1948.

-Y.Eche: *Les Bibliotheques Arabes, Publiques et Semi Publiques en Mesopotamie, en Syrie et en Egypte au Moyen Age*. Damascus: Institut Francais. 1967.
-H. Edwards: *Patterns and Precision: The Arts and Sciences of Islam*; Washington; 1982.
-G.T. Emeagwali in Science and Public Policy; *Jounal of the International Science Policy Foundation*, Surrey; UK; Vol 16; No 3; 1989; at http://members.aol.com/Sekglo/racism.htm
-*Encyclopedia of Islam*, Leyden; Brill.
-M. Erbstosser: *The Crusades;* David and Charles; New ton Abbot; First published in Leipzig; 1978.

-A.M.Fahmy: *Muslim Naval Organization*; Second edition; Cairo; 1966.
-N.A. Faris editor: *The Arab Heritage*; Princeton University Press; New Jersey; 1944.
-H.G. Farmer: *Clues for the Arabian Influence on European Musical Theory*, Journal Royal Asiatic Society, 1925/1, pp 61-80.
-H. G. Farmer: *Historical facts for the Arabian Musical Influence*; Verlag; Hildesheim; 1970
-O.A. Farukh: *The Arab Genius in Science and Philosophy*; American Council of Learned Societies, Washington, D.C, 1954.
-I.R. al-Faruqi and L. L al-Faruqi: *The Cultural Atlas of Islam;* Mc Millan Publishing Company New York, 1986.
-G. Ferrand: *Instructions Nautiques et Routiers Arabes et Portugais des XV et XVI Siecles*, 3 Vols, Paris, 1921-8.
-G. Ferrand: *Relations de Voyages et textes geographiques Arabes, Persans and Turks relatifs a l'Extreme orient du VIIem au XVIIIem Siecles*; E. Leroux, Paris, 1913-4. re-edition by F. Sezgin, Frankfurt, 1986.
-S.Ferber ed: *Islam and the Medieval West*; State University of New York at Binghamton; 1975.
-Abu al-Fida: *Geographie d'Aboulfeda*, ed. and tr. M. Reinaud. 3 vols. Paris, 1840-83.
-W. Fischel: The Origins of Banking in Medieval Islam: *JRAS* Vol 1933 pp 339-52.
-Sir Banister Fletcher: *A History of Architecture*: revised by J. C. Palmes: University of London, The Athlone Press, 18th edition, 1975.
- J. Fontana: *The Distorted Past, Blackwell*, 1995.
-R.J. Forbes: *Studies in Ancient Technology*; vol II, second revised ed, Leiden, Brill, 1965.

-F.L. Ganshof: The Middle Ages; in *The European Inheritance*, Ed: Sir. E. Barker, G Clark, and P. Vaucher, Vol I, Oxford, at the Clarendon Press, 1954.
-R. Garaudy: *Comment l'Homme devint Humain,* Editions J.A, 1978.
-M. Garcia-Arenal: Historiens de l'Espagne, Historiens du Maghreb au 19em siecle. Comparaison des stereotypes *ANNALES: Economies, Societes, Civilisations*:Vol 54 (1999): pp; 687-703.
-J.C.Garcin et al: *Etats, Societes et Cultures du Monde Musulman Medieval*; vo2; Presses Universitaires de France; Paris; 2000.
-D. J. Geanakoplos: *Medieval Western Civilisation, and the Byzantine and Islamic Worlds,* D.C. Heath and Company, Toronto, 1979.
-F. and J. Gies, *Cathedral, Forge, and Waterwheel* subtitled "Technology and Invention in the Middle Ages". Harper Perennial, 1995.
-T.Glick: *Islamic and Christian Spain in the early Middle Ages*, Princeton University Press, New Jersey, 1979.
-John Glubb: *A Short History of the Arab Peoples*; Hodder and Stoughton, 1969.
-S.D. Goiten: *A Mediterranean Society*, 5 Vols, Berkeley. 1967-90.
-V.P. Goss ed: *The Meeting of Two Worlds*; Medieval Institute Publications, Michigan, 1986.
-E. Grant: *A Source Book of Medieval Science*; Harvard University Press; 1974.
-E.Grant: *Physical Science in the Middle Ages*; John Wiley and Sons, London, 1971.
-Wang Gungwu: Transforming the Trading World of Southeast Asia[i] at http://hometown.aol.com/wignesh/5Wanggungwu.htm
-A. Gunny: *Images of Islam in Eighteenth Century Writing*; Grey Seal, London, 1996.

-S.K. Hamarneh: Editorial: Arabic-Islamic science and technology; *Journal of the History of Arabic Science*; 1 (1977); pp 3-7.
-S.K Hamarneh and G. Sonnedecker: *A Pharmaceutical View of Albucassis Al-Zahrawi in Moorish Spain,* Leiden, coll. Janus, suppl. 5, 1963.
-S.K. Hamarneh: *Health Sciences in Early Islam*, 2 vols, edited by M.A. Anees, vol I, Noor Health Foundation and Zahra Publications, 1983.
-R. Hammond: *The Philosophy of al-Farabi and its Influence on Medieval Thought*; New York; The Hobson Book Press; 1947.
-J.B. Harley and D. Woodward ed: *The History of Cartography*; Volume 2; Book 1; Cartography in the Traditional Islamic and South Asian Societies; The University of Chicago Press; Chicago and London; 1992.
-W. Hartner, ``The Principle and use of the astrolabe," in W. Hartner, *Oriens-Occidens*, Hildesheim, 1968, pp. 287-318.
-W. Hartner: The Role of Observations in ancient and medieval astronomy; in *The Journal of History of Astronomy*; Vol 8; 1977; pp 1-11.
-J.Harvey: *The Master Builders: Architecture in the Middle Ages*: Thames and Hudson, London, 1971.
-J. Harvey: The Development of Architecture, in *The Flowering of the Middle Ages*; ed J. Evans; Thames and Hudson; 1985; pp. 85-106.

-J.H. Harvey: `The Origins of Gothic Architecture,' *Antiquaries Journal* 48 (1968), pp. 91-4.
-C.H. Haskins: *Studies in the History of Mediaeval Science*.Frederick Ungar Publishing Co. New York. 1967 ed.
-C.H. Haskins: *The Renaissance of the Twelfth Century*, Harvard University Press, 1927.
-C.H. Haskins: England and Sicily in the 12th century; *The English Historical Review*: Vol XXVI (1911) pp 433-447 and 641-65.
-A. Y. Al-Hassan; D.R. Hill: *Islamic Technology*: Cambridge University Press, 1986.
-J.R. Hayes ed: *The Genius of Arab Civilisation*, Source of Renaissance, Phaidon, Oxford; 1976.
-B. Hetherington: *A Chronicle of Pre-Telescopic Astronomy*; John Wiley and Sons; Chichester; 1996.
-W. Heyd: *Geschichte des Levantehandels im Mittelalter* 1, 1879. Fr ed: W.Heyd: *Histoire du Commerce du Levant au Moyen Age*; Leipzig; 1885-6; reedit; Amsterdam 1967.
-D.R. Hill: *Islamic Science and Engineering*, Edinburgh University Press, 1993.
-D. R. Hill, *The Book of Knowledge of Ingenious Mechanical Devices*, Dordrecht, Boston, 1974.
-P.K.Hitti: *History of the Arabs*, MacMillan, London, 1970 edt.
-E.J. Holmyard: *Makers of Chemistry*; Oxford at the Claredon Press, 1931.
-S.M Hossain: A Plea for a Modern Islamic University; in *Aims and Objectives of Islamic Education*; Ed by S.M.al-Attas; Hodder and Stoughton;King Abdulaziz University, Jeddah;1977; pp 91-103.
-G.F. Hourani: *Arab Seafaring in the Indian Ocean in Ancient and Early Medieval Times*; Princeton University Press; 1971.
-Paul Egon Hubinger: *Bedeutung Und Rolle des Islam Beim ubergang Vom Altertum Zum Mittelalter*, Darmstadt, 1968.
-S.F.D. Hughes: Scandinavia in Arabic Sources; *Dictionary of the Middle Ages*; Vol 10. pp 706-8.
-D. Hunter: *Papermaking: The History and Technique of an Ancient Craft*; Pleiades Books; London; 1943; 1947.

-H.D. Isaacs: Medicine, Science and Technology: Islamic reactions to Western learning; in *Renaissance and Modern Studies*; Vol 31: pp. 43-57.
-Al-Istakhri: *Das Buch der Lander*, tr. A.D. Mordtmann. Hamburg, 1845.

-Al-Jazari: *The Book of Knowledge of Ingenious Mechanical Devices*, tr D.. Hill Dordrecht, Boston, 1974.
-G.G. Joseph: *The Crest of the Peacock*; Penguin Books; 1991.
-Ibn Jubayr: *The Travels of Ibn Jubayr*; Trans; R.J.C. Broadhurst; London; 1952.

-E.S. Kennedy: *Astronomy and Astrology in the Medieval Islamic World*; Aldershot; Variorum; 1988.

-Al-Khazini: *Kitab Mizan al-Hikma*, Hyderabad; partial English translation by N. Khanikoff (1859); *Journal of the American Oriental Society* vol 6: pp. 1-128.
-A F. Klemm: *History of Western Technology*; tr by D. Waley Singer. George Allen and Unwin Ltd, London, 1959.
-D.A. King: Astronomy, in M.J. L. Young, J.D. Latham and R.B. Serjeant ed: *Religion, Learning and Science in the Abbasid Period.* Cambridge University Press, 1990; pp 274-89.
-P. Kraus: *Jabir Ibn Hayyan.* Textes choisis, Paris, Cairo, 1935.
-I.J. Krckovskij: *Izbrannye Socinenja* (chosen works); Vol 4, Moscow, 1957.
-K. Krisciunas: The Legacy of Uluh Beg; at http://www.ukans.edu/~ibetext/texts/paksoy-2/cam6.html
-P.Kunitzsch: *The Arabs and the Stars: texts and traditions on the fixed stars, and their influence in medieval Europe*; Variorum; Aldershot; 1989.
-Al-Khwarizmi: *Surat al-Ard*, Ed. Hans v. Mzik, Leipzig, 1926.

-P. Lacroix: *Science and Literature in the Middle Ages*, Frederick Ungar Publishing Co, New York, 1964.
-V. Lagardere: La Riziculture en Al Andalus (VIIIem-Xvem siecles), in *Studia Islamica*, vol 83, 1996, pp 71-87.
-E. Lambert: L*'Art gothique en Espagne aux 12 et 13em siecles*; Paris; 1931.
-E. Lambert: L'Art Hispano Mauresque et l'Art Romant; *Hesperis*; 17; pp. 29-43.
-G. Le Bon: *La Civilisation des Arabes*; IMAG; Syracuse; Italy; 1884.
-N.L. Leclerc: *Histoire de la medecine Arabe*; 2 vols; Paris; 1876.
-W.R. Lethaby: Medieval Architecture: in *The Legacy of the Middle Ages*, edited by C.G. Crump and E.F Jacob: Oxford at the Clarendon Press, 1969 edt, pp 59-93.
-M. Levey: *Early Arabic Pharmacology*; E. J. Brill; Leiden, 1973.
-M.Levey: The Manufacture of inks, Liqs, Erasure Fluids and Glues-A Preliminary Survey in Arabic Chemical Technology; in *Chymia*; Vol 7; (1961) pp. 57-72.
-E. Levi Provencal: *Histoire de l'Espagne Musulmane*; Vol III; Paris, Maisonneuve, 1953.
-D.C. Lindberg: *Studies in the History of Medieval Optic*s; London, Variorum; 1983.
-D.C. Lindberg ed: *Science in the Middle Ages*. The University of Chicago Press. Chicago and London. 1978.
-D.C. Lindberg: Introduction, in *Optica Thesaurus: Alhazen and Witelo;* editor: H. Woolf. Johnson Reprint Corporation, New York, London, 1972. pp v-xxxiv.
-M. Lombard: *The Golden Age of Islam*; tr J. Spencer; North Holland Publishers; 1975.
-M.Lombard: Quand l'Islam Brillait de Mille feux. The article is in *Le Temps stratégique* No 20, Spring 1987; and at http://www.archipress.org/batin/ts20lombard.htm.
-R Lopez: Les influences orientales et l'Eveil economique de l'Occident; *Cahiers d'Histoire Mondiale*; Vol 1: 1953-4; pp 594-622.

-R.P. Lorch: The Astronomical Instruments of Jabir Ibn Aflah and the Torquetom; *Centaurus,* 1976; vol 20; pp 11-34.
-C.G. Ludlow and A.S. Bahrani: Mechanical Engineering during the early Islamic Period; in *Chartered Mechanical Engineering*; Nov 1978; pp. 79-83.
-J L. Abu-Lughod: *Before European Hegemony*, Oxford University Press, 1989.
-Lynn White Jr: `Technology in the Middle Ages,' in *Technology in Western Civilisation*, Vol 1, edited by M. Kranzberg and C.W. Pursell Jr, Oxford University Press, 1967, pp 66-79.
-Lynn White Jr: Cultural Climates and Technological Advance in the Middle Ages; *Viator*; 2; pp 171-201.
-Lynn White Jr: The Act of Invention; *Technology and Culture,* Vol 3; pp 486-500.

-S. C. Mc Cluskey: *Astronomies and Cultures in Early Medieval Europe*; Cambridge University Press; 1998.
-M. Mc Vaugh: Constantine the African,' *Dictionary of Scientific Biography*, 16 vols, New York, 1970-80, vol 3, pp. 393-5.
-E.B. Macdougall and R. Ettinghausen ed: *The Islamic Garden*, Dumbarton Oaks; Washington; 1976.
-R.S. Mackensen: Background of the History of Muslim libraries.' *The American Journal of Semitic languages and Literatures* 51 (january 1935) 114-125, 52 (October 1935) 22-33, and 52 (January 1936): 104-10.
-R. Mackensen: Moslem Libraries and Sectarian propaganda, in *The American Journal of Semitic languages*, 1934-5, pp 83-113.
-G. Makdisi: *The Rise of Colleges*, Edinburgh University Press; 1981.
-G Makdisi: *The Rise of Humanism in Classical Islam and the Christian West*; Edinburgh University Press, 1990.
-E. Male: *Art et artistes du Moyen Age*; Paris 1927.
-William of Malmesbury: *History of the Kings of England,* tr. Revd John Sharpe (London, 1815).
-G. Marcais: *Manuel d'Art Musulman*; Paris; 1926.
-G. Marcais: *l'Architecture Musulmane d'Occident,* Paris 1954.
-G.Marcais: Les Jardins de l'Islam; in *Melanges d'Histoire et d'Archeologie de l'Occident Musulman;* 2 Vols; Alger; 1957; pp 233-44.
-F.S. Marvin ed: *Progress and History;* Oxford University Press, 1916.
-L. Massignon: l'Influence de l'Islam au Moyen Age sur la formation de l'essor des Banques Juives; *Bulletin d'Etudes Orientales* (Institut Fr de Damas) Vol 1; year 1931: pp 3-12.
-D.Matthew: *The Norman Kingdom of Sicily*: Cambridge University Press; 1992.
-L.A. Mayer: *Islamic Astrolabists and Their Works;* Albert Kundig; Geneva; 1956.
-Maria Rosa Menocal: *The Arabic Role in Medieval Literary History,* University of Pennsylvania Press, Philadelphia, 1987.

-D. Metlitzki: *The Matter of Araby in Medieval England*, Yale University press, 1977.
-M. Meyerhof: Ibn Nafis and his theory of the lesser circulation. *ISIS* 23 (1935). Pp.100-20.
-M. Meyerhof: `Esquisse d'histoire de la pharmacologie et de la botanique chez les Musulmans d'Espagne,' *al-Andalus* 3, 1935, pp. 1-41.
-*Micrologus (Nature, Sciences and Medieval Societies;) Sciences at the Court of Frederick II;* Brepols; Paris; II. 1994.
-A.Mieli: *La Science Arabe et son role dans l'evolution scientifique mondiale.* Leiden: E.J. Brill. 1938.
-J.M. Millas Vallicrosa: *Estudios sobre historia de la ciencia espanola*, Barcelona, 1949.
-J. M. Millas Vallicrosa, `Sobre la obra de agricultura de Ibn Bassal,' in *Nuevos estudios sobre historia de la ciencia Espanola;* Barcelona: Consejo Superior de Investigaciones Cientificas, 1960.
-W.E. Minchinton: Early tide Mills: Some problems; *Technology and Culture*; Vol 20. pp 777-86.
-A. Miquel: *La Geographie Humaine du Monde Musulman*, Vol 4, Ecole des Hautes Etudes en Sciences Sociales, Paris, 1988.
-E.A. Moody: Galileo and Avempace: The dynamics of the leaning tower experiment in E.A. Moody ed: *Studies in Medieval Philosophy, Science and Logic*; University of California Press; London, 1975; pp 203-86.
-R.P. Multhauf: *The Origins of Chemistry*; Gordon and Breach Science Publishers; London, 1993.
-J.H. Munro: Technology Treatises in *Dictionary of the Middle Ages*; vol 11; C. Scribner's sons; N York; pp 641-2.
-Al-Muqaddasi: *The Best Divisions for Knowledge of the Regions*, a translation of his Ahsan… by B.A. Collins, Centre for Muslim Contribution to Civilization, Garnet Publishing Limited, Reading, 1994.
-E. A. Myers: *Arabic Thought and the Western World.* Frederick Ungar Publishing, New York, 1964.

-A.S.S.Nadvi: *Arab Navigation*; S. M.Ashraf publishers; Lahore; 1966; pp. 55-8.
-M. Nakosteen: *History of Islamic Origins of Western Education: 800-1350*; University of Colorado Press; Boulder; Colorado; 1964.
-C.A. Nallino: *Raccolta di scritti Editi e Inediti*, Roma, 1944.
-J.Needham: *Science and Civilization in China;* 7 vols.; Cambridge University Press, 1954 -.
-G.G.Neill Wright: *The Writing of Arabic Numerals*; University of London Press; London; 1952.
-J.D. North: ``The Astrolabe,'' *Scientific American* 230, No 1, 1974, pp 96-106.
-J. D. North: *Astronomy and Cosmology*; Fontana Press, London, 1994.
-John J O'Connor and Edmund F Robertson at:
http://www-history.mcs.st-andrews.ac.uk/history/index.html In the chapter devoted to: Arabic mathematics: a forgotten brilliance.

-Z. Oldenbourg: *The Crusades*; trans from the French by A. Carter; Weinfeld and Nicolson; London; 1965.
-S.B. Omar: *Ibn al-Haytham's Optics*: Bibliotheca Islamica; Chicago, 1977.
-J. Owen: *The Skeptics of the Italian Renaissance;* Swan Sonnenschein &Co; London; 1908.

-A.Pacey: *Technology in World Civilization, a Thousand year History*, The MIT Press, Cambridge, 1990.
-R. Palter edition: *Toward Modern Science*; The Noonday Press; New York; 1961.
-J.Pedersen: *The Arabic Book,* (1928) tr by G French; Princeton University Press; 1984.
-R Pernoud: *Pour en Finir avec le Moyen Age*: Editions du Seuil, Paris, 1977.
-S Pines: *Studies in Arabic Versions of Greek Texts and in Mediaeval Science,* The Magnes Press, Brill, Leiden, 1986.
-O.Pinto: `The Libraries of the Arabs during the time of the Abbasids,' in *Islamic Culture* 3 (1929), pp. 211-43.
-H. Pirenne: *Mohammed and Charlemagne*; F. Alcan; Paris-Bruxelles; 7th edition; 1937.
-E.L. Provencal: *La Civilisation Arabe en Espagne*; Paris; 1948.
-E.L.Provencal: *Documents arabes inedits sur la vie sociale et economique en Occident Musulman au Moyen Age*; Cairo; 1955
-H. Prutz: *Kulturgeschichte der kreuzzuge*; Berlin, 1883.

-R. Rashed (with collaboration of R. Morelon): *Encyclopedia of the History of Arabic Science*, 3 vols, Routledge, London and New York, 1996.
-J. Read: *The Moors in Spain and Portugal*; Faber and Faber, London, 1974.
-E.Renan: L'Islamisme et la science' in *Oeuvres Completes*; Vol 1; Paris; 1942.
- J. Ribera: J. Ribera. Disertaciones Y Opusculos, 2 vols. Madrid 1928.
-D.S.Richards ed: *Islam and the Trade of Asia*; Oxford; 1970.
-B.Z. Richler: Translations and Translators; *Dictionary of The Middle Ages;* vol 12; pp. 133-6.
-M.Rodinson: les Influence de la Civilisation Musulmane sur la Civilisation Europeene Medievale dans les domains d la Consommation et de la Distraction: l'Alimentation. In *Academia Nazionale dei Lincei; Convegno Internazionale* 9-15 April 1969; Roma; 1971.Pp 479-99.
-S and N. Ronart: *Concise Encyclopaedia of Arabic civilization; The Arab West*; Djambatan; Amsterdam; 1966.
-V. Rose: `Ptolemaus und die Schule von Toledo' in *Hermes*, viii. 327; 1874.
-F.Rosen, ed: *The Algebra of Mohammed ben Musa (al-Khwarizmi).* London: Oriental Translation Fund, 1831, Reprint: Hildesheim, Olms, 1986.
-F.Rosenthal: *Knowledge Triumphant: the concept of Knowledge in Medieval Islam*, Leiden; E.J. Brill, 1970.
-J. Ruska: *Das Buch der Alaune and salze*, Berlin, 1935.
-J.Ruska: `Al-Rasi (Rhases) als Chemiker', *Zeitschrift fur Angewandte Chemie* 35, 1912, pp 719-24.
-J. Ruska: `Die Alchemie des Avicenna,' *Isis* 21, 1933: 14-51.

-J. Ruska: `Die Alchemie ar-Razi's', *Der Islam* 22, 1935, 281-319.

-H.M. Said; A. Z. Khan: *Al-Biruni: his Times, Life and Works*; Hamdard Foundation, Pakistan, 1981.
-George Saliba: Whose Science at:
http://www.columbia.edu/~gas1/project/visions/case1/sci.1.html
-G.Sarton: *Introduction to the History of Science*; 3 vols; The Carnegie Institute of Washington; 1927-48.
-G.Sarton: *The Appreciation of Ancient and Medieval Science during the Renaissance (1450-1600)*, University of Pennsylvania Press, 1955.
-G. Sarton: *The Study of the History of Mathematics*: Harvard University Press, 1936.
-G. Sarton: *The Incubation of Western Culture in the Middle East*, A George C. Keiser Foundation Lecture, March 29, 1950. Washington DC; 1951.
-E. Savage-Smith: `Gleaning from an Arabist's workshop: Current trends in the study of medieval Islamic Science and Medicine,' *ISIS* 79 (1988): pp. 246-72.
-E. Savage Smith: *Islamicate Celestial Globes*; Smithsonian Institute Press; Washington, D.C, 1985.
-A.Sayili: *The Observatory in Islam;* Publications of the Turkish Historical Society, Series VII, No 38, Ankara, 1960.
-T. Schioler: *Roman and Islamic Water Lifting Wheels;* Odense; 1973.
-J. Schnitter: *A History of Dams*; A.A. Balkema, Rotterdam, 1994.
-L.A. Sedillot: *Traite des Instruments astronomiques des Arabes*; Paris, 1834.
-L.A.Sedillot: Memoire sur les instruments astronomique des Arabes, *Memoires de l'Academie Royale des Inscriptions et Belles Lettres de l'Institut de France* 1: 1-229; Reprinted Frankfurt, 1985.
-H.Selin ed: *Encyclopaedia of the History of Science, Technology, and Medicine in Non Western Cultures*, Kluwer Academic Publishers. Boston/London, 1997.
-K. I. Semaan ed: *Islam and the Medieval West*. State University of New York Press/Albany.1980.
-M. Serres: *A History of Scientific Thought;* Blackwell, 1995.
-F.Sezgin: *Geschichte des arabischen Schrifttums* (vol vi for astronomy); 1978.
-A. Shalaby: *History of Muslim Education*: Dar Al Kashaf; Beirut; 1954.
-F.Sherwood Taylor: *A Short History of Science*; William Heinemann Ltd, London, 1939.
-M. Sibai: *Mosque Libraries: An Historical Study*: Mansell Publishing Limited: London and New York: 1987.
-C.J. Singer: *The Earliest Chemical Industry*; The Folio Society; London; 1958.
-C.J. Singer et al: *History of Technology*; 5 vols; Oxford At The Clarendon; vol 2 (1956); particularly pp 753-77.
-D.E. Smith: *History of Mathematics*; Dover Publications; New York; 1958.
-N. Smith: *A History of Dams,* The Chaucer Press; London; 1971.
-R.B.Smith: *Mohammed and Mohammedanism*; London; Smith Elder; 1876
-M.S.Spink and G.L.Lewis: *Abulcasis on Surgery and Instruments*; The Wellcome Institute, London, 1973.
-M. Steinschneider: Etudes sur Zarkali; *Bulletino Boncompagni*; vol 20.

-H. Suter: *Die mathematiker und Astronomen der Araber und ihre Werke (1900)*; APA, Oriental Press, Amsterdam, reedit; 1982.
-K. Sutton: Qanats in al-Andalus; the continued presence of Moorish irrigation technology in the Campo Tabernas, Almeria; Spain; *The Maghreb Review*; vol 26; 1; 2001; pp. 69-78.
-J. Sweetman: *The Oriental Obsession*: Cambridge University Press, 1987.
-N. Swerdlow and O. Neugebauer, Mathematical Astronomy in Copernicus's *De revolutionibus*, New York: Springer Verlag, 1984.

-D.Talbot Rice: *Islamic Art;* Thames and Hudson; London; 1979 ed.
-H.Terrasse: *L'Art hispano mauresque des origins au 13em siecle;* Paris; 1933.
-G.Thery: *Tolede Grande Ville de la Renaissance Medievale*; Oran; 1944.
-J.W. Thompson: Introduction of Arabic Science into Lorraine in the Tenth Century," *ISIS* 12 (1929): 187-91.
-M.A. Tolmacheva: Geography and Cartography: Islamic; *Dictionary of the Middle Ages*; Vol 5; pp 391-5.
-K A Totah: *The Contribution of the Arabs to Education;* New York: Columbia University Press, 1926.
-T.F. Tout: The Place of the Middle Ages in the teaching of history, *History*, New series, Vol 8 (1923-4); pp 1-18.
-J. S. Trimingham: *The Influence of Islam upon Africa*; Longman, Librairie du Liban; second edition 1980.
-H.R.Turner: *Science in Medieval Islam*, Austin Texas, 1997.

-A.L Udovitch: At the origins of the Western Commenda, in *Speculum* 37 (1962): pp. 198-207.
-A.L. Udovitch: Trade, in the *Dictionary of the Middle Ages*; vol 12; pp. 105-8.
-A.L.Udovitch: *Bankers Without Banks; The Dawn of Modern Banking*; N. Haven; Yale Univ Press; 1979.
-A.L. Udovitch: Credit as a mean of investment in medieval Islamic trade; *Journal of Economic and Social History of the Orient* (JESHO); 1967; pp 260-4.
-A. Udovitch: An Eleventh century Islamic treatise on the law of the sea: In *Annales Islamologiques*, Institut Francais d'Archeologie du Caire; Vol 27; pp 37-54.
-A.L. Udovitch: Urbanism; *Dictionary of The Middle Ages*; 12; pp 306-10.
-Ibn Abi Ussaybia: *Uyun al-anba fi tabaqat al-attiba'*, edited by A. Mueller, Cairo/Konigsberg; 1884, reprint, 1965.

-Carra de Vaux: *Les Penseurs de l'Islam*, Paris, Librairie Paul Geuthner, 1921.
-J.Vernet: *Ce que la culture doit aux Arabes d'Espagne*, tr by G Martinez Gros, 1985, Paris; German tr: *Die spanisch arabische Kultur in Orient und Okzident,* 1984, Zurich/Munich.
-M. Vintejoux: *Le Miracle Arabe*, Charlot, Paris, 1950.

-J. Waardenburg: Some institutional aspects of Muslim higher learning, *NVMEN*, 12, pp.96-138.

-T. Walz: Writing Materials, *Dictionary of the Middle Ages*; 12; pp 697-9.

-A.M. Watson: *Agricultural Innovation in the Early Islamic World*; Cambridge University Press; 1983.

-W. M. Watt: *The Influence of Islam on Medieval Europe*, Edinburgh, 1972.

-M. C. Welborn: `Lotharingia as a center of Arabic and scientific influence in the eleventh century,' *ISIS* 16 (1931) pp.188-99.

-A.Whipple: *The Role of the Nestorians and Muslims in the History of Medicine*. Ann Arbor, Michigan, 1977.

-D.Whitehouse: Glass in *Dictionary of the Middle Ages*; pp. 545-8.

-G.M Wickens: The Middle East as a world centre of science and medicine; in *Introduction to Islamic Civilisation*, edited by R.M. Savory; Cambridge University Press, Cambridge, 1976; pp 111-8.

-G. M. Wickens: `What the West borrowed from the Middle East,' in *Introduction to Islamic Civilisation*, ed by R.M. Savory, pp 120-5.

-E. Wiedemann:*Beitrage zur Geschichte der Natur-wissenschaften. X. Zur Technik bei den Arabern*. Erlangen, 1906.

-E. Wiedemann:`Zur mechanik und technik bei der Arabern' in *Sitzungsherichte der physikalisch-medizinischen Sorietat in Erlangen* (38), 1906.

-G.Wiet; V. Elisseeff; P. Wolff; and J. Naudu: *History of Mankind;* Vol 3: The Great Medieval Civilisations; Tr from French; G Allen & Unwin Ltd; UNESCO; 1975.

-J.K. Wright: *The Geographical Lore of the Time of the Crusades*; Dover Publications; New York; 1925.

-E. Wright: General editor: *The Medieval and Renaissance World*; Hamlyn; London; 1979.

-F. Wustenfeld: *Geschichte der arabichen aertze und Naturforscher*; Gottingen; 1840.

-M.J. L. Young, J.D. Latham and R.B. Serjeant ed: *Religion, Learning and Science in the Abbasid Period*. Cambridge University Press, 1990.

-R de Zayas: *Les Morisques et le Racisme d'Etat;* Ed Les Voies du Sud; Paris, 1992.

Index